RICE

TROPICAL AGRICULTURE SERIES

The Tropical Agriculture Series, of which this volume forms part, is a series of books on tropical agriculture which are being published under the editorship of D. Rhind, C.M.G., O.B.E., B.SC., F.L.S., F.I.BIOL.

Already published

Child, R. *Coconuts*

Eden, T. *Tea*

Harris, W. Victor *Termites*

Simmonds, N. W. *Bananas*

Smith, F. G. *Beekeeping in the Tropics*

Urquhart, D. H. *Cocoa*

Williamson, G. and Payne, W. J. A. *An Introduction to Animal Husbandry in the Tropics*

1. Typical terraced paddy field near Kandy, Ceylon

RICE

by

D. H. GRIST

DIP. AGRIC. (CANTAB.), F.L.S.

Formerly Agricultural Economist,
Colonial Agricultural Service,
Malaya

FOURTH EDITION

LONGMANS

5/1969
йн

LONGMANS, GREEN AND CO LTD
48 Grosvenor Street, London W.1
*Associated companies, branches and representatives
throughout the world*

New editions © D. H. Grist 1959 and 1965

*First published 1953
Second Edition 1955
Third Edition 1959
Fourth Edition 1965
Second impression 1968*

PRINTED IN GREAT BRITAIN
BY LOWE & BRYDONE (PRINTERS) LTD.,
LONDON

FOREWORD

by

Sir Harold Tempany, C.M.G., C.B.E., D.Sc., F.R.I.C.

Late Agricultural Adviser to the Secretary of State for the Colonies

THERE is no more important crop in the world to-day than rice; it is the staple food of the teeming millions of south-east Asia, whose numbers are increasing rapidly. Even before the war rice supplies barely sufficed to satisfy their needs at a rather substandard level of subsistence; to-day populations in these regions have already increased by over 10 per cent beyond the pre-war level, while production only slightly exceeds that of the pre-war years. The increase of rice production is one of the major world agricultural problems; upon its solution world peace and security are largely dependent.

The urgency of the matter has induced the United Nations, acting in conjunction with the Food and Agriculture Organization and other associated bodies, to set up the International Rice Commission. A large part of the activities envisaged under the Colombo Plan are also concerned with the augmentation of rice production in certain Eastern countries.

In such circumstances a work dealing with the various aspects of rice production is obviously badly needed. So far as I am aware the only book on the subject is E. B. Copeland's work published nearly thirty years ago. Since that was written, however, there have been a number of important changes and developments in the situation. Accordingly the present work by Mr. D. H. Grist is timely. He spent many years in the Far East where for a long period he served as Agricultural Economist in the Malayan Department of Agriculture, where I was closely associated with him as a friend and colleague. So he is intimately acquainted with rice production under Eastern conditions. Moreover, he has also recently visited certain countries in South America where rice is grown. He is thus well qualified to undertake the compilation of this book. In it he has collected and summarized a large amount of information drawn from numerous sources concerning the characteristics of the crop, its irrigation, cultivation, and manuring, the pests and diseases which attack it, and its milling and processing. In the concluding chapters he has discussed

v

factors which affect production and the prospects of increasing it. Throughout he has also drawn largely on his wide experience.

It is hoped that the book will serve a useful purpose by bringing within the compass of one volume reasonably full and up-to-date information concerning this vastly important and in some respects unique cereal.

7 North End House   H. TEMPANY
  London, W.14

PREFACE TO FOURTH EDITION

EVERY aspect concerning the cultivation and preparation of rice has been the subject for study at rice research institutes and experiment stations in all countries where paddy is considered an important crop. The result is an ever-increasing flow of scientific and technical publications which adds to our knowledge of the crop and contributes to the improvement of yields.

In this book I have endeavoured to present a picture of paddy cultivation throughout the world and to summarize the results of the more important investigations on the crop. I can only hope to achieve a measure of success with the help of the institutions concerned and of individual investigators.

The more I study this subject, the more I am convinced that both basic and applied research on rice is some years ahead of its application in the field, and that this gap between knowledge and its application is widening. If only the more simple cultivation methods recommended were put into practice, methods that are not beyond the capacity of the peasant farmer, the increase in world rice production would be startling. Sir E. John Russell reminds us that "the food for the vast majority of mankind is produced by peasants, mostly illiterate, bound by custom and tradition, often shrewd in using their methods skilfully, but unwilling to change unless they are completely satisfied that the new one is better." The extension services must play an important part in guiding cultivators towards improving the techniques of cultivation and the use of fertilizers. Improved extension services are, therefore, the most important key to increased yields.

D.H.G.

London.
8 *January* 1964

PREFACE TO FIRST EDITION

Rice is perhaps the most remarkable of cultivated crops, for although possessing the roots of a dry-land plant, it flourishes in swamps or under irrigation, and in Asia has produced one or more crops annually for centuries. This continuous rice growing—almost unexampled in the crop world—produces yields at a surprisingly high level, despite the fact that in many regions the land is never manured.

The crop is grown over a very wide range of climatic, soil and water conditions, from wet tropical to regions of semi-arid, warm temperate climate; in heavy clays or poor sandy soils; on dry land or in swamp land in water that may be fifteen to twenty feet deep; in fresh or brackish water. The thousands of varieties of rice that exist account for this cosmopolitan nature, for it is true to say that a variety may be found to suit almost any condition, provided that the plant is subject to abundant sunshine and given water sufficient for the requirements of the particular variety.

While rice is not a complete food in itself, as a grain it has a very high nutritive value, second only to wheat. Unfortunately, much of these nutrients (proteins, fats, and water-soluble vitamins of the B complex) is eliminated in the processes of milling and cooking. Many of the diseases suffered by rice-eaters are caused by malnutrition and are preventable by such means as improved milling, parboiling and cooking, by which the vitamins, in particular, are retained in the finished product. Improvements in health are already evident in some countries as a result of the application of scientific research to this subject.

It is estimated that an annual increase of 1·3 million tons of rice is necessary to meet the needs of the growing rice-eating population. While the ultimate solution of the problem of meeting demand by supply must be by limitation of population, the immediate necessity for larger rice supplies may be met by an increased area under the crop and by improved yields. If the price of rice is maintained at a reasonably high level, the area may be expected to increase in many countries, the chief deterrent to development being the high cost of bringing land into cultivation.

The possibility of improving productivity is discussed in some detail in the following pages. The four main channels leading to improvements in yield appear to be, in order of importance: improved drainage and irrigation; more effective control of pests; the addition of humus to the land, with or without fertilizers; and the selection and breeding of varieties.

Drainage and irrigation are of paramount importance; efficient water control results in direct improvement in yield; in addition, it aids in the control of pests, diseases, and weeds, and renders fertilizers more effective.

Losses caused by pests are enormous, and largely preventable; for this reason the necessity for better control over pests is given priority over manuring or the improvement of varieties. It is possible that the new and very potent insecticides now on the market may prove of value against certain pests of the rice crop which hitherto have been difficult to control.

It is usual to assume that increased yields will result from fertilizing the crop. While some improvement may be expected by this means, it is probable that undue emphasis has been given in some quarters to the need for fertilizers. The requirement of first importance in many areas is humus, with or without the addition of fertilizers. It is probable, therefore, that by such means as green manuring, fallowing, rotation of rice with a grass ley and cattle grazing, the application of fertilizers on a more modest scale may be found sufficient, while in many areas fertilizers may be found unnecessary.

Considerable research work has been directed towards the improvement of varieties and in the study of varieties in relation to their environment. This will, for a long time, be a fruitful line of research, leading to the production of varieties resistant to particular pests and diseases and capable of producing optimum yields under varying conditions.

Rice is intimately bound up with the economy and well-being of Asia. The total area under the crop exceeds 200 million acres, of which over 90 per cent is grown in Asia. Yet the demand for rice in Asia exceeds present world supplies. It is the staple diet of over half the world population, including countless millions in Asia who subsist almost entirely on rice. If, therefore, in the following pages the author appears to have laid undue stress on rice in Asia, his defence is the urgency of the many problems as they affect the life of an immense population that lives near to starvation and which is sustained almost entirely on rice.

Stoke-by-Nayland
Suffolk
August 1951

D. H. GRIST

ACKNOWLEDGEMENTS

In writing this book and preparing subsequent editions I have corresponded with many rice experts, visited libraries, abstracted or made use of abstracts prepared by others, and shamelessly importuned all who were in a position to give me information and advice. Invariably I have been treated as a colleague to whom one willingly gives every help and encouragement. While this attitude towards me rendered my task very pleasant, it makes my acknowledgements very difficult, for to include all who have helped me with information, advice, criticisms, illustrations, or who have read my manuscript would make a lengthy list, which would still omit some whose research work has either directly or indirectly assisted me. To all these I tender my respectful thanks.

Throughout this book and in the Bibliography, I have endeavoured to acknowledge and do justice to the research work on rice. There can, however, be no finality to a book such as this. I am constantly coming across both old and new work to which I should make reference. The subject is such a wide one and the literature on it so scattered that mention of important research work may have escaped my attention and therefore been omitted. I can but offer my apologies for such omissions both to the scientists concerned and to my readers.

In previous editions of this book I have expressed my gratitude to the following for their kind assistance in various directions: Mr D. S. Byers, Dr F. P. Coyne, Dr D. S. Fernandes, Mr F. Garibaldi, Dr R. M. Gorrie, Mr J. M. Hector, Dr G. A. C. Herklots, C.B.E., Dr C. F. Hickling, C.M.G., Dr J. C. Hinton, Dr W. F. Jepson, O.B.E., Mr J. E. Jessup, Professor M. C. Kik, Mr G. E. Mann, M.C., Mr J. E. Mayne, Mr E. J. McNaughton, Mr P. McNee, C.B.E., Mr N. C. E. Miller, Mr Ng Beng Cheng, Dr G. Watts Padwick, Mr H. C. Pagden, Professor R. L. Pendleton, Professor B. S. Platt, Mr W. Poggendorff, Mr Soong Min Kong, Mr R. Vamos and Mr G. Wrigley. I am also indebted to members of the staffs of Plant Protection Ltd., Fisons Pest Control Ltd., and Shell Petroleum Co. Ltd. for advice.

In connection with the preparation of the present edition, I gratefully acknowledge the courtesy extended to me by the Director,

Royal Botanic Gardens, Kew, in allowing me access to the Kew Library, to the Assistant Director, Mr C. E. Hubbard, C.B.E. for checking the botanical section of the book and Mr Russell for many corrections to the text. Mr A. G. Leeks, Chief, Rice Section, FAO, Rome, has kindly supplied me with information and publications from time to time.

Dr E. F. Edson has checked the section he prepared for the third edition, on the risk of pesticides to fish and has brought the subject up to date by additional information.

Since the inception of this book I have consulted a number of libraries, in particular the Tropical Products Institute, the Colonial Office, Rothamsted Experimental Station, India House, the Commonwealth Relations Library and the Library of the Royal Botanic Gardens, Kew. I would again like to thank the staffs of these excellent libraries who are always so helpful.

Rice owes its inception to the encouragement and wise guidance of my former chief, the late Sir Harold Tempany. Mr D. Rhind, C.M.G., O.B.E., Advisor on Agricultural Research, Department of Technical Co-operation and the General Editor of this series of books on tropical agriculture, has contributed the chapter on Rice Genetics and supplied me with much material in connection with the chapter on selection and breeding techniques, which I have freely drawn upon in writing Chapter VII. Mr Rhind has invariably placed at my disposal his wide knowledge of rice; I greatly value his generous help and continue to profit by his wide experience and knowledge.

I am indebted to Dr Seijin Nagao and the Academic Press Inc., New York, for material from *Advances in Genetics Volume IV*, The Rice Journal for material from *The Production and Marketing of Rice* by J. N. Efferson, and J. M. Hector for material from *Introduction to the Botany of Field Crops, Vol. I, Cereals*.

For permission to reproduce photographs I am indebted to the following:

Plate 1, Camera Press, Ltd.; Plate 40, Mr H. H. Croucher; Plate 4, Crown Copyright Reserved; Plate 54, The *Daily Argosy*, British Guiana; Plates 2, 6, 28, 57, E.N.A.; Plate 58, Messrs. John Gordon and Co.; Plates 59, 61, 62, 64–6, Messrs. Lewis C. Grant Ltd.; Plates 30, 35, 48, Dr G. A. C. Herklots; Plate 47, Mr F. Hal Higgins; Plate 16, Dr J. J. C. Hinton; Colour Plates I and IV, Fenno Jacobs of Three Lions; Plates 7, 8, 14, 26, 27, 32, 36, 37, 38, 43, 55, 56, Sunil Janah; Plates 44, 49, 50, 51, 52, Department of Agriculture, Federation of Malaya; Plates 23, 25, 33, 34, 41, Department of Public Relations, Federation of Malaya; Plates 10, 11, 13, 22, 29, The Malayan Information Agency; Plate 60, Messrs. Wm. McKinnon and Co. Ltd.; Plate 31, Menzies, Griffith, N.S.W.; Plate 9, Mrs H. Morrison; Plate 3, The Netherlands Embassy; Plate 45, Mr J. B. Norton; Plate 63, Messrs. Thomas Robinson and Son Ltd.; Plate 53, Rotary Hoes Ltd.; Plate 21, S.I.P.M.A., Milan; Colour Plate II, Corsini, Standard Oil Company, New Jersey; Plate 24, Toko Boeki K. K., Japan; Plates 15, 39, 67, 68, U.S. Information Service; Plates 42, 46, Bureau of Plant Industry, Soils and Agricultural Engineering, U.S. Department of Agriculture; Plate 69, Mr M. Eden; Plate 70, Mr R. Wijiwardene.

Colour Plate III is reproduced from S.S. and F.M.S. Bulletins, Scientific Series 1–12, by permission of the Department of Agriculture, Federation of Malaya.

For permission to reproduce or redraw diagrams I am indebted to the following:

The Ceylon Government for Fig. 3 from Senaratna: *The Grasses of Ceylon*; The Commonwealth Mycological Institute for Figs. 23–30 from Padwick: *Manual of Rice Diseases*; Dr G. A. C. Herklots for Figs. 7 and 10; Mr L. Nicholls and the British Council for Fig. 31 from *British Science News* 2, No. 28; Mr L. Nicholls and the Editor of *Research* for Figs. 34 and 35 from *Research* 2 (1949); Messrs. Thomas Robinson and Son Ltd. for Figs. 32, 33 and 36; Saiosha Works Co. Ltd., Japan, for Figs. 8 and 9; Toho Boeki K. K., Japan, for Fig. 12; Longmans, Green and Company Ltd. for permission to reproduce Table 66 from *Genetics and Breeding of Rice* by Dr M. F. Chandraratna; *The Rice Journal* for Fig. 35 and Sir Bruce White, Wolfe Barry and Partners for Figs. 11–14.

CONTENTS

PART II

PADDY: PRODUCTION

PART III

RICE: THE PRODUCT

xx *Contents*

LIST OF PHOTOGRAPHS

PART I

ORYZA SATIVA LINN.:
THE PLANT

The rice problem is over 90 per cent Asian: the real experts are those millions of human beings who have inherited green fingers down the centuries.

—*The Economist.*

2 January 1954.

c

Chapter I

THE ORIGIN AND HISTORY OF RICE

RICE has been cultivated for such countless ages that its origin must always be a matter for some conjecture. Botanists base their evidence as to its origin largely on the habitats of the wild species. It is presumed that the cultivated species have developed from certain of the wild rices; it is possible, but considered unlikely, that any of the wild rices are descended from cultivated rice.

The genus *Oryza* L. comprises about 25 species, distributed in tropical and sub-tropical regions of Asia, Africa, Central and South America and Northern Australia.* They are probably derived from two genetical sources, the main one in Asia, the other in Africa which has also given the species in South America. Chevalier and Viguier[124] suggest two centres of origin, *viz.*: *Oryza fatua* Koenig and *Oryza sativa* L., both of Asian origin, and *Oryza stapfii* Roschev. and *O. glaberrima* Steud. from West Africa. *Oryza fatua* Koenig and *Oryza minuta* Presl., states Burkill,[98] occur in moist places from the Eastern Himalayas to Ceylon and from the southern-most edge of China through Burma and Indo-China to Java, Borneo and the Philippines. In the fields of south-western and western India, he adds, "*Oryza fatua* is exactly like the annual *Oryza sativa* L. in every respect except that it shatters at maturity. In the Gangetic plains it is seen in a different form, but is still like *Oryza sativa* L. except for shattering. The poor do not ignore it, but tying the awns together before maturity, save the grain for themselves, or they collect the fallen grain, which is made an easier process by the length of the awns." *Oryza stapfii* Roschev. and *Oryza glaberrima* Steud. are assumed to have been cultivated on the margins of the neolithic Sahara. The historian Ibn-Datouta (A.D. 1350) mentions the existence of rice in Nigeria, which was certainly *O. glaberrima* Steud. Portères states that *O. glaberrima* was introduced into Northern Nigeria in the sixteenth century. The earliest cultivation of *Oryza sativa* L. in Nigeria was about 1890 when upland varieties were introduced to the high forest zone in Western Nigeria. Shallow swamp varieties from British Guiana and Ceylon were established in the smaller tributaries of several rivers where they rapidly replaced the swamp

* See Appendix VI.

3

varieties of red rice (*O. glaberrima*), then most extensively grown. *O. glaberrima* is now mostly confined to the far north of Nigeria and to Sierra Leone.

Various authorities consider *Oryza sativa* L. a polyphiletic species, resulting, according to Gustchin,[238] from crossing wild forms of great diversity with cultivated varieties. Amongst these wild Asian forms, two appear to be basic: *Oryza sativa* L. form *spontanea* and *Oryza officinalis* Wall.[682] Roschevicz[571] states that in addition to the species *Oryza fatua* Koenig and *Oryza officinalis* Wall., other forms may have entered into the origin of certain varieties of cultivated rice. Thus, possibly, *Oryza breviligulata* A. Chev. et Roehr. and *Oryza glaberrima* Steud. may be connected with the origin of some of the cultivated forms in West Africa. It is also thought that some of the forms of small rice, *Oryza sativa* L. ssp. *brevis* Gust. may be closely connected with *Oryza minuta* Presl. *Oryza perennis* Moench., a perennial which multiplies by means of rhizomes, is even now cultivated in a small area in Equatorial Africa.[682] *Oryza punctata* Kotschy, states Bain,[62] occurs wild in rain-flooded depressions in the Sudan; its seed as well as that of other wild species still occur and are harvested in times of shortage. It was held by Chatterjee[722] that *Oryza sativa* L. var. *fatua* Prain (syn. *O. sativa* L. f. *spontanea* Rosch.) was worthy of specific rank but the name *O. fatua* Koen. could not be used. The most acceptable name seems to be *Oryza rufipogon* Griff. It is this plant which sometimes occurs as a noxious weed in paddy fields. (See Chapter XII.)

The so-called wild rice of North America is *Zizania aquatica* and is not a true rice although it is one of the genera of the Oryzeae. This aquatic wild plant is traditionally harvested by Chippewa Indians in Minnesota and the adjoining States of Wisconsin and Michigan. According to Johnston,* *Zizania* of poor quality is indigenous to the river areas of the northern Congo basin. He adds that rice was practically unknown in the central basin until the German explorer, Dr Pogge, introduced it in 1875 or 1876, about the same time as the Arabs introduced the crop into the eastern Congo.

According to Vavilov,[683] the longer a group has been established in an area, the larger will be the number of species to be found there. He concludes that the wealth of forms and varieties of rice found in the south-west Himalayas which are closely allied to many Chinese varieties points to this region as the centre of origin of rice. It may well be that this and other places in India, south-east Asia, the Phillippines and Africa are centres of origin of cultivated forms of rice.

Copeland[135] adds linguistic evidence to prove that rice originated

* In *George Grenfell and the Congo*, Hutchinson (1908).

in south-east Asia. "Rice," he states, "was not a crop of the Egyptians or Chaldeans in very ancient times. It is therefore improbable that its culture originated in Africa and spread thence to Asia, a possibility which the botanical evidence would admit." He points out that in Chinese and many other languages in south-east Asia, agriculture and rice or food and rice are synonymous, pointing to the conclusion that paddy was first cultivated in this part of the world.

Specimens of rice have been discovered in China dating from the third millennium B.C., and the Chinese term for rice appears in inscriptions dating from the second millennium B.C. The Chinese term for rice, *tao*, is believed to correspond etymologically to similar terms for rice in Indo-China and Thailand, but the Malayan and Indian terms for rice appear to be unrelated. Ting[656] concludes that in view of the number of wild rices found in southern China, rice cultivation is believed to have started in this region and to have spread northward. The same writer states that a study of rice glumes found in the Yangtse River in red burnt clay, thought to belong to the late Neolithic, are classified as *O. sativa* f. *spontanea* ssp. *Keng* and show strong resemblances to the rice cultivars now grown in eastern China.[657] Excavators at Mohenjodaro in West Pakistan discovered rice grains in earthern vessels, thus providing evidence that rice was an important food in the Indus valley civilization which flourished as early as 2500 B.C.[19]

Paddy cultivation probably dates back to the earliest age of man, and long before the era of which we have historical evidence it was probably the staple food and the first cultivated crop in Asia. Earliest historical references are found in Chinese writings of about five thousand years ago, when it was stated that the privilege of sowing paddy was reserved for the Emperor alone, the less important cereals being reserved for the less exalted members of his family. Ramiah[511] points out that the original homes of plants are characterized by the great diversity of forms, rich in varieties, and it is in south-east Asia, India, China and Indo-China that this great diversity is to be found. All the Hindu scriptures mention rice and all offerings to God are given as rice, denoting its antiquity. Ramiah adds that some of the very ancient Tamil *puranas* contain descriptions of particular varieties of rice which are to be used in certain religious offerings, showing that even in those ancient times varieties with definite grain characteristics were recognized and that Susrutha (1000 B.C.) in his Ayurvedic *Materia Medica* recognized the differences among rices that existed in India, separating them into groups based on their duration, water requirements, and nutritional values.[509] The religious aspect has persisted throughout the ages in Eastern countries; it enters into the religious rites of Borneo and Sarawak, while in Java rice is considered as the offspring of the Goddess Dwie Srie. Usually, the religious significance is connected with fecundity and plenty. Rice cakes are eaten at certain festivals in Asia to symbolize long life, happiness and abundance. The custom at weddings in Europe of throwing rice at the bride and bridegroom is borrowed from the East.

According to Chi,[125] the first authentic record of irrigation for paddy cultivation is to be found in the *Book of Poetry* supposed to have been written in the Chow dynasty about 781–771 B.C., wherein the writer refers to water flowing northwards from the river to the rice-fields in the Wei Valley of Shensi. The historian Ssu-ma Ch'ien in 148 B.C. wrote of conditions in the Yangtse Valley, "where the land is tilled with fire and hoed with water," which is held to refer to the burning off of trees and undergrowth, flooding the land and planting paddy.

We do not know the country of origin of rice, but the weight of evidence points to the fact that it originated in the continent of south-east Asia, spreading northwards in Asia before the later movements of the Aryan dispersal, for the name is alike in Zind and Sanskrit and similar in Old Persian. From the mainland of the continent it also spread south and east through the Malay archipelago with the flow of human culture. It was introduced into Indonesia by the Deutero-Malays when they immigrated there about 1500 B.C. The legend that paddy cultivation was introduced by the Hindus has been disproved.[395]

In Ceylon, paddy has been grown from time immemorial. Before about 543 B.C. it was probably grown on the island as a dryland crop. The earliest references to tanks to conserve water for irrigation of paddy in Ceylon are about 420 B.C. While some of these tanks were undoubtedly used to supply water for domestic purposes, it is certain that a network of tanks to supply water for paddy cultivation was built up from the time of the early Sinhalese kings. During subsequent invasions these irrigation systems were severely damaged, while malaria so reduced the population that the cultivation of paddy rapidly declined. Many of these ancient tanks have been repaired recently and are again doing good service for their original purpose some thousand or more years ago. It is thought, however, that the area cultivated with paddy in Ceylon may now be very much less than in ancient times. It has been suggested that in early history the island became the granary of the East and that an export trade in rice developed with neighbouring countries.[474]

Paddy cultivation is of great antiquity in the Philippines. It is thought that the wonderful system of terraces on the mountain-sides of the island of Luzon was constructed by the immigrant people from south China in the second millennium B.C. These people were driven into the hills by subsequent invasions of Malays. The present-day cultivators, said to be descendants of the original Ifugao immigrants, continue to cultivate this crop by methods brought down to them through thousands of years.[48]

Japan has for long been famous for the excellence of its rice. The country was known in very early times as Mizumono Kuni—the Land of Luxurious Rice Crops. Rice was introduced into Kyushu, Japan, from China about 100 B.C. From this island its cultivation spread eastward, but it was not until the end of the eighteenth century that paddy cultivation was introduced into Hokkaido, the most northern of the four Japanese islands.[379]

Rice did not reach Western Asia and the highly civilized Egypt, Greece and Rome until much later. No references to rice are found in ancient Egyptian tombs or writings, ancient Persian writings are silent on the subject, while it is not mentioned in the Bible. On the other hand, the Talmud, written at a later date, refers to the cultivation of rice. The Greeks learned of rice from the Persians, and medieval Europe got it from the Saracens. Theophrastus, born about 375 B.C., refers to the cultivation of paddy in Egypt, and the Greek historian Diodore of Sicily, a contemporary of Augustus, describes the plant and its cultivation from reports made to him by Aristobule who took part in the expedition of Alexander the Great to India *circa* 344–324 B.C. Rice was therefore known to the ancient Romans as a result of their conquests in the East, and its cultivation in Sicily may have existed in very early times.[649] The crop was introduced into northern Italy in the fifteenth century, the first authentic mention of its cultivation in this region occurring in a letter written by the Duke of Milan in 1475.[442] During the time of the Roman Empire rice was imported and it was not cultivated in the Mediterranean basin until the Arabs introduced it in the Nile Delta. The Malays are said to have brought the crop to Madagascar and the Indians to the East African islands. The Moors brought rice to Spain, the Spaniards brought it to Italy, and the Turks introduced it over much of the south-eastern part of Europe, from whence it spread to the Balkans. The spread of paddy cultivation was sometimes opposed for reasons of health (malaria) and in the sixteenth and seventeenth centuries cultivation near towns was forbidden.[699]

Piacco,[487] however, considers it probable that rice was introduced to Italy from the Orient through Venice rather than Spain. This, he suggests, gave rise to the rice known as Nostrale (Local). The variety Bertone was apparently introduced from France in the 1820s on account of its greater resistance to "brusone" disease. Its name is taken to mean an awnless rice. Chinese was a synonym for Bertone, whereas Originario was introduced by selection from Japanese seed, introduced in 1903.

The Portuguese introduced rice into Brazil and the Spaniards to Central America and parts of South America. Paddy cultivation in Brazil is mentioned in some of the earliest records of European settlement. The crop was introduced into Hawaii in 1853; the French brought it to New Caledonia and the Germans to New Guinea.

Paddy cultivation in the United States of America dates from about 1685 when it was introduced into the colony of South Carolina, probably from Madagascar. About 1718 it was introduced into Louisiana, but it did not assume importance in that State till 1887 when it was shown that the crop could be cultivated profitably by machinery on the prairies in the south-western part of the State. The commercial rice crops of the United States are now grown almost entirely in the State of Arkansas, where it was introduced early in the present century, California, where the first commercial crop was grown in the Sacramento Valley in 1912, Louisiana and Texas. In the last-named State, early plantings were of dry-land paddy. The first known attempt to grow paddy was in 1850, when 110 acres were planted. The success of the crop depended entirely on rainfall. The first attempt to cultivate the crop with irrigation is said to have been made by the Port Arthur Canal Company which installed a large pumping plant in Jefferson county.[43]

Unsuccessful attempts were made to develop paddy cultivation in British Guiana early in the eighteenth century. It was not until 1886 when, using irrigation facilities for a sugar estate and employing East Indian and Chinese labour with knowledge of methods of cultivation, the crop was successfully grown.[533]

Paddy has been grown on a commercial scale in Australia since 1924, but as early as 1891 farmers in New South Wales tried to grow dry-land paddy. Further trials with wet paddy were equally unsuccessful, because unsuitable varieties were planted. About 1914, a Japanese settler, I. Takasuki by name, developed a rice variety which bears his name in the Murray River area and cultivated it successfully. The Murrumbidgee Irrigation Area was already well established when paddy cultivation commenced there in 1923. Paddy cultivation materially assisted further development of the area and is today, with the exception of fruit, its most valuable product.[281] In

2. Paddy fields in Thailand

3. Paddy fields north of Bandoeng, Java

4. Terraced paddy field in southern China

5. Terraced paddy field in Java

6. Typical paddy fields showing terrace cultivation in Shan States, Burma

7. Paddy fields in Bihar

8. Paddy fields on terrace with stone embankments Orissa

9. Paddy fields in Peiping The Summer Palace is in the background

the Northern Territory of Australia small areas were cultivated to rice by Chinese about 1887 and small areas are still cultivated in the Aboriginal Compound. Large-scale mechanized cultivation started in 1954. Paddy cultivation in Queensland, introduced in 1869, is practically confined to the upland type. Some hundreds of acres were grown annually during the period from 1880 to 1890, but the crop was eventually displaced by sugar-cane.

Chapter II

CLIMATE AND SOILS

LATITUDE

THE paddy plant will flourish under such widely differing climatic conditions that it is difficult to define those most suitable for its development. Evidence is advanced in Chapter XIX showing that while the highest yields are obtained in countries enjoying a sub-tropical or warm-temperate climate, the crop also thrives over a wide range of conditions within about 45° latitude north and 40° south of the Equator. These are not, however, the extreme limits at which successful cultivation is possible. For instance, in Europe cultivation has moved northwards to 49° latitude in Czechoslovakia, and in the Soviet Union it extends to 47° N. latitude and may be extended later to 50°–53° N. latitude.[186] Generally considered a crop suited to the wet tropics, where indeed the greater part of the total area is situated, it also flourishes in such countries as Egypt and Australia, and among temperate climate localities in Spain, Portugal, Italy, Hungary and France. In fact, the highest yields are recorded between 30° and 45° north of the Equator. The area within latitudes 45° north and 40° south, where the most extensive areas under the crop are found, embraces Central America, half of the United States of America, the West Indies, most of South America, the entire continent of Africa, the whole of Australia, India, most of China, Japan, the Malay Archipelago and the Pacific islands. The water requirements of the crop are such that cultivation tends to be concentrated in regions where there are flat lowlands, river basins and deltas, with high temperatures and abundant sunshine. Wickizer and Bennett[699] have remarked on the absence of extensive and heavy concentrations of rice production in Asian lands lying directly upon and within 5° north and south of the Equator, where annual rainfall is very heavy and so evenly distributed throughout the year that there is virtually no dry season.

The conclusion is evident that within the above-stated range of latitude (excluding the high mountainous regions) the chief limiting factor to the growth of paddy is water supply.

ALTITUDE

The altitude at which paddy may be grown depends on latitude. It has been grown at 10,000 feet in the Himalayas, 6,000 feet altitude in the Philippines, over 4,000 feet in South America, while in many tropical countries it is extensively cultivated at altitudes exceeding 2,000 feet. Over one million acres of paddy are grown in the mountainous areas of India, but yields are usually low because of unsuitable varieties of paddy and poor cultivation. Pawar reports[477] exceedingly high yields from two imported *japonica* varieties which were heavily fertilized, which suggests that *indica* varieties commonly employed in these areas are quite unsuited to the conditions.

In practice, the area cultivated at considerable elevations is small because in such regions there are difficulties in water supply and control, and in finding extensive areas of reasonably flat land.

There is no conclusive evidence as to whether differences in altitude alone affect yield; available data on this point are conflicting, but the nature of the plant is such that it is unlikely that altitude itself exercises any great effect on yield although lower night temperatures may reduce respiration losses and so raise yields.

TEMPERATURE

Paddy is adapted to regions of high temperature and prolonged sunshine. The average temperature required throughout the life of the plant ranges from 68° to 100° F. In Louisiana, a very high temperature accompanied by increased wind velocity on clear, bright days was observed[670] to cause scald of paddy, the injury appearing immediately after panicle emergence. On the other hand, Yamagata found[709] that the number of tillers, ears and grains increased with the intensity and quality of light up to a light intensity of about 200 per cent normal.

The total temperature required (sum of daily mean temperatures during the growing period) is between 3,000 and 4,000 degrees F. This is probably the lower range of requirement, for in many countries this figure is very considerably exceeded. In Hungary,* for instance, one of the most northerly situated rice-producing countries, a total temperature of 5,500° F. and 1,200 hours of sunshine are considered the lowest limits for successful paddy-growing.

Temperature has an important bearing on growth and this is particularly evident at the latitudinal boundaries of paddy cultivation. It is found in the northern regions of Japan[379] that low temperatures in the early growth stages retard development of seedlings,

* Private communication from Mr J. Simon.

delay transplanting and reduce tiller formation. Plant height and number of leaves are affected adversely, causing delay in heading. Low temperatures after heading cause a decrease in the number of fertilized kernels and in their weight. Furthermore, extremes in diurnal temperatures have an important bearing on plant growth. Low night temperatures are advantageous, variation between day and night temperatures promoting maturity of kernels. Yamada[733] has shown that the temperature coefficient of respiration of paddy has a value of $Q_{10}=$ approx. 2. while for photosynthesis Q_{10} is little over unity. The gap between carbohydrate synthesis and loss by respiration represents the dry matter accumulation and this would decline with a rise in night temperature. Under daylight intensities which are not themselves limiting the lower temperatures of higher latitudes, particularly night temperatures, would tend to enhance carbohydrate accumulation and so raise yields.

The view that paddy requires a humid atmosphere is probably erroneous, for in many countries where growth and yields are satisfactory, such as Egypt, California and parts of Japan, humidity is very low. In parts of Northern India and Pakistan irrigated paddy is grown in areas of less than 11 inches rainfall. Paddy, however, provides its own micro-climate, raising the relative humidity within the crop much above that of adjacent unirrigated areas.

LENGTH OF DAY

It is certain that, whatever the range of climatic conditions the plant will tolerate, it will not flourish unless it is subjected to long periods of sunshine. Shade has been observed greatly to retard the attainment of the "critical" stage of tiller formation. Kiyosawa,[337] has shown that shading causes a decrease in the number of spikelets per panicle, but does not affect the percentage of fertile grains. So adaptable is the paddy plant, however, that at least one variety is known[511] which in Malabar grows successfully in shade under trees, while it is reported[483] that in the Korat region of Thailand, paddy planters do not cut more trees than are necessary, because, they say, trees fertilize the paddy land on which they grow.

Summarizing factors affecting rice production, Ramiah[512] points out that paddy is grown in warm temperate regions mainly in the summer months when there is a difference of up to four hours between length of day and night, while in the tropics the maximum difference is only about one hour. Based, therefore, on their response to photoperiod, paddy varieties can be grouped as sensitive and non-sensitive. Sensitive varieties flower when the day length is decreasing and when it reaches a critical value for induction of the flowering phase.[113] Such varieties are frequently of medium or long maturation period. The inducement of flowering by the shortening day length influences their ripening period, so that they are "date fixed" as regards maturity date, though their growing period can be extended by earlier sowing. Non-sensitive varieties do not respond to differences in photoperiod, their length of life being independent of day length so that they can be grown at any season. They are "period fixed" as regards length of maturation and earlier or later sowing has little influence on the length of life. They may, of course, be influenced by factors other than photoperiod, such as temperature. Among sensitive varieties there are variations in degree of response to photoperiod.

One of the main reasons for the wide range of climatic conditions under which the crop will grow is the great diversity of paddy varieties. Varieties differ greatly in their resistance to drought and flooding, some being drought-resistant while others are flood-resistant; some must be grown in fresh water while others will tolerate brackish water. The climatic conditions under which paddy is grown in Japan vary enormously, varieties having been found suited to this wide range of climatic conditions. There are many varieties of paddy in Upper Burma grown in the cool season which are photoperiod insensitive and able to stand temperatures down to 50° F. or lower. These, collectively known as *Mayin* paddies, are sown at various times from November.

Much study remains to be done on the environmental conditions favoured by different varieties. Whyte[698] suggests a global review of the present state of knowledge and experience as the basis for a new series of experiments under the International Rice Commission. In this connection, Roberts[569] has described the design of chambers for growing paddy under controlled light and temperature in the tropics which merits attention.

SOILS

Dudal[183] is of opinion that the term paddy soils is unsatisfactory when used as the name for a soil group, it merely gives an indication of the land use but gives no information on the soil. In a concise statement of present knowledge on paddy soils, he points out that these soils used for paddy cultivation are kept for varying periods in an artificially flooded condition which brings about a movement of iron and manganese compounds from the upper layers and their subsequent reprecipitation at a lower depth. This reduction of the top soil starts through the metabolism of anaerobic bacteria. The surface soil remains in an oxidized stage because of oxygen supplied from the irrigation water, but in the reduce zone iron and manganese compounds are carried down and, when they reprecipitate, form a layer 5 to 20 cms. thick at a depth ranging from 20 to 60 cms. This "ploughpan" may occur in the upper layers of paddy soils as a consequence of the breakdown of aggregates by continuous flooding and is not necessarily related to ploughing. When considerable amounts of silt are deposited successively by floods or irrigation water, the paddy soil formation process may start again in the fresh material, so that the profile shows several superimposed accumulation layers.

The formation of paddy soils has been observed on alluvial soils, Grumosols, Latosols, Andosols and Regosols. To a lesser extent, paddy soils are also known to occur on Red-Yellow Podsolic soils, Grey Hydromorphic soils, Planosols and Grey-Brown Podsolic soils. The following is part of Dudal's comments on the paddy soil development of the main soil groups.

The alluvial soils, which consist of young marine and river deposits, occupy the major part of the wet-land rice areas. Due to their topographical position, ground-water level is high. When very poorly drained, the whole soil is in a reduced condition and the special features due to irrigation do not show. When imperfectly to moderately well drained, the profile shows two mottled horizons, one formed by surface and the other by ground water. Alluvial soils vary widely in texture, colour, pH and base status, according to the source of the material. For paddy cultivation, soils of heavy to medium texture are more commonly used.

The Grumosols, also called Regur or black tropical soils, are generally formed from marine clays, lime materials or marls. They have a heavy clay texture, crack deeply and form a mulchy granular structure at the surface when drying. They are neutral to alkaline and may contain free lime, partly in the form of concretions. They are relatively low in organic matter. When moistened the clay swells, the soil becomes sticky, plastic and almost impervious. Iron accumulations seldom occurs in these soils.

The Latosols occur in sloping topography and are terraced for wet paddy cultivation. These soils are deeply weathered and strongly leached, showing an accumulation of sesquioxides when silica is leached out. They are mostly of heavy texture, but have a favourable structure and good permeability.

The Andosols are characterized by a thick crumbly surface layer, rich in organic matter, medium to light textured, porous and fairly acid. Occurring in undulating to hilly country, they must be terraced for use under irrigation.

The Regosols used for wetland paddy cultivation are commonly composed of volcanic ash. The unconsolidated and porous material is light to medium textured, showing no profile development. A certain stratification may occur due to successive deposits. The accumulation of iron-manganese forms concretions or a slightly cemented pan.

Dudal concludes by summarizing the soil-water-plant relationships as follows:

> The chemical conditions in the reduced surface layer can be summarized as follows: anaerobic decomposition of organic matter, low oxygen tension, high concentration of carbon dioxide and ammonia, reduction and migration of iron and manganese compounds, reduction of sulphates and nitrates respectively to sulphides and nitrogen, formation of hydrogen sulphide, increase in pH (ferroxide being a stronger base than ferrioxide and hydrogen sulphide being a weaker acid than sulphuric acid), increase solubility of silica.
>
> A most important feature is the formation of hydrogen sulphide which harms plant growth. . . . Sulphides, however, combine with ferrous iron so that their harming effect may be neutralized if sufficient iron is present. Excess of hydrogen sulphide or of ferrous iron is known to cause physiological diseases. . . . The reduction of naturally occurring ferric phosphates is likely to increase the availability of phosphorus to the plant; it seems also favoured by the increased solubility of silica. With the downward movement of iron and manganese compounds, a temporary excess due to higher solubility may be followed by a marked shortage of these elements.
>
> From the physical standpoint, consequences of a pan formation are impeded drainage and limited rooting depth. The upholding of the water table decreases the water consumption but poor drainage increases the reduction range. . . .

The soil may vary considerably, sometimes within relatively limited areas—yet knowledge of the soil is essential in connection with choice, quantity and timing of fertilizer application. However, the effect of variation in soil types is often much less than that due to variation in husbandry. For example, transplanting medium-term paddy varieties at, say, 50 days instead of 25 days may reduce yield by more than half, thereby completely masking the effects of soil differences.

The types of soil suitable for paddy cultivation depend more on the conditions under which the plant is grown than upon the nature of the soil. The semi-aquatic conditions under which it is cultivated necessitate a heavy soil through which the irrigation water will not easily percolate, for the demands of the plant regarding water are more precise than are its demands on soil conditions. "Rice," states

Pendleton,[483] "is doubtless the most adaptable food crop man grows, and if enough water remains on the soil until the maturing of the crop, it can produce at least a little grain on soils that are unbelievably poor in plant nutrients." Paddy has been grown with excellent results on the poorest classes of land on the Murrumbidgee Irrigation Area of New South Wales. The consequent improved condition of the land and the payable yields of wheat and oats obtained in rotation with paddy proves that paddy cultivation is the best means of utilizing profitably much of the once unwanted land in this area. On most areas during certain times of the year it is essential to conserve water on the land owing to uncertain future supplies; loss of water through free percolation may therefore be a critical point in the development of the plant. Furthermore, in many areas great reliance is placed on water provided by special irrigation works; such water may be expensive and is usually not available in unlimited quantities.

Most of the extensive areas in Asia are situated in the deltas of great rivers, or are spread along their banks. Thus, the situation of paddy areas is governed rather by considerations of water supply than by the nature of the soil. It has been concluded by some writers that paddy apparently makes no special demands regarding soil, but though this may be true—or what is more likely, types of paddy have been found particularly suited to certain types of soil—the influence of soil characteristics must be of importance, not alone when related to the requirements of the crop but also in conjunction with response to manuring.

Apart from the desirability of growing the crop on a heavy soil capable of holding water on the land, there appears to be direct evidence that it grows better on heavy clay soil than upon the lighter soils containing a higher proportion of sand. Provided that sufficient water is available to maintain irrigation, satisfactory yields are frequently obtained on quite sandy soils when they are given heavy dressings of organic matter, and frequently, too, if they are given fertilizers. The "mucks" and peat soils are usually considered less suitable for this crop, a decision doubtless due, at least in part, to the difficulty in draining and cultivating such soils. While, therefore, exceptional circumstances may determine the suitability of a soil for paddy cultivation, there appears to be no doubt that the heavier types, especially if they contain a satisfactory amount of organic matter, are most suited for paddy growing, and most good paddy-yielding areas will be found to consist of a soil wherein the finer particles—clay plus silt—are high, being generally about 70 per cent. Ramiah,[512] summarizing information supplied by workers in a number of Asian countries, states that variations in soil conditions and the extension of paddy cultivation to unsuitable soils appear to be two of the reasons for the wide disparity of yields; in Burma, for instance, average yields are reported to be declining as a result of extension of cultivation to unsuitable areas. He adds that historical records show that yields in India were about 50 per cent higher during the Mongol period than at present.

Chemical analysis of a soil does not appear to provide a very sure guide to its suitability for paddy cultivation. The fact that soils may be made to produce satisfactory paddy crops annually for centuries shows that the case is one that can find no parallel in agriculture. Thus, paddy soils are found to be very dissimilar in chemical composition, yet yielding equally good crops. The apparent paradox may be partly explained by the nutrient-carrying rôle of irrigation water.

SOIL STRUCTURE

Soil structure, of such great importance to most crops, is of little or no significance for swamp paddy. The ideal condition of the soil for paddy is a creamy mud devoid of crumbs, and underwater tillage is designed to produce this condition in addition to suppressing weeds. The case is otherwise with upland (dry) paddy and in certain mechanically-cultivated irrigated areas where a good structure promotes penetration of rain water.

ACIDITY OF SOILS

It is noted that good paddy soils are almost invariably acid in reaction, the pH value usually varying from about 5·5 to 6·5. Thorp[654] has related soil reaction and salinity to crop yields in China. While admitting that the figures of yield on the saline soils are based on insufficient data, he gives the following results of yields (lb. per acre): 2,678 from soils pH below 6·5; 2,614 from neutral soils with pH 6·5 to 7·5; 2,320 from saline alkaline soils pH above 7·5; 1,920 from non-saline alkaline soils above pH 7·5. The figures appear to confirm results elsewhere; while paddy is tolerant of considerable variation in soil reaction, it does appear to show a preference for the acid types. Most of the highly productive paddy soils of China are either slightly or strongly acid. In India, Bal and Misra[64] found that the light rich soils in the area of their investigations had a lower pH value than the heavy soils, and concluded that the paddy plant prefers a slightly acidic or neutral medium to an alkaline one. In Malaya, Grantham[227] stated that there is no apparent connection between fertility and acidity shown by lime absorption; in fact, the best paddy soils, he concluded, are the most acid. Examining the cause of unproductivity of a certain volcanic soil for paddy in Japan, Kamoshita[322] found, as a result of pot experiments, that the alkaline reaction of the soil is harmful to paddy during the first period of growth. Despite this concensus of opinion paddy is found growing successfully on highly alkaline soils with pH over 8 along the coastal areas of Bengal, Orissa, Madras, and small isolated patches in the interior of Bihar and the East Punjab States.[512] On the successful Murrumbidgee area in New South Wales the pH is 7·5 to 8. Paddy soils in Peru are also highly alkaline: it is stated[190] that paddy will not develop on these soils unless water supply is abundant at all times and the crop is transplanted.

The pH of a paddy soil influences the availability and uptake of mineral elements by the plant. Aoki[53] found that the solubility of soil phosphate increased when the reaction changed beyond the range pH 5 to 7. The degree of increase was larger under paddy-field conditions than under dry-land conditions.

The pH of a paddy soil, however, is not static. Dennett[168] showed that paddy soils in a flooded condition and during fallow showed large differences in pH value, changes being from pH 4·5–5·0 to 6·5–7·0, the values being reversed as soon as irrigation water is run off. Ponnamperuma[496] also studied changes of pH when the land is flooded; the largest change observed in 8 days was 0·5 units and in 51 days 1·6 units, while Karunakar and Daniel[326] showed that the variation occurred irrespective of manurial treatment, but corresponded to definite growth fluctuations of the plant. In Louisiana[521] the pH of virgin soil in flooded condition increased; with cultivated soil the pH was higher to begin with, but still increased with flooding. The pH showed a tendency to rise in the presence of organic matter.

Recently, Tomlinson showed[667] that in the West African Rice Research Station at Rokupr, Sierra Leone, there is a marked seasonal variation of pH on the surface soil of cleared mangrove swamp which has been used for paddy cultivation for some fifty years. The pH value rises during the wet season and falls during the dry season and in some cases the magnitude of the fluctuation is as great as three pH units. He suggests that this fluctuation is a result of translocation to and from the soil surface of water-soluble acidic compounds. In this investigation Tomlinson also found that the fluctuation of soil pH value is accompanied by fluctuations in the level of availability of iron, aluminium and phosphorus in the soils. He points to two important consequences of this phenomenon; firstly, soils of this type are cultivated in Sierra Leone with trans-planted seedlings, the time of transplanting usually being dependent on the salinity of the soil. However, the same investigator has shown[666] that seedlings do not survive if transplanted into soils of pH value less than about 3 units and make poor growth unless the pH is greater than about 5 units. It follows that if the pH value of the surface soil fluctuates through these values, the time of transplanting may be of great importance. The second point concerns soil sampling for analysis in connection with fertilizer advisory work. He shows that, particularly in the case of phosphate, the fluctuation of surface soil pH value would complicate seriously the assessment of soil fertility by analytical methods and careful account must be taken of the time of soil sampling if attempts are made to assess the fertility of soils by these methods.

Fertilizers applied to the soil may change the pH value of the soil to a considerable degree. Long-continued application of ammonium sulphate increases acidity and decreases the content of bases. Bal and Misra[64] found that the pH value of the soil is lowered by an adequate application of sulphur.

Studies by Bartholomew[70] to estimate the effect of irrigation on the pH of paddy soils showed that calcium, iron and aluminium, and the pH of the water used, caused reversion of large amounts of soil phosphate. Irrigation also induced alkalinity in the surface of the soil. The same writer also found[69] that the use of water containing a high proportion of bases renders added phosphate unavailable to plants.

It is evident that in some countries excellent crops of paddy are obtained in alkaline soils while in other regions it may thrive equally well in an acid soil. It is also shown that soil acidity is not static but varies under irrigation, plant growth conditions and season. One can but support the doubt expressed by Went[695] as to whether the pH of the soil really is of any importance in the growth of the plant other than by influencing the availability of nutrient elements.

SULPHIDES IN SOILS

Soils in some areas carry large amounts of sulphides. Such soils occur frequently in coastal areas as tidal swamps carrying mangrove and other species tolerant of very acid conditions. When cleared for paddy cultivation these soils present special problems. In Malaya they are known as "gelam" soils.[139] In West Africa Tomlinson[666] has studied their properties in regard to their suitability for paddy cultivation. Under oxidizing conditions such soils can produce extremely low pH values, even down to pH 2. He found that below pH 4 growth of paddy was greatly reduced and below pH 3 it could not survive. As the pH falls, free iron and aluminium ions appear in the soils. Tomlinson estimated that 1,000 ppm. of iron is harmful to paddy and 10,000 ppm. toxic. Corresponding levels for aluminium appeared to be 250 and 1,500 ppm. respectively. It seems probable that the damage to the paddy is mainly due to free iron and aluminium ions. In these sulphate soils there are very rapid fluctuations in pH values according to changes in the water regime, there being a very rapid drop on drying due to oxidation changes. Though good crops can be raised on such soils they need special management and ample water to remove toxic substances.

Hesse[270] points out that the nature of the muds in a coastal swamp appears to decide the kind of mangrove they support. Compared to the *Avicennia* swamp mud, that from the *Rhizophora* swamp has a higher pH value and a higher content of oxidizable sulphur, nitrogen, phosphorus and carbon. The apparent high rate of decomposition of the *Rhizophora* swamp mud as compared to that of mud under *Avicennia* is due to high oxygen uptake during sulphur oxidation.

SALINITY OF SOILS

Proximity to the sea resulting in occasional flooding of the land with sea water results in salinity of the soil. Certain varieties of paddy will flourish in a slightly saline soil, but the majority are adversely affected by salt. Pendleton[484] records that during the first few years that paddy is grown in the saline coastal clays of Thailand, the growth of straw is luxuriant but yields of grain low and of poor quality. The effect of sodium chloride at different concentrations on the growth of paddy has been studied by Del Valle and Bebé.[167] In pot experiments using clay loam soil, paddy plants 30, 60 and 90 days old were subjected until 164 days old to one of five concentrations of sodium chloride (0·15 to 1·0 per cent), the pH remaining at 7. The treatment retarded flowering by 5 to 15 days and the salt content of the plants varied directly with the salt concentration and length of irrigation from 0·25 per cent in the control without salt to 6·21 per cent in the 30-day plants subjected to a 1 per cent concentration. Concentration of 0·15 and 0·25 per cent greatly lowered the number of grains produced by the 30- and 60-day groups respectively; 0·25 and 0·35 per cent decreased grain size with two groups, while 0·5 per cent prevented grain formation and killed some of the plants in 60 to 110 days. Ninety-day plants were hardly affected by the concentrations used. Symptoms of sodium chloride toxicity are darkening of the green colour, withering of leaf tips, followed by yellowing and death.

Cultivators in Thailand[484] classify saline soils as bitter, salty and sour, others referring to certain soils as astringent. The experienced cultivator can decide on the suitability of the water on his land by taste, while others use betel juice, spitting some of the red mixture into the water standing on the field; if the colour remains red, the water is considered safe for planting; if it turns black the water is considered "sour" and planting is delayed.

Along the Malabar coast of south-west India, in the Tellichery District, there are some 15,000 to 20,000 acres of low paddy land which is flooded with salt water once or more annually. Under the "kai pad" method, the surface soil from each square yard over the area is heaped into mounds before the monsoon breaks. Sufficient paddy seed is planted on each mound to plant the soil when it is eventually levelled. The seed grows during the rainy season and at the end of July, when most of the salt has leached from the mounds and the floods have somewhat subsided, the mounds are levelled and the seedlings from each planted in the freshly-spread soil.

In Burma, Thailand, Malaya and British Guiana, and in some other regions, paddy is grown on coastal areas of clay, in some cases reclaimed from the sea or from old mangrove swamps, the soil being a blue, greasy-feeling clay of considerable depth which turns to a grey-blue colour on exposure. When the salt has been washed out of such soils they grow excellent crops. Salinity of soil has also been noted in Egypt (see page 50), successive flooding being resorted to with success to rid the land of excess salt. In Spain,[303] paddy is cultivated over a period of seven years on lands which have accumulated salinity. A similar method is adopted in the Punjab for irrigated land which has accumulated saline salts. The heavy irrigation for paddy washes out the salt and the land is thus restored for cultivation of crops other than paddy. The system of drains and canals established for paddy cultivation prevents a repetition of salt contamination. High yields are obtained in British Guiana, the crop being cultivated on the coastal areas characterized by the prevalence of heavy, sodium-magnesium sea-borne clays. Such soils may be alkaline, but with cultivation they become acid, a change which is ascribed to the removal of salts by irrigation water. While the soils are satisfactory in that they are of considerable depth and reasonably rich in plant nutrients, they are peculiarly susceptible to drought, due, it is said, to the soil shrinking and packing on drying and to their high content of salts which induces physiological drought. They therefore benefit considerably from periodic submergence and this has led to a system of "flood fallowing" for periods varying from four to twelve months. "The beneficial effects are attributable to washing out of injurious salts, combined with an improvement in soil texture apparently consequent upon an increase in the available iron content of the soil which tends to aggregate the finer soil particles."[527] This system of flood-fallowing in British Guiana is a unique feature of sugar-cane cultivation in the Colony, in which connection it has been shown to be responsible for an increase in yield up to 40 per cent spread over three years. Investigations show that the effect is associated with an increase in the ammonium nitrogen content of the soil, equal to a dressing of 2 cwt. sulphate of ammonia per acre to the soil, and improvement in texture ascribed to the formation of a hydrophobic film of ferric oxide on the colloidal particles, and to an increased activity of micro-organisms concerned with the supply of plant nutrients.

SOME PADDY SOILS

The following notes are intended to give a generalized account of soil conditions relating to some of the more important rice regions. Unfortunately, the data are insufficient to enable one to correlate these soil analyses with yields.

Bruce[93] compared analyses of Asian paddy soils with those of Ceylon. He gives the following "average" of analyses from each area. (See Table 1.)

TABLE 1

COMPARISON OF PADDY SOILS FROM CEYLON AND OTHER COUNTRIES
(percentage)

Country	Coarse	Silt	Clay	Water absorbition	N	CaO	MgO	K_2O	Citric K_2O	P_2O_5	Citric P_2O_5
Ceylon	63	24	7	48	0·184	0·285	0·351	0·314	0·160	0·114	0·012
South India	52	29	10	51	0·070	1·398	0·801	0·618	0·019	0·169	0·017
Burma	14	55	21	66	0·112	0·600	1·127	0·921	0·016	0·188	0·012
Malaya	34	48	11	71	0·132	0·270	0·438	0·008	0·008	0·074	0·005
Thailand	8	48	27	60	0·248	0·270	0·280	0·131	0·014	0·047	0·007
Philippines	45	34	13	60	0·098	1·880	1·001	0·405	0·016	0·109	0·015
Japan	52	32	10	58	0·179	0·465	0·288	0·431	0·017	0·176	0·017

The detailed chemical analysis of paddy soils studied by Bruce still further accentuates the wide differences to be found in soils considered satisfactory for paddy cultivation. (See Table 2.)

Graham[224] states that the rice-producing soils of the Central Provinces of India are formed almost entirely upon pre-Cambrian rocks of the Purana and Archaean groups. The actual material derived from the weathered rock is greatly modified in many cases

TABLE 2

CHEMICAL ANALYSES OF SOME ASIAN PADDY SOILS
(percentage)

	Moisture	Organic matter and combined water	Oxide of Fe and Mn	Oxide of alumina	Lime	Mg	Potash K_2O	Soda	Sulphuric anhydride	P_2O_5	Chlorine	Silica	Containing nitrogen
Galle District of Ceylon ...	3·000	13·340	4·240	24·026	0·200	0·087	0·154	0·337	0·123	0·128	0·035	54·330	0·230
Rich soil in C.P. India	3·340	14·720	13·760	17·554	0·180	0·230	0·378	0·509	0·096	0·141	0·012	49·080	0·235
Coimbatore District of India	5·400	4·200	4·000	11·738	0·940	1·325	0·942	0·525	0·014	0·154	0·012	70·750	0·056
Pegu District of Burma ...	4·800	7·800	6·720	11·780	0·440	1·210	0·903	0·515	0·069	0·205	0·038	65·520	0·134
Krian District of Malaya...	6·200	9·600	2·400	14·034	0·400	0·490	0·695	0·816	0·233	0·077	0·086	64·770	0·140
Alabang, Rizal, Philippines	5·200	7·400	7·040	13·604	1·040	0·677	0·347	0·769	0·069	0·102	0·012	63·740	0·101
Rangsit District of Thailand	6·070	13·650	1·530	5·400	0·260	0·240	0·106	—	0·810	0·514	—	—	0·434
Tokyo Chiba Prefecture, Japan	2·200	10·880	6·720	9·342	1·041	0·432	0·270	0·579	0·110	0·230	0·027	68·170	0·286

by rain-wash and admixture with soils of other types. "The typical rice soils of the Central Provinces have a high proportion of coarse particles and a correspondingly low proportion of clay, being suitable only for single cropping. The heavier soils suitable for double cropping are much finer in texture and therefore more retentive of moisture."

This attempt to relate type to suitability for double cropping is interesting. It would appear that the requirement is a "nice" balance between sand and clay, but it would be dangerous to assume that these requirements for double cropping are applicable to conditions in other countries, for the factors relating to double cropping are too diverse to be settled on the soil factor alone. Graham's observation is a valuable one and should be related to the soil analyses of areas where double cropping is customary. (See Table 3.)

TABLE 3

COMPOSITION OF TYPICAL PADDY SOILS IN THE CENTRAL PROVINCES OF INDIA
(percentage)

	Soils				
	1	2	3	4	5
Coarse sand 1 to 0·2 mm. diam. ..	22·59	43·38	5·66	12·69	16·45
Fine sand 0·2 to 0·04 mm. diam. ..	37·57	20·15	19·08	28·51	11·53
Silt 0·04 to 0·01 mm. diam. ..	17·77	7·88	38·82	24·79	13·66
Fine silt 0·01 to 0·002 mm. diam. ..	7·93	10·83	19·22	14·31	15·76
Clay below 0·002 mm. diam. ..	11·10	13·05	11·67	13·90	34·79
Calcium carbonate ..	0·31	0·20	0·08	0·04	1·18
Loss on ignition	2·42	4·47	3·58	3·19	5·02
Nitrogen	0·57	0·27	0·44	0·45	0·48

Pendleton[484] has described the formation, development and utilization of soils on the Bangkok Plain of Thailand, a low flat area with dark, grey clays, with rather higher land along the western, north-western, northern and north-eastern parts, where the soil is younger and of a light greyish-brown to light brown silt loam to light clay loam. These latter soils, he states, are less intensely cultivated, producing mostly upland crops, but when irrigated are superior paddy soils. The writer concludes that the soils of this vast plain exemplify many stages in the development of laterite from river-borne alluvium. Some stages are marine clays, young clays producing good paddy, mature and less fertile clays, senile unproductive soils and laterite. Except on silts recently deposited from the rivers, paddy is the only crop which can be grown on these soils. Pendleton describes how the sediments brought down by the rivers continue to extend the land southwards, besides periodically depositing finely grained alluvial materials over the area. The coarsest particles are deposited on the banks of the rivers, thus building up natural and fertile levees on which villages are established, the finer particles being deposited over the back country. It is because these soils have developed from very finely grained alluvial material, and because weathering has continued in the uppermost portions of these materials, that the soils of the plain are almost entirely clay. Floods deposit silt and clay from higher upstream, bringing plant material in addition to inert leached material.

The soils of the Central Plain of Thailand[534] are almost impermeable, being heavy clay. In some places crystals of gypsum are found near the surface. Thailand soils were reported on by Bruce,[93] who described them as clay silts, the coarse particles being 8 per cent, silts 48 per cent, and clay 27 per cent. Ladell has shown that the yield of paddy increases as the percentage of fine fractions ranges from 63·8 to 72 per cent. But in practice no reconnaissances to determine whether or not the soil is likely to be suitable for paddy cultivation are carried out in Thailand, water supply being held to be the dominant factor, so that light, rather sandy soils are considered suitable provided that sufficient water is available to compensate for their poor water-holding capacity.

Except for small areas in the coastal strip and the Shan Plateau, the important agricultural soils of Burma are situated in the Central belt consisting of the basins of the rivers Chindwin, Irrawaddy and Sittang. Most of the belt is covered by tertiary sediments and alluvium. The soil texture is fine, so that percolation is almost nonexistent and drainage is therefore by surface run-off. The level topography restricts surface drainage so that extensive areas are waterlogged during the south-west monsoon rains from June to September and are therefore suited only for paddy cultivation.[7]

The physical characteristics of Malayan paddy soils are 27 to 46 per cent of fine sand, while the fine fractions are approximately 40 per cent clay and fine silt, and 20 per cent of coarse silt. The best land in Malaya, producing exceptionally high crops, contains 21 per cent fine silt, 15 per cent silt, and 58 per cent of clay. Land in Kedah, immediately south of Thailand, showed on analysis 31·7 per cent of fine silt, 27·2 per cent silt, and 31 per cent of clay.[76]

Buck[94] has classified the paddy areas of China (see Fig. 1). He shows that the rice regions in that country lie between latitudes 23° and 32° north, and extend from sea-level to 1,500 metres. Except in

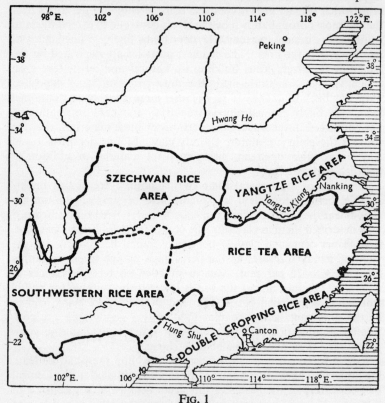

FIG. 1
The rice areas of China
(After J. L. Buck, *Land Utilization in China*)

the coastal province of Kiangsu, the amount of rice produced north of the 32nd parallel is comparatively small, while for some distance south of it rice is not the staple food of the inhabitants. The climate in the rice region is temperate and sub-tropical, considerably tempered by maritime influences along the coast. Humidity is high, and average rainfall about 50 inches. The growing season is about 326 days, the average temperature being 67·1° F. The summers are very hot and humid, but winter frosts are experienced in some areas. In the northern half of the area winter crops, such as wheat and barley, are followed by paddy in the summer; in the southern half of the region there are no winter crops, therefore paddy is followed by paddy. Double cropping extends over two-thirds of the area. Thorp[654] states that in some places a small third paddy crop is obtained in the year by interplanting before the second crop is harvested. Buck's divisions of the Chinese area are —the double-cropping area of Kwang Tung 113° E. longitude, the South-western area 30° N. latitude, and the Yangtse area 116° E. longitude; south of this is the rice-tea area. Paddy is thus grown on a wide range of soils in China, varying in origin and composition. Thorp states that the highest yields are obtained from the dark-coloured, slightly podzolized or unpodzolized soils, but adds that good yields are also obtained from the podzolic types developed from the recent alluvium in the large valleys. There are also large areas of paddy soils in China that are but little podzolized, most of which are dark in colour and some almost black. They occur in the flood plains of the great rivers and lakes of Szechwan eastwards to the China Sea, and south-west along the sea-coast on the deltas of the various small rivers. These dark soils are characterized by the almost complete absence of sand, and the approximately equal amounts of clay and silt. Podzolized paddy soils developed from the Old Red Earths are very poor, but by continual cultivation and very heavy dressings of manure they are made to give surprisingly high yields of paddy. The red paddy soils developed from the grey-brown and brown podzolic soils or from alluvium in the small valleys between them are more fertile, and are able to retain fertilizers longer than the soils derived from lateritic materials.

Many of the paddy soils in the fertile Szechwan Basin are developed entirely from the purple-brown and purple soil materials washed down from the hills. Most of these soils, derived from the purple-brown materials, are slightly acid in reaction and are quite productive. The Old Red and Yellow Earths, though very poor, are made to produce high yields by heavy and continued manuring.

Thorp says that most of the soils on which paddy is grown in the Yangtse rice-wheat area are non-calcareous, heavy-textured, stiff and plastic, where drainage conditions are imperfect or poor. Good crops can, however, be produced on the friable, light-textured types of soil, provided there is a heavy substratum to hold up the water. Much of the paddy lands in China, as is pointed out by both Thorp and Buck, have been changed materially by cultivation and manuring until they have been adapted for paddy cultivation, regardless of their original characteristics, and Thorp states that practically all the

alluvial lands have been renewed many times by periodical deposi-
tions during the past forty centuries.

Thorp has attempted to correlate types of paddy soils in China
with yields obtained. His data show that the highest yields are
obtained from the grey-brown podzolic soils, the dark-coloured silty
paddy soils, and the non-calcareous grey silty and clayey alluvium.
The poorest yields are obtained from the podzolic grey-brown clay
pan, many of the podzolic Red and Yellow Earths, and consistently
from the calcareous alluvium.

"The use of night-soil as a manure and the cost of transporting
it for more than a limited distance," observes Richardson,[559] "has
led to the building up of a ring of highly fertile soils around the cities,
with a corresponding degree of impoverishment of the country farther
away. . . . In the hilly parts of China the fertility of the soil is
generally lower than on the plains, crops are poorer, and the effects
of nutrient deficiencies are evident to the eye." This heavy manuring
around the cities has also been noted in India.

The soils of Formosa are mainly composed of sandstones and
shales of a fairly light and free-draining nature and are of moderate
fertility. Owing to the rapid decay of vegetable matter and heavy
leaching, they are poor in humus throughout the island. From
the extreme north down to the western plain to approximately
mid-point, soils contain very little clay, are acid in reaction, and are
lacking in plant food. South of the Tropic, the soils are more clayey,
the proportion of clay reaching its maximum near Tainan and
decreasing further south. Certain of the soils on the east derived
from limestones and schists, with mixed sandstones and shales, are
alkaline in reaction and poor in nitrogen.

In contrast with the heavy soils usually associated with paddy
cultivation in Asia, the soils of the paddy-growing area of Italy
are generically more or less sandy clays. In the Vercellese region
of high yields the soil is described[649] as alluvio glacial types except in the neighbourhood of river-beds where they are replaced
by recent alluvium. Luigi Borazio[727] gives the following four
mechanical analyses of typical soils in this area.

TABLE 4

MECHANICAL ANALYSES OF ITALIAN PADDY SOILS
(percentage)

Description	Soils			
	1	2	3	4
Coarse earth about 1 mm. diam.	10	5	2·5	2·0
Fine earth below 1 mm. diam. ..	90	95	97·6	98·0

The chemical analyses of the first two of the above samples is stated to be:

	Percentage	
Moisture	1·40	1·34
Organic matter ..	3·40	2·90
Total nitrogen ..	0·19	0·15
Total phos. anhydride	0·17	0·12
Pot. oxide	0·11	0·11
Calcium oxide ..	0·49	0·65
Magnesium oxide ..	0·79	0·67
Acidity (*p*H) ..	6·6	6·8

Soils on which paddy is grown on the Murrumbidgee Irrigation Areas and also in south-eastern Australia, usually belong to the soil groups of "red-brown earths" and "grey and brown soils of heavy texture". The former group are brown or red-brown soils with strong texturally differentiated surface and subsoil horizons, and a definite zone of lime accumulation in the subsoil. The second group contains both brown and grey soils with shallow (generally less than 4 inches) surface horizons of medium to heavy texture or with little or no development of a surface horizon. Profiles are heavy throughout, often with only slight accumulation of carbonates and usually with gypsum in the deep subsoil. These "grey and brown soils of heavy texture" often occur as a Gilgai complex, the puff component of which may be referred to as calcareous, crumbly soils. In this group also occur soils commonly called self-mulching soils, characterized by a strong grade of structure in the surface, giving rise to the appearance of a freshly-cultivated soil. They are of heavy texture throughout the profile, with little differentiation apart from the structural development at the surface.

A typical "red-brown earth" soil is the Birganbigil, which occurs extensively in the Murrumbidgee Irrigation Areas. This soil has 5 to 6 inches on a compact loam surface, beneath which occurs a dark brown or reddish-brown, medium-blocky, heavy clay with a gradual change with depth to a light yellow-brown, fairly dense, medium clay, at about 36 inches. Some concretionary carbonates occur below 18 inches. There is very little change with depth unless some unrelated material is present. Gypsum sometimes occurs at a depth below 36 inches.

Typical members of the great soil group referred to as "grey and brown soils of heavy texture" are soils of the Wilbriggie series. Wilbriggie clay has 1 to 2 inches of compacted light brown brittle surface soil of light texture, below which is a dark brown, heavy clay

continuing to considerable depths. Slight amounts of concretionary
carbonate are found below 15 inches, while gypsum may be present
below 24 to 30 inches. Wilbriggie clay loam, another member of the
same series, is transitional to the "red-brown earths" and has 2 to
4 inches of clay loam surface; gypsum appears at a slightly greater
depth. All other morphological characteristics are comparable with
those of the clay type. Both soils are widespread on the Murrumbidgee Areas and adjoining irrigation areas where paddy is
grown.[84, 632]

Commenting on the above and on the general conditions governing paddy cultivation in Australia, Jessup states:*

> All the soils on which rice is grown are high in clay except for the
> surface horizons of the red-brown earths. Consequently, infiltration
> rates are generally low. However, soil is only one aspect of suitability
> of land for rice-growing. Where rice-growing under irrigation is con-
> cerned, land classification as distinct from a soil classification depends
> on an integration of both soil and the underlying geological conditions,
> which control ground-water behaviour.
>
> The deep percolation component of rice water consumption and lia-
> bility to salting and development of water-tables in rice lands is a func-
> tion of the underlying geological conditions. This has been found to be
> completely independent of the actual soils on which rice is grown,
> when considered from an agronomic aspect.
>
> Several aspects of rice production vary with the two great soil groups,
> i.e. red-brown earth and grey and brown soils of heavy texture. Firstly,
> the capacity of red-brown earth soils to respond more rapidly to increasing
> air temperature than the heavier soils, permits earlier sowing and gener-
> ally results in more rapid germination and brairding. In the case of the
> grey and brown soils, careful attention must be paid to time of sowing
> and subsequent germination "flushings", to control soil moisture and
> reduce the effect of soil surface crusting. It is well recognized that a
> successful germination and establishment is one of the main contri-
> buting factors governing high yields. Owing to the greater difficulty
> in obtaining satisfactory establishment on the grey and brown soils,
> yields on the average are somewhat lower than those obtained from the
> warmer red-brown earths. However, with careful management indivi-
> dual growers, in suitable seasons, are producing crops of $3\frac{1}{2}$ to 4 tons
> per acre on these heavy soils.

One soil type in the Murrumbidgee Irrigation Area in New South
Wales is described as shallow, medium to heavy clay soil overlying
a stiff clay subsoil which had previously proved unproductive when
sown to other crops. This soil, under a rotational system, yields an
average of 1·8 tons of paddy per acre.[281] The best yield in the 1954–5

* Private communication from Mr J. E. Jessup.

season was $2\frac{1}{2}$ tons an acre, a world record for a paddy crop produced by completely mechanical methods.

In California[694] paddy is grown on a soil that is described as sticky and waxy. It holds water well, but cracks badly when thoroughly dry. Grey to black soil of this type, known as Stockton clay adobe, is said to be typical of most of this paddy-growing area of California. In the Sacramento Valley the principal soils on which paddy is grown are the clays and clay adobes of the Stockton, Willows, Sacramento, Capay and Yolo series. The mechanical analyses of these soil types are shown in the following table.

TABLE 5

MECHANICAL ANALYSES OF SOME CALIFORNIA PADDY SOILS
(percentage)

Soil	Fine gravel	Coarse sand	Med. sand	Fine sand	Very fine sand	Silt	Clay
Stockton clay adobe:							
Surface 0–28″ ..	0·2	0·4	0·9	3·5	16·7	32·2	46·0
Subsoil 28–40″	0·6	0·9	0·1	3·5	20·7	30·4	42·3
Substratum 40–							
70″	0·3	2·3	2·8	6·6	26·6	40·2	21·7
Sacramento clay:							
Surface 0–40″ ..	0·7	1·9	1·4	6·7	22·4	34·9	32·6
Subsoil	0·9	1·4	2·1	7·1	24·0	31·8	32·9

Chapter III

WATER SUPPLY AND CONTROL

DRAINAGE AND IRRIGATION

SUCCESSFUL paddy cultivation depends on adequately inundating the fields during the greater part of the growth period of the plant. This sounds simple enough, but in practice this desideratum is reached only after solving a number of problems that vary in importance in each particular case. In many areas it becomes not so much a matter of supplying sufficient water as to control the water; not always the supply of water but its drainage; or again, it may be the supply of water at one time of the year and its drainage at a later date. Ramiah[512] has pointed out that there is no relationship between the total quantity of rain and yield, countries such as Egypt, Italy, Australia and the United States being characterized by moderate rainfall but provided with irrigation facilities, whereas in parts of East Pakistan, Burma, Thailand, Cambodia and Viet-Nam and a number of other countries, there is often too much water during the season; drainage is therefore impossible, planting delayed and carried out in deep water with overgrown seedlings. Crops, therefore, suffer from poor planting conditions as well as floods in their active growing stage.

Irrigation implies not only an adequate and controlled water supply, but also efficient drainage of excess water whenever desirable. The supply and control of water, in fact, is the most important aspect of irrigated paddy cultivation; given an adequate and well-controlled water supply the crop will grow in a wide range of soils and in many climates. It is therefore more important than the type of soil.

It is generally agreed that paddy should be planted in a well-soaked field but with little standing water and that the depth of water should be increased with the plants' growth until the depth is from six to twelve inches. This applies to transplanted paddy; other conditions are desirable with broadcast or drilled paddy. When the plant flowers the water should be gradually drawn off till at harvest time the field is dry. During growth of the plant the water should not be stagnant, but gently flowing. Paradoxically, the objective of the rice grower in New South Wales is to supply just enough water to

10. A brushwood dam, Malaya

11. A new dam to replace a brushwood dam, Malaya

12. Final cultivation, British North Borneo—work with dignity

13. Asian primitive water-wheel

his crop to compensate for losses with no overflow, and his yields are amongst the highest in the world. Soil aeration, in part, is achieved by cultivation, but it is also attained by the movement of water over the area and by algal activity. It is believed that certain soils in Java and one valley in the extreme south of Madras State produce high paddy yields because their soils are pervious, the percolating water carrying oxygen with it. Where the paddy field remains under stagnant water for any length of time growth is affected, probably because decomposition of organic matter depends largely on oxygen and in the absence of oxygen nitrates cannot be formed. It is possible, too, that chemical reactions induced by anaerobic conditions lead to the formation of substances toxic to the plant.

This simple statement of the water requirement of paddy may be open to question, for the optimum depth of water appears to vary in different countries. It is, however, generally accepted that adequate tillering is desirable with transplanted paddy and, except possibly in the cultivation of special varieties of paddy, deep water inhibits tillering and results in a decreased crop. Necessarily, this is a counsel of perfection, for over the vast majority of paddy fields in the East the cultivator has incomplete control over the water supply. Considering the difficulties, the degree of success achieved by Asian cultivators in harnessing water for irrigating their fields must be recognized.

WATER REQUIREMENTS

The actual amount of water required by the crop depends on a number of factors. An excessive depth of water on the land will not influence transpiration of water by the plant, for this remains constant regardless of the degree of saturation of the soil, although transpiration is increased by the application of phosphate, the effect being greater the drier the soil.[263] In India it has been found that manuring lowers the water requirements of the crop and that farm-yard manure is more effective in this respect than artificials. The paddy plant, in fact, takes no more water than dry-land crops, but evidence[635] suggests that swamp conditions provide constituents such as silica, which are not ordinarily readily available in dry soil.

The principal factors influencing water consumption are field evaporation, seepage, preparation of land and initial flooding; while the conditions that have an important effect on these factors are— climatic conditions, characteristics of the soil, length of irrigation period, ground water-table, yield and method of planting, as well as method of irrigation. Temperature, humidity and wind velocity are the main factors affecting surface evaporation and transpiration in paddy-fields.

Matsushima,[28] working in Malaya, found that the transpiration ratio was 446, i.e., the amount of water necessary to produce one gram of dry matter was 446 c.c. From this figure the amount of water transpired by the paddy crop can be estimated. Thus, for a field yielding 3,000 lb. paddy per acre, the volume of water transpired would be 263,300 gallons per acre.

In Japan[356] the water requirement of paddy varies from 2·3 to 4·3 acre feet for the entire season, the standard depth of water in the field being one or two inches. Leonard,[356] who quotes these figures, adds that immediately after transplanting, the water should be rather deep to hold seedlings upright, but should be shallow at the tillering stage. Fields are dried for weeding or for application of a top-dressing of fertilizer. Irrigation is delayed for several days after top-dressing to prevent loss of fertilizer through leaching. Fields are finally drained when the crop begins to ripen. In many fields, however, this degree of water control is impossible.

In Thailand it is considered that the total amount of water required by the crop is six acre feet, but in most parts of the Central Plain the quantity of rainfall normally received during the growing period from June to November falls short of this amount by about 2·5 feet, so that the aim of the Irrigation Department is to utilize the natural water resources to augment this deficiency in rainfall and to regulate the quantity of water admitted strictly in accordance with crop requirements. It is stated that the ideal in this respect is to hold the depth of water on the field at about 30 per cent of the height of the growing plant.[97] In Indo-China it is considered that the amount of water required during the five months when paddy is planted out is four feet, but this figure does not take into account the water required for nurseries and preparation of the field. In Ceylon, six feet are considered necessary for a dry-season crop of from three to four months.[367] The average amount used on the Murrumbidgee Irrigation Area of New South Wales is about six feet per season, the actual requirement being influenced by the underlying geological and hydrological conditions, the season, density of the crop and layout of the field.[281]

Poorly constructed bunds will increase water requirement through loss by seepage and further, unskilled use of water supply results in waste. In Japan[287] a saving of 18 per cent can be made, with little detrimental effect on yield, by draining the field for ten days between late tillering and flowering. Where paddy is sown direct into the field, water may be saved by delaying irrigation until the tillering stage is reached.

In Louisiana and Texas,[310] forty-eight to sixty acre-inches of water are required to produce the crop; of this, a quarter to one-half may be supplied by rainfall during the growing season, the remainder being supplied from wells and streams. The actual requirements, however, vary according to topography of the land, as the presence of natural sloughs or draining courses passing through the area will drain off some of the irrigation water. In California, from sixty to seventy-two inches of water are required. Evapotranspiration from a Caloro paddy crop growing on Stockton clay adobe, grey phase, during a 160-day season was found to be between 2·8 and 3·0 acre feet. This study revealed the fact that, in practice, the water requirement for field production always exceeds 3 acre feet because of percolation losses and water spilled at the outfall weir.[516]

In the Hunan Province of China, total water requirement for medium-duration paddy is reported[462] to be about 34 inches, 55 per cent of which is used through transpiration, 25 per cent through soil percolation and 20 per cent through evaporation. Loss of water through evaporation can be very great under tropical conditions. Over a twelve-month period in Malaya[298] the loss amounted to 56·54 inches. Similar losses have been recorded in British Guiana.

The temperature of water depends partly on the rate of evaporation. Mono-molecular films of long-chain organic compounds such as celyl or stearyl alcohol, when spread on the water surface, reduce evaporation and thereby maintain water temperature. By spreading a mono-molecular film of a compound known as OED. the Japanese found it possible to raise the temperature of water on paddy fields by several degrees.

Though it has been shown that a slow continuous flow of water over the fields gives better yields than when water is held on the field and changed at intervals, the additional yield obtained from the high consumption of water required for continuous flow irrigation is not great enough to warrant this extravagant use of irrigation water. As water consumption rises, yields certainly increase, but on a diminishing scale so that, unless there is a superabundance of water, it is more economical to restrict water supplies to some 5 or 6 acre-feet, i.e. about 1 cusec for 60 acres (rainfall plus irrigation) and to increase the area irrigated.

QUALITY OF WATER

Yield of paddy depends in no small measure on the quality of water used for irrigation. Water may have a considerable fertilizing value because of its mineral nutrients, or may cause damage to the crop by poisonous or indirectly harmful substances.

Quality of water is dependent on its origin. River water is generally preferable to that from other sources. In addition to the fertilizing elements dissolved in such water, it carries silt and clay. While large masses of silt must be avoided, a reasonable quantity of coarse silt deposited on the land has a favourable effect on the soil. Very fine silt carried to the land in like manner frequently has an unfavourable effect on the plant's growth.

Der Berger's[79] experiments in Java showed that paddy-land distant from the source of irrigation water received less water than that situated nearer the source of supply, and the silt content of the water also decreased quickly as the water flowed over the land. The crop decreased also with the distance from the source of water supply, the difference in yield between fields irrigated with first-hand and second-hand water being very marked. It was concluded that plants in the first field retained a great part of the fertilizing substances in the water.

In controlled irrigation schemes, provided with separate drainage and irrigation canals, it may prove necessary in times of water shortage to pump water from drainage canals to replenish water in irrigation canals. While such a course may be employed to keep the land inundated for a few days to tide over a water crisis, the practice of using water more than once for irrigation must be deprecated, as it will be reflected in decreased yields of crop.

WATER CONTROL

Water control is essential if the growing crop is to be provided with adequate supplies as needed. It is customary in many countries to drain the land at least two or three times during growth of the crop, usually in connection with weeding and fertilizing. Periodical drainage is impossible, however, if water supply is uncertain, or its control imperfect, as inability to reinundate the fields would endanger the growing crop. The yield is seriously affected if the supply is insufficient, especially at the time of earing. Small quantities of water given at frequent intervals are more conducive to high yields than are larger quantities given at less frequent intervals.[534] In most countries, however, the irrigation periods are less frequent. In Italy, for instance, the fields are dried twice during growth, first for four or five days about twenty-five days after sowing and again after the last weeding, water is withheld for a few days. It is stated that this drying has a beneficial effect on soil aeration and root penetration. On the other hand, the custom of irrigating by day and draining by night is considered useless and often in-jurious.

In California, Mikkelsen reports[400] that *japonica* varieties grown under continuously flooded conditions produce better vegetative growth and at least 50 per cent more grain than when grown under intermittently irrigated conditions. Earlier work indicated that unflooded paddy yields were depressed because certain enzyme systems destroy growth substances and soils which are aerated allow nitrification to proceed with consequent losses of nitrogen by deni-trification after flooding. On the other hand, Lee Chow shows[353] that in Formosa intermittent irrigation is as good as, if not better than, continuous flow and results in a saving of 20 per cent of the water—a factor of considerable importance where two crops of paddy are grown each year and where water supply is not too plenti-ful. Bulanadi and Aldaba in the Philippines concluded,[96] as the result of an experiment with four varieties of paddy, that inter-mittent irrigation produced higher yields than continuous flow. There appears little doubt that intermittent irrigation with adequate water control is superior to continuous flow of water over the fields.

WATER CONTROL BETWEEN SEASONS

Whether the land be flooded or retained in a dry condition between paddy seasons is a debatable point. In many regions the cultivator has no choice in the matter; the crop is grown during the rainy season and there is no water available to flood the land in the off-season. In south-west China[279] the water fallow practice in winter on the paddy-fields is considered an important measure to store water for paddy cultivation in the coming spring and also to main-tain soil fertility by the process of waterlogged weathering. It is suggested, however, that in this area the cultivation of wheat on paddy-fields during the winter instead of using the land to store water is to be recommended, provided that manures are available and that storage of water is not essential for the subsequent irrigation of paddy.

Drying the land in the off-season is generally considered benefi-cial, as the process releases some of the nitrogen and phosphorus tied up in the soil organic complex. In Japan[531] so important is this drying considered that in some areas where the practice is rendered impossible by reason of inadequate water control, soil is removed from the field, dried under shelter and returned to the land a few days before transplanting commences. Paddy planters on the Bang-kok Plain, Thailand, believe that the longer and hotter the dry season, the more successful the subsequent paddy crop. In the Inrin district of Central Formosa, soil weathering is accomplished after ploughing by piling clods in lines several feet high.[634] In the Sudan Gezira area, the effect of a fallow is claimed to be equal to a dressing of 40 lb. of nitrogen per acre.

PRIMITIVE METHODS OF IRRIGATION

Asian manipulation of water for paddy cultivation is almost always directed towards lifting water from natural supplies and directing it to the paddy-fields. Methods to conserve water are usually beyond their power or resources, so that cultivation depends upon the ability to utilize seasonal rainfall. For this reason the vast and historic paddy-growing areas occur in the wet tropics, or are found adjacent to rivers that seasonally overflow their banks and inundate the surrounding country. The amount of rainfall considered necessary has therefore but local significance, for it depends upon the nature of the country and the natural facilities for maintaining flooded conditions sufficiently long to enable the crop to grow.

Development of irrigation works by government achieves two objects; firstly, as applied to existing paddy-fields, it relieves the grower of anxiety over seasonal variations of rainfall and secondly, by making better use of available water, it enables an extension of paddy planting in areas that otherwise would be considered unsuited to the crop.

The two chief methods used by the cultivator for raising water to flood the land are damming streams and lifting water from rivers and wells by waterwheels or gear operated by hand or other means.

Building a dam[229] is usually carried out on a communal basis; that is, cultivators whose land will benefit as a result of the dam assist in its construction. The river banks above and below the proposed dam are strengthened by wooden stakes and split bamboo. A row of very thick stakes is driven into the river bed from bank to bank. The distance between the stakes will depend upon the strength of the current and river depth. Between these stakes, which may be three feet apart, are placed smaller stakes, but still of no mean size. Thus a row of stakes is formed from bank to bank of the river. At a distance of about three feet up-river from this row of stakes a second row is erected, parallel with the first, composed of wood of about two inches diameter.

Meanwhile, bundles of sticks tied with roots or rotan have been collected and brought to the site. The bundles are about fifteen inches in diameter and are placed at right angles to, and between the two rows of stakes. In placing the bundles into position, care is taken that they are well pressed down, with the thick ends close to the stronger line of stakes. This erection of bundles of wood is carried to the ultimate height of water over the dam. When this work is completed it is seen that a great quantity of water finds its way between the bundles and the water level above the dam is not materially altered. Sods of turf, earth and grass, freshly dug, are then packed behind the dam, till the level of this mass rises to the height of the dam. The water has now risen on the upstream side of the dam and flows into a watercourse which carries it to the paddy-fields. Surplus water flows over the dam. In cases where there is a considerable weight of water behind the dam, the dam is further strengthened by placing large poles diagonally from below the dam, the upper and forked ends of which support the large upright posts first erected. Below the dam, at a distance of perhaps ten yards, a small fragile dam is made of a row of stakes against which are placed split bamboo. This is a necessary precaution against the danger of the dam being undermined.

It will be realized that construction of a dam calls for great patience and much hard work. The resultant dam is frequently quite inadequate to withstand a strong flood such as frequently results from torrential tropical rain and such a catastrophe may spell ruin to the growing crop by withholding the water supply at a critical period.

The waterwheel is usually undershot and designed to lift water from a river to irrigate land on one bank, but occasionally land on both sides of the river is irrigated from a single wheel. The diameter of the wheel is from twelve to fifteen feet and supplied with bamboo internodes from ten to fifteen in number for lifting the water. The hub of the wheel is of hard wood, fixed at either end to a wooden platform. The wheel cannot rise and fall according to the height of the river. The spokes are of bamboo and the circumference of the wheel is constructed of twisted rotan. Water when lifted falls into a wooden trough which delivers it to the watercourse serving the paddy-field. The amount of water lifted is usually sufficient for about three acres of land.

In the vast areas of Lower Burma, from which the bulk of the exportable crop of that country comes, real swamp conditions exist and there appears to be little or no control of the water supply. Further up-country irrigation is practised, in addition to which small areas also exist, bordering rivers and subject to flood, where successive plantings are possible, level by level, as the flood water subsides.

TERRACING

Terraces for paddy cultivation on mountain sides may be seen in various parts of Asia, particularly in northern Luzon in the Philippines and in parts of Java, Japan and Ceylon. The Ifugao terraces in Luzon cover an area of about 250 square miles and are a remarkable piece of engineering, even judged by modern standards. In Ceylon hill areas of paddy fields occupy the sides and spurs of narrow valleys up to about 4,000 feet altitude and are beautifully terraced. Tobata,[660] writing about the terraced fields in Japan states that he once counted 250 "fields" (divisions) in an area of only three-quarters of an acre. The smallest "field" contained only four "hills" of paddy when fully planted. Terraces of this description are irregular, conforming to the configuration of the land, and must have entailed a tremendous amount of work in construction. The water is obtained from mountain streams, irrigation channels being made so that the whole area is supplied. Great ingenuity is shown in the employment of water, which sometimes has to be carried over chasms.

Terraced paddy-fields on steep hillsides may lead to erosion and landslides. Gorrie[220] instances such damage in Ceylon, where heavy and continuous irrigation renders the whole hillside unstable. He states that far too much water is supplied to the fields with no separate storm drains to lead away the surplus runoff. The result is waterlogging which works into the deeper layers of montmorrillonite or china clay, transforming them into a greasy slipway over which the whole mass creeps or skids. The remedies, he states, are strict economy of irrigation water, provision of storm drains and rotation of non-irrigated crops with paddy, thus giving the ground a chance of drying out between paddy crops.

LIFTING WATER

The Asian has shown considerable skill in the methods employed in harnessing water for irrigating his paddy-land. For instance, surveys of the ancient irrigation canals of Angkor show that a moat 4 kilometres long gave an error of about 1 cm., while the sections of a canal 60 kilometres long ran dead straight.[233] Levels have to be worked out by eye on a trial-and-error basis—and the errors are few. The main weakness of the work is usually its impermanence, for most of the dams, waterwheels, waterways and other devices last but one season, while heavy rain may destroy the work soon after its completion. The employment of such methods usually restricts cultivation to areas of heavy rainfall or to natural undrained swamps. Paddy cultivation, however, does not depend on heavy rainfall, but on adequate irrigation, and where this is possible by the construction of modern irrigation works on a large scale, cultivation may be extended to areas of low rainfall.

The Persian waterwheel and the Shadouf are two ancient and primitive methods of lifting water for irrigation, still in common use in the Middle East and India. Tothill[668] describes the former as a large wooden wheel with wooden teeth on the outer rim, mounted on a vertical shaft, from the upper part of which projects a horizontal arm, to which are yoked two bulls. This wheel drives a similar but smaller wooden-toothed wheel, mounted on a horizontal shaft, the other end of which carries a large open-spoked wheel with a wide periphery. The latter carries two parallel endless ropes, joined by spacing bars, to which are attached a series of water containers. The loop of the parallel ropes dips into the water and, as the wheel revolves, the filled containers are carried to the top of the wheel, where they spill their contents into a trough, whence the water flows to the field. This waterwheel can raise water three to eight metres, but is considered an inefficient method of lifting water.

Tothill describes the Shadouf as a very primitive but effective and cheap method of raising water by man-power through two or three metres, with the added advantage of being easy to construct and maintain. It consists essentially of two posts supported by a crossbar on which is pivoted a long wooden lever, to the shorter end of which is fixed a weight to act as a counterpoise to a rod or rope and dipper attached to the long arm. The rod is seized high up and pulled down until the dipper enters the water. The full dipper is then allowed to rise, pulled up by the counter-weight, until it reaches the level of a trough or channel into which it empties, the water flowing to the field. At a lift of two metres it is stated to raise from three to five cubic metres of water per hour.

A common method of raising water, practised in China, is by means of a locally-made foot-pedal machine, light enough to be carried by one man from one terrace to another. It is described by Efferson[190] as being built of wood, bamboo and paddy-straw rope. It is composed of a long, narrow wood trough from twenty to forty feet long, about a foot wide and a foot deep. Moving up this trough is part of a wood and paddy-straw circular chain with paddles about every foot that fit into the trough. The circular chain is attached to a roller on the upper end by means of wood gears, and on the roller there are several footrests, similar to the spokes of a wheel. The power, when applied to these footrests, turns the roller which moves the circular chain up the trough, pulling water from the lower terrace or stream to the field being irrigated. The power is human, the worker treading the footrests with a movement similar to that used when riding a bicycle. The more typical machines have positions for two people and on large farms there may be four or sometimes six people operating one of the larger machines. A more elaborate wooden-gear attachment is sometimes constructed so that the power may be supplied by buffalo; these outfits, however, are not movable and are used only for the first lift from the stream to the lowest terraces of the field.

In Japan, irrigation is supplied by numerous artificial ponds, called *plate* ponds, scattered over the fields, and an elaborate network of canals. These ponds and canals are the results of many years of hard work. Their maintenance also requires much labour because they are always threatened by floods and typhoons. In Kagawa Prefecture in Shikoko, where drought often threatens the paddy crop, there are hundreds of thousands of small artificial ponds, the total acreage of which is estimated at 15 per cent of the acreage of paddy land. In Saga Prefecture in Kyushu, the creeks for artificial irrigation occupy 10 per cent or more of the acreage of paddy land, while in Hyogo Prefecture there are 50,000 small ponds, all of which are shallow and very inefficient.[660]

In contrast to the above and perhaps indicating a sign of the times, the writer has seen a Tangye pump, owned by a small cultivator in British Guiana and let on hire to neighbours, for pumping excess water from paddy-fields.

MODERN IRRIGATION

Irrigation schemes may have any of the following objects in view: firstly, replacement of primitive means of raising water by modern and permanent works, such as concrete dams; secondly, construction of permanent works for irrigating new areas, by such means as empounding water in reservoirs, pumping schemes and dams; and thirdly, by devising drainage schemes. Drainage is often more important than irrigation and many existing areas have been improved by the adoption of schemes to drain the land as required.

While the paddy plant is tolerant of considerable variation in the quality of water in which it will grow, there is no doubt that to produce the best results the plant should be supplied with water which carries no contamination. One would expect that well-aerated water is best, but this is not always possible to obtain. Water in movement will ensure a degree of aeration. Temperature of the water affects paddy growth. Observations in Japan[379] have shown that a decrease of about 10 per cent production may be expected for each 1° C. (approx. 1·7° F.) fall in temperature of irrigation water at noon within the scope of 22° to 29° C. (69° to 81° F.). If the water temperature falls below 22° C. (69° F.) there is a sharp decrease in production. Growth and tillering may be more vigorous at the head of valleys that receive cold water newly emerged from a mountain stream than downstream, but this improved growth may well be caused by fertilizer material dissolved in the water, or to aeration of the water. Ueki found[671] that the number of tillers and spikelets per unit area decreased as the temperature of irrigation water at tillering increased from 71° to 86° F. The number and weight of grains per unit were greatest when the mean water temperature was 77° to 79° F. and the maximum temperature was under 86° F. Water temperature of 100° F. and over are frequently observed in paddy fields containing newly-planted paddy. There appears to be no information of the effect of this water temperature on paddy growth. The optimum temperature for tillering, according to the Japanese,[379] is 89° to 93° F., but this will vary with the variety and the stage of growth. Thus, the optimum temperature in the young ear stage or in the heading stage is higher than in the early seedling and fruiting stages.

It has been pointed out that the primary work of a drainage and irrigation department is the provision of permanent works to replace the temporary works constructed by cultivators. Land cannot be irrigated to its greatest advantage by primitive methods. Permanent works may be expected to result in better controlled water systems with fewer dams and with less work on maintenance. "Irrigation practice," states Murray,[422] "concerns itself with the elevation of river flows to riparian areas by means of dams or pumping plants. The usual system of feeder channels is provided on a pattern to suit local conditions, and a comprehensive system of drainage to remove excess water from unseasonal rainfall is an essential feature. . . . In addition, certain areas which have no available supply of irrigation water are operated as controlled drainage areas in which the water-table is carefully controlled by drainage works, and rainfall in the area is retained or drained off as circumstances demand. Areas of this type are found in the flat coastal belt (of Malaya) and in small tributary valleys adjacent to the large rivers." Murray continues by pointing out that irrigation practice in Malaya aims at supplying water adequate for growth of a long-term paddy with an eight-months' maturation period, as this gives the heaviest yield and consequently the best return for capital outlay. The present writer has yet to be convinced that this view is incorrect, although some authorities hold that there is no correlation between yield and duration of growth. Murray instances that during the Japanese occupation of Malaya a variety of paddy was introduced from Formosa capable of producing two crops a year, but the two crops produced in the aggregate no more than one long-term crop. This bears out the present writer's experience with Japanese short-term varieties. The explanation probably is that one was attempting to grow *japonica* varieties under *indica* conditions.

It is imperative that irrigation systems be devised to supply water throughout the customary growth period of the area. In some cases this will entail water for one long period; in other cases, such as districts where two crops are grown per annum, the water supply will be required for two comparatively short periods during the year.

The prerequisite of efficient and economic paddy production is adequate control of drainage and irrigation throughout the season. During this period the water should be available for each field as soon as it is ready for planting. A drainage and irrigation system cannot, however, be based on average conditions, it must be designed to supply adequate water during seasonal shortage and to drain sufficiently rapidly in periods of excessive rain. Where this entails the provision of reservoirs it may not always be possible, or where possible, the capital outlay may not be justified by the area which may be expected to benefit by the improvement. In tropical areas reservoir sites should be deep in relation to surface area because of the large evaporation that may be expected.

The great objection to native-made dams is that they often result in breaking down river banks and in silting up rivers. Furthermore, they make provision for raising the water level to irrigate the fields, but not for draining water during periods of heavy rain. For this reason they often cause sweeping torrents of water to flow over the fields, doing damage to the crop and causing erosion. Concrete dams, constructed by irrigation engineers, are provided with gates so that this sudden flow of excess water may be rapidly drained off. The action serves also to flush out the river and thus maintain the depth of the bed.

EROSION DANGERS

With the advent of the high dam as a factor in agricultural development in the tropics, states Gorrie,[219] interest has moved in many countries from the well-established pattern of scattered cultivation to large irrigated areas. Priority of conservation guidance has been given to clearing the land to be irrigated and cultivated and then to the control of floods and destructive erosion in the catchment area. Logically, of course, these should be undertaken in the reverse order, but inevitably irrigation development is far ahead of erosion control at the sources of the river.

Dams and reservoirs arrest all the heavier suspended silt. Thus, through neglect to prevent erosion in the watershed, the useful life of reservoirs is limited to a comparatively few years. Many writers have pointed to the serious situation threatened by the silting up of reservoirs. Gorrie, writing of the irrigation projects in the dry Western States of America,[217] says:

> Most of them were built with the knowledge that some silting took place, and their life as estimated by their builders varied from 100 to 300 years. Many of them, however, will not last even 100 years, and apart from the investments involved, there is the growing prospect of drifting and unstable social conditions for the populations of these irrigated tracts with the capacity of the reservoirs shrinking at their present pace and already impaired for storage of a drought reserve.

Such danger from silting is not confined to the United States. Many of the expensive dams in Asia may have an even shorter life unless drastic action is taken to prevent erosion. The permanence of dams already constructed must be ensured, states Gorrie,[218] by carrying out whatever can be done to stop erosion. Conservation measures should be brought into practice before the dam is built and those countries contemplating irrigation development should take early action to ascertain how far it is going on in their catchments and arrange for public acquisition and protection of catchment areas wherever these are liable to suffer from misuse by their private owners.

EMPOLDERING

Empoldering is a method of restricting floods and thus securing adjacent areas from submergence. The Dutch are probably responsible for introducing this system into British Guiana in the eighteenth century. Today, all the land developed for paddy cultivation in this colony and in the adjacent Dutch colony of Surinam is protected by this means.

A tract of swamp land is completely surrounded by a dam or dyke, thus denying to the enclosed area unrestricted quantities of water from outside. Through the centre of the empoldered area an irrigation canal is constructed, in which the water is controlled by suitably-placed sluices. Drainage canals are made on two sides, parallel with the irrigation canal, the water in the drainage canals being kept at a lower level than that in the irrigation canal. Thus, the amount of water within the polder is controlled by using the slight difference in level towards the sea, or the difference in level between high and low tide. In the absence of sufficient natural fall, pumps are installed to give adequate water control.

The system, if extensively developed, is liable to lead to grave trouble, due to the enforced restriction of flood water, resulting in occasional breaking of dams and consequent widespread flooding as a result of abnormally high rainfall.

IRRIGATION IN SOME COUNTRIES OF PRODUCTION

From early times tanks were constructed and used in Ceylon to store water from rain and rivers in the wet season so as to ensure the water supply for the paddy season. The Irrigation Department has restored or improved many of these ancient works which now adequately serve a considerable area. The Department has also developed irrigation from rivers whereby water is led from a river through a channel as a result of a masonry anicut constructed across the river. Further schemes of this nature are under consideration which will probably irrigate some 200,000 acres, much of it in the "Dry Region" of the island. Other more primitive systems of irrigation practised in Ceylon include basin irrigation, whereby a temporary dam is placed across a small stream, resulting in raising the water in the stream above the dam till it overflows its banks and floods the surrounding country; lift irrigation, the primitive method practised in the dry district of the Jaffna peninsula, whereby water is lifted from wells usually by a well sweep; and collection by direct rainfall only, or by rainfall supplemented by run-off from neighbouring high land, a method satisfactory only in the wetter regions of the island.[474]

In Lower Burma, empoldering is used as a protection in some regions against floods, and canals for drainage. One of the oldest, constructed in 1880, protects 140,000 acres; the Irrawaddy Embankment, completed the following year, protects 630,000 acres. In Upper Burma, improved irrigation dates from 1890; major works include the Mandalay Canal controlling 90,000 acres, completed about 1902, the Shwebo Canal constructed about four years later and irrigating 29,000 acres, the Mû Canal in 1911 serving 70,000 acres and the Ye-u Canal completed in 1918 and irrigating 90,000 acres. In 1920 two million additional acres of the sea-coast were made available for paddy, but these low-lying areas are only cultivated efficiently when prices are high.

In Thailand[97] there are a number of irrigation schemes in operation and projected, which if and when completed will embrace the whole of the Central Plain. The Chao Phya project, on which work is now proceeding, will provide efficient control over nearly 2 million acres. This project will complement earlier projects connected with the irrigation of the Chao Phya Plain. In the meantime, the crop is still largely dependent on the vagaries of rainfall, and the existing irrigation schemes cannot supply water irrespective of the rainfall on the Plain.

The general trend of the rivers of the Central Plain is north-east and they are intersected by a series of canals. At appropriate intervals there are sluice gates, usually of the undershot type, by means of which the level of water in the canals can be regulated. During the off-season, when there is little rainfall, the control gates are kept closed with the object of maintaining the water-level as high as possible in the canals, thus keeping up the water-table in the fields, so that, with the advent of the monsoon rains, the soil quickly becomes saturated and the water-table reaches the surface. As the rain continues and water in the canal rises, water can be forced into the fields to supplement rainfall. If, on the other hand, the depth of water in the fields becomes excessive, the sluice gates are opened and water is drained off the fields. The canals thus function as irrigation canals or drains.

Water supply and control appear to depend on the height to which the rivers of the Plain, the Menam Chao Phraya in particular, rise and inundate the fields. The rise depends on the amount of rain in the mountains where the rivers have their source. The rise should not be too early or the crop may not be sufficiently well grown to withstand inundation, nor so deep as to inhibit tillering or damage the crop. If the inundation is delayed, the crop may be too far advanced to take full advantage of the water. An exceedingly late flooding may affect flowering or interfere with harvest. It is therefore evident that there are considerable variations from year to year in water supply and also of date when inundation may be expected. These variations result in great uncertainty from year to year as to the supply of rice that may be expected.

There is some attempt in Thailand to supplement early rainfall by pumping water from the canals, the endless chain being used and often operated by wind power. Although the quantity of water lifted is not great, it may be of great assistance to the nurseries in areas where transplanting is practised. There are, however, no large pumping schemes in operation.

Where irrigation schemes exist, the construction of minor canals to lead water to specific lots is left to the cultivator, the irrigation authorities indicating the most suitable alignment. It is understood that cultivators co-operate with the Irrigation Department in this matter.

The levels of the Plain change so gradually that little bunding is required in the fields—an advantage, for it not only saves time and renders cultivation easier, but tends to lessen damage to the crop by rodents and reduce the incidence of weeds.

In northern Thailand, streams of clear water are plentiful and the catchment area of the border is enormous. This plentiful supply enables two crops of paddy to be raised annually. Basin irrigation is largely practised, much of the work being done by cultivators under the leadership of their headmen. In the north-east region lack of water is more marked and the soils are light and non-retentive of water. The streams have small catchment areas and may cease to flow in the dry season. Rainfall in southern Thailand is about 100 inches a year, supplying ample water for irrigating the crop, even where the soil is light and unretentive.

The Ganges-Kobadak Scheme in East Pakistan is expected to double rice production on nearly 2 million acres. Despite the fertility of the soils which border this river area, crop yields have always been low and uncertain. The existence of a dependable water supply such as will be provided by this Scheme will enable two paddy crops to be produced each year, and it may even be possible to grow a third crop other than paddy.

In Indo-China the need of irrigation facilities is reported to be greatest in the Tonkin Delta plain, where the density of population is high, the size of the individual holding small and where an appreciable proportion of the area is made to yield two crops of paddy a year. Irrigation is at present available on about 600,000 acres of the total area of nearly two million acres planted with paddy. About 25,000 acres are supplied by pumped water and the remainder by gravitation with water impounded by dams. Earthworks to protect low-lying areas along the Rouge Fleuve were first put in hand some seven hundred years ago by Annamites and have now been improved and extended. Lowlands adjacent to the sea are protected from sea-water inundation by bunds. In areas where the crop is timed to be harvested in May, the superabundance of water derived from rainfall or rivers is removed as quickly as possible to allow transplanting to be completed before dry weather sets in.

About 222,000 acres are irrigated in Annam, mostly by dams on the rivers. In northern Annam on the Tonkin border, where double cropping is carried out, a number of irrigation works have been installed. In Cambodia the need for irrigation is less urgent. There are already public irrigation works in the area in addition to works constructed by private enterprise, often pumps to lift water into or remove it according to the needs of the crop.

The principal paddy areas of Cambodia are located near the

14. Watering fields from a well, Madras

15. Flooding and ploughing paddy fields in China

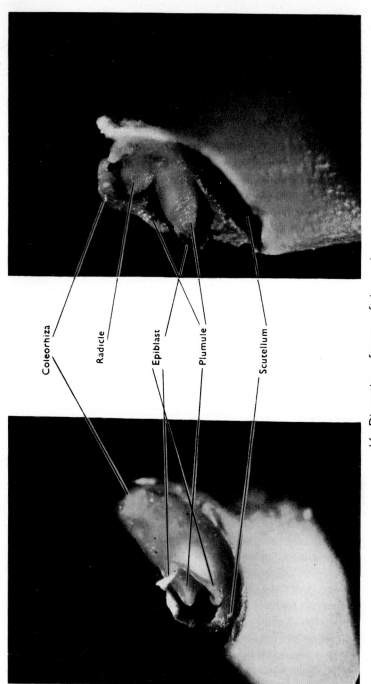

Coleorhiza

Radicle

Epiblast

Plumule

Scutellum

16. Dissection of germ of rice grain

Cochin-China border. This area and an extensive one along the Mekong comprise the floating rice regions. The key factor in water supply is not so much the actual rainfall in the region but utilization of inundation water with the rise of the Mekong. The level of water in the river commences to rise towards the end of June, maximum inundation takes place during late September, after which the fall is rapid. The annual depth of inundation is remarkably constant, being about six feet, and in this connection the Great Lake appears to function as a sort of gigantic regulator.

In the adequately watered Mekong-Brassac delta in Cochin-China the problem is more one of drainage than of irrigation, and the reclamation of swamps. Rainfall is normally sufficient to raise a satisfactory crop. The plain is traversed by a network of large canals which run more or less at right angles to the flow of the several channels of the Mekong. Secondary canals interlink with the main canals and there are numerous tertiary canals, many of which are communally or privately constructed. The general layout resembles that of the Menam Chao Phraya in Thailand and the method of operation also appears to be similar, namely, the rise and fall of the tides, between which there is a difference of 0·5 to 2 metres, is utilized to hold up or drain water according to crop requirements.

Most of the paddy-growing region of Burma has an annual rainfall of 100 to 250 inches, all of which falls during the five-month growing season. Consequently, little formal irrigation is practised.[189] The extent to which the Burma crop is rain-fed may be gauged from the fact that only about 10 per cent of the 12·6 million acres under paddy just before World War II was classed as irrigated. About one million acres of this was irrigated from government sources in the dry zone. Of the rest, about half was under supplementary irrigation in the wet zones.

With Government help, Korean farmers have started irrigation associations and are building reservoirs and canals. Giant pumping stations are now operating to draw river water for the paddy fields. About 700 irrigation associations are now operating, covering 813,000 acres of paddy fields and an additional 160 new projects are being organized.[39]

In Java and Madura[210] paddy cultivation dates from very early times. The rapidly increasing population in the nineteenth century, however, led to difficulties in meeting the demand under the somewhat precarious native irrigation system. In the season 1848–9, famine from crop failure caused the death of about 200,000 people. In consequence, the government built in the plain of Demak a dam on the Tuntong River, simultaneously constructing the western and eastern irrigation canals, thus controlling irrigation over some 30,000 acres. Following a further famine in 1872, the government undertook a complete technical irrigation of the whole plain.

In 1871, a committee investigated the possibilities of technical irrigation in several regions in Java. In 1885 a special service was formed charged with the complete project of irrigating all land considered suitable for paddy cultivation. Four years later this work was decentralized.

The most important irrigation works in Java have been constructed during the present century and especially since 1916 much government money has been spent on these developments. The total area controlled by irrigation schemes by 1940 was over 3¼ million acres.

Government intervention in irrigation is considered desirable when large areas in flat country have to be irrigated, or when the peasant irrigation causes crop failure or excessive damage. Such irrigation systems are mainly in the northern coastal regions and in the plains of mid and east Java; less water is usually available in these regions than elsewhere and the dry east monsoon is protracted.

Over 180 million guilders have been spent in construction of irrigation works, or about 94 guilders per acre. Naturally, the costs varied; the well-known Pemali works, for instance, cost 48 guilders per acre, whereas the Krawang project cost about 203 guilders per acre.

In Egypt[182] paddy cultivation depends entirely on artificial irrigation from the Nile. There are two systems of irrigation; in the older system the land is divided into basins which are flooded during the annual rise of the Nile, the water so obtained being known as *Nili* water. The basins are surrounded with embankments to hold water in the basin as the Nile falls, from thirty to forty days, the crop being sown on the sediment deposited with no further water and little tillage. It follows that only one short-duration crop can be planted, the fields being fallowed after removal of the crop until the following year.

The second and more modern method of irrigation from the Nile aims at regulating the distribution of water and storing a portion of water for summer irrigation. This is therefore a perennial irrigation and the water so obtained is known as *Seifi* water. Under this system a chain of public canals totalling over 11,000 miles carries water throughout the year to the fields, giving to each a fixed share by means of outlet culverts placed at the mouth of cultivators' private ditches. It is therefore possible to obtain two crops a year—

not necessarily paddy. Drainage as well as irrigation is necessary with the perennial irrigation system because the high water-table is detrimental to growth of plant roots. Public drains for this purpose total some 7,700 miles.

Under controlled modern irrigation in Egypt paddy is planted frequently with the main purpose of washing the land of alkalinity, and doubtless on this account a technique of water manipulation has developed which not only serves the purpose of cleansing the land but is beneficial to paddy. The land is flooded for cultivation purposes, smoothed down and germinated seed planted. It is then left for ten or twelve days in cold weather or five or six days in warm weather, after which the water is drawn off, leaving the plants well established. The water is removed in the evening and, should the weather be hot, must again be run on the land as soon as possible next day. Water then remains on the land for four days. This operation is repeated every four days for a period of one month; thereafter the water is drained off and replenished every eight days for about a month. The drain and canal are then left open together so that water is flowing in and out of the fields at the same time. After this, the water is changed every eight days until harvest time. The technique of irrigation varies somewhat according to the variety of paddy under cultivation. The above refers to Sultani; with the varieties Yamani and Subieri the land is left for two or three days after drawing off water before again inundating. With Yamani the land may be allowed to become dry enough to walk on before irrigating again.

Paddy cultivation in Italy depends entirely on irrigation, some of the canals used dating to the fifteenth century. All these irrigation works draw water from the River Po or its tributaries by means of barrages erected across the water course. The most famous of these canals, the Canal Cavour, was opened in 1866; it takes its origin from the Po at Chivasso, where an elaborate barrage has been constructed. The canal is fifty-three miles long and has a maximum capacity of over 3,500 cubic feet per second. A number of hydraulic elevators and electric power stations have been established, the largest of which elevates the river water to a height of 175 feet, when it is delivered into irrigation channels.[649]

The main paddy areas in the United States[310] are situated in the States of Louisiana, Texas and California. Irrigation water for Louisiana and Texas is obtained by powerful pumps from the sluggish streams that flow through the prairies to the Gulf of Mexico and also by pumping water from deep wells. Provision of water for the areas is usually undertaken by private companies who sell water to growers at from $8 to $10 per acre each season. This service includes not only the provision of water but construction and maintenance of the canals which carry it to the fields.

In Arkansas most of the irrigation water is carried from wells that may be anything from twenty-five to sixty feet deep. The size of pump necessary depends on the depth of the well and the acreage to be irrigated, but usually the pump is designed to supply up to five or six gallons of water per minute per acre. Cost of pumping is usually about $8 to $10 per acre.

Irrigation water for the interior valleys of California is obtained chiefly from the Sacramento and Feather Rivers by gravity and pumps. Here too, provision of water for irrigation is in the hands of private companies who sell water on an acre-foot basis or at an annual charge per acre. Basing the water rate on volume rather than on a flat rate per acre tends to conserve water and to confine paddy growing to the heavier types of soil where the quantity of irrigated water required may be less than on the lighter types of soil where there is loss of water by seepage.

Deep wells are not often employed in the Sacramento Valley, but in the San Joaquin Valley they are often the only source of supply. The official opinion is expressed that deep wells are expensive to dig, equip and operate, and should not be depended upon for paddy cultivation unless they have been thoroughly tested before paddy cultivation is undertaken.

Water flows by gravity through canals from the pumping unit to the paddy-fields, where it is distributed through shallow irrigation ditches which run along the higher side of each field. The water is then applied to fields through control gates, as required. At convenient places in the bunds irrigation boxes are installed. They are placed deep enough so that the bottom boards will not hold water back when fields are being drained. The depth of water is controlled by shutters which are placed in a horizontal position across the opening of the irrigation box. By taking out or replacing a narrow board shutter, the water can be lowered or raised as desired. Copeland[135] recommends the box-gate and describes it as follows: ". . . a box, open on top except as may be desired by the flash-boards on the upper side. A sill, about 6 inches deep, keeps water from eating under it, and the ends are similarly carried out and embedded. Forty-two inches wide and 14 inches deep is a convenient size of opening. For control of the water each gate is provided with one 6-inch, one 4-inch, one 2-inch and two 1-inch flash boards. The bottom of the opening of the gate should be in the plane of the ground surface, never any higher. The gate should be placed where it will drain the check thoroughly; very large checks require several gates in each dyke."

It will be realized that irrigation methods in the United States aim not only at the supply of adequate water, but at effective water control at all times, from the initial preparation of the land up to harvest. By this means not only is the crop assured of an adequate supply of water when required, but the system provides for control over land drainage. Without provision of control of drainage and irrigation, the system of mechanized cultivation in the form it takes in America would not be possible.

The manipulation of water for cultivating paddy under the American mechanized system is detailed in Chapter X. Under this system the importance of good drainage is emphasized by American writers, who point out that "poorly drained land is usually expensive to cultivate, difficult to obtain good stands on, and seldom produces maximum yields. . . . Harvesting is usually more expensive on poorly drained than on well-drained land, and there is often a loss due to over ripeness which results in shattering."[310] The same authority points out that before paddy is sown or irrigated, adequate drainage for the low places should be effected, so that they can be well drained during the flooding season and before harvest.

SPRAY IRRIGATION

Paddy is grown commercially in Israel, mainly in the well-watered Hulah Valley on the borders of Syria and Lebanon, where irrigation plans envisage reclamation of a considerable area of fertile clay land. As the amount of rice which can be grown in this region is insufficient to satisfy Israeli requirements, experiments on spray irrigation have been conducted in the more arid regions of the country because the quantity of water required to produce a paddy crop under this system is about 2,000 cu. metres, as compared with about four times this quantity for the inundation method in the Hulah Valley. Spray experiments have proved sufficiently successful to justify official publication of instructions to farmers on spray irrigation for paddy cultivation.[346]

Spray irrigation in Israel is said to be very successful on soils containing a high percentage of sand, 85 to 90 days' short-straw *japonica* varieties of paddy from China, obtained from Bulgaria, being drilled in well-prepared and fertilized soil, 10 to 12 inches between rows, with a space of 4 to 5 feet after every five rows to allow for spraying equipment.

The seed is drilled at the rate of 90 to 150 lb. per acre in April–May, selective weedkiller, usually 2,4-D being sprayed about 20 days after germination. Combine harvesting takes place in July–August, yield of paddy being about 2,500 lb. per acre, while yields approaching 3,000 lb. per acre are considered possible. All cultivation is mechanized; only two days of manual work are involved.

Emphasis is laid on the importance of spraying at regular intervals and in correct quantities. Ten to thirteen sprayings are applied, the first two between sowing and germination, 80 cu. metres of water being applied each time. Thereafter, 5 to 7 sprayings, 140 to 160 cu. metres each time, at intervals of 8 to 10 days followed by 3 to 4 applications at 5-day intervals will bring the crop to maturity.

ECONOMICS OF IRRIGATION WORKS

Governments are frequently concerned with the high cost of irrigation systems for paddy cultivation and the small return that may be expected on capital investment. This is inevitable, for one is dealing with a crop which has a low market value in comparison with most other crops. In their development of the rice industry in Java the Dutch took a most realistic view of this problem. To judge whether a system of irrigation would be justified, data were first gathered on the agricultural and economic conditions of the region and also on the probable profit from the project, the quality of the water and on other agricultural aspects. A financial estimate was based on these data. Irrigation works were usually undertaken only when they were at least 50 per cent "fiscal remunerative"; in other words, interest on the invested capital has to be at least 50 per cent of the rate determined beforehand. Thus, if the project yielded an interest of 3·6 per cent and the determined normal rate of interest was 6 per cent, the scheme was considered 60 per cent "fiscal remunerative." Consideration was given in this way to the indirect advantages of a scheme of a social nature.[210]

CULTURAL REGULATIONS

Cultural regulations are in most countries enforced to minimize damage to the crop by pests and to ensure an economical use of water. The more general application of regulations to ensure a fair distribution of water in areas where supplies are limited or where several parties are interested in water distribution may take the form of limiting the total amount of water used, prescribing dates of planting so that only part of the total area requires water at one time, and limiting the total area planted with the crop annually. In most countries where such regulations are necessary, the control is usually entrusted to committees or water boards which include representatives of interested parties. A fully representative water board, supported by the necessary legislative authority, can usually arrive at a workable arrangement which ensures a fair distribution of available water.

In 1936 the Netherlands East Indies Government promulgated the General Irrigation Act, designed to utilize available irrigation water as efficiently as possible and to prevent waste of water. Under this Act, the date is prescribed on which east and west monsoon irrigation is to start for each irrigation area separately. These dates may differ each year, depending on the rainfall and discharges of the rivers concerned. A culture project for the east monsoon planting within an irrigation region will concern rice, sugar cane and secondary crops. After fixing the area of each, water is allocated in definite proportion for each region. The water is thus distributed in such a way that every crop should have an equal chance of success.

Chapter IV

CHARACTERISTICS OF THE PLANT

RICE is a grass (Gramineae) belonging to the genus *Oryza* Linn. of which two species are cultivated, *O. sativa* Linn. and *O. glaberrima* Steud. The former is by far the more important, *O. glaberrima* being confined to small areas in West Africa. Though undoubtedly distinct types, the morphological differences are small, *O. glaberrima* having shorter, truncate ligules (6 mm. against 15 to 45 mm.), fertile lemma and palea, and simple undivided panicle-branches as compared with *O. sativa* which bears short branchlets. Because *O. glaberrima* is relatively unimportant, this book is concerned with *O. sativa*, although much will apply equally to the West African species.

Oryza sativa is widely grown in tropical and sub-tropical regions, either as a dry-land crop but more usually in water. The ripe seed is the staple food in many Eastern countries. It is not, however, an aquatic plant, for the roots of aquatics produce but few branches and no root-hairs, whereas the roots of paddy—whether grown as a dry-land crop or in water—are much branched and possess a profusion of root-hairs.

The term "paddy" is applied to the land on which the plant is grown, and to the unhusked seed. In countries where this cereal forms an important part of the diet, the vocabulary is particularly rich in words descriptive of every stage in the cultivation of the crop and its preparation as a food. As is to be expected, the importance of rice in commerce has led to numerous terms descriptive of various grades of the product as sold in world markets. As this multiplicity of terms is apt to be extremely confusing, an attempt has been made to reduce terms to the minimum, which it is hoped may become universally accepted (see Appendix III). In the following pages two terms are used throughout, namely, paddy—the growing plant or the unhusked grain, and rice—the husked grain.

The genus *Oryza* contains both annual and perennial species. Perennial wild species can sometimes be troublesome weeds (e.g. *O. perennis* Moench). The cultivated forms are generally grown as annuals and behave as such when conditions after harvest bring the plant's life to an end by drought or cold. They are, however, capable of more than annual growth and where moisture and

56

temperature permit there is commonly a re-growth after the first harvest. This ratoon growth is made use of in some places, thus avoiding the labour of cultivating a second time. Examples of this practice are found in India, Ceylon, China and Swaziland.[193, 235, 584, 643, 713]

ROOT

On germination, the radicle develops from the base of the grain, quickly followed by two additional roots, all subsequently giving rise to short lateral roots. The main rooting system, however, develops from the nodes of the stem below ground level. In the "floating rices," whorls of adventitious roots are formed from the first three very short nodes, giving rise to whorls of permanent adventitious roots. Tillers are produced at the nodes and further adventitious roots are produced from the lower nodes of these culms, so that the plant quickly develops a mass of adventitious roots. The tiller produced directly from the main stem is the "primary" tiller; it is quickly followed by further tillers until the peak tillering stage is reached, after which "invalid" tillers are produced which die without forming panicles. Under normal conditions the root system is fairly compact, the roots tending to develop horizontally rather than vertically; the plant, therefore, draws its nutrients from near the surface of the soil. Sasaki showed[585] that under standard conditions the roots after transplanting developed at first near the soil surface, then gradually penetrated deeper in the soil. The zone occupied by the mature root system is large and inversely oval. The extreme depth reached was 90 cms. Root development is influenced by soil texture, cultivation, water and air in the soil, the amount of available food supply and by the system of transplanting.

Sethi[596] states that after a fortnight's growth two distinct types of root are evident; long, flaccid, light brown and much-branched roots, and comparatively short, thicker, unbranched roots with a white waxy appearance. About six weeks after sowing, the white roots begin to branch and become weak and flaccid. These white roots increase in number from the fifteenth day till the appearance of the flowers. At maturity all roots are thin, branched and flaccid. As the plant develops the older roots die, their function being assumed by the younger roots, so that towards the period of maturity, when few new roots are formed, the plant possesses a mass of living and dead roots until, when the plant reaches maturity, most of the roots are dead.

Sato[589] observes that the number of roots increases gradually from the early period of growth towards tillering, and the shooting period reaches the maximum at heading time, and decreases gradually until harvest time. The ratio of weight of root to top gradually decreases towards the shooting or heading time.

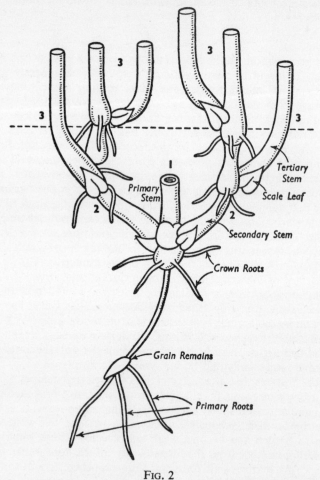

FIG. 2

Diagrammatic representation of tillering in cereals
(After Schindler)

Development of the root system is largely governed by method of cultivation and nature of the soil. Doi and Yamagata found[178] that roots of plants grown on "degraded" soil were white and severely damaged while those grown on good soil had a brown coating of ferric oxide and were mostly uninjured. Tillage and weeding caused roots to spread laterally and ridging and weeding caused them to penetrate more deeply into the soil. The reducing action of paddy soils was injurious to the roots, but on non-weeded areas this injury was surprisingly light. It is suggested that this could be attributed to the oxidizing action of the roots of weeds. Varieties also exhibit characteristic root systems: short duration types have a less developed root system than late varieties while coarse-grained varieties have a coarse root system compared with the more delicate roots of the finer types. Downward as well as lateral spread of roots is more pronounced in the taller than the shorter varieties while there is a high positive correlation between the number of tillers and the number of roots. Root development continues until all the tillers finish flowering but there is no appreciable increase in length. Typical swamp-land varieties develop a more intensive root system under puddled soil conditions than when grown under dry-land conditions, whereas the typically dry and the wild rices behave in the reverse way.[509]

New roots start in greatest numbers at maximum tillering and nitrogen, phosphorus and potassium are absorbed at the greatest rate at this time. Maximum rate of absorption of iron, magnesium and sulphur is ten days later and silica and manganese twenty days later.

Anatomy of the Root. The young root has an epidermis of thin-walled cells which towards the apex grow out to form the root hairs. Beneath the epidermis and separated from it by a single layer of thin-walled cells is a single-layered exodermis of thick-walled cells. The remainder of the cortex consists of large thin-walled cells, the innermost constituting the endodermis.

The central cylinder is at first unlignified and at an early stage develops a number of very large central vessels—either a single central vessel or six vessels arranged starwise. To the exterior, groups of smaller vessels alternating with phloem and separated by thin walled parenchyma, form a vascular ring. The xylem of these groups abuts on a single layered percycle. The remainder of the cylinder is constituted of thin-walled parenchyma.

As the root ages, the epidermis of the layer immediately beneath are sloughed and the exodermis replaces them. This layer then thickens further and its outer walls become suberized. Thickening of certain of the adjacent layers of the cortex may follow. Simultaneously, the radially arranged intermediate cells of the cortex separate from one another and alternate strands or groups of strands so formed may shrivel and die. There is formed a cortical structure strongly resembling that of many water plants. Adjacent to the epidermis, which gradually thickens, two or three layers of cortical cells tend to remain more or less unaltered. At maturity the central cylinder is thus invested by a loosely pleated jacket-like cortex. The central cylinder also becomes modified. The vessels become lignified and in time the cells of the parenchyma are strongly thickened, thus forming a solid core of the root.[264]

The above statement is important in explaining the adaptation of the roots of the non-aquatic paddy plant to aquatic conditions.

STEM

The main axis of the stem is differentiated from the growing point of the embryo, enclosed at first by the coleoptile. The ultimate height of the stem depends on the number of internodes and their length and may be much affected by environment, but under comparable growth conditions is characteristic of varieties. Early strains of short maturation period generally have fewer internodes than those of long maturation period, but there are exceptions to this rule. The number of internodes may vary from about ten to twenty.

In the early stages of growth there is little difference in height between varieties; later, elongation commences, reaching its maximum at flowering. Varieties of short duration grow more rapidly than those of long duration. Internodal growth is from the base, taking place mainly in the area immediately above the node. The terminal internode ends in a node bearing a ring of hairs and bearing above the branched open panicle.

The culm is more or less erect, cylindrical, smooth and hollow except at the nodes. It varies in thickness from about six to twelve millimetres. Nodes are clearly defined by a distinct thickening and the transverse septum. Leaves arise from just below the septum (sheath node) and buds in the axils of basal leaves may give rise to new culms (tillers) which later emerge from the top of the leaf-sheaths (intravaginal) forming a tuft of culms. The primary main culm is not a tiller, a term proper to the vegetative shoots.

Pigment may be present in the internode or in the node, varying from a tinge of pink to deep purple. When pigment is absent the culms are green or whitish until ripening, when a dull yellow "straw" colour develops. Pigment in the coloured forms may be diffuse in the epidermis or in the parenchyma, or it may be confined to the sheaths of the vascular bundles, appearing as fine coloured streaks. Pigment may appear early or late in the life of the plant and may be permanent or temporary.

LEAF

The leaves are alternate and borne in two ranks along the stem. The leaf consists of two parts, a sheath enveloping the stem and a blade or lamina. The number of leaves borne on an axis is equal to the number of nodes. Since the number of nodes is progressively fewer than on the main axis, the number of leaves on the tiller is correspondingly fewer.

The first leaf of the plant is the sheathing leaf or coleoptile. The second leaf, emerging through the lateral slit of the coleoptile, is reduced in size and has practically no blade. The remaining leaves are normal, except the uppermost or "flag," which is slightly modified. The bud—a potential tiller—is enclosed in the prophyll. The normal vegetative leaf has sheath, ligule, auricles and blade.

The Sheath. The sheath is always present, encircling the whole or part of the internode from the node upwards. At the base the sheaths tend to exceed the length of the internodes and consequently enwrap the base of the succeeding sheath to a variable extent. From the tenth leaf upwards, however, the internodes are longer and the sheaths relatively and progressively shorter than the internodal length. Growth of the sheath is mainly from the base and may continue after the blade has attained about its maximum length. The sheath is split to the base, is finely ribbed and glabrous. Colour, if any, may be confined to the base or may be distributed through the sheath, and may be visible either on the outer or inner surface, or both. The pigment occurs in the epidermal cells, in tissues surrounding the bundles, or distributed throughout the parenchyma.

Ligule. The ligule arises from the junction at the top of the sheath and is present in almost all varieties of paddy; it is about 2 cm. long, membranous, and tends to split as it develops. The ligule may be colourless or coloured a faint pink or purple. A coloured ligule is always associated with colour in the sheath.

Auricles. The auricles are situated at the junction of the sheath and blade and are sickle-shaped. Long, slender teeth are normally present on the convex face of each ligule. Colour, if present, is always associated with colour in the node. If the auricles are coloured, so also is the sheath, but the converse is not true. Some strains of paddy are devoid of auricles.

The Blade. The blade is long and narrow, usually pubescent or hispid, with distinct mid-rib, but varying considerably in length. Leaves of many varieties are coloured, the colour being usually concentrated in the mid-rib region and on the margins, though occasionally the whole leaf is coloured.

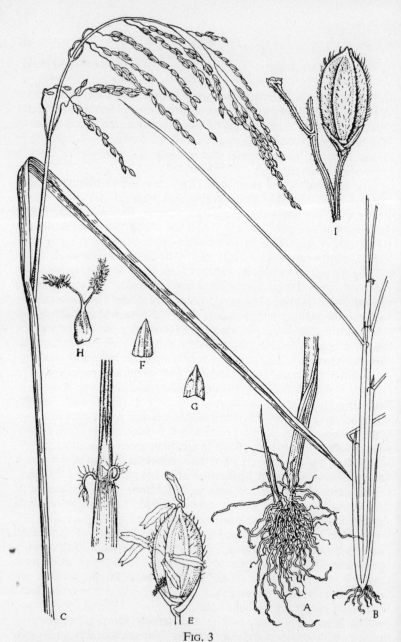

Fig. 3

Oryza sativa. L. A: plant base and roots × ½; B: portion of stem showing leaf × ¼; C: panicle × ½; D: ligule and auricles × 1½; E: spikelet × 5; F: lower empty lemma; G: upper empty lemma; H: ovary; I: part of raceme showing one mature spikelet attached and the reduced glumes ("collar") remaining after the rest of another mature spikelet has fallen—

F–I × 5

The uppermost leaf, or "flag", of the axis possesses a blade always shorter and broader than the lower leaves. As the panicle emerges from the sheath, its blade is nearly parallel to the panicle axis. After the panicle has emerged the blade falls, ultimately standing either at an acute angle to the axis, more or less horizontal thereto, or definitely drooping.

INFLORESCENCE

The inflorescence is a panicle, more or less lax, much branched and bearing spikelets. The homology of the parts of the spikelet of paddy is at first confusing because of the suppression of some parts to mere vestiges bearing little resemblance to their homologues in less specialized genera.[55] The spikelets are laterally compressed, oval, oblong or lanceolate, with or without awn, borne on a short pedicel, the rachilla disarticulating below the lower floret and not produced beyond the uppermost floret. There are three florets in each spikelet but the two lower florets are reduced to sterile, scale-like lemmas. Only the terminal floret is fertile and forms the easily-recognized "grain." There are two glumes but they are very small and obscure, being reduced to a minutely two-lobed or annular rim on the tip of the pedicel. Next above this smooth, polished rim are found the two sterile lemmas. These are thin and narrow, pointed, usually much shorter than the fertile lemma and palea (the non-flowering glumes of Fig. 3) above but in some uncommon varieties as long as the fertile lemma. These two sterile lemmas are all that remain of the two lower florets. The fertile lemma is tough or coriaceous, rigid, keeled and on the outside, scabrid or rough with silica excrescences and hairs on its outer surface, awned or not from the tip, strongly five-nerved with the two outer nerves near the margins. The awn, when present, may be a mere tip of about 1 or 2 mm. or may be as much as 10 cm. long. The palea is similar to the fertile lemma in texture, slightly smaller and its outwardly rolled edges fitting into the in-rolled edges of the lemma; keeled but with no strong mid-nerve on the back, two-nerved close to the edges; unawned. The fertile lemma and the palea together form the fertile third floret and enclose the grain when ripe. They constitute the bulk of the "husk" but, at threshing, carrying with them the rudimentary remains of the two lower florets and the glumes which unite them at the base. The vestigial glumes are not carried with the rest of the spikelet at maturity but remain attached to the tip of the pedicel.

Inside the boat-shaped lemma and palea of the fertile floret are two rounded, smooth bodies, the lodicules whose swelling at flowering time assists the opening of the floret. There are six stamens with slender filaments bearing versatile anthers. The pistil consists of a one-celled ovary with a single ovule. The style is short and bears two plumose stigmas. The fruit (caryopsis) or grain is the ripened ovary containing the ripened ovule and closely invested by the fertile lemma and palea but free from them (not fused). The pericarp, formed from the wall of the ovary, is tightly fused with the ripened ovule. It is that part which is removed as bran on milling and it is

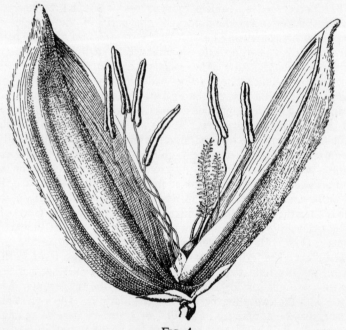

FIG. 4
Spikelet of rice

important to note that it is formed from tissue of the parent plant (the ovary wall) and is not part of the succeeding generation resulting from fertilization of the ovule. This has important bearing on the inheritance of grain characters, such as red grain (see Chapter VI).

The rudimentary panicle may be felt as a swelling in the uppermost leaf-sheath at the time when the stem grows rapidly. Finally, the stem elongates and the panicle appears. The latter, usually, fully emerges within a week.

The time of day when the flower opens and the period of flowering depend on humidity and temperature and also sometimes on the variety. The lemma and palea separate and the stigmas protrude, followed rapidly by the anthers bursting, or they may dehisce before they are extended, in which case the stigmas have probably become pollinated before extension. Normally, however, the pollen is liberated while the spikelet is opening and rarely later.

Paddy is normally self-pollinated but cross-pollination is possible and does indeed take place to some extent, the amount depending largely on climatic and varietal differences. Normally, the amount does not exceed 1 per cent, although as much as 30 per cent has been observed in some instances. Lord,[367] in a carefully-controlled experiment, found that in two climatically different districts in Ceylon, the amount of natural crossing varied from 0·34 to 0·67 per cent, while Brown in Malaya[90] obtained the figure of 0·41 per cent for natural cross-pollination. Srinivasan and Subramanian[627] in India found that natural cross-pollination ranged from 0·04 to 0·03 and the distance up to which it took place ranged from six to seven feet from the pollinating agent.

The flowers open from the tip of the panicle downwards, over a period of a few days. The time they remain open doubtless depends on air humidity, the period being from as little as six minutes to rather more than an hour. While the flowers may open at any time of the day, they usually open in the forenoon. Burkill[98] observes that flowers opening in the afternoon are quite likely to do so with anthers already dried, but adds that opening so late is unusual and happens only in dull weather.

The maximum, minimum and optimum temperatures for germination of pollen are 50, 10 and 30–35° C. respectively. Low temperature is more serious to the function of pollen than to the pistil. For this reason it is possible, in hybridization work, to sterilize pollen without damage to the pistil (see page 118). The fertilization rate is lowered sharply by low temperature within thirty minutes after pollination. Pollen which contacts the stigma germinates immediately, the pollen tube entering the embryo sac within thirty minutes of pollination.

Naturally, the flowering stage should be as short as possible so that the whole crop becomes evenly ripe. The period from flowering to ripening of grain is about thirty days; there are, however, varieties that mature in less than a fortnight from flowering and others that take over two months to ripen.

Santos[583] summarizes the morphology of the mature grain as follows. The mature grain coat consists of a filmlike covering composed of the following structures: the ovary wall or pericarp, the inner integument and nucellus which are pressed together flatly in

G

a somewhat compact form. The kernel is oblong oval, usually smooth and glistening, whitish or translucent white, with or without abdominal white. Sometimes it is red or purplish-black. The endosperm is built up of thin-walled, elongated parenchyma cells filled with starch grains and some protein substances. The outer part of the endosperm is limited by a layer of rectangular cells known as aleurone cells, which are rich in proteins and fat or oil globules.

During the ripening process the spikelet becomes shorter and turgid. At this "milky" stage the embryo is fully developed and the endosperm cells filled with a watery sap in which starch grains are suspended. During this period of development, the colour of the lemma and palea changes from pale to dark green, owing, according to Santos, to the resorption of some of the contents of the several layers of the ovary wall and their subsequent compression caused by the enlargement of the endosperm through which the chlorophyllous layers become more conspicuous. The spikelet then gradually loses its green colour, the endosperm becomes tough and waxy, the hull contracts, the cell layers become considerably distorted, and the spikelet develops into a hard grain.

The grain (caryopsis) is tightly enclosed by the lemma and palea (the "hull"). The general appearance of the mature grain is so familiar as to need no description. Its colour is usually that of the pericarp, although rarely the colour is also found in the endosperm. In the white varieties of rice there is usually a chalky, white portion at the middle ventral side, known as abdominal white. While the translucent, waxy, white appearance of the endosperm is general, occasional grains are found that appear dull, due to the fact that the endosperm is starchy on the outside and horny within. Grains with dull areas here and there are also not uncommon.

The main points of the morphology of the mature rice grain as described by Santos are as follows. The aleurone layer is composed of a single layer of quadrangular or rectangular parenchyma cells with thin walls. Since Santos wrote the above several workers have shown that there are two or three aleurone layers on the ventral side of the grain and five or six layers on the dorsal side. Cho (1942) states that the aleurone layer on the dorsal side of a rice grain of the *japonica* type is composed of five or six layers, while there are three layers, without exception, in the *indica* type.[379] The endosperm is built up of thin-walled parenchyma cells which are generally elongated radially. The endosperm cells in the sector towards the ventral side, which corresponds with the part occupied by the abdominal white, contain practically only starch grains. The protein contents of the endosperm cells mixed with the starch grains decrease

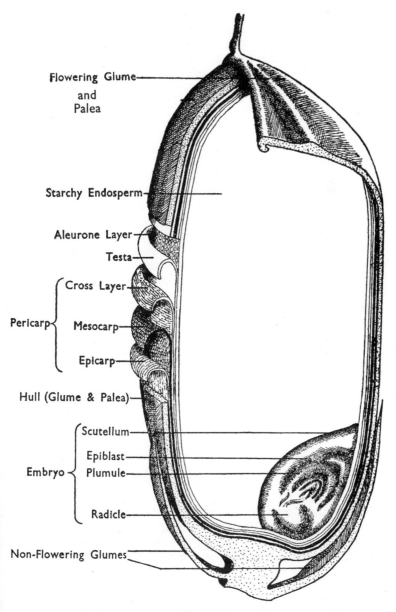

Flowering Glume
and
Palea

Starchy Endosperm

Aleurone Layer

Testa

Cross Layer

Pericarp

Mesocarp

Epicarp

Hull (Glume & Palea)

Scutellum

Epiblast

Plumule

Embryo

Radicle

Non-Flowering Glumes

FIG. 5
Structure of the rice grain

proportionately from the periphery towards the region of abdominal white.

The embryo is about one-third the length of the caryopsis and located near the base towards the lemma or ventral side of the grain.

In the middle part the plumule and primary root are arranged in the form of a capital L, the plumule corresponding to the long arm, the primary root corresponding to the short horizontal arm. These are joined to each other by a short stem, more or less at right angles, and embedded or surrounded by a mass of thin-walled polygonal parenchyma cells, which form the scutellum, epiblast and coleorhiza. The ventral side of the embryo is protected by the prolongation of the aleurone region from the upper part of the embryo to the base and serves as an epidermis. This epidermis in turn is covered by the pericarp, which is pressed together with the seed coats.

The plumule or primary bud is somewhat ovate in outline, pointing obliquely away from the apex of the grain. It is composed of a minute growing point, one or more foliage leaves, and a leaf or coleoptile which encloses the growing point and immature foliage leaves which are attached to the upper end of the hypocotyl. The plumule is bounded at the inner side by the scutellum or cotyledon, which lies next to the endosperm and is attached to the hypocotyl. The epiblast is seen as a protruding structure which extends towards the upper end of the tip of the plumule and overlaps with the upper end of the scutellum. The epiblast is devoid of vascular tissue. Between the plumule and the primary root there is a short stem, the hypocotyl, which terminates at the anterior end in a short growing point and at the posterior end into the primary root.

The outermost layer of the scutellum, towards the endosperm, consists of radially elongated thin-walled parenchyma cells, which are arranged in palisade form. This layer is known as the epithelium. The epiblast, like the scutellum, is composed of thin-walled rectangular or polygonal parenchyma cells. It is surrounded by the epithelium.

Some knowledge of the morphology of the mature grain is necessary to an understanding of the distribution of protein, fat and vitamins in different parts of the grain. While the cells constituting the greater part of the endosperm contain practically only starch grains, the parts of the grain commonly designated "the germ" and the pericarp contain varying but considerable quantities of protein granules and deposits of fatty cells. In milling, the germ is usually knocked off together with the scutellum, while in the polishing process the pericarp is removed with the remains of the

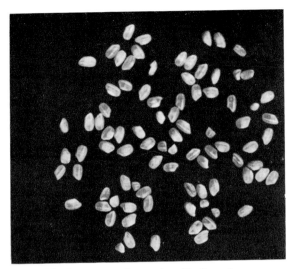

17. Commercial sample of Italian rice

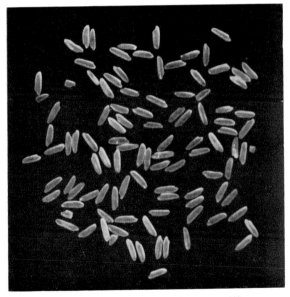

18. Commercial sample of "Converted" rice
from U.S.A.

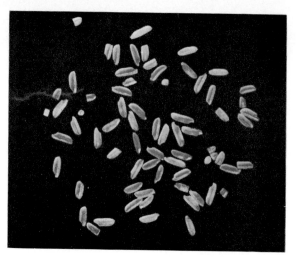

19. Commercial sample of parboiled rice from British Guiana

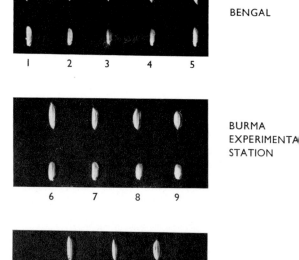

BENGAL

BURMA EXPERIMENTAL STATION

BURMA

20. Paddy and Rice from some types of *Oryza sativa*, L.

1. Patnai. 2. Chingrighusi. 3. Kalaktara. 4. Bhasamanik.
5. Indrasail (Winter Rice).
6. Type 28-8. 7. Type XA-97. 8. Type E-30-42 (1938). 9. Type D-17-88.
10. Emata. 11. Theikpan. 12. Khayangya.

embryo and the aleurone layers. This matter is treated in greater detail in the chapter concerning nutrition.

GROWTH-REGULATING SUBSTANCES

Rampal and Bhatt have summarized[515] available information on the response of paddy to growth-regulating substances. They state that in Gopalachari's sand culture experiments[216] there was an increase in grain as a result of α-naphthalene acetic acid when applied with the nutrient solution. Misra and Sahu observed[405] a significant increase in tiller and leaf formation in plants obtained from grains treated with 250 and 500 ppm of indole acetic acid and 2,3,5- triiodobenzoic acid solutions, but differences in grain yield were not significant.

Rampal and Bhatt[515] tried several growth regulators—α-naphthalene acetic acid (NAA), indolyl-acetic acid (IAA), phenoxyacetic acid (PAA) and 2,4,5-triiodobenzoic acid (TIBA). Only TIBA produced some beneficial effects on growth and yield of paddy in pots and field experiments, suggesting the desirability for further investigations as regards effects of auxins on flowering behaviour of paddy. Other treatments produced deleterious effects on plant development. There was no effect on earliness.

With higher concentration and excessive auxin treatment, Sircar and Kundu[606] observed early ear emergence with the variety Rupsail, but no such earliness was noted by Misra and Sahu using other varieties of paddy.

GERMINATION

Properly ripened and harvested paddy should reach a maximum germination of nearly 100 per cent when it attains the correct condition of maturity. Newly harvested seed may have a low germination; with storage this will increase to its maximum, thereafter falling off rapidly unless special precautions are taken. A six-month variety in British Guiana gave very poor germination for at least a month after harvesting. It then improved rapidly and approached the maximum of nearly 100 per cent about two months from harvesting. This figure was maintained for about five months, after which the viability began to fall off gradually up to a period of eleven months after harvest, when germination practically ceased. At germination peak, hand-threshed paddy gave practically 100 per cent germination as compared with about 90 per cent with machine-threshed paddy. There are possible differences in rate of dormancy loss, depending on storage conditions of the seed.

The resting period, during which germination has not attained a high figure, depends on the variety. Research in India has shown that varieties which have a long maturation period in the field require a correspondingly long resting period; much of the seed will therefore fail to germinate immediately after ripening and harvesting, but quick-growing varieties may require no resting period. On the other hand, Roberts in West Africa[567] and Dore in Malaya found[181] no correlation between maturation period and dormancy period. Commenting on this, Roberts points out that the extremely short duration varieties common in India were not used in West Africa; it is possible, therefore, that West African varieties lie outside the range of duration in which correlation with dormancy may be evident. Furthermore, even where dormancy is associated with short duration, it is also evident that the association is not inevitable. Shanmugasundaram, for example, found[732] that 22 of 140 varieties of less than 120 days' maturation period were strongly dormant after harvest. Matsuo[379] states that *japonica* type seed requires no dormant period. Chandraratra and his colleagues show[117] that seed dormancy for a variety may be a function of its photoperiodic sensitivity. Regarding the survival value of dormancy and its absence they observe that seed of a sensitive variety which exhibits no dormancy would germinate at a time when the natural photoperiod would inhibit flowering. The possession of dormancy prevents germination in the sensitive variety until favourable photoperiods supervene. On the other hand, dormancy is disadvantageous to an insensitive variety grown in both seasons. Seed dormancy and irregularity of germination are caused by incomplete ripening. The completion of this ripening process may be promoted by thorough drying at a moderate temperature.

Roberts has discussed[568] the influence of temperature, moisture and gaseous environment and suggests that dormancy be broken by sun-drying the seed to 11 per cent moisture content or less and then placing it in shallow containers in an incubator at approximately 120° F. Seven days of this treatment removes the dormancy of all seed in most varieties without danger of loss of viability during the treatment. Umali *et al.* found[672] that dormancy is broken by smoking the seed at 120° F. for 84 hours in a smoke chamber using wood fuel.

ENVIRONMENT

Considerable differences in growth are found under varying conditions; investigators frequently find that varieties achieving a considerable reputation in one country prove extremely disappointing when cultivated in another country. This was found to be the case with the early-maturing varieties from Japan when grown in Malaya and experience in Burma has been similar. The Department of Agriculture, Burma, reports:[525] "Of exotic paddies over a hundred have been tried. The sub-tropical ones, as represented by the rices of Japan, Spain, Italy and America, which are now so much in demand in Europe, have all proved precocious when grown under the tropical conditions of Burma, and have given yields barely half those of local selections. The purely tropical exotics have shown no superiority in quality or yield over pure lines isolated from indigenous types."

There is probably no important cereal crop that is more influenced by environment than paddy. This is a point of considerable importance in considering extension of the world area under this crop. It is probable that the areas suitable are far more extensive than is usually supposed. The bulk of the world's production is grown in the humid regions within the tropics, yet high yields are obtained as far north as Manchuria, about 45° north of the Equator, and as far south as New South Wales, about 35° south of the Equator. It is said to ripen at an altitude of 7,000 feet in Kashmir.

WATER REQUIREMENT

Varieties exist which grow satisfactorily under "dry" conditions, while others demand water for their development, and others again will grow on either dry or flooded land. The "dry" varieties will not tolerate arid conditions, so that, in practice, their cultivation is restricted to regions where there is an assured rainfall over three or four months, or where irrigation is available.

The depth of water for optimum growth of "wet" varieties differs somewhat with the variety under cultivation; while some do best in moving water, or will thrive in stagnant water, others will withstand flood water up to twenty feet in depth. The great majority of varieties demand fresh water, but there are a number that will tolerate up to about 0·3 per cent of sodium chloride in the water.

The depth of water required by the plant depends on the variety; in general, however, it has been found that where the water is too deep for a particular variety, tillering is reduced and this adversely affects the yield. Investigations in the Philippines[96] showed that there was no significant difference between submergence depths—0 to 25 cm.

HEIGHT OF PLANT

Apart from the so-called floating varieties, the ultimate height of the paddy plant is from four to six feet. Many of the tall varieties are weak in the straw and are therefore unsuited to situations subjected to high winds or rapid movement of water. The dwarf varieties grow to a height of not more than two feet. Kikkawa[335] considers that they have little practical value, adding that they are often grown for the sake of curiosity. Graham[224] observes that as far as the Central Provinces are concerned, the short habit is associated with poor tillering and a small panicle. Kikkawa found that there is a correlation between the height of the plant and the tillering and weight of ear, tall plants giving more tillers and a heavier crop than short plants. The present writer has been unable to trace any such relationship in a large number of varieties tested by him in Malaya. Furthermore, he found that dwarf varieties produce as many tillers as tall varieties.

The deep-water varieties, or "floating rices", are usually sown broadcast during the months March to May and are harvested at the end of the year. The monsoon in June gradually floods the land until in places it reaches a depth of twenty feet. As the level of the water rises the paddy grows, so that its tip is maintained above flood level. Ramiah and Ramaswami[508] state that the stems grow rather zigzag under the water and have a tendency to crawl on the surface and this habit is responsible for their being called "floating." Tillers and roots are produced at nodes above the stem base, such roots supplementing the rather poorly developed root system of the plant. Should the flood water fall and leave the weak stems prone on the mud, there follows a rapid root development at the nodes.

TILLERING

The number of tillers is approximately constant for any one variety under comparable conditions, but tillering is influenced by cultural conditions, spacing of plants, weeds and water supply. If the seed is not planted too deep, tillering commences about a fortnight from sowing. The plant may continue to form tillers for a short period, or their formation may continue until shortly before inflorescence appears. The ultimate number of tillers is not necessarily the maximum number formed, since during growth of the plant a number of tillers may be formed which do not produce inflorescence; in fact, some of them die before the plant reaches maturity. If the tillers are few in number and produced within a short period of time, the ripening period of all is approximately equal, but if tillers are numerous or produced over a lengthy period of time, a variable number of unproductive tillers must result. A large number of tillers is therefore not necessarily conducive to high yield, for it may result in unequal ripening. In a variety which does not tiller profusely it is

Paddy fields in Po Valley, Italy

11. Paddy field, Bandoeng, Java

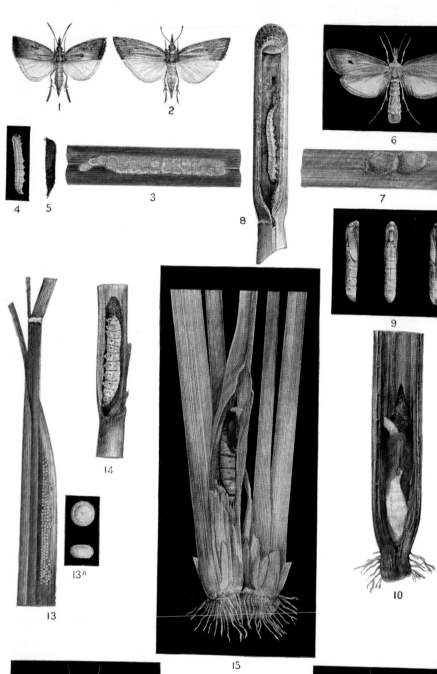

EXPLANATION OF PLATE III

1. *Proceras polychrysus* (Meyr.), male
2. *Proceras polychrysus* (Meyr.), female
3. Ova of *Proceras*
4. Larva of *Proceras*
5. Pupa of *Proceras*
6. *Schoenobius incertellus* Walk, female
7. Ova of *Schoenobius*
8. Larva of *Schoenobius*
9. Pupa of *Schoenobius*
10. Cocoon of *Schoenobius* in stem
11. *Sesamia inferens* Walk, male
12. *Sesamia inferens* Walk, female
13. Ova of *Sesamia* on inner surface of leaf-sheath which is laid back
    to expose them
13A. Ova of *Sesamia* enlarged
14. Larva of *Sesamia*
15. Pupa of *Sesamia* in leaf-sheath

With the exception of Figs 3, 4, 5, 8, 13 and 14 all figures slightly enlarged.
Fig. 3 enlarged 4.5

IV. Paddy Terraces in Northern Luzon, Philippines

usually possible to obtain the approximate number of earheads by planting more closely.

Tillering is subject to considerable variation due to environment and method of cultivation. Ashby observes[57] that deep cultivation of both "wet" and "dry" paddy checks growth and delays tillering, resulting in late and uneven ripening, owing probably to late-formed tillers, which are not, however, too late to develop normal ears. Rhind[555] points out that early tillers bear larger panicles with plumper grain of more even size than do late tillers. Because ripening and harvest are fixed by seasons and water supply, the earlier planting can be carried out the longer the tillering phase and hence the greater the number of surviving tillers. It follows that every endeavour should be made to transplant as early as possible. In one experiment a gain of one-quarter bushel yield per acre was obtained for every day by which transplanting was advanced.

In some varieties the stems are more or less stiff and the resulting habit of the plant is compact. In other cases the stems are more prostrate and the plant habit is therefore spreading. Ramiah found that the compact habit behaves as a simple dominant to the spreading habit. In plants with the compact habit, the basal internodes were always short, while in those with a spreading habit the basal nodes were definitely longer and tillering succession more obvious.

LODGING

Lodging may be the result of environmental conditions or may be specific to the variety. In rich soil the sequence appears to be hyper-nutrition, low carbon-nitrogen ratio, a preponderance of vegetative growth and consequent straw weakness. On poor soils the reverse is true—a high carbon-nitrogen ratio, a reduction in the proportion of vegetative growth and straw strength. Hector[264] has drawn attention to the work of Revera (1916) on wheat, who concluded that lodging was due to the high water content of the tissues, and to Weldon (1928), who showed the reverse condition, i.e. lodging resulting from low dry matter content per unit length of culm. This may be the result from a relatively low content of lignin and various reserve materials, such as disaccharides and polysaccharides, or from the development of relatively small slender culms. This condition in turn is due to a low carbohydrate-nitrogen ratio, the result of shade, hyper-nutrition or relatively high temperatures. He adds that though nitrogenous manures decrease the silica and ash content, the lignin is increased. Experiments by Tubbs have shown that nitrogen deficiency tended to strengthen the lower nodes and concluded that weakness of the internodes is due to loss of strength in the mechanical tissue, and that this mechanical tissue can only develop effectively in the presence of a sufficiency of potassium. Sato studied the starch contained in the tissues of paddy.[590] He found that the plant is most susceptible to lodging about three weeks after heading, at which stage the parenchymous cells of the culm have been depleted of starch grains. Varieties resistant to lodging have abundant foliage, high starch content in the culm and are late maturing.

External factors responsible for lodging are high wind, shading, hyper- and unbalanced nutrition, temperature and disease. If plants are crowded, light is shut off from the stems, resulting in some etiolation at the base of the plant, the cell walls of the tissues being smaller and thinner, and the mechanical tissue much reduced. Excess nitrogen and water produce a similar result, while lack of potash induces weakness of the mechanical tissue. Relatively high temperatures result in much the same condition, while several fungus diseases may cause stem weakness. Transplanting tends to reduce lodging. Harada and Edo discovered[248] that plants sprayed with 2,4-D 33 to 25 days before earing produced longer lower internodes while if sprayed 23 to 25 days before earing they developed longer upper internodes and greater culm length. For resistance to lodging, therefore, the best time for spraying is before the beginning of internode elongation.

Hector also refers to the internal factors responsible for lodging which are specific to the variety. In general, somewhat stout, short-strawed varieties are more resistant, as may be expected, but some of the long-strawed varieties are also resistant. According to Bhide and Bhalerao,[82] the more resistant types have stems with a thicker band of sclerenchyma at the periphery than have strains that tend to lodge, more fibro-vascular bundles, and exhibit, in particular, a narrow layer of small sclerenchymatous cells behind the air cavities, loosely linked to the sclerenchymatous sheaths of the bundles which lie between these cavities.

Breeding for non-lodging habit in otherwise valuable strains is comparatively easy and successful. Ramiah[504] asserts that there is a genetic association between character of straw and such characters as tillering and maturation period; non-lodging being linked with poor tillering and long maturation, but there appears to be no relation between plant height and straw character, nor between straw character and floret sterility. Ramirez and Umali found[514] that dryland paddy lodging was mostly in the stalk and wet-paddy mostly in the root. High breaking strength of straw and shortness of the first two internodes may be used as an indication of stiffness of dryland paddy culm. The thickness of culm wall and of the sclerenchyma cells at the second internode are related to resistance to lodging of both types of paddy.

MATURATION PERIOD

In most Asian countries of rice production, considerable importance is attached to the classification of paddy varieties according to time of ripening. The date of sowing must depend on the water supply and climatic conditions; the classification of varieties according to time of ripening must therefore be of local interest only, while the total number of days from planting to maturity is the real measure and is likely to lead to no misunderstanding. Taking maturation period as the measure, Graham[224] states that in the Central Provinces of India early varieties mature in 121 days, the range being from 106 to 145 days; medium varieties in 125 days, the range being 110 to 169 days, and the late varieties in 133 days, the range being from 119 days onwards. The period between sowing and appearance of ears in the three classes is almost identical, viz. 87, 90 and 91 days, so that earliness or lateness of a variety depends not so much upon the vegetative period of growth as upon the reproductive period during which the fruit matures and ripens.

The maturation period of paddy may be anything between 90 and 260 days, and, within limits, maturation period varies with environmental and climatic conditions. Generally, tillering varies with maturation period, i.e. varieties with a long maturation period produce more tillers than those with a short maturation period. But even on this point one should not be too dogmatic, for it is obvious that where conditions are particularly suitable for a particular variety, that variety will produce a greater number of tillers than it would under less favourable conditions. Of all the varieties tested by the writer in Malaya[229] those from Thailand were the most luxuriant in growth and of shorter maturation period than Malayan varieties. In almost every case the former gave nearly double the number of tillers, greater number of seeds per panicle, but were from 20 to 40 days earlier than the Malayan varieties.

The relationship between maturation period and yield remains uncertain. Many authorities consider that the highest yields are obtained with growing periods of about five months and that late varieties give smaller crops. Ramiah states:[512]

It is not true that early varieties are always poor in yield, as yields comparable with those of the medium growing period varieties have also been obtained with early varieties with, say, growing periods of 100 to 110 days, in parts of peninsular India. Such high yields of early varieties are dependent on the conditions of the growing season and the fertility of the land. Thus it is clear that, while the agricultural conditions of an area determine the length of the growing period of the varieties to be grown, it is possible to choose high yielding varieties of any length of growing period suitable to such conditions.

Larter asserts[348] that there is little, if any, evidence that long-term varieties are, as a class, intrinsically higher-yielding than medium-term varieties, or the latter than short-term varieties. It is difficult to reconcile this view with that of his colleagues Allen and Haynes,[12] who state as one of the advantages of mechanization that it may lengthen the growing season sufficiently for yields to be appreciably increased. The present writer maintains the general principle—yield increases with the number of tillers. It follows that in order to obtain from a short maturation crop a yield comparable with that from one with a long growth period, planting distance must be considerably reduced to compensate for fewer tillers.

STERILITY

Sterility may vary from a few empty glumes to the entire panicle. Lack of fertilization due to unfavourable weather conditions may account for the occasional empty spikelet, or it may be due to inherited degeneration. The top of the panicle may exhibit rudimentary spikelets, white and papery in appearance, which tend to dry up and break down shortly after they emerge. This condition, known as "sponginess" in Java, may be due to environment, but in many cases appears to be caused by abortion of both the anthers and the ovaries. In hybrids between the *japonica* and *indica* varieties a high degree of sterility may be found in the progeny.

Sterility of the entire panicle may be due to borers, eel worms, fungus infection, physiological conditions, or it may be inherited. In New South Wales,* the yield of the rice crop, all other conditions being equal, can be related directly to low temperatures during flowering. Below 35° F. partial sterilization of pollen cells in anthers approaching emergence occurs, but without any subsequent signs of "frosting." At 32° F. sterilization is complete. Many writers have observed a high proportion of sterile spikelets on rice grown in cold water.

SHATTERING

Premature shedding of grain from the panicle is known as shattering. There are considerable differences in tendency to shatter between cultivated varieties and it has been shown to depend to a large extent on the conformation of the joint between the pedicel and the rachilla,

* Private communication from Mr W. Poggendorff.

the point at which the ripe grain disarticulates. Where this joint is a deep ball-and-socket form there is less tendency for shattering. The other extreme can be found where the grain is so tightly attached to the pedicel as to make threshing laborious.

Wild rices as well as red rices shatter as they ripen, but considerable loss of grain may also be experienced with varieties not particularly prone to shatter, should harvesting technique be unsuitable. Time and method of harvesting are important factors in this connection. Should harvesting be unduly protracted or the grain overripe, which usually takes place when the area is large or machinery and labour insufficient, losses may be serious. A ripe crop subject to a hot sun by day and dew by night is particularly liable to shatter. Combines and binders treat the crop somewhat roughly and will cause more shattering than hand-reaping. Ramiah[509] states that in Madras, varieties with a strong tendency to shatter show it more when grown out of the appropriate season; some varieties shatter more when harvests come in summer, others in autumn and also when grown at higher altitudes. Bhalerao[81] reports that cultivators believe that such conditions as stiff clay soil, large quantities of humus, stagnant water, deep water in fields at harvest time, rapid drying after maturity contribute to shattering. It may well be that these are contributory causes of shattering.

The main precaution to be taken to minimize loss by shattering, especially to be observed with varieties prone to shatter, or when combining, is to harvest when the straw is green and allow the crop to dry in the field before threshing. If the crop is to be harvested by machinery, varieties should be cultivated which do not readily shatter.

DROUGHT AND FLOOD RESISTANCE

The hazards of drought and flood in paddy cultivation in Asia are very great and the annual loss of crop attributable to these causes is considerable, although frequently obscured by the current practice of basing yields per acre on the area harvested rather than on the planted area.

Drought as applied to paddy cultivation usually means insufficient water for the needs of the varieties grown in the area. But the drought resistance of paddy varies enormously—from dry-land conditions for "hill" paddy to very deep water for "floating" rices.

Drought resistance is an inherited character associated with certain morphological characters, such as a highly developed root system. Hybrids with the shortest duration of flowering are said to be the most drought resistant. It follows that among the "wet" rices there is considerable variation in resistance to drought and flooding. Graham[224] places such varieties into three categories in regard to their water requirements, viz. drought-resistant, normal, and flood-resistant, and states that the highly drought-resistant varieties can exist twenty days to one month without water, while the longest period that a paddy can withstand submergence is about fifteen days. He suggests the probable explanation of the phenomenon that among the late varieties both drought-resistant and flood-resistant varieties are met with, may be that the danger of flooding to which late varieties growing in the lowest fields are exposed in their early stages, and the late date of maturing after the seasonal rainfall has ceased, have evolved a type which may be both flood- and drought-resistant.

As regards flood resistance, observations in India have established that:

(*a*) seedlings which are older by the time floods occur show greater resistance to submersion;

(*b*) the initial height of seedlings at time of transplanting is no index to their capacity to survive submersion, and

(*c*) yield and flood resistance are not correlated and rapid growth is not necessarily accompanied by high yield.

Many varieties will grow for a short time under water without adverse effect on yield and almost any variety will survive protracted flooding provided that a small portion of the plant—even a leaf or two—is above water level.

While the principal method of preventing disaster to the crop is to be found in controlled drainage and irrigation, yet in some places and under certain circumstances losses may be mitigated or even prevented by timely precautions, especially as regards time of planting, method of raising seedlings in the nursery and the choice of varieties that manifest a degree of resistance to unseasonable conditions.

TOLERANCE TO SALINITY

Paddy is salt-sensitive, for which reason salt should be removed from the superficial soil layers that constitute the shallow root zone of the plant. Therefore, if irrigation water is good, paddy may be grown in soil of initially high salinity.

Experiments have been conducted in a number of countries to determine the effect of salt on the growth and development of paddy. These investigations showed that the plant is most affected by salt in the early seedling stage, and that some varieties have a much greater tolerance than others. Work in Hungary showed that some paddy varieties have a high tolerance to sodium sulphate, although the height and dry weight of aerial parts of the plant were reduced by increasing salt concentration.

Investigations in Egypt showed that salinity reduced weight of straw and number of tillers less than yield of grain and number of productive tillers. As salinity increased, flowering was progressively delayed, panicles were shorter and contained more sterile spikelets. The tolerance of transplanted seedlings increased appreciably as they developed.

In another classic experiment in Cuba,[167] paddy plants of 30, 60 and 90 days old were subjected to various concentrations of sodium chloride (0·15 to 1·0 per cent). Concentrations of 0·15 and 0·25 per cent greatly lowered the number of grains produced by the 30 and 60 day groups, 0·25 to 0·35 per cent decreased grain size and 0·5 per cent prevented grain formation and killed some of the plants. Ninety-day plants were hardly affected by the concentrations used. The seedlings should be planted on the crest of the ridge.

Ridge cultivation of paddy is practised in parts of Italy as a means of coping with very heavily weed-infested land and it should be possible to obtain crops of paddy by this method on saline soil. In the cold regions of Japan,[446] ridge cultivation on non-saline land, produced shorter hulms. Yields were higher from a 3-foot than a 2·4-foot wide ridge, and in a 3-foot ridge, yields were greater with 3 rows than with 2 rows per ridge. Ridging for paddy on saline soil is, of course, only an expedient; it is not a cure for salinity. It is possible, however, that this method of planting might prove an interim means of utilizing very saline areas.

The following green manure plants have been recommended[296] for cultivation in areas influenced by tidal water: *Kandelia rheedii*, *Bruguiera conjugata* Merr., *Excoecaria agallocha*, *Dolichandroe aquathecea* K. Schum and *Derris uliginosa*. For coastal sandbanks the following are recommended: *Morinda citrifolia*, *Scaevola frutescens* Krause and *Pavetta indica*. All the above are woody plants—trees or large shrubs and therefore not particularly suitable for green manures. However, their leafy branches could be lopped and ploughed in as is often done in Ceylon with *Gliricidia* (see page 213). For saline paddy fields the following legumes may be useful: *Crotalaria striata*, *C. verrucosa* and *Rothia trifoliata*.

AROMA

Aroma in rice is more common than is generally supposed and may well explain the popularity of some varieties. In the less scented rices the aroma becomes evident when the uncooked grain is ground, but in the more scented varieties it is recognized when the grain is boiled, while the flowers and even the vegetative parts may emit the perfume.

Some varieties have a peculiar aroma said in India to resemble that of the flower of the tree *Bassia longifolia* Koenig (*Madhuca longifolia* Macbr.). Such rices are not liked by Europeans, who describe the taste as "mousy", but in parts of Asia they are highly esteemed and command high prices. In Ecuador[397] and certain other parts of Latin America, the population has consumed musty rice for so long that clean white rice is rejected by them. This induced mustiness is known as Sierra rice and is prepared by fermenting moist rice (17 to 22 per cent moisture) in piles on hard floors in the open. The piles of rice are covered with tarpaulins and turned after 4–5 days and again after another 6–15 days. The resultant product is light-golden to cinnamon-brown in colour. A somewhat similar fermented rice is prepared in the Yangtze Delta of China[463] where polished rice is mixed with rice bran in the proportion of 10 to 1 and piled in heaps which are covered with rice-straw mats on which are spread a thick layer of rice hulls. After about six months, during which time the rice undergoes fermentation, the heap is opened and the rice screened. The kernels in the middle of the heap have acquired a yellow colour, those near the outside retaining their original colour. The white and yellow kernels are mixed for sale in the proportion of 1 to 2. It is stated that this fermented rice has a smaller expansion on cooking and is more easily digested.

Studies on the inheritance of the scented character of rice have been made by Ramiah, Kadam and Patankar, and by others in India. Aroma in rice is a varietal as well as an environmental character, but neither the active principle nor its distribution in the grain is fully understood.

Chapter V

VARIETIES AND THEIR CLASSIFICATION

THE varieties of cultivated rice are legion and the variation of characters exhibited by them enables the crop to be grown with success over a wide range of climatic and cultural conditions; from dry land, in more or less arid conditions with irrigation, to deep undrained swamps, and in varying depths of water.

REASON FOR LARGE NUMBER OF VARIETIES

The perpetuation of such a large number of varieties is probably due to the Asian custom of harvesting ear-by-ear with the implement (*pangani* in the Philippines, *pisau penuai* in Malaya) which cuts the ears of paddy singly. Copeland[135] suggests that this is the original harvesting implement and records its widespread use in the Philippines and Java. The result of harvesting the crop ear-by-ear is that the attention of the harvester is naturally drawn to any striking variation from the normal. The present writer's experience is that the Asian cultivator is attracted by differences in varieties and is prone to cultivate any paddy which strikes the eye as different, often merely to impress his neighbours. (Has not one seen a similar vanity exhibited by gardeners the world over?) It is, therefore, reasonable to ascribe the persistence of this wide range of varieties as due mainly to the traditional method of harvesting.

Curiosity, however, was not solely responsible for this multiplicity of varieties, for under primitive conditions the cultivator was faced with the necessity of finding varieties which would prove suitable for cultivation over a wide range of cultural conditions, and these varying conditions may, and indeed do, exist in close proximity within small areas of country. Thousands of varieties are grown in India, each suited to a particular condition of soil, rainfall or climate. Varieties which can thrive under a wide range of conditions are rare. There are said to be over 600 improved varieties in India. Richharia *et al.* state[564] that steps are now being taken to reduce the number by testing the varieties in different regions where similar conditions prevail, so as to widen their adaptability. These writers give the following reasons for the huge accumulation of improved varieties in India.

81

(*a*) In evolving superior varieties, major attention was paid to "selection" of local popular varieties without considering the area to which each variety was suited;

(*b*) lack of assured irrigation facilities necessitated breeding many short-duration varieties to escape the uncertain monsoon or drought periods;

(*c*) more uplands—which would be better utilized for growing other crops—are cultivated to paddy;

(*d*) no major attempts have been made to test existing varieties to evaluate their cosmopolitan nature;

(*e*) there is an orthodox approach in preferring one's own varieties and

(*f*) there is no effective system to withdraw the older varieties and multiply rapidly the newly-evolved varieties to replace them.

SUB-SPECIES OF ORYZA SATIVA L.

Oryza sativa L. is divided into four sub-species,[682] described as follows:

(1) *Indica.* Caryopsis elongated, thin, narrow and slightly flattened. Ratio of length to width 3·1 to 3·5:1. Usually awnless or possessing short and smooth awns. Glumellae and leaves slightly pubescent, with short, thin hairs. Leaves pale green, the upper leaf frequently forming an acute angle with the culm.

(2) *Japonica.* Broad, thick caryopsis, rounded in transverse section. Ratio of length to width 1·4:1 to 2·9:1. Awned or awnless, also intermediate forms. Glumellae hairs long and fairly thick. Leaves narrow, dark green, the upper leaf forming an obtuse (in many cases an acute) angle with the culm.

(3) *Brevindica* (Portères) Vasc. Short caryopsis, about 4 mm. in length and narrow; greatly resembling in form the sub-species *indica.*

(4) *Brevis* Gustchin. Short caryopsis, 4 mm. in length and almost equal in width, i.e. short and wide.

The morphological basis for distinguishing these sub-species is often obscure owing to the great number of intermediate forms and hybrids. Their status is therefore debatable except that there are good physiological and genetical grounds for separating the sub-species *indica* and *japonica.* The *japonica* forms are typical of the more northerly (and southerly) areas of paddy cultivation and flourish under very long photoperiods. When grown in tropical areas where the day length is short, they respond to the shorter photoperiod by greatly curtailed life-periods and often become so precocious as to be useless. Further grounds for distinguishing these sub-species is given by the partial sterility of the progeny of *japonica* × *indica* hybrids. Though the chromosome numbers are the same and no morphological differences can be distinguished between the chromosomes of the two sub-species, there is clearly some incompatibility between the genes of the two forms. There are other characters which often, but not invariably, separate these sub-species. For instance, the grain of *japonicas* is commonly shorter and broader than is usual for *indicas*; *japonicas* usually have broad leaves, rather hairy glumes and translucent endosperm. These differences are, however, by no means constant and if taken individually would not serve to distinguish one from the other. Another difference of great importance is in the cooking character of the rices; *japonicas* tend to soften rapidly after a certain time of cooking and to become "mushy" if only slightly overdone: *indicas*, in contrast, tend to resist some over-cooking and to give a rice with each grain separating and not sticky. Strong preferences for particular types of rice dictate the forms which will be acceptable in each area amongst people whose diet is normally rice. These differences are not to be confused with those between the "glutinous" and "non-glutinous" types; both of these can be found in *japonicas* and *indicas*, but the above description deals with differences within the non-glutinous types.

TYPES FAVOURED IN DIFFERENT COUNTRIES

The types of paddy favoured in a country depend on climatic and cultural conditions, and whether the rice is destined for export or local consumption. Racial preferences are very pronounced. In the Philippines, for instance, a long-grained, hard rice is favoured, white and highly milled. The Japanese demand is for a short-grained, semi-glutinous rice; while of the total production in India and Pakistan, about 13 per cent is long-grain, 32 per cent medium-grain and 55 per cent short-grain rice.

In Burma[525] the cultivator recognizes four groups of paddy, classed according to maturation period; they are:

Kaukyin or early varieties, with a maturation period from 100 to 150 days.

Kauklat or varieties with a medium-length maturation period, from 150 to 170 days.

Kaukkyi or varieties with a long maturation period, from 170 days and upward.

Mayin or varieties insensitive to photoperiod and grown in the winter months, having life-periods of about 140 days.

Douglas[157] divides types of rice into three categories:

(1) Relatively long and bold type, known as Carolina rice.

(2) Long, thin, cylindrical grain, known as Patna.

(3) Short, stout grain, known as Spanish-Japan.

In Indonesia[189] there are four main grades of milled rice, the highest quality being obtained from a long-grained, awned paddy with an indifferent yield. The second quality is a slightly smaller grain, while the third grade, which is in main demand in the area, is a short-grained rice. The fourth grade is a glutinous rice.

In Malaya, local varieties are divided into four categories, depending on the size and shape of the grain, though no exact limits appear to be made as to the dimensions of the grain, or the ratio of length to breadth.

The *Seraup* type, which has a distinct shoulder on the anterior extremity of the grain. This type is the most acceptable to millers because of its weight and good milling qualities. Varieties in this type have a long maturation period, over 230 days, and are amongst the highest yielding varieties. The size and shape of grain may vary widely between varieties, especially in length of grain.

The *Radin* type, which is very uniform in outline and is of medium length. Less popular with millers because of its lightness and small size of grain, but it is popular with growers for home consumption. The maturation period is very variable, from 120 to 270 days.

The *Rangoon* type is a rice which is broad and thick in proportion to its length. It is unimportant. The maturation period varies from 120 to 180 days, according to variety.

The *Siam* type, with a very long and sometimes slightly curved grain. It is grown entirely for local consumption and is not favoured by millers. The maturation period of varieties may vary from four to seven months.

In practice, there is no hard and fast division between varieties that grow in water and those that grow on dry ground. There are many varieties of "wet" paddy that will not tolerate dry conditions and *vice versa*, but there are also many varieties that will flourish under either wet or dry conditions.

A feature of rice production in the United States of America is the trend to produce long grain rice in place of short grain. Long-grain varieties now account for over one-half of total production. A similar trend to long-grain varieties is evident in Italy.[415]

The origin of practically all the cultivated rices of America is Asia; over five thousand varieties of paddy from various parts of the world are said to have been introduced in the past thirty years, but very few have proved suitable for cultivation in the United States. Of the varieties at present widely grown, many are pure-line selections from certain of these importations, while some are the result of crosses effected by the Department of Agriculture in the United States.

Considerable attention has been given in the United States to the improvement of varieties by selection and breeding to meet the needs of particular districts. It would appear that, in common with most other countries, continual efforts are needed to maintain the purity of the stock seed distributed by the Department of Agriculture. Whereas in Asia this difficulty is often caused by the desire of the cultivator to grow several varieties, and by the smallness of the individual holding, in America a frequent source of trouble is the threshing machine, which is not always properly cleaned when it has to thresh paddy of more than one variety.

Varieties of Japanese rice[356] are usually short and small-grained, the stem and leaves short and tough and the leaves narrow. Experimental stations have distributed new and improved varieties, making it possible to grow satisfactory crops under the varying climatic conditions in the country. Early varieties are resistant to low temperatures and have been developed for cultivation at the higher elevations in the warmer districts, or where two annual crops are grown. The cool districts grow relatively tall varieties with a heavy weight of grain per ear, although the number of ears per plant is few. Where summer is short and cool, short-stemmed types with many tillers are grown; in the warmer districts varieties are cultivated with less weight per ear, but the ears are numerous and the straw short. The problem of crop failure in low-temperature regions is being met by selection of cold-resistant varieties, early sowing in the nursery, early transplanting, warming the irrigation water and by improving fertilizer practice.

In regions of high temperature in Japan, a rank vegetative growth, lodging and low yield are met by growing sound seedlings, transplanting at a suitable time, covering the plants with soil high in iron ions and by improving fertilizer practice. Of varieties grown, the Norin varieties have been developed at the Stations. Strains of Asahi, Aikoku and Gimbozu are extensively grown, while other varieties distributed include Rikun No. 132 in Tohaku, Norin No. 1 in Hokuriku and Aikoku in Kanto. In the warmer south-west districts Asahi is widely grown, the varieties in this region being well adapted to short-day conditions.

Efforts have been and are still being made in Formosa to breed varieties which are adapted to high and low temperatures and hence are suitable for planting in the first and second half of the year respectively. The high-yielding variety Horai was introduced in

1922 and has proved very successful. It is stated that over 60 per cent of the cultivated area is now planted with this variety and contributes about 70 per cent of the total rice output of Formosa. The Horai paddy of Formosa requires a soil well supplied with nutrients; consequently, during World War II, when fertilizers were scarce, native varieties largely replaced Horai paddy because they thrive without the aid of fertilizers. Ponlai rice is a common name for improved varieties introduced from Japan and also for those obtained by crossing these Japanese varieties with the native rices of Formosa. Ponlai rice has a stiff straw and a short round grain, is insensitive to day-length, is early maturing and a high yielder.[119]

West Pakistan rices are divided into fine and coarse varieties. Of the former, the Basmati group contains the finest varieties. They are grown for quality rather than quantity. The outstanding character of the Basmati is that on cooking the kernels elongate considerably without bursting or becoming sticky.

In Hungary, Dunghan Shali, one of the finest varieties in Europe as regards yield, milling and cooking qualities, is widely cultivated, but unfortunately proves very susceptible to brusone disease. The Italian varieties Agostano and Precoce Allorio and the Roumanian variety Linia 45 are also grown in Hungary and are resistant to this disease. They are, however, inferior in quality and have an extremely long maturation period. Attempts are therefore being made by backcrossing, employing Dunghan Shali as the recurrent partner and the resistant varieties as donor parents, to produce high-quality brusone-resistant varieties suitable for Hungarian cultural conditions.

Soviet Russia aims at selection for earliness, moderate water requirement and selection of varieties grown under conditions of flood and tolerant to saline soils. It is claimed that Assam types can supply the four types of plant needed by Soviet rice breeders.[185]

INFLUENCE OF MECHANIZED CULTIVATION ON VARIETIES GROWN

Many of the difficulties recently encountered in mechanization of paddy cultivation in British Guiana were found to be due to the unsuitability of local varieties to mechanized conditions, and the production of new varieties is therefore being undertaken in this region to overcome these objections. It is pointed out[539] that present varieties are suited to the requirements of a transplanted crop where free tillering is desirable. Where the crop is drilled or broadcast and harvested by machinery, tillering has proved to be a distinct disadvantage, as it causes uneven ripening, reaping is delayed and there is a greater tendency for the crop to lodge, thereby increasing the difficulty of using harvesting machinery.

Furthermore, British Guiana experience is that the local variety has the habit of prolonging or shortening its maturation period according to date of planting, i.e. it is season-fixed, so that, regardless of the date of sowing, maturation takes place at one time. It is therefore impossible to arrange a series of sowings with the object of prolonging the harvesting period. Another objection to the local varieties is the length of straw, a feature that not only encourages lodging, but increases handling costs and interferes with the working of harvesting machinery. It is considered that the ideal variety for mechanized rice production should have a stiff, stout straw, should not tiller freely and should not readily shatter. The grain should be long, to facilitate the separation of red rice by mechanical means (red rice usually having slightly smaller grains than the cultivated varieties) and because long-grained rice is more popular on the markets.

It would seem, therefore, that any widespread development in mechanization will necessitate a reconsideration of the present ideas on desirable qualities in paddy.

HARD AND GLUTINOUS VARIETIES

Varieties are divided into two main classes: those with a hard, starchy grain having a vitreous fracture and those with soft, dextrinous grains having an opaque fracture. The first-named form the rices of world commerce, the latter so-called glutinous rices being of more local importance. Glutinous varieties appear to be facing a shrinking demand. Originally developed to meet consumer tastes in Japan, Korea and certain other regions in South-east Asia, Thai exports rose from nil in 1950 to a peak of 156,000 tons in 1953, but have since declined to about one-half this level.[194] Much of this rice was used in making beer. Mickus, however, states[397] that flour made from glutinous rice solves the problem of curdling in white sauces and gravies used in pre-cooled frozen foods.

The glutinous rices possess a dull and soft grain, the cut surface being described as paraffin-wax-like in appearance. The straw is usually soft and pliable, making it more valuable although more liable to lodge; the grain is usually large and in many varieties coloured, the colour being confined to the epidermal layer.

The glutinous rices, in fact, contain no gluten; the sticky nature of the cooked grain is due to the constitution of the carbohydrates in the endosperm, although opinion differs as to its exact nature. The commonly accepted belief is that the endosperm is not entirely filled with granules of starch, but that it contains soluble starch and dextrin, with some maltose. Burkill[98] considers that this deposition of dextrin in the grain instead of starch can be regarded as a deferring of ripening, adding that it is obvious that on the whole it is a very small change and likely to be the result of selection work of man. He quotes Mitra[409] in stating that the grains of some glutinous rices seem to become non-glutinous during storage. In many Asian countries a specific name is given to glutinous rices as distinct from the general name for rice, while they also recognize intermediate forms between the hard rices and the glutinous rices, which they designate soft rices.

The main characteristic of glutinous rice is that when treated with iodine the endosperm stains a yellow- or reddish-brown colour due to erythrodextrin (as does dextrin) instead of the usual blue reaction of starch. Compared with the hard rices, glutinous rices are usually of poorer quality, the protein being lower though the fat content is distinctly higher.

When boiled, the glutinous rices become sweeter, sticky and cloying, for which reason they are not eaten with curry; they are, however, widely used in the preparation of special dishes, pastries, cakes for ceremonial purposes and for making beer.

Glutinous rice possesses a distinct type of grain and should not be confused with "soft rices". There are "sticky" rices within the "hard" and "soft" groups which go mushy if overcooked, but glutinous rice when cooked is not merely sticky or mushy, it goes into a jelly.

Glutinous rices are practically unknown in international trade, yet they are widely grown in Asia where a large number of varieties are recognized. Cultivators usually grow a small area with a much-prized local variety for home consumption or local sale at a premium over hard rice. About 10 per cent of the rice produced in China and Japan is stated to be glutinous and it is cultivated in India, Burma, Java, Thailand and the Philippines, and in almost all Asian countries. This glutinous rice is said to be similar to the mochi gomi rice produced in small quantities in the U.S.A. and commonly called "sweet rice."[548] On the other hand, Graham[224] states that "so far as the present collection has gone, no examples of glutinous rices have been found in the Central Provinces." In no country does glutinous rice replace hard rice. It is probable that the cultivation of these special rices will persist, but they are unlikely to become important.

SYSTEMS OF CLASSIFICATION OF VARIETIES

Successive writers have pointed out the desirability of instituting an internationally recognized system for the classification of varieties of rice, yet little advance in this direction has been made. Copeland[135] refers to the resolution presented at the Rice Congress at Valencia in 1914 urging the "formation of a real botanical classification of the varieties of cultivated rice," yet although valuable contributions have been made to this end, both before and since Copeland wrote, little has been achieved on an international level towards the adoption of a comprehensive international system of classification. Indeed, in many countries where investigations on rice have extended over many years, no attempt has been made to classify the local varieties. The Food and Agriculture Organization of the United Nations publish a World Catalogue of Genetic Stocks in which some classification is attempted. Classification in Burma is largely based on millers' requirements and Malaya has been influenced in the same direction. There is much to be said for this system based on local purposes. In many other countries classification has been made on physiological characters—maturation period, height, tillering and so on. These characters are valueless as a basis for international classification, because the behaviour of a variety differs according to climatic, soil and other conditions.

Valuable contributions towards botanical classification have been made in India, which are discussed later, and much good work has been done in Japan and elsewhere. But these attempts at classification are usually restricted to the country in which the investigator works, no attempt being made to correlate results in different countries and to agree on a comprehensive system that could be internationally recognized.

During the past century many attempts have been made to devise a botanical classification of rice varieties. Many of these systems are so rudimentary as to be of little practical value, or of only local significance. Gushchin[237] has pointed out many of the weaknesses of these attempts, amongst which he notes that only a small number of types are usually encountered in the classifications and there is no attempt to classify on genetic characters.

Kikkawa[335] suggests two systems of classification, one based on agronomic characters, or as he states it, "with regard to its cultivation," the second on the characters of the grain. His first system must be dismissed, for many of the characters upon which the system relies are variables; for instance, the two main divisions are Aquatic Rice and Upland Rice, but, as he himself points out, "we can hardly draw a line between common or aquatic rice and upland rice." His classification based on the grain has much to recommend it. The distinctive points are summed up as follows:

(*A*) Non-glutinous rice.
    (I) Slender-grained. (II) Long-grained. (III) Short-grained.

(1) Large grain. (2) Medium grain. (3) Small grain.
    (*a*) Common-coloured.
        (*a*) Ordinary. (*b*) Scented.
(*B*) Glutinous rice.
    (I) Slender-grained. (II) Long-grained. (III) Short-grained.
    (1) Large grain. (2) Medium grain. (3) Short grain.
        (*a*) Common-coloured. (*b*) Specially coloured.

Graham[224] presents a more critical view of the characters which are admissible for the purposes of classification. His simple classification is summed up by him as follows:

> All rices fall into one of two groups, viz. rices with a green leaf sheath and those with a coloured leaf sheath. The second class may be subdivided into those with a red leaf sheath and those with a purple leaf sheath.
>
> These classes further sub-divide on their vegetative characters, those of the spikelet and those of the grain. In addition to these morphological characters, the time of ripening, though not definite enough to form a main point in the classification of rices from a large area, is of considerable local importance.

The necessity of confining the characters for classification purposes strictly to those that do not vary cannot be too strongly urged. Graham would admit time of ripening, at least for local purposes, but this character may be extremely variable, depending on environment, water supply and control, method of cultivation, manuring, soil, and even variations of climate from year to year: in fact, upon almost every possible factor that may affect growth.

Kashi Ram and Ch. V. Sarvayga Chetty[499] in a study of the rices of Bihar and Orissa, pointed out that most investigators based their main divisions on classification of the grain, whereas it must be founded on qualitative characters. Most quantitative characters are difficult to define sharply and are subject to fluctuations through changes in environment. These investigations stress the value of colour characters as criteria, the primary divisions being based on the chemical constitution of the kernel, the presence or absence of clustering in the spikelets, length of the outer glume, and upon the presence or absence of elongated internodes such as occur in deep-water varieties. Subsequent divisions are based on the colour of the inner glume, apiculus, outer glume, kernel, and internode, in the order named. The ultimate classes are distinguished by differences in the size and shape of the grain.

In working out the above excellent basis of classification, its authors were probably influenced by previous work on this subject

in India. For instance, many years earlier, Hector classified varieties at Dacca on the following basis:
(1) Leaf-sheath, apiculus and stigma coloured.
(2) Leaf-sheath, apiculus coloured but stigma colourless.
(3) Apiculus and stigma coloured, but leaf-sheath colourless.
(4) Apiculus only coloured.
It is doubtful whether (3) and (4) exist.

Development of the work in India is shown in the schemes devised by Beale[74] based mostly on the characters of the grain. Certain standard types are defined, to one of which any variety must conform. Where varieties are similar, reference is made to floral and other characters.

Beale divides the varieties of Burma into five groups; they are as follows:

The *Ngasein* Group which comprises the largest number of Burma varieties. The grain is bold and hard and fairly translucent, though the defect known as "abdominal white" is inherent in many of the varieties. Milling out-turn is considered good and the type is popular. The type is defined thus: Short medium grain, apiculus prominent, straight. Shape obliquely obovate. Kernel usually translucent, sometimes with "abdominal white."

The *Medon* Group probably comes next in importance to the *ngasein*. It has a short plump grain and in spite of being softer and more chalky than the *ngasein* group, its milling out-turn is higher. Locally, it commands a higher price owing to it being considered more tasty and more easily digested. It does not travel very well, but there is a growing export for it in the East. The type is defined: Short, roundish, bold grain; apiculus-end round without a "beak" and usually hairy. Shape broadly elliptic, kernel opaque and chalky.

The *Emata* Group. The main character of this group is a long hard grain, in which the breakage on milling is high, but which gives an attractive rice capable of high polish. On account of the difficulty they present in milling, the lower qualities of *ematas* are parboiled. The type is defined as follows: Long, slender grain, apiculus very prominent and often curved. Shape of grain linear; kernel translucent.

The *Letywezin* Group comprises a large number of varieties. In appearance and character they lie midway between the *ematas* and *ngasein* groups. The grain suffers in milling, for which reason they are frequently parboiled. When parboiled, they find the same market as the *ematas* and when milled as white rice they are classed as an inferior *ngasein*. The grain is described as slender, apiculus prominent but not curved; shape lanceolate; kernel translucent.

Varieties of the *Byat* Group do not play a very important part in trade. They are, however, grown in small areas and are much appreciated for home consumption. The grain is large and bold and mills well. The milled product is chalky in appearance and soft. The grain is broad and large; apiculus-end round, beak absent, usually hairy. Shape elliptic; kernel opaque and chalky.

Beale's five groups are more closely defined by him into seven types:

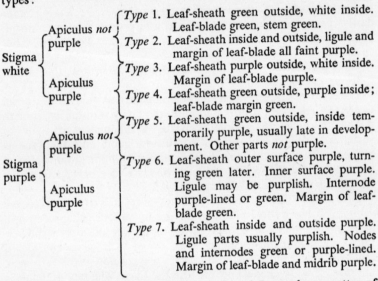

Stigma white

Apiculus *not* purple

Type 1. Leaf-sheath green outside, white inside. Leaf-blade green, stem green.

Type 2. Leaf-sheath inside and outside, ligule and margin of leaf-blade all faint purple.

Apiculus purple

Type 3. Leaf-sheath purple outside, white inside. Margin of leaf-blade purple.

Type 4. Leaf-sheath green outside, purple inside; leaf-blade margin green.

Stigma purple

Apiculus *not* purple

Type 5. Leaf-sheath green outside, inside temporarily purple, usually late in development. Other parts *not* purple.

Apiculus purple

Type 6. Leaf-sheath outer surface purple, turning green later. Inner surface purple. Ligule may be purplish. Internode purple-lined or green. Margin of leaf-blade green.

Type 7. Leaf-sheath inside and outside purple. Ligule parts usually purplish. Nodes and internodes green or purple-lined. Margin of leaf-blade and midrib purple.

He adds that the difference between 6 and 7 may be a matter of intensity of purple colour, and it may be possible to eliminate 6, making 7 cover both. Colour of stem, of both the nodes and internodes, does not appear to be as important as that of the leaf-sheath. The main objection to this system is that the types are not linkage groups and are therefore unstable.

Mention has been made of Beale's five groups. These are defined by length and breadth of grain in Table 6.

Thus, there are five groups and seven types. It is claimed that within these thirty-five divisions any variety may find a place. It is appreciated that the division of grain into five groups according to size and shape of grain may appear arbitrary, but it has proved to be a workable scheme in the largest rice-exporting country in the world and as such merits consideration.

Objection can be advanced against any scheme of classification of rice, and the problem is undoubtedly complex. It is suggested that,

TABLE 6

DIMENSION OF GRAIN OF BURMA RICES

Class	Group name	Dimensions of grain			
		With husk		Husked	
		Length in mm.	Length breadth	Length in mm.	Length breadth
A	Emata	Over 9·4	Over 3·3	Over 7·0	Over 3·0
B	Letywezin	8·4 to 9·8	2·8 to 3·3	6·0 to 7·0	2·4 to 3·0
C	Ngasein	7·75 to 9·0	2·4 to 2·8	5·6 to 6·4	2·0 to 2·4
D	Medon	7·35 to 8·6	2·0 to 2·4	5·0 to 6·0	1·6 to 2·0
E	Byat	9·0 upwards	2·25 to 3·0	6·4 to 7·35	2·10 to 2·5

in the first place, a simple scheme of classification be adopted which is capable of elaboration as a result of experience and by general consent of an international body.

The consultative sub-committee of the FAO has recently published a list of rice terms which include definitions of different classes as follows:

Shape				*Ratio of length to breadth*
Slender	..	..	..	Over 3
Medium	..	..	..	2·4 to 3·0
Bold ..	..	..	..	2·0 to 2·39
Round	..	..	..	Under 2

Size				*Length in mm.*
Extra long	..	..	..	Over 7
Long ..	..	..	..	6 to 7
Middling	..	..	..	5 to 5·99
Short	..	..	..	Under 5

Size is also defined by weight:

				Weight in gr. of 1,000 *kernels of milled rice*
Very large	..	..	..	Over 28
Large	..	..	..	22 to 28
Small	..	..	..	Under 22

These are proposed trade grades: it remains to be seen whether they are universally adopted by the trade.

Reference is frequently made to coarse (or bold) rice. Such rice has a length-breadth ratio of over 3. Varieties of rice grown in warm temperate regions are usually coarse. The finest rice is probably produced in Thailand. It is considered that coarse rice yields are higher than fine rice, are hardier, respond better to manures, retain viability longer in storage, mill better and are more nutritious in processed form.

SUITING THE VARIETY TO THE ENVIRONMENT

No expert can, by visiting an area, or by examining climatic conditions and the chemical nature of the soil, prescribe with any certainty the variety of paddy to which the situation is suited. He may, however, with reservations, indicate varieties which may prove suitable. The many factors influencing the growth of paddy are so complex and so much is incompletely understood, that the vagaries of the crop can only be countered by the process of trial and error. A study of the literature on paddy-growing will reveal the many apparent contradictions, so that only by tests over comparatively small areas can the most suitable variety be selected. Furthermore, selection of the most suitable variety for a given area does not depend entirely on which variety will produce the greatest crop; the selected variety must also be suited to market requirements.

In finding a suitable variety for an area, acclimatization is relatively unimportant. Maácz,[370] however, states that Italian rice varieties grown for a few years in Hungary developed shorter caryopses and were lighter in weight. Decreases in grain diameter were accompanied by decrease of plant height. These changes are thought to be due to cooler weather and to the sensitivity of the plant to photoperiodic conditions. Should a variety prove unsuitable under a given set of climatic and soil conditions, continuous cultivation is unlikely to render the variety more tolerant to these unfavourable conditions.

From the discussion of the cultural conditions of growth, together with a realization of the diversity of varieties, it will be appreciated that the cultivation of paddy is possible over a wide range of climatic and soil conditions. The task of selecting the right variety for any given area is extremely complex; its complexity will be lessened when the classification of varieties is standardized, and with increased knowledge of crop requirements.

Chapter VI

THE GENETICS OF PADDY*

It is not intended to give a detailed account of the genetics of paddy in this book. The inheritance of many characters, though occasionally of local importance, is of little economic importance in breeding paddy for general consumption. The specialist reader will naturally turn to the original publications to which reference is made in this chapter.[321] A summary of the mode of inheritance of some characters affecting the agricultural value of paddy is necessary in order to understand plant improvement measures; a full account is given by Chendraratna.[721]

THE CYTOLOGY OF PADDY

Kuwada[344] in 1910 first reported the haploid chromosomes of *Oryza sativa* L. to be 12 ($2n = 24$) and this has been repeatedly confirmed. Parthasarathy[472] found ten pairs and four single chromosomes. In somatic prophase two chromosomes were observed with terminal knob-like processes which remained attached to the single nucleolus or, if two nucleoli were present, one such chromosome was attached to each nucleolus. Parthasarathy also found that there were varieties having two or four nucleoli and it has further been shown that the *japonica* group is characterized by two nucleoli while the *indica* group commonly has four in somatic cells.

Studies of association during meiosis, notably by Sakai,[579] showed that there were commonly two groups of three and three groups of two chromosomes indicating that the basic number is 5, but the studies of Audulov[717] provide strong evidence that the basic chromosome number should be regarded as 12. In studies on haploid plants Takenaka *et al.*[645] found three bivalents and two trivalents. They inferred that the genome is composed of *a b c d e a' b' c' d' e' a" b"*.

Other species of *Oryza* having $2n = 24$ are *O. glaberrima* Steud., *O. officinalis* Wall and *O. longistaminata* Chev. (= *O. perennis* Moench.). They are reported to cross readily with *O. sativa* but with much sterility in the progeny. The other species for which records are available have $2n = 48$. Crosses between these and *O. sativa*[312] have generally been unsuccessful, but in the few cases where

* Contributed by Mr D. Rhind, c.m.g., o.b.e.

viable seed has been obtained, the progeny have been sterile. Indeed, even between such close relatives as the *japonica* and *indica* sub-species of *O. sativa* sterility in the progeny is often high.

Haploids and polyploids occur occasionally in crops and induced polyploids have been produced. Haploids appear like miniature diploids, sterile unless artificially pollinated. Autotriploids some-times occur in pure lines where they are sterile, usually larger than the diploid and generally with long awns.[416, 501] Allotriploids have arisen in crosses between *O. sativa*, *O. minuta* and *O. officinalis*. Autotetraploids showing gigantism but highly sterile have been reported,[417] and these have been studied in Japan.[447] Polyso-mics, having one or more chromosomes additional to the diploid complement, have arisen from triploids by irregular meiosis giving plants with twenty-five to thirty chromosomes.[327, 501]

ANTHOCYANIN PIGMENTATION

Many genes have been described which control anthocyanin pig-mentation in different parts of the rice plant. Earlier accounts generally over-simplified the inheritance of these characters, often assuming a single gene which later studies have shown to be two or three complementary genes. Ramiah and Rao[509] have summarized the earlier work. Later results (*vide* Nagao (1951)) recognize five alleles for chromogen, $C^B > C^{Bp} > C^{Bt} > C^{Br} > c$ and three at the *Sp* locus, $Sp > Sp^d > sp$. Anthocyanin colour in the apiculus depends on the combination of genes from the *C* and *Sp* loci. Genes producing colour in the apiculus also produce colour in other parts of the plant and they are therefore basic genes, colour in other parts only developing when the apiculus is coloured. Thus colour in the leaf and leaf-sheath depends on *Pl*, *Pla* or *Plm* in combination with a gene at the *C* locus (*C*, C^B, C^{Bt} or C^{Bp}) and one at the *Sp* locus (*Sp* or Sp^d). *Pl* is epistatic to both *Pla* and *Plm* and *Pla* is epistatic to *Plm*. Stem and internode colours depend on *Pn* together with *CSp* or other alleles at these loci. Many other genes expressing anthocyanin colours exist but since these characters are generally of little agri-cultural importance details are omitted here.

RED GRAIN

The red pigmentation of the pericarp of the rice grain is of great commercial importance because of its effect on quality and milling behaviour. Except for a few restricted markets, red grain is highly undesirable and special care is necessary to exclude this character from crops.

The pigment, which is not anthocyanin, is generally inherited as if a single gene pair is involved with red colour dominant. Work by Nagao and Takahashi (1947)[425] showed, however, that two complementary genes may be concerned, *Rc* and *Rd*. *Rc* is responsible for pigment production in the so-called grey-brown rice which has brown irregular flecks on a reddish-brown background. *Rd*, when present, together with *Rc*, causes a spreading of the colour of *Rc*, so producing red rice. *Rd* itself does not produce any pigment. Red rice is assumed to be *RdRc*, grey-brown rice *Rcrd* and white rice either *rcRd* or *rcrd*. Crosses between red- and white-grained rices segregate, either 3:1 or in some cases 9:3:4.

The genes *Rc* and *Rd* occur in different linkage groups, *Rd* being very closely linked with *Sp* (recombinations less than 0·3 per cent), and *Rc* being in the *lng* group.

MORPHOLOGICAL CHARACTERS

STEM

The habit varies from spreading to compact. A too wide angle of tillers is undesirable, a compact to intermediate habit being preferable. The inheritance of angle of tillering has been little studied, but Ramiah found the compact habit a simple recessive though the spreading form is variable. In some wild species the habit is procumbent and this extreme form has occurred as an ageotropic mutant due to a single gene.

The floating habit was studied by Ramiah and Ramaswamy[508] who obtained a ratio of 15 normal to 1 floating, duplicate genes being concerned. Normal erect varieties vary in height, which is controlled by multiple genes. Dwarf types, like that from Burma studied by Parnell *et al.*,[470] also occur as well as various mutants, the dwarf habit being nearly always recessive. Stem thickness shows polygenic inheritance.

LEAF

Length and breadth of leaf vary considerably and some association of narrow leaf with slender grains has been observed. Grant[225] found an approximate ratio of 3:1 from a cross broad x narrow leaf, while Ramiah found a polygenic inheritance. Hairiness varies between varieties, the character "hairy" being dominant over "smooth" with either one or two genes involved.

CHLOROPHYLL

Deficiencies in chlorophyll production are common in paddy and these are detrimental to the plant, ranging from lethal to slight loss of vigour in the homozygous state. Lethal deficiencies giving rise

I

to *albino* or *lethal yellow* forms are commonly due to a single recessive gene but ratios of 15:1, 63:1 and 9:7 have been reported. Albino and lethal yellow seedlings die after a few days. It appears that the genes concerned are somewhat unstable because in every paddy nursery, whether of pure lines or farmer's mixtures, a few such seedlings can always be found in the first week after sowing. Even in pure lines which have been selfed for upwards of twenty generations these lethals still occur and necessitate the selfing of more than a single plant for purity maintenance, to guard against accidentally choosing one heterozygous for a lethal chlorophyll gene.

Deficiencies which are not lethal though weakening are *virescent* and *chlorina* in which the seedling is first pale yellow or very pale greenish-yellow which slowly changes to green. Rhind (unpublished) measured the amount of chlorophyll in such recovered plants and found they never attained the full development of chlorophyll of normal plants and they remained weaker. Inheritance was due to one or two genes in most cases, though Kadam[318] found six genes controlling the virescent character.

Striped patterns are occasionally found, the commonest being longitudinal stripes of green and white or yellow and white. As a seedling character it is often evanescent with one or two genes involved. As a character of older plants it appears not to be inherited in a Mendelian manner.[507] Tillers showing the variegated character when separated from the parent plant gave mostly white or green progeny only. The variegated character is not transmitted by the pollen.

PANICLE

Probably the most important panicle character is length, which is associated with yield. Panicle length is strongly correlated with plant height and is probably controlled by the same polygenes. It is important that the panicle shall be fully exserted from the leaf-sheath, some varieties being carried well clear of the junction of the sheath and the flag-leaf while others remain partly enclosed, the degree of exsertion being due to multiple genes. Panicle density (grains per unit length) is a compound character dependent on degree of branching, length of rachilla of each spikelet, grain length, etc. The very lax type (e.g. the Madras variety GEB 24) appears to be dominant to the common compact types and this has been found in interspecific crosses also. Association of dense panicle with smaller sized grains is common, though the extremely lax panicled GEB 24 has notably small grains. "Clustering" of spikelets occasionally occurs, Rhind finding it common in varieties from the extreme north of Burma. In this character, two to seven spikelets are found close together on the secondary branches, some appearing as if reversed in position. A single partially dominant gene for "clustering" has been found.

GLUMES

Apart from colour characters the only other variations in glume of cultivated paddy is that of length. There are varieties which have glumes as long as or longer than the lemma and palea. In crosses with normal short-glumed varieties ratios of 3 normal:1 long or 1:2:1 have been recorded, as well as 15:1.

LEMMA AND PALEA

Much work has been done in India on the colours of the lemma and palea, both in the young state and when ripe. For details, the original papers should be consulted[262, 410, 470] or the summary given by Ramiah and Rao.[509] There is probably little commercial importance to be attached to these colour differences, though varieties with very dark glumes are likely to give a dirty-looking rice when milled, due to dark powder from the husk.

AWN

Though they are reputed to confer resistance to birds, the presence of awns is undesirable in commercial crops. The inheritance of the awned character is complicated by the influence of environment. Iso,[293] for instance, considers that moist conditions encourage awn development, particularly during the heading stage. Often short awns occur on some tillers of a plant but not on others, while sterile spikelets may bear awns on an otherwise awnless plant. Auto-triploids arising from a completely awnless pure line may bear awns two to three inches long. Using a broad grouping into "tipped," "awned" and "fully awned," Ramiah[509] has shown that mono-, di-, and trihybrid ratios can be recognized. It is probable, however, as Ramiah himself points out, that the inheritance of the awned character cannot be so simply explained.

PISTIL

"Double-grained" rice appears occasionally though the small, misshapen grains make it commercially worthless. The multi-pistilate condition is a simple recessive to the normal. Cases of polyembryony also occur, Ramiah[510] mentioning it as frequent (1 in 1,000) in GEB 24. It is probably due to the development of two embryo-sacs in one ovule.

GRAIN (CARYOPSIS)

Grain size and shape is subject to a limited amount of variation due to environment, which was studied in detail by U Tin.[674] The grain size changes so induced are probably less than in most other cereals, so that this character is of considerable diagnostic value for pure lines. Inheritance of grain size characters is polygenic though, using broad groupings, attempts have been made to explain the segregations on the basis of up to four pairs of genes. Size and shape differences in the progeny of crosses are subject to such a wide range of continuous variation that a simple scheme of inheritance could not be expected.

ENDOSPERM

This is the part of the plant of greatest value but comparatively little is known of factors involved in its characters. Probably the best known genetically are the starchy and so-called glutinous characters. Glutinous is inherited as a simple recessive to starchy, the F_2 segregation taking place on the panicles of the F_1 plant. There is nearly always a small deficiency in the number of recessives;[120] a significant deficiency but not invalidating the monohybrid theory.

Amongst the starchy types, the chief rices of commerce, differences in hardness, translucency, presence or absence of abdominal white, etc., are important. Their inheritance has not yielded any simple scheme except in a few cases. Grant[225] crossed opaque with translucent endosperm rices and observed a ratio of 1 translucent: 2 abdominal white: 1 opaque. Dave[526] and Rhind observed xenia in a similar cross which segregated 3:1 on the F_1 panicle and this was also studied by Yamaguchi.[710]

A character occasionally found in bold-type grains is "notched belly" caused by uneven growth of endosperm cells.[427] It is an undesirable character leading to increased breakage in milling.

SHATTERING

Too easy shedding of grain is obviously undesirable but the opposite, too hard threshing, can cause farmers to reject a variety. Even machine threshing may not overcome the latter difficulty entirely, because pieces of rachilla may remain attached to the spikelets and so lower bushel weight. Considerable differences in degree of shattering are found between varieties. The shape of the depression at the base of the fruit into which the tip of the rachilla fits influences the ease with which the grain separates; the deeper the depression the tighter the grain is fixed.[224] There is an abciss layer at this juncture, and if the cells of this layer dry up early, grain is liable to shedding, but if their drying occurs later shedding is reduced. Cases of absence of the abciss layer occur and such paddies thresh with difficulty. In a cross between cultivated and wild rices (which shatter excessively) ratios of 3:1 and 15:1 were recorded with shattering dominant. Crosses between cultivated varieties, which do not involve the extreme degree of shattering found in some wild species, present difficulties in classification of degrees of shattering and Ramiah and Hanumantharao[505] found a polygenic inheritance though probably not many genes were involved.

PHYSIOLOGICAL CHARACTERS

Response to length of day is one of the most important agricultural characters of paddy on which the suitability of a variety to a particular locality largely depends. The inheritance of this response to photoperiod is therefore described in some detail.

The factors which govern photoperiod response are complicated by the fact that flowering date is influenced positively or negatively by the photoperiod, so that a single record of flowering date is one point only on the curve which relates flowering to different photoperiods. Proper appreciation of this fact was first recognized by Chandraratna[113] who, in an elegant analysis of the problem, described the genetics of inheritance of sensitivity to differences to photoperiod. In a mineographed report to the International Rice Commission in 1954 Chandraratna wrote as follows:

> The germination-heading interval drops to a minimum value at a photoperiod characteristic of the variety. Extension or shortening of the photoperiod beyond this optimum value delays heading. Second degree polynomials of the form
>
> $$y = a + bx + cx^2$$
>
> where y is the germination-heading interval in days, and x is the photoperiod in hours, provide satisfactory fit to curves relating flowering date of a rice variety to the photoperiod.
>
> The germination-heading interval reaches a maximum value when the first differential coefficient is zero. As
>
> $$\frac{dy}{dx} = b + 2cx = 0,$$
>
> the optimum photoperiod assumes the value $-\dfrac{b}{2c}$. The germination-heading interval corresponding to this optimum photoperiod may be designated the minimum heading duration, and can be shown by substituting $x = -\dfrac{b^2}{2c}$. in the equation $y = a + bx + cx^2$ to have the value $a - \dfrac{b^2}{4c}$. The best estimate of photoperiod sensitivity, which must

be related to the rate of change of curvature of the parabola, is furnished by the second differential coefficient,

$$\frac{d^2x}{dx^2} = 2c.$$

The parameters $2c$, $-\dfrac{b}{2c}$ and $\dfrac{a - b^2}{4c}$ thus provide estimates of photoperiod sensitivity, the optimum photoperiod and minimum heading duration. The age expression of a rice variety can accordingly be resolved into these three measurable components, the genetics of each of which can be the subject of separate study.

Having thus analysed the factors involved in photoperiodic response, Chandraratna then studied the genetics of sensitivity to photoperiods in crosses between an insensitive or nearly insensitive variety and four varieties highly sensitive to day length. To evaluate the parameter $2c$ a series of photoperiods would be necessary but, while these could be applied to a homozygous population, it was not possible to do so to a segregating F_2 population in which each individual is unique. It is, however, possible to separate sensitive from insensitive segregants when these are clearly defined (not polygenically controlled) and when the parents have comparable optimum photoperiods and minimum heading durations. By utilizing a season of short days, indications of sensitivity were obtained. The F_2 segregations agreed with a ratio of 3 sensitives : 1 day-neutral, the gene pair being designated *Se se*.[114, 116] While a monohybrid segregation of the main gene is indicated, the wide variation in degrees of sensitivity would seem to need a series of alleles at the *Se* locus, with possibly modifiers at other loci. Chandraratna, commenting on previous results of studies on the inheritance of earliness and lateness, notes that these either show a 3 : 1 segregation in F_2 or a unimodal distribution of the polygenic type. The former possibly result from the action of genes at the *Se* locus under long days, while the latter would occur when either the two parents were day-neutral or when the F_2 was grown under day lengths of about the optimum.

An association of much economic importance was found between *Se* and high tiller number, which may account for the perpetuation of sensitive types despite the restriction this places on their adaptability.

Recent work by Fuke[203] indicates at least six genes controlling heading time each giving a specific response to day length and temperature. Of the sixty-four possible genotypes Fuke claims to have identified twenty-two amongst eighty Japanese varieties tested.

LINKAGE GROUPS

There is only a limited amount of information on linkage groups in rice, much of it relating to colour characters. Of the twelve possible linkage groups Jodon[307] describes eight but some of these are uncertain. Reviewing this subject Nagao[424] considered only four were established with certainty. The following account follows Chandraratna.[721]

The "Waxy-Chromogen" group. Jodon's Group I

In this group a number of characters are linked with glutinous endosperm (*wx*), the best example being apiculus colour. Of the two complementary genes responsible for apiculus colour, *C* and *Sp* or their alleles, only *C* is linked with *wx*, recombinations being about 23 per cent. This suggests that *C* is identical with other genes described for apiculus colour such as *Ap* of Jodon.[307] Other genes of this group include dwarf (d_3), Hara's male sterile *sf* linked with *wx* and *C*, genes for virescent, clustered grain and for floating habit. Chandraratna found photoperiod sensitivity (*Se*) linked with apiculus colour.

"Purple Leaf-Liguleless" group. Jodon's Group V

Nagao includes six genes in this group, purple leaf blade *Pl*, liguleless *lg*, ebusi dwarf d_2, colour reaction to phenol *Ph* (a dark violet colour produced on fruit and husk), red or purple palea and lemma *Rp* and semi-sterile *sk*. The gene *Rp* is probably identical with *Ap* and *Rbe*. The gene order suggested is d_2–d_3–*Pl*–*lg*–*Ph*–*Pr*.

"Long Glume-Brown Bran" group. Jodon's Group IV

In Jodon's Group IV there is close linkage between spikelet length and outer glume length. Nagao includes three genes, long empty glumes *g*, lop-leaved d_6, and brown pericarp *Rc*. Recombinations reported are 30·2 per cent between d_6 and *Rc* and the same between *Rc* and *g*. The apparent linkage between red pericarp and glume length must be between *Rc* and *g* because the complementary gene for pericarp colour, *Rd*, belongs to the *Sp* group.

"Activator-Purple Node" group.

Five genes seem to belong to this group, *Sp*, *Pn*, *Rd*, *pa* and *lax*. *Sp* is the complimentary gene to *C* for coloured apiculus. It is closely linked (recombinations 0·3 per cent or less) with *Rd*, the complementary gene for red pericarp. It is linked with purple node *Pn* (recombinations 17·2 per cent in coupling). Depressed palea, Morinagas' gene *pa*, is linked with *Sp* with recombinations about

20 per cent. Sparse spikelets, *lax*, is linked with *Sp* with recombinations about 31 per cent.

"*Inhibitor-Purple Stigma*" group

This group is based on the linkage of *Ps* (purple stigma) and *I-Bf*, an inhibitor of brown furrows on the lemma and palea.

"*Dwarf-Gold Hull*" group

This is the linkage of Daikoku dwarf (d_1) and gold hull (*gh*), which are also linked with "white stripe", *gw*.

"*Fine Stripe-Undulate Rachis*" group

In this group "fine stripe" (*fs*) and "undulate rachis" (*Ur*) are linked and also with *Dn*, dense panicle.

"*Spreading-Shattering*" group

This group has only one known linkage between spreading habit *sg* and grain shattering, *sh*.

"*Neckleaf-Verticillate*" group

The only known linkage is between neckleaf (*nl*) and verticillate rachis (*ri*).

"*Mottled Leaf-Tillering Dwarf*" group

The basis of this group is mottled leaf, *mt*, and d_5, one of the three complementary genes of Bunketsu-waito dwarf.

"*Brittle Culm*" group

The brittle culm gene, *bc*, is assumed to be in this group but no linked gene is known.

"*Glabrous*" group. Jodon's group VII.

It is assumed to contain the glabrous gene *gl* but there is only an uncertain linkage with *An*, one of the genes controlling awns.

SYMBOLIZATION OF GENES

Varying symbolization of genes described by different authors has led to confusion, which Kadam and Ramiah[320] first attempted to regularize. Nagao made a further revision in 1951 and the International Rice Commission in 1959. These three systems are reproduced in Table 7.

TABLE 7

GENE SYMBOLS IN RICE
(after Chandraratna)

Character	Kadam and Ramiah (1943)	Symbol proposed by Nagao (1951 et seq)	International Rice Commission (1959)
Albino	*w*	*al*	*al*
Anthocyanin activator (complementary gene for apiculus colour)	*Ap*	*Sp, Sp*^{d}	*A, A*^{d}
Awned	*An*	*An*	*An*
Awned sterile	*fan*	*ans*	—
Auricle absent or rudimentary	*au*	—	*au*
Barren sterile	*fbs*	*bs*	—
Beaked hull (lemma tip recurved over palea) ...	—	—	*Bd*
Brittle culm	*bc*	*bc*	*bc*
Brown furrow (dark brown colour in furrows of lemma and palea)	—	—	*Bf*
Black hull (complementary gene)	*H-b*	—	*Bh*
Brown pericarp (chromogen or chromophelein) ...	*Pbr*	*Rc*	*Rc*
Cercospora oryzae, resistance to	*Ce*	*Ce*	*Ce*
Chlorina	—	*ch*	*chl*
Chromogen (complementary gene for apiculus colour; higher members of multiple allelic series influence internode colour pleiotropically)	*C*	*C, C*^{B}, *C*^{Bp}, *C*^{Bt}, *C*^{Br}	*C, C*$_B$, *C*^{Bp} *C*^{Bt}, *C*^{Br}
Claw spikelet	—	*clh*	*clw*
Cleistogamous spikelet ...	—	—	*cls*
Clustered spikelets ...	*Scl*	*Cl*	*Cl*
Compact-panicle sterile ...	—	*cps*	—
Complete sterile	*fo*	*cs*	—
Dwarf (general)	*d*	*d*	*d*
Daikoku dwarf	—	*d*$_1$	—
Esibu dwarf	—	*d*$_2$	—
Tillering dwarf	—	*d*$_3$, *d*$_4$, *d*$_5$	—
Top-leaved dwarf	—	*d*$_6$	—
Double awn	—	*da*	*da*
Dense panicle	*dn*	*dn*	*dn*
Depressed palea	—	*pa* (Morinaga's symbol)	*pa*
Early flowering (photoperiod-insensitive)	—	—	*Ef*
Enhancer or intensifier ...	—	—	*En-* (precedes character symbol)

TABLE 7 (continued)

GENE SYMBOLS IN RICE

(after Chandraratna)

Character	Kadam and Ramiah (1943)	Symbol proposed by Nagao (1951 et seq)	International Rice Commission (1959)
Female sterile	*ffs*	*fes*	—
Floating habit	*ef*	*fh*	*fl*
Fine stripe	—	*fs*	*fs*
Fragrant flower	*Fgr*	*Fgr*	*Fgr*
Glabrous leaf	*Lh*	*gb*	*gl* (hypostatic to *Gm*)
Gold hull (recessive to straw)	—	—	*gh*
Green-and-white striped	*gs*	*gs*	—
Green-and-yellow striped	*gy*	*gy*	—
Glutinous or waxy endosperm	*wx*	*gl*	*wx*
Helminthosporium oryzae, resistance to	*Hm*	*Hm*	*He*
Inhibitor	*I*	*I*	*I-* (precedes character symbol)
Late flowering (photoperiod sensitive)	—	—	*Lf*
Lazy or ageotropic habit	*la*	*la*	*la*
Lax panicle	*lx*	*lax* (Morinaga's) symbol)	*lx* or *I-lx*
Lemma-palea colour	H (alleles indicated by additional lower-case letters)	—	H (alleles indicated by superscript letters)
Lemma-palea ripening black	*H-b*	*Rl*	—
Lemma-palea ripening gold	*H-go*	*Rg*	—
Leptosphaeria resistance	*Le*	*Le*	—
Lethal	—	—	*l*
Liguleless	*lg*	*lg*	*lg*
Lodging	*Ld*	—	*Ld*
Long empty glumes	*g*	*lng*	*g*
Lutescent	*l*	*lu*	*lu*
Minute spikelet	—	*Mi*	
Multiple embryos (poly-embryonic)	—	—	*me*
Multiple pistils (polycaryoptic)	*mp*	*mp*	*mp*
Male-sterile	*fm*	*ms*	—
Mottled green (glumes and leaves tinged dirty brown as if diseased)	*hm*	*mg*	*bl*
Neckleaf (panicle partly enclosed by supernumerary bract)	—	*hk*	*nl*
Notched kernel	—	—	*nk*

TABLE 7 (continued)

GENE SYMBOLS IN RICE

(after Chandraratna)

Character	Kadam and Ramiah (1943)	Symbol proposed by Nagao (1951 et seq)	International Rice Commission (1959)
Open spikelet (lemma and palea fail to close after blooming)	—	*op*	*o*
Open-spikelet sterile (same as previous but sterile) ...	—	*ops*	—
Paleaceous sterile (stamens and pistil replaced by glumes)	*fp*	*pas*	—
Phenol positive (grain stains violet with phenol) ...	—	*Ph*	*Ph*
Piricularia oryzae, resistance to	*Pi*	*Pi*	*Pi*
Purple leaf blade	*Lp*	*Pl*	*Pl*
Purple leaf apex and margin	—	*Pla*	—
Purple midrib	—	*Plm*	—
Purple node	*Np*	*Pn*	*Pn*
Purple stigma	*Sp*	*Ps*	*Ps*
Purple hull	*Hp*	*Rp*	*Pr*
Purple pericarp	*Pp*	*Pp*	*Prp*
Purple root	*Rp*	*Pr*	—
Red pericarp	*Pr*	*Rd* (complementary action with *Rc*)	*Rd* (complementary action with *Rc*)
Round kernel	—	—	*Rk*
Rolled leaf	—	—	*rl*
Scented kernel	—	—	*Sk*
Sclerotium oryzae, resistance to	—	—	*Sc*
Semisterile	*fs*	*ss*	—
Shattering of grain	*Sh*	*Sh*	*Sh*
Sinuous neck of panicle (See "Undulate rachis") ...	*ne*	*ne*	*sn*
Spreading habit (the "motsure" character) ...	*Es*	*Sg*	—
Staminoidal sterile	*fst*	*sts*	—
Sterility (general)	*f*	*s*	*s*
Triangular hull	—	*th*	*tri*
Twisted leaf (midrib absent)	—	*tw*	*tl*
Undulate rachis ... ... (See "Sinuous neck") ...	—	—	*Ur*
Verticillate arrangement on rachis (the "rinshi" character)	—	—	*ri*
Virescent	*v*	*v*	*v*
White belly or abdominal white (endosperm) ...	*wb*	—	*wb*
White core (endosperm) ...	—	—	*Wc*
White hull	—	—	*Wh*
Xantha (lethal yellow) ...	*y*	*xa*	*l-y*
Zebra stripe	—	—	*z*

Chapter VII

IMPROVEMENT BY SELECTION AND BREEDING*

THE paddy population commonly found in the field consists of plants of different types, habits and yielding power. Natural crossing between these types produces plants which are heterozygous and which do not breed true but continue to add to the mixture at each generation. This mixed population offers a promising field of work on crop improvement since, if only the highest-yielding and more desirable forms are cultivated, yields can be greatly increased and quality improved. There are four methods by which this object may be achieved, viz. mass selection, pure line selection, pedigree and bulk-population breeding.

The most obvious advantage to be expected from selection and breeding is enhanced yields. It may be anticipated that increases over the unselected mixture may amount to 10 to 25 per cent or more. Other advantages include even ripening of the crop, uniformity of grain size resulting in better milling behaviour, lower breakage, disease resistance and elimination of undesirable characters such as lodging of straw, shattering, elimination of red grain and absence of awns—and hence higher bushel weight.

MASS SELECTION

Cultivators in Asia have unwittingly practised mass selection of paddy from time immemorial by choosing plants they like for cultivation in future seasons. It is this practice which has given rise to the multitude of varieties now grown.

In mass selection, the seed of a number of individual plants of apparently desirable characters is bulked for cultivation in the following season. The procedure is as follows: Seed from which the selection is to be made is grown in a nursery and transplanted with a single seedling per hill on land which is not especially fertilized for the crop. By this method variability caused by environment is greatly reduced and genetic variability allowed full play. A selec-

---

* Based largely on an unpublished account prepared by Mr D. Rhind, to whom the author is indebted. Use has also been made of Mr K. Ramiah's excellent book on Rice Breeding and Genetics.

tion of individual plants is made from this crop all of which conform to the desired type. At harvest the seed from the selected plants is bulked for planting.

Mass selection of individual plants of similar appearance but irrespective of their genotypic value often results in some immediate improvement, but the method is by no means entirely satisfactory and has only limited scope for success. For example, unless the resulting crop is regularly and systematically rogued to eliminate aberrant and undesirable types, the progeny will rapidly deteriorate. In fact, more often than not, it will be found that the work of mass selection must be repeated annually.

PURE LINE SELECTION

Pure line selection produces a homozygous population with some genetical advance within the limits of available variability but with loss of adaptability. It is, however, a necessary procedure where large commercial crops are grown but the number of pure lines issued to growers should be kept to a minimum. The high degree of inbreeding in rice rapidly reduces heterozygosity so that within a farmer's crop there is only limited scope for improvement, though this may be well worth having.

In this method of crop improvement a critical examination is made of the mixed plant population of paddy so planted as to allow single plants to be selected and their characters recorded. For this purpose, about 2,000 plants are set with single seedlings spaced two feet between rows and one foot between plants in the row. Initial selections are made by examining the plants, taking those which appear to have the most desirable characters, such as approximate flowering date desired, numerous tillers, long panicles with many grains, absence of awns, medium tillering angle, absence of disease, light-coloured glumes, white grain, absence of lodging, grain size and shape desired, absence or near absence of abdominal white. Similarly, selection for other improvements may be made, such as resistance to lodging and disease, spikelet sterility.

Selection of about forty to fifty plants is made in the field and recorded for each plant. These data are recorded for each selection as a check on its behaviour in the subsequent year and for this purpose a register must be opened. When the panicles have been further examined in the laboratory, many will be discarded and only about fifteen to twenty of the most promising retained. The following standard technique should be followed to produce pure lines from these selections:

PLANT TO ROW (FIRST-YEAR SELECTIONS)

For each selection a separate small nursery (about one yard square) is prepared. A series of such nurseries can be made with small bunds about 6 inches wide and 6 inches high, with small watering channels between from which the soil is taken to construct the bunds. When sufficiently grown, 300 strong seedlings of each selection are transplanted, singly, in three rows of 100 plants, the rows being spaced 2 feet apart and 1 foot between plants in the row.

To avoid mistakes, careful numbering of plots and seedlings is necessary. Mark the tenth plant in each row with a stick two to three feet taller than the plants so that any particular plant can quickly be found by counting the sticks and then the plants. A register for use in the field is made for field records with spaces 1–100 for each plant. The characters for record are:

Field Records: flowering date, tiller number, height, tiller angle, lodging.

Laboratory Records: panicle length, grain dimensions, abdominal white, awns, panicle weight, bushel weight, hulling percentage, breakage, life period.

Flowering Date. Daily recording must start as soon as a panicle appears. Flowering extends over ten to twelve days; if it extends beyond two weeks it is an undesirable character. Record the date on which the first flowers appear on the plant. To recognize whether a plant has been recorded as flowered, a knot is tied in one leaf when recorded. When the whole plot has flowered the records are examined to find the median flowering date (not the mean), which is then accepted as the flowering date of the selection.

Tillering Number. This is recorded when grain has set and is the total number of fertile panicles borne by each plant. The average tiller number is entered in the selections record.

Height. This is measured from ground level to the top of the tallest stem measured at the ring of hairs below the panicle (junction of culm and peduncle), excluding the panicle. Use the metric system for all these observations.

Tiller Angle. The angle made by tillers to the perpendicular can vary from 90° to nearly upright, the majority being around 30° to 35°. It is sufficient to record the tiller angle as either (*a*) very close, (*b*) medium, or (*c*) very wide. Close and medium angles are satisfactory, but a very wide angle is to be avoided.

Lodging. The behaviour in wide-spaced breeding plots is not a certain guide; very tall varieties lodge more than shorter ones, while wider spacing, a large number of tillers and large panicles all conduce to lodging. Nevertheless, records of lodging in the selection plots are a guide and those which appear to lodge may be discarded.

When field records are complete and the plants are ripe, the middle row of each selection is harvested and reserved for seed. The plants are tied in bundles with about ten inches of straw, threshing being postponed until later. The two outside rows are reaped separately and threshed. The weight of grain gives a rough guide to yield in comparison with other plant-to-row selections, but is not statistically reliable. Should, however, any line give exceptionally low yield one is justified in taking this into account in deciding whether to keep or discard the line.

Panicle Length. This is correlated with yield and is a useful guide in selection work. Twenty or thirty panicles are measured from the ring of hairs at the junction of the peduncle and culm to the tip of the most distal grains.

Grain Dimensions. For grain classification purposes the length and breadth of both paddy and rice are needed. They are measured with a special grain-measuring instrument, which is fixed to the bench with a clamp. The grains are picked up with forceps in the right hand and the measuring instrument worked with the left hand. To avoid the necessity of writing down each measurement, a series of small receptacles marked with class intervals is prepared and when each grain has been measured it is dropped into the appropriate pot. A count then gives the frequency distribution and a simple calculation the mean and standard deviation. A separate set of receptacles is needed for length and breadth, but the same set of grains are used for both. Class intervals of 0·2 mm. are appropriate.

Grain dimensions should show one mode. If bimodal, impurity is definite but the converse is not necessarily true because the impurity may not lie in grain size characters and, moreover, the mixture may be such as to give an approximate normal curve. It is as well to record the frequency distribution as well as the mean calculated from it; the distribution indicates the range and prevalence of undesirable undersized grains.

Awns. Presence or absence of awns is recorded. Awns are undesirable if long, but occasionally good varieties produce short awns 2–3 mm. long which, if not too prevalent, may be disregarded.

Panicle Weight is a good indication of yield since the total weight is about nine-tenths due to grain and only one-tenth to the rachis. One hundred panicles are weighed and recorded as mean weight in grams.

Bushel Weight. This is related to milling out-turn. With only small quantities of grain available, a chondrometer is used. The bushel weight is, of course, the struck bushel of eight Imperial gallons.

Hulling Percentage. Varieties differ in hulling out-turn, which is the percentage of edible rice (whole plus broken grains) and selection can eliminate poor milling lines. The first milling test is done on grain from the outside rows of the plant-to-row plot, using a laboratory mill, which is a miniature of the large cone-type mill but carries out the whole operation of hulling and polishing in one stage. The weight of the whole rice gives the hulling percentage; bran and chaff cannot be separated easily, but are not sufficiently important to warrant separate recording. Hulling small samples must be done on raw paddy since it is not possible to parboil small lots with reproduceable results.

Two characters are involved with hulling percentage; firstly, the quantity of edible rice, both whole and broken grain, which can differ between varieties and should be as high as possible—up to 68 per cent—and secondly, the amount of whole grain produced. While the first is essentially a genetic character, the second is only partly so. No field treatment can make a large difference to the out-turn of total rice, although small differences are possible.[674] The degree of breakage can be greatly affected by field treatment and handling of grain. With many breeding plots to record and harvest it is often impossible to reap at the optimum time for milling; consequently grain may be overripe or too dry. Breakage may, therefore, be above normal. It may be possible to obtain more reliable breakage figures at a later stage in the selection programme, when larger quantities are available for yield tests.

Abdominal White. Whether abdominal white is to be avoided depends on the type of rice which the market demands. Unless the demand is for a chalky grain it should be avoided because it is more liable to breakage in milling.

Life Period. This is best expressed as the number of days from sowing to flowering plus thirty. The date of reaping is not sharply defined, but flowering date is measurable and except for varieties insensitive to photoperiod, is fairly constant. From flowering to ripeness is 28 to 35 days, depending on weather, but a standard of 30 days may be accepted.

The above completes field and laboratory examinations of the initial selections. Discarding unsatisfactory selections should be done strictly, otherwise there will be an accumulation of lines which are unlikely to prove satisfactory.

Numbering Selections. When new selections are made from a mixture it is of little use to retain the name and number of the original, although there should be a record of the origin of each selection and its history. If Beale's classification is used (see page 92) the class letters can be used as prefixes followed by the year in which it was first grown as a separate line and then by the number of the selection.

SECOND YEAR SELECTIONS

Selections are subject to yield trials against the local variety or unselected mixture as control. The line is also grown for maintenance of purity because the seed from yield trials is liable to crossing and accidental mixing. The maintenance is done with seed from the centre row of the First Year plot in a separate nursery and planted in three lines of 100 plants spaced 2 × 1 feet as before. It is advisable to repeat the observations on the Second Year Maintenance plot, but milling tests are carried out on the produce of the Yield Trial plots.

Yield Trials. Only really promising lines in the First Year plots are subject to yield trials in the second year. Plots of 1/50 to 1/100 acre, each about three times as long as broad, are prepared for this purpose, and planted about three plants per hill at the customary spacing. If the plots are measured and marked with ropes pegged down, leaving one foot space between plots, there should be little border effect within the experiment. Only varieties having about the same flowering date should be included in each trial. The whole experiment should be surrounded with a blank three feet wide.

The statistical layout will depend on the number of varieties to be tested. It is doubtful whether the more complicated designs, such as Balanced Lattice, give as much information as a number of simpler trials such as Randomized Blocks and Latin Squares, while the more complex designs call for much more work and care.

Nursery for Yield Trials. A nursery measuring about 10 × 10 feet should be sufficiently large to accommodate the seedlings for one trial. Seed from the centre row of the First Year plot may be sufficient, but it may be supplemented from the side rows if necessary. Once the Second Year nurseries have been established, excess seed may be disposed of after preserving samples of both paddy and rice for record. All varieties are sown on the same day, pulled together and, if possible, transplanted on the same day. The border may be planted with mixed seedlings left over.

Reaping and Threshing. First, border plants are removed and discarded. Signs of lodging are recorded. Each plot is then separated by passing along the blank spaces and turning the paddy inwards. Sheaves from each plot are distinctly marked and carried to the

K

threshing floor. Threshing many small plots needs constant watching to avoid mistakes. Hand threshing and winnowing are best as there is no satisfactory laboratory thresher and winnower.

Results of yield trials, expressed in pounds per acre and as percentages of the mean, provide the most important test of a variety. It is risky to make a final selection on the basis of a single year's trial.

After weighing, the produce from the separate replications can be bulked and used for milling tests. It is desirable at this stage to obtain a trade opinion on rice of varieties which appear satisfactory in other respects. For milling a bushel or so it is necessary to hand-pound or use a small Planter's mill type of machine. It is also desirable to make cooking trials because cooking behaviour, especially as regards stickiness, varies enormously. Any paddy remaining from yield trials which is not used in these tests is discarded because it cannot be regarded as of sufficient purity for further use.

The Second Year Maintenance plots provide the pure seed supply from the centre row and this is carefully checked for purity in the field. Differences in flowering date or height indicate impurity and any such off-type plants and their neighbours are removed at once. The outside rows are not taken for seed purposes.

THIRD YEAR SELECTIONS

Selections retained from the second year are again put through yield trials and also maintained in purity plots as in the second year. After the Second Year trials the number should have been considerably reduced. It is risky to decide finally on the merits of a new selection on the basis of one year's performance; the trials should be repeated twice (three trials in all).

MULTIPLICATION OF PURE SEED

The multiplication and purity maintenance programme is, briefly, as follows:

    I   Bag four plants.

    II (*a*) Four single plant nurseries.

        (*b*) Four plots of 300 plants spaced 2×1 feet.

        (*c*) Centre line of one plot retained, three plots discarded.

        (*d*) Bag four plants from centre line.

    III (*a*) $\frac{1}{4}$ acre plot from II (*c*).

        (*b*) Maintenance plots from II (*d*).

    IV   Twelve to fifteen acres multiplication with seed from III (*a*).

Multiplication. Four carefully chosen plants in the centre row of the maintenance plot are placed under muslin bags to prevent cross-pollination. When flowering is over the bags are removed and the plants allowed to ripen normally. These four plants are the insurance against accidental loss of the pure line. Each is examined with particular care for conformity to the original type. If all prove acceptable, they are sown in separate nurseries and later transplanted into separate maintenance plots of three lines each. These are checked for impurity and one only chosen to provide seed for the first multiplication stage. This seed is taken from the centre row. Within this row four plants are again bagged to provide seed for the next year's maintenance.

All the seed from the centre row of the chosen plot is sown in a nursery and later transplanted at 2×1 feet spacing, giving a plot of about $\frac{1}{4}$ acre. This wide spacing allows individual plants to be examined and also permits more tillering and more rapid multiplication.

Seed from the $\frac{1}{4}$ acre plot is further multiplied and there should be sufficient to plant twelve to fifteen acres. This bulk production should be carefully examined for impurity at flowering and shortly before harvesting. Any rogues as well as their neighbouring plants are removed. If the preceding work has been done with care there should be few, if any, off-types but it is no longer possible to ensure complete purity. Particular watch is kept for red-grained plants. These show up against the sun when wet with dew. Their presence must be regarded as especially undesirable.

Seed from this ten to fifteen acres can go direct to farmers or be used for bulk multiplication.

By following the above programme there is a continuous series from a single bagged plant with the insurance that the type is not lost through accidental crossing or seed failure. It is important that this series be maintained and a proper seed supply scheme evolved; otherwise in a few years seed to farmers will be hopelessly mixed and the benefits of the work irretrievably lost.

DESCRIPTION OF PURE LINES

It is advisable to have complete and detailed descriptions of established pure lines for record purposes, as well as herbarium specimens of the whole plant and samples of the paddy and rice. These records should be very complete and should include vegetative characters not of economic importance but which may serve as aids in identification. One of the most valuable aids to identification is the dimensions of the grain; consequently, in permanent records of pure lines, the length, breadth and thickness should be accurately recorded as the mean of 500 grains.

It should be noted that selection within a pure line offers little scope for further improvement in yield, although there is evidence that improvement in other directions may be possible, for a strain the purity of which is determined by morphological characters need not necessarily be so for other characters, such as disease resistance or spikelet sterility.

Specimen forms for recording field and laboratory examinations are given in Appendix V.

HYBRIDIZATION

Rice was at one time regarded as anemophilous, but in 1898 Takahashi in Japan proved that it was mainly self-pollinated and succeeded in producing new varieties by crossing. In 1904 Kano in Japan started rice breeding by hybridization; as a result, by 1913 twenty new varieties selected through crossing were in farmers' hands. The work has been further developed in that country.[379] Concurrently, investigations of a similar nature were conducted in Java and in 1913 van der Stok produced a new variety by this method which possessed economic value.[135] Hybridization has since been used successfully by investigators in many countries.

Hybridization for the purpose of producing new and improved types involves a delicate technique. The anthers must be removed before they mature and pollen from another variety used to fertilize the stigma. This fertilized stigma must then be protected to prevent further cross-fertilization from neighbouring plants until the flowering period has passed.

Technique of Hybridization. Many investigators have evolved their own technique of emasculation for rice hybridization. Those evolved by Mendiola[390] and Niles[435] involve clipping the glumes and this necessitates germinating the seed produced on nutrient agar, while the hot water method developed by Jodon[306] suffers from the disadvantage that the straw is easily broken just below the panicle when it is bent over. Perhaps the two most commonly used methods at the present time are Ramiah's[503] and a development of this evolved by Rhind[554] and used by Jordan.[315]

In Ramiah's method a panicle which started blooming the previous day is selected, spikelets already fertilized removed and the panicle enclosed in a dark paper envelope, both the panicle and envelope being held in position by a bamboo stake driven into the mud near the plant. The enclosing in an envelope is done an hour or an hour and a half before the probable time of natural opening. The envelope is removed after about ten to fifteen minutes when it is found that all the spikelets which are to open that day have opened in a flush, the undehisced anthers hanging out. The anthers are immediately removed and pollination carried out when the pollen parent is ready. The spikelets close again but by the time pollen is ready re-opening them is easy. After pollination, the rest of the unopened spikelets are cut away and the panicle covered with a muslin bag for two or three days. It is desirable to allow the pollinated spikelets to develop in the open to attain their full development.

The method of forcing flowering developed by Rhind depends upon surrounding the panicle with warm saturated air and has been described by Jordan,[315] who has successfully employed the technique in Sierra Leone.

Water at 43° C. is carried to the field in a vacuum flask. A panicle in the third day of flowering is chosen for the female parent and all spikelets that have already flowered are removed. The absence of stamens in these spikelets is readily seen when the panicle is viewed against the light. A little warm water is poured into an empty vacuum flask, shaken up and emptied. The panicle is then inserted in the flask which is closed by holding the fingers across the mouth. The flask is kept in this position for one to three minutes by which time stamens will protrude from several spikelets. The flask is removed and the anthers pulled from the open spikelets with forceps. It is found that a number of spikelets open shortly after removal of the flask and if the panicle is held bent to one side the stamens of these all come out together and may be removed in one operation. The stamens are removed by their filaments, but if only the anthers are approachable, a grip on these enables them to be removed without dehiscing. If any anthers are left inside the glumes a gentle beating of the panicle with the hand will dislodge them and they can then be pulled off. Any other unopened spikelets are then cut off. The emasculated spikelets are then examined with a hand lens and any whose stigmas show signs of pollen are cut off.

The technique of pollination is thus described by Jordan:[315]

While the panicle of the female parent is inside the vacuum flask one or two panicles of the male parent, in their third day of flowering if possible, are picked and when the flask is removed from the female parent, are placed inside it, being held in position by the inserted cork. The temperature of the flask is still sufficient in normal weather . . . if found necessary, however, pour a little more warm water into the flask, shake up and leave at the bottom of the flask while the panicles of the male parent are being treated. The panicles remain inside the flask during emasculation, removal of unopened spikelets and examination of the female parent. They are then removed and it is found that a fair number of spikelets have opened and their stamens are hanging out. The stamens are promptly removed with a pair of fine forceps into a lidless 2-inch Petri-dish or watch glass, taking care to handle them by their filaments. This dish can be held conveniently in the palm of the left hand, leaving the fingers free to support the spikelets during pollination. Ripe anthers, which are immediately obvious by their lighter colour and swollen appearance, are picked up by the forceps and held inside the glumes of the emasculated spikelets. Tapping the forceps on the edge of the lemma is sufficient to cause the anther to dehisce and shower pollen on to the stigmas. When dealing with rice varieties in which the stigmas protrude between the glumes as soon as the spikelets open, it is necessary to rub the anther sacs on the stigmas, as the pollen released inside the glumes does not always reach them. After pollination the plant is labelled and the panicle enclosed in a cloth bag for twenty-four hours.

By means of ice water in a vacuum flask, Poggendorff* in New South Wales has successfully effected sterilization of pollen for crossing purposes.

An emasculation technique used in Hungary has been described by Gruber.[234] By breathing on a spikelet in which the yellow anther is visible through the glumes, the glumes open and the indehisced anthers protrude from the spikelet. A 60 per cent hybrid grain set has been obtained by this method.

The choice of method must remain with the worker. Ramiah states that his method gives nearly 90 per cent success under Coimbatore conditions and is also time-saving. Jordan states that Rhind's technique used in Sierra Leone gave an average of 74 per cent of the pollinated spikelets setting seed. A similar technique is now used in Malaya[719] and a number of other countries, while Ramiah's method is also followed in a number of countries.

BULK-POPULATION BREEDING

The purpose of hybridization is to enhance genetic variability or to synthesize varieties combining desirable characters from two or more parents, and it is desirable to define the aims before embarking on a programme of crossing. The pedigree method of individual selection from within a segregating F_2 population is laborious and slow but a good deal of work can be avoided by the experienced breeder without recourse to elaborate recording of data. With a largely self-fertilized crop like rice the F_2 heterozygosis is rapidly reduced to near-homozygosity so that delay in selecting individuals from a cross greatly reduces work. Further, to obtain the widest range of new combinations the greatest number of gene linkages need to be broken and this is maximal in the earlier generations. To

* Private communication from Mr W. Poggendorff.

exploit this rapid approach towards homozygosis the method of bulk-population breeding can be used. Essentially, it consists of leaving a segregating population from a cross to "settle down", to reach a state when many characters are true-breeding, and so permit methods of selection approximate to those of pure line selection to be used. By the F_7 generation a high degree of homozygosis is reached but it is useful to eliminate in earlier generations any plants showing recognizable deleterious characters. Though genotypes more vigorous than others may quickly dominate a population at about F_7, it is unlikely that any gene combinations of reasonable vigour will be entirely lost.

Bulk-population breeding is particularly valuable where quantitative characters are concerned, such as yield of grain. It has the great potential advantage of reducing work in the early generations, as well as the demands on field space, so enabling the breeder to handle a larger number of crosses.

BACKCROSSING

Backcrossing consists essentially in re-crossing the hybrid progeny (F_1) of an original cross with one of the original parents with the object of perpetuating a particular character possessed by the donor parent. Its success depends on the transference of one dominant character to a strain which is desirable in other respects. When the character to be transferred is recessive, the programme must be extended by periodic selfing to bring to light the recessive character. Repeated backcrossing of one parent carries the initial cross towards homozygosis at the same rate as would continuous selfing but produces a genotype approximating to the recurrent parent. The genes from the donor parent, however, remain heterozygous throughout the backcrossing generations and to reduce them to a homozygous state a period of selfing is necessary to complete the process. Backcrossing is particularly useful in increasing resistance to particular diseases. When it is desired to add resistance to two different diseases, separate programmes are mapped out for each disease and the end product crossed together.

VEGETATIVE MULTIPLICATION OF CLONES

Carpenter and Roberts[105] have recently developed a method for increasing the F_2 seed by vegetative multiplication of the F_1 plants by means of hydroponic culture. The composition of the medium for this purpose is shown in the following table.

TABLE 8

HYDROPONIC CULTURE MEDIUM USED FOR CLONAL
PROPAGATION OF PADDY PLANTS

Major nutrients	$MgSO_4, 7H_2O$	0·35 g./litre
	$Ca(NO_3)_2$	0·92 ,,
	KH_2PO_4	0·38 ,,
	KNO_3	0·85 ,,
Minor nutrients	Ferric EDTA	0·07 g./litre
	H_3BO_3	1·86 mg./litre
	$ZnSO_4, 7H_2O$	0·29 ,,
	$MnSO_4, 4H_2O$	2·23 ,,
	$(NH_4)_6MO_7O_{24}$	0·035 ,,

pH about 4·5. Osmotic concentration 1·0 atm.

The investigators explain the procedure as follows:

The medium is stored in the form of five stock solutions, viz. one for each of the major nutrients, and a mixture of all the minor nutrients. The stock solutions are made up at very high concentration such that 1·4 ml. of KH_2PO_4 stock solution, 2·8 ml. of each of the other major stock solutions, and 1·0 ml. of the minor nutrients stock solution, are made up to each litre of the final medium. In this way preparation of the final medium is greatly simplified and, owing to the high concentration of single salts, no growth of micro-organisms occurs in the major nutrient stock solutions at ambient temperature. The minor-nutrient stock must, however, be stored in a refrigerator. The plants are grown from seed in this medium in small containers for about six weeks and then transferred to glazed stoneware pots of approximately 7·5 litres capacity. The small containers or pots are kept topped up with distilled water (tap water could probably be used) at regular intervals to make up for transpiration loss, and the medium is changed about every three weeks. Under these conditions the plants produce copious tillers—well over 100 per plant are often developed. Towards what would normally be the end of the tillering phase, the plants are split up into portions each containing two or three tillers together with the attached roots, which are then transplanted into similar pots of liquid culture medium. This splitting has the effect of prolonging the tillering phase and each portion of the original plant thus continues to tiller for some time before sexual primordia are formed; far more seed is thus finally produced from the original plant than is produced under field conditions.

A possible simplification of this routine would be to transplant the separated sections of the clone from the hydroponic pots directly into the field or into buckets of waterlogged soil . . . it might save the plant breeder the task of maintaining liquid culture media for several months.

21. Italy: mechanized transplanting with the ILCMA Transplanter

22. Sowing germinated seed on a floating nursery, Malaya

23. Tilling the paddy field with a wooden plough, Malaya

24. Merry tiller, Japan

A wooden ribbed roller used for making the mud soft and reducing all lumps, Malaya

26. Smoothing the mud—the final operation before transplanting, Bihar

27. Removing seedlings from nursery, Bihar

28. Planting out paddy seedlings in the flooded fields, India

29. Cutting roots and tops preparatory to transplanting, Malaya

30. Removing seed-
lings from nursery,
Hong Kong New
Territories

31. Layout of paddy fields in the Murrumbidgee Rice Area, New South Wales

32. Harvested paddy fields, Bihar

Harvesting paddy with the tuai, a knife that cuts ear by ear, Malaya

34. Harvesting with the sickle, Malaya

35. Threshing paddy in the field, Hong Kong New Territories

36. Threshing paddy with a bullock team, Bihar

37. Threshing paddy by treading, Malabar

At the Central Rice Research Station, Cuttack, advantage has been taken of the perennating habit of some varieties to multiply stock. Formation of tillers by the development of dormant buds is more pronounced in photo-periodically sensitive, long duration varieties than in insensitive varieties. Richharia considers that vegetative propagation may prove useful in breeding, genetical work and multiplication of pure varieties.[561]

INDUCED MUTATION

Induced mutation by gamma radiation or by chemicals is now used in many countries to produce wider mutants than are usually obtained by conventional hybridization. It is also noted that mutations have been induced by nutritional deficiencies. Noguchi,[439] for instance, obtained mutations affecting chlorophyll formation, awning, plant size and sterility by growing plants in nutrient water cultures from which phosphorus was lacking except for a few weeks at the seedling stage.

Those responsible for work of this nature apparently disregard the unselective character of mutagenic action, the huge preponderance of deleterious mutations—and nearly all those quoted are changes for the worse—serious chromosome aberrations and the pleiotropic action of nearly all induced mutations.

It is premature to venture a conclusion regarding the possibilities of induced mutation, but the following remarks by D. Roy Davis in his Fernhurst Lecture in 1960 are pertinent:

> With the present status of mutation breeding and the inefficient techniques available to us today, there is little justification for the plant breeder seeking variability from irridiated material, if it is already available naturally. There are exceptions, but in general it has yet to be shown conclusively that the required variability can be produced more quickly, more economically, or with less utilization of space and labour by mutagens than by hybridizations. . . . Claims that mutation breeding is essential because we are running out of variability do not appear to be justified. . . .
>
> Future work, especially with chemical mutagens, may drastically modify our concept regarding the status of mutation breeding, but it is obvious that much research work has to be undertaken before a full evaluation of its true potential is possible.

As to rice, there is fortunately no necessity to resort to artificial mutations, for the multitude of varieties provides a prodigious range of unexplored variability upon which the rice breeder can draw in his endeavours to improve this crop.

IMPROVEMENTS BY SELECTION AND BREEDING

Over vast areas in Asia the varieties cultivated are so mixed that marked improvements in yield can be obtained in one or two seasons by selection based upon a single character. From a practical point of view the aim should be the cultivation of a single strain in any one field, thereby eliminating the competition which is bound to arise when a number of different forms are grown together, e.g. tall forms and short forms. Mass selection has often been used as a first step to such improvement; pure line selection is more arduous but has been followed in many countries and, although the results have not been uniformly satisfactory, in the majority of cases it has led to marked improvements in yield. In Thailand, for example, the increases which have resulted from its employment are stated to amount to 15 per cent, while in Malaya they are placed at 25 per cent.

The production of new rice varieties by hybridization may be expected in the long run to give the best results, since not only can it provide higher yielding types, but it can also eliminate or reduce losses from lodging and improve resistance to pests and diseases. The production of hybrids is long-term work of a very laborious character but of absorbing interest. It demands a high degree of skill and much more precise knowledge of the characters of existing strains than is at present available, although considerable advances have been made in this direction during the past decade. The characters must be classified and catalogued so that the performance of each type under different environmental conditions can be better understood. Nevertheless, such work is likely to be amply rewarding. It has produced spectacular results in the case of wheat, for example, and there appear no obvious reason why equally striking results should not follow its application to rice.

HYBRID STERILITY

In recent years much work has been done on the hybridization of *indica* and *japonica* varieties in attempts to combine the desirable characters of both groups, particularly the high response to fertilizers often shown by the *japonica* varieties. The work has been handicapped by the sterility barrier which separates these two groups. The cause of the sterility shown by *indica* × *japonica* hybrids has been attributed to genetic causes and to structural differences between homologous chromosomes contributed by each parent.

Meiosis in *indica* × *japonica* hybrids is regular but a proportion, often high, of the pollen and embryo sacs abort. A possible explanation is that small structural differences occur in chromosomes, too small to interfere with pairing at meiosis, but enough to interfere with gametes. The theory that intervarietal sterility is caused by cryptic structural hybridity explains the regular behaviour of chromosomes at meiosis and the occurrence in F_1 of a range of sterility from nearly zero to 100 per cent. A supposition of genes affecting gamete development seems unnecessary. The practical breeding result is that progeny of *indica × japonica* crosses are difficult to obtain with full fertility and in some cases it has proved impracticable. A similar sterility effect has accompanied irradiated rice where reciprocal translocations in the chromosomes leads to semi-sterile progeny.

DIFFERENTIAL FERTILIZER RESPONSE

Over large areas of rice-growing lands in Asia fertility is relatively low and centuries of unconscious selection has produced types able to grow moderately well at low fertility levels but which have lost most of their capacity to respond to higher fertility or fertilizer applications. Early Japanese research showed that types existed in the *japonica* group which had the ability to respond to high fertility and this was successfully exploited in the provision of high-yielding varieties. The desire to achieve similar fertilizer responses in tropical varieties was the central theme of the *indica × japonica* hybridization project started by the International Rice Commission in 1950. Further study of fertilizer responses in the *indica* group showed, however, that although these had largely lost the ability to respond to fertilizers, they were not all without this character and that they vary widely in their reactions to high fertility levels. This opens a possible field for breeders which may not suffer the handicaps of hybrid sterility and the cooking quality of *japonicas* which makes them generally unacceptable to Asian consumers.

Responses to increased fertility may occur as higher numbers of tillers or as higher numbers of grains per panicle, or as a proportion of both, and varieties differ in their mode of response. Responses may even be negative in some *indicas* which show neither higher tiller nor lower yield under high fertility conditions. This often happens when new land is first cropped with rice, the plants being excessively leafy, the result of poor starch accumulation. This in turn stems from the high initial rate of nitrogen uptake which is shown by most *indicas*. There is excessive vegetative growth which increases losses due to respiration, thus reducing starch reserves which otherwise could have been utilized for grain formation.

The high absorption of nitrogen shown by many *indicas* in early growth emphasizes the advantage of late dressings of nitrogenous fertilizers for such varieties and where trials are intended to reveal variety differences in fertilizer responses time of application treatments should be included (see also Chapter XI).

PART II

PADDY:
PRODUCTION

It is my chief duty to gather up an abundance of grain by all that lieth in my power. . . . In the kingdom that belongeth to me there are many paddy lands that are watered chiefly by the waters from the rain clouds; but the fields that depend upon a perpetual supply of water from the rivers and tanks are verily few in number. . . . In a country like unto this not even the least quantity of water that is obtained by rain should be allowed to flow into the ocean without profiting man.

—Words of Parakrama Bahu (1153–86), *Mahávansa*,

pt. 2, reans. L. C. Wijesinha.

Chapter VIII

METHODS OF CULTIVATION

TRADITIONAL METHODS

As a result of centuries of experience, systems of cultivation, although simple, have reached a high degree of efficiency in many Asian countries, but the implements continue to be most primitive, in many cases improvised to suit local conditions. The reluctance of the cultivator to accept innovations may, to some extent, be due to conservatism, but there are additional reasons for his apparent apathy. He is a peasant, cultivating usually from one to five acres, and without co-operation or other financial assistance he lacks the capital to enable him to purchase new and to him expensive implements and, although his customary methods are expensive in labour, this is of little moment, for he and his family perform the necessary tasks. It is, therefore, the traditional methods of cultivation that are still of first importance, methods that have changed but little in the past thousand years, that must be largely considered in this place. It must be admitted that it has seldom been possible to offer the cultivator modern implements which are improvements on his own under the conditions in which they are required to work.

Jordan has questioned[316] the necessity of persisting in using the traditional methods of cultivation. Is it not a fact, he asks, that paddy will tolerate standing water rather than requiring it; and have comparisons of yields between transplanting and direct seeding been strictly valid, i.e. may not differences found have been the result of greater uniformity of spacing? Further, he asks, now that weed-killers appear to be bringing the weed problem under control, is it still necessary to hold standing water on the fields to the present extent, and are transplanting and puddling still essential?

One cannot answer these questions in a few words. It is indeed possible that the results of research should lead to a re-appraisal of current methods of cultivation. But about 90 per cent of world production is obtained in Asia on small holdings by peasants most of whom are illiterate, and most of whom cannot afford anything but the simplest implement, and cannot afford chemicals of any sort. If the recommendations of the various rice institutes were put into effect—recommendations which are but simple improvements on present methods of cultivation, the rice crop in Asia would be vastly increased. There is hope that the Extension Services will persuade cultivators to accept these innovations; there is little chance, however, that drastic changes in methods of cultivation can be introduced in the foreseeable future.

WET AND DRY SYSTEMS

There are two main systems of paddy cultivation; the dry system, in which the crop is grown on dry ground, very much in the same way as other cereals; and the wet system, in which the land is inundated and the crop grown in water from the time of planting or transplanting until harvest approaches. "Dry" paddy cultivation is relatively unimportant at the present time, for "wet" paddy supplies practically the entire world market. This latter system, therefore, is the subject under consideration in this chapter.

FLOATING PADDY

In parts of Asia, notably in East Pakistan and in Burma the so-called floating paddy is cultivated in areas subject to deep flooding. In East Pakistan is found the most extensive area cultivated by this method, there being about 5 million acres. About twenty-five local varieties are recognized, grouped according to whether they are suitable for shallow, medium or deep water. The long-stemmed plants often become entangled with each other during the later stages of growth, when they are liable to become uprooted and carried away in the water. These uprooted plants can still grow and produce ears. Alim and Sen[10] have described the conditions under which floating paddy is grown in East Pakistan.

The soil is mostly clay and therefore hardens and becomes impenetrable in the dry months of March and April. Consequently, the land must be ploughed either before it dries out (January) or on the advent of the monsoon which will delay the time of sowing and probably cause damage to the crop by the early flood. Paddy straw of the previous crop is left on the field and burnt before ploughing to facilitate cultivation and prevent the incidence of *Ufra* eelworm disease. As the land remains submerged for five months or more in the growing season, all dry-land weeds are killed, but aquatic weeds, mostly water hyacinth, are abundant and persist. Four ploughings are considered sufficient for dry-land sowing, a light iron mould board plough being used for the purpose.

The seed is sown either wet or dry. For dry sowing, ungerminated seed is used and covered with earth by ploughing. This assists germination and protects the seed from rodents and birds. March and April dry-sown seed frequently fails to germinate because of uncertain rainfall. For wet sowing, germinated seed is broadcast on puddled land, the surplus water being drained off before sowing. Rate of seeding is 75 lb. for dry sowing and 100 lb. per acre for wet sowing.

The early varieties ripen in September and are harvested from boats. The yield is low, rarely exceeding 900 lb. per acre. Medium varieties are mostly heavy yielders, giving 2,400 lb. paddy per acre under favourable conditions.

SOWING SEED IN THE FIELD

Seed may either be broadcast or drilled direct in the field or it may be cultivated in nurseries and subsequently transplanted when the seedlings have reached a suitable stage of development.

Broadcasting or drilling has for long been commonly practised in India and Ceylon, and is usual in large-scale mechanized methods of cultivation.

In Ceylon, two methods of sowing the field are recognized, viz. dry-land and wet-land sowing. The first method is stated to be necessary where the rainfall or irrigation facilities are inadequate for puddling the soil. The seed is usually broadcast or drilled without previous germination, though if the rains can be depended upon to fall soon after sowing, the seed may be germinated before sowing. The seed is covered by the plough or local hoe—the *mamoty*—and remains dormant in the soil until the advent of rain. Subsequently, the land is flooded as the plants grow, the water being drawn off when the ears are past the "milk" stage. Where there is a sufficient supply of water for the fields to be puddled, sprouted seed is sown as soon as final levelling of the soft mud has been effected. In this case the seed is invariably broadcast as there are practical difficulties in drilling sprouted seed in soft mud. The seed sinks into the mud and soon develops, the depth of water on the field being regulated in the usual manner as the plants grow.

Jack[297] states that in Malaya direct broadcasting in the field is resorted to only where the water can be run off the field a few days after sowing unsoaked seed and run on again after the young plants are several inches high.

Cultural methods of sowing in Japan depend on the climate of the region. Leonard states[356] that in the cold regions (Hokkaido) it is usual to sow the seed in the field, because, explains Matsuo,[379] of the short growing season, but as a result of the introduction of protected nurseries and cold and hot frame seed beds, transplanting is becoming more usual. In the cool climate of Tokaku transplanting

L

is practised with early sowing in protected nurseries with early varieties. In the medium climate of mid-Honshu the ordinary transplanting system is followed, while in the warm climate of south Honshu, Shikoku and Kyushu, transplanting is carried out with somewhat late sowing and with late varieties.

Broadcasting is the usual method in the Central Provinces of India, although in recent years the practice of transplanting has been introduced and its popularity is increasing. The seed, sometimes already germinated, is broadcast just before or after the rains have started. Another system mentioned by Graham[224] is broadcasting followed by a second ploughing when the plants are about a foot high. The method has been more fully described by Clouston[129] who states that the system, known as *Baisi*, consists of ploughing once before sowing the seed. The seed is broadcast at the rate of 100 lb. per acre. When the plants are one foot high, the land is ploughed, which uproots many plants and covers some with mud. The plants are thus thinned out and the root system of those that remain is strengthened. Five to six days later the field is levelled, which flattens all surviving plants. In five to six days weeding commences, followed by further weeding on two occasions at intervals of about a fortnight.

Water seeding of paddy is often practised in the United States, especially on the so-called bottomlands, characterized by clay or clay loam soils which are difficult to manage but have a high fertility level.

The land is levelled, usually disc harrowed twice, followed by a spring-tooth harrow to remove the prominent harrow marks. The field is then covered with four to six inches of water and seeded immediately. The recommended rate of seeding is three bushels (135 lb.) per acre. Presoaked seed will sink and seed treated with fungicide, insecticide or both will sink better than untreated seed. After seeding, the depth of water should be maintained at 4 to 6 inches for five to six weeks. The field may then be drained for nitrogen fertilization.[243]

THE DRY NURSERY

An alternative to broadcasting or drilling seed is to raise seedlings in a nursery to be transplanted when they have attained sufficient development. The nursery may be situated on dry land or in a "wet" situation, the latter being usual. The main difference between a dry and wet nursery is that the seedlings may remain in the former for as long as three months before transplanting, whereas seedlings from a wet nursery must be transplanted after about forty days or they become too developed for the purpose. In cases where the water supply is precarious it is therefore an advantage to be able to postpone transplanting till field conditions are suitable. The writer found no evidence that the crop is in any way inferior when seedlings from a dry nursery are employed, provided that it is efficiently cultivated and, if necessary, manured.

The dry nursery should be well cultivated and manured, and adequately protected from fowls, ducks and birds. The seed is steeped in water for a few hours and immediately broadcast on the nursery bed and covered with an inch or so of fine soil. A common error of many cultivators of both wet and dry nurseries is to sow the seed too thickly. Seedlings from such a nursery may be transplanted at any time after forty days, or even earlier if the plants are sufficiently developed,

The use of the dry nursery is common in parts of Malaya. In British Guiana[527] the seed is planted either by broadcasting (locally known as "shying") or by transplanting at six weeks plants raised in either a wet or dry nursery. On the saline soils of Sind, Pakistan,[403] the seedlings are raised in a dry nursery.

THE WET NURSERY

The land is usually fenced off and ploughed or dug. All weeds are removed and lumps of clay broken down so that the land is brought to a condition of fine mud. In Burma, the soil is worked to a depth of five or six inches. The water is then drained off. Meanwhile seed has been steeped in water for a night and kept in a cool place for a further two days, by which time it will have germinated. The germinated seed is broadcast in the nursery, but no soil is placed over it. Should there be any standing water on part of the nursery it is unlikely that the seed will survive. In a week's time the seedlings are perhaps two or three inches high and the growth is dense. In this condition seedlings are capable of surviving a deep flood for three or four days, but are easily swept away by water in motion. As the seedlings develop, water is sometimes let out of the nursery until the time of transplanting, when the nursery may be moderately dry.

"Broadling" is claimed[482] in Ceylon to be a promising new technique in paddy cultivation. The plants are raised in a nursery and the three weeks' old seedlings broadcast in the recently-drained field. Tillering starts about a week or earlier after broadling. Only four-month varieties of paddy respond well to this treatment. It is claimed that broadling requires less seed, produces quicker tillering and more tillers and is easier to operate than transplanting.

In many countries manuring the nursery is considered to be of secondary importance and over-manuring a mistake, as it is said to cause the plants to become too developed and the stems weak. In Japan, however, as well as in China, infinite care is exercised in the preparation of the nursery. Leonard[356] gives a precise account of the system obtaining in Japan. He states that the preparation of seed for planting consists in sifting to remove small and withered seed and then placing the good seed in a salt solution of specific gravity 1·13 to separate the heavy from the light seed—the latter being discarded. This practice is common in many rice-producing areas in Asia; sometimes instead of salt a "thin" mixture of clay and water is used for the purpose.

In many districts in Java nurseries are manured with organic matter, such as stable dung, waste products or compost, and for this purpose fallen leaves and green material of various plants are gathered.[210] Recent experiments in Malaya indicate a positive response to manuring the nursery. The Japanese[418] recognize the value of phosphate fertilizers in paddy nurseries. Seedlings grown in upland nurseries with adequate phosphate fertilizers showed, on transplanting, better adaptation to poor environmental conditions (low temperatures and low light intensities), better rooting ability, growth and yields than did seedlings grown with lower levels of phosphate. Coating seeds with agar containing phosphorus promoted root growth. In the northern areas of Japan seedlings are raised in hotbeds in order to produce satisfactory growth despite the low temperature. Mixed or organic manures are dug into the seed bed and sulphate of ammonia or other water-soluble fertilizers are mixed with the soil before sowing and wood ash applied when the seedlings are about one inch high. More nitrogen is applied in cold than in warm areas. The seedlings are thinned in the seed bed several times, weeds being removed at the same time. The beds are drained of water in the mornings to raise the temperature and irrigated in the late afternoon to maintain the temperature during the night. In southern Japan, however, many nurseries are not manured and experiments show that the quality of seedlings has little relationship to yield of grain.[287] In Korea,[189] because of severe winters and the short growing season, nurseries are planted as early as possible. Frequent frosts are therefore likely after seed germinates. To protect the growing plants from frost, the nursery is flooded every night so that the plants are completely inundated, the water being drained off in the mornings.

In the cool northern districts of Japan seed germination is accelerated by overnight soaking in warm water at 86° F. and retaining the seed in a warm room until roots about 6 mm. long have developed. The germinated seed is spread on the nursery and covered with sifted, burnt soil. The bed is submerged for a short period, drained and burnt rice hulls then spread over the surface. This is then covered with oil paper or vinyl sheet placed in close contact with the seed by sealing the edges with mud and weighing down the paper with straw rope. Thus cold air is prevented from circulating beneath the paper. Water is maintained in the surrounding channels but is not allowed to cover the bed. In about fifteen days the seedlings are about an inch in length and push up the paper, which is then removed.[379] This technique results in stronger seedlings at transplanting while early maturity protects the plants from cold weather damage and from typhoons at harvest time. In 1956, over half a million acres of paddy were planted by this method and the area thus treated increases yearly.

In China, great care is taken in preparing the nursery. In Hong Kong,[269] the nursery is twice manured after thorough cultivation. The first manuring is made four days before transplanting and for a nursery of 500 sq. ft. about 10 lb. bone meal, 5 lb. fish meal and 130 lb. of a mixture of 80 per cent finely ground cow dung and 20 per cent ashes from grass and brushwood are applied. The second dressing is given the night before transplanting and may consist of about 10 lb. powdered peanut cake or fish meal. For the first crop, paddy germination begins the third day after soaking and the seed is ready for sowing when the first roots are about ¼ inch long. For the second crop, germination takes place the day following soaking and the grain is then ready for sowing.

In western India, a specialized method of seed-bed preparation is practised, known as *Rab*. Copeland,[135] quoting from an Indian publication,[373] describes it as follows. The method consists in burning the seed bed and is practised from Nerbudda in the north to Kanara in the south wherever quality of rice is important. This area is characterized as one of very heavy, sticky soil, exceedingly hard when dry and tenacious when wet. The seed bed is covered with a layer of cow dung superimposed with a layer of branches and other combustible matter, the whole being covered with a layer of soil. The burning is done shortly before the rains are expected, after which the bed is thoroughly cultivated and planted. When the field has been transplanted with seedlings from this nursery, the seed bed itself is transplanted and is said to produce the finest crop, which is saved for seed.

Copeland also describes a seed-bed method used in the Philippines whenever early maturity is required.

The seed bed is placed where water is at hand, and puddled and smoothed in the usual way. Banana leaves are then split down the middle to the mid-rib, the narrowed ends cut off and placed edge to edge, and pressed in so that a very little mud oozes over them. Holes and torn pieces in the leaves, and places where they do not quite meet, are covered with pieces of leaf. To be sure that there can be no open holes left, the beds may be made more than one leaf thick. The beds thus formed are a yard or a metre wide, and indefinitely long. At the ends they are closed by leaves laid crosswise with the edge inwards, so that each whole bed is surrounded by a raised border, made by the mid-ribs. As a matter of convenience, two or more such beds may be made side by side. A cavan* of seed will plant two such beds about fifty feet long, which is accordingly the usual length. The beds are then covered with a layer of rice hulls or finely cut straw about an inch thick, which is wet with muddy water.

The seed is soaked and germinated in the usual manner, and scattered thickly over the bed. Constant care is required to keep it wet, at first by sprinkling, and then, as the roots grow and begin to make a mat, by flowing water. If the weather is hot and clear, the beds need to be shaded, which is done with banana leaves or bamboo branches placed on frames. Transplanting is performed within two weeks after germination. Only early varieties are handled in this way.

Japanese investigations[412] show that a dry nursery gives better results than either use of a wet nursery or direct sowing. In the wet nursery, growth of seedlings after transplanting is delayed for several days, during which time potassium and silica content in the plant decrease and total sugar and crude starch contents increase, tillering is delayed and lower tillers do not emerge. Under the dry nursery system, the higher temperature promotes growth and nitrogen and phosphorus accumulation in the plants, tillering period is extended and the lower tillers emerge. With direct sowing in the field, the seeding time is later although tillering starts earlier than in the wet nursery; narrow leaves and many small ears are characteristic.

MULTIPLE NURSERIES

The nursery method of raising seedlings in the Krian District of the State of Perak in Malaya has been described by Jack.[297] The method appears to be peculiar to this district, in an area noted for high yields. Grass is cut and piled in a long strip, about three or four feet wide and standing about an inch above water level. Mud is plastered on this to make a compact, solid bed, and more mud, rich in humus, is superimposed. The seed is broadcast thickly over the

---

* The cavan is the usual "sack" (about 100 lb. seed).

bed in the cool of the evening. The allowance is about 18 lb. seed for the eventual planting out of an acre. The nursery is watered twice daily and when the seedlings are about four to five inches high the nursery is lowered by pulling out grass from underneath. This ensures thorough wetness and also protection against the mole cricket, *Gryllotalpa borealis*, which otherwise would attack the rootlets. When the seedlings are ten to twelve inches high, usually after twelve to sixteen days in the nursery, they are pulled up in clumps of 150 to 200; these clumps are placed, still as clumps, in a second nursery of ploughed land where they remain for about six days in about two inches of water. Each clump is then subdivided into about six smaller clumps which are placed in a prepared bed of mud. Twenty days later, by which time the plants are about 2½ feet high, the clumps are again divided into bunches of ten to twelve plants, the clumps being planted in rows and spaced two feet apart. Final transplanting into the field takes place about forty days later.

Commenting on this system of multiple transplanting, Jack[297] makes the following observations:

> The physiological factors involved in transplanting are somewhat obscure, but the conclusion at present, based on a number of experiments, is that transplantation acts in a similar way to root pruning, the injury to the root system stimulating growth of the sub-aerial portion and resulting in increased tillering. The root system of transplanted rice is developed from the lower nodes of the stem, the first or seedling root system dying completely in most cases. In very rich soil like that in Krian complete amputation of the original root system is the usual practice. It was found that, in the best soils of Krian where three transplantations are the rule, seedlings that had been transplanted once gave a large vegetative growth but practically no grain. It was also found that if the original root system was not heavily pruned at the final transplantation the resulting plants were slow growing and eventually gave little grain.

In British Guiana[130] double transplanting was found to result in a higher yield, stronger seedlings, more efficient weed control and economy in seed. The additional expenditure was more than counterbalanced by the increase in yield. Double transplanting, nevertheless, is not commonly practised in British Guiana.

FERTILIZING THE SEEDLINGS

In some cases, the roots of seedlings are steeped in a semi-liquid mixture containing fertilizer of some sort, usually guano or cattle manure, before being planted in the field. In some parts of Kyushu, Japan[531] where soils are derived from volcanic ash and fix phosphates very strongly, a thin mud paste is made by mixing one part of super-phosphate with about five parts of soil. The roots of the seedlings are dipped into this "mud" just before transplanting. The practice of concentrating phosphates around the roots tends partially to reduce loss of phosphates through phosphate fixation.

The quantity of seed required to transplant an acre varies, rich land requiring fewer seedlings per "hill" and wider spacing than poorer land. The amount required also depends on the variety of paddy. The usual rate is about 20 lb. per acre for good land, up to 40 lb. for poorer land or for short-maturation varieties.

Seedlings should be allowed to grow in the nursery for twenty-eight to fifty days, the period depending on rate of growth and not infrequently on the state of preparation of the field in which they are to be planted. They should, however, be transplanted as soon as they are sufficiently large because the subsequent tillering stage ends at a time fixed to the photoperiod; that is, a fixed date, so that the only way to lengthen the tillering phase is to extend it backwards by starting it sooner.[554] With early varieties they should possess five or six leaves, with late varieties six to seven leaves. Seedlings suitable for planting are seven to nine inches long, robust, uninjured by pests or diseases and have light-coloured, tough leaves.

Trials in Malaya[91] showed very clearly that a marked decrease in yield can be expected if seedlings are transplanted after they reach the optimum stage of development. A delay of 30 days in transplanting resulted in a drop in yield of 780 lb. paddy per acre, a delay of 60 days in a reduction of 1,720 lb. per acre. Therefore, every effort should be made to transplant seedlings which have developed five to six leaves—and this has held good for varieties of paddy of different maturation periods.

BROADCASTING *versus* TRANSPLANTING

Some 200 years ago a Dutch Governor of Ceylon wrote: "If only the Singalese could be induced similarly as in Java and elsewhere to plant paddy instead of sowing it, they would appreciably contribute to making Ceylon richer in grain."[195] Experience and experiment in all the more important areas of production in the East confirm that higher yields may be expected from transplanted paddy than from direct broadcasting or drilling. Lord states[368] that experiments in Ceylon have shown that with six or seven months' paddy, transplanting increases the crop by 30 to 46 per cent; with the three to four months' varieties, which occupy most of the paddy area in Ceylon, it is doubtful whether transplanting will prove profitable.

Paul[474] considers that transplanting in Ceylon is superior to broadcasting, but not necessarily to drilling, while a Report[541] on rice production in Ceylon states that transplanting gives increases ranging from 30 to 40 per cent and saves seed. Field trials in Ceylon[700] have also confirmed the conclusion that yields of paddy sown broadcast can be considerably increased by harrowing the crop when the seedlings are three to four weeks old. When the standard of cultivation is poor the response to harrowing is said to be greater. In India, the increase in yield through transplanting has been 15 to 30 per cent.[512] Experiments in the Philippines[461] proved that transplanted paddy develops faster, is more uniform, taller and matures later than broadcast seed. The mean yields were 2,880 lb. and 1,920 lb. per acre for transplanted and broadcast seed respectively. Clouston[129] states that a transplanted field can easily be detected as tillers are numerous and the crop less weedy.

In Italy, paddy is either drilled or broadcast, or transplanted by mechanical means. It is held[649] that transplanting induces a higher yield, gives a more regular stand, facilitates weeding and reduces the amount of supplying necessary; it also shortens the period during which the crop occupies the land.

In many quarters, however, doubt is expressed as to whether transplanting paddy results in higher yields, or whether it is justified only by enabling the land to carry more than one crop per annum and by assisting to maintain the land reasonably free from weeds. Wickizer and Bennett[699] point out that "in some parts of Japan rice has been sown directly on the paddy-field as thickly as is customary with transplanted rice, and the yields have been approximately the same. Furthermore, although there is no transplanting in California, yields there compare favourably with those obtaining in parts of the Orient (other than Japan) where yields are fairly high." Adair *et al.*[4] in the United States, too, has stated that as a result of trials over a period of three years, no significant differences in average yield resulted from the two procedures. Wickizer and Bennett should not, however, compare the yields of broadcast seed in the United States with yields in tropical Asia, but with yields in countries with climatic conditions similar to those of paddy-growing areas of the United States.

Peru[190] is the only American country where transplanting is usual. In the early 1920s paddy was grown by primitive methods and the average yield was 34 bushels per acre. The present yield per acre of 65 bushels is attributed to improvement in cultivation methods and a change over from broadcasting to transplanting.

One can but emphasize the fact that the weight of evidence

throughout the paddy areas of the world is that transplanting is beneficial to the plant and results in increased yields. While other factors must be taken into account to explain the high yields obtained in certain countries, notably Japan, China and Spain, in all these countries transplanting is the accepted custom and not the exception, and very great care is taken in preparation of the nursery.

It must be admitted that transplanting offers difficulties, the chief of which is the necessity of hand labour, but where these difficulties can be overcome, or circumvented by the use of mechanical transplanters, transplanting should be the invariable practice in paddy cultivation.

It has been rightly pointed out that one of the main virtues of transplanting (but not the most important) is the opportunity it offers to control weeds in the field. This weed problem is proving a limiting factor in rice production in the United States and may perhaps be solved only when economic conditions make it possible to introduce transplanting in this region. Wickizer and Bennett[699] would appear to retain an open mind on the subject, for they state: "On lands where at present only one rice crop and no other crop is grown each year, some of the chief potential advantages of transplanting cannot be realized. Future changes that may involve an extension of the practice are unpredictable. Some potentialities for bettering rice yields by this method undoubtedly exist, but their magnitude remains unknown."

PREPARATION OF THE LAND

Local custom, the nature of the soil and water supply are among the principal factors responsible for the various methods employed in preparing land to receive paddy seedlings. Where the water is under good control the earlier operations may be similar to those usual in cultivating a dry-land crop, but where the land is really swampy, other methods are necessary and have become customary.

By far the greater area planted with paddy is on land subject to seasonal flooding, and the cultivator's aim, therefore, is to take the fullest advantage of the rains. In Burma,[525] for instance, there are three sets of conditions under which the crop is raised: low-lying swamp land where rainfall is sufficient throughout the growing period to keep the plant in its necessary state of submergence; land less low-lying, or with less rainfall, but having supplementary water available from natural drainage and seepage, or from irrigation schemes; and land bordering tanks or rivers and subject to flood on which successive plantings can be made, level by level, as the flood water subsides.

Somewhat similar variations are found in most paddy-growing countries. By growing the appropriate variety of seed and by adopting the system of cultivation which meets local variations of soil and water supply, widely varying types of land are cultivated, in conditions where water supply is uncertain and at best not plentiful to the planting of deep and undrained swamps. It frequently happens, too, that widely varying conditions are encountered within a comparatively small area.

The first field operation is usually that of repairing and cleaning waterways and making and repairing bunds. A paddy-field is divided by bunds, the size and shape of divisions depending on the land contours. In fairly flat country a division may embrace an acre or more, the bunds being in straight lines, whereas if hillside land is utilized and irrigated from a stream, the divisions will be small and irregular, the bunds conforming to the contours. Contour bunding should always be adopted in open country only after a careful contour survey of the area. The bunds are constructed of compacted clay, stiff mud and weeds, openings being made at convenient places for ingress and egress of water. Land within a division is approximately level, so that should it be necessary to conserve water within a division, the exit is closed with mud and the water contained in the division will be at one level.

It is obvious that where the bunded divisions are small, ploughing is difficult and in some cases impossible, and recourse is then made to hand-cultivation. However, many animal-drawn implements are light, being made of wood, and so may be employed in fields that are much divided by bunds, the operator lifting the implement over the bunds. One division is usually cultivated at a time to limit the necessity of lifting the implements. It is usually not possible to plough before bunding because the bunds are necessary to impound water and thereby render the soil sufficiently soft for the primitive plough.

The soil is turned over with a plough or one of the various hand implements and in this way weeds are turned under the mud. This work is preferably done with three or four inches of water on the land. The choice of implement varies according to the nature of the land. Heavy weed growth may be cut down before ploughing. The plough is single-furrow, composed of wood with the exception of the coulter, which is usually of iron. Light iron ploughs are frequently seen in place of the wooden ploughs. Ploughs are drawn by one or two buffalo or oxen and usually till the ground for two or three inches. Deep ploughing for paddy is usually unnecessary and inadvisable.[12]

Where the nature of the land does not permit ploughing, the *chankol* may be used. This is an implement known and widely used throughout the East. It is a draw hoe with a blade of varying weight and shape according to the nature of the work, but is usually about fifteen inches long and twelve inches wide, set at an acute angle to the handle. A somewhat similar implement but with prongs instead of a blade is also used to break up very heavy land. Nowhere in the East does one find a spade used by Asians, probably because they work with bare feet.

A wooden ribbed roller is used for making the mud soft and reducing lumps. It is drawn over the land just before transplanting, yoked to a buffalo or drawn by hand. A hexagonal roll, with a row of teeth about six inches long protruding from each side of the hexagon, is used for puddling the mud, or a serrated board may be used for the purpose. This implement is sometimes used instead of the plough or *chankol*. The teeth turn in the weeds and render the mud soft. On the other hand, it can be used with good effect on land once ploughed, or in place of the ribbed roller. It is drawn by a buffalo or ox, and on suitable land will do one acre a day.

The harrow is entirely composed of wood, measures about four feet across and is provided with a single row of teeth about nine inches long. Drawn by a buffalo or ox, it can rake three-quarters acre a day. It is sometimes provided with a handle to enable the driver to press the implement into the ground. If the rake is not provided with a handle, the driver must frequently put his foot on the rake to drive it into the mud. The action of the rake is not to draw off the weeds but to drag them under the mud. A hand-operated implement, very similar to the rake except that instead of teeth it is provided with a plank of wood (sometimes serrated) is occasionally used. It is employed for making the surface smooth especially just before transplanting.

Ploughing finished, the land may be left for three or four weeks. It is about this time that nursery planting is completed. At the end of this period the land may be again ploughed or harrowed, the weeds that have grown since the first ploughing being turned in or drawn off and allowed to die on the bunds, or drawn into heaps to rot and then trodden under the mud. Lumps of soil are broken down by working the land with the bare feet or with a harrow or ribbed roller. The depth of mud is a factor deciding the type of implement that should be used. Land with deep mud (and it may be anything from an inch or two to three feet deep), cannot be ploughed with the native implement. In deep mud, cutting down weeds and treading them under the mud alone may suffice. In very deep mud, such as may occur in very low-lying natural swamps, the land is cultivated merely by driving water buffaloes round the divisions till they have trodden in all weeds and worked the mud into a regular soft consistency.

Finally, where possible, excess water is drawn off, leaving the mud covered with about an inch of water. The surface may be made smooth with an implement which is virtually a plank of wood yoked to an ox or buffalo and drawn over the land. In Italy the levelling is done with a *speanoni*, a long plank drawn by a horse.

The amount of cultivation and the implements used vary with local circumstances. In Japan, in areas where only one paddy crop is grown a year, ploughing is done in winter or early spring, so that the soil may be well aerated and organic matter decomposed before paddy planting. Where paddy is followed by winter crops, the fields are ploughed as soon as the winter crop is removed. In Burma, cattle are usually employed for ploughing. The recognized rates of working for a pair of cattle per day of six hours are one-third acre for ploughing, or over an acre with a blade harrow (*set-htun*). In Malaya, the rate of ploughing is much less, being about seven days per acre and three days to harrow, up to as much as ten days to plough an acre with a buffalo on heavy land.

As soon as the land is finally prepared for planting with seedlings from the nursery, transplanting commences. Thus one sees preparation of land and planting proceeding at the same time. Weeds grow very rapidly and it is essential, therefore, to transplant as soon as possible after final cultivation so that the paddy shall be ahead of the weeds.

TRANSPLANTING

Seedlings in the nursery are pulled up in small bunches without regard to the amount of roots that are retained on each plant. In Hong Kong[269] and in parts of China, however, the seedlings are removed from the nursery with care by means of a sharp, flat hoe of special design. The blade of the hoe is pushed into the bed so as to lift a patch of seedlings together with the soil and fertilizer in the immediate vicinity of the seedlings. It is to be noted that in contrast to the system obtaining elsewhere, seedlings with adhering soil are planted in the field. Sometimes seedlings for a second crop in the year are removed by hand in Hong Kong. The rough treatment of seedlings for the first crop is avoided because the seedlings are smaller, having been in the nursery for about twenty-five days. It is also possibly intended to retain the fertilizer applied to the nursery in close contact with the roots.

The usual practice in most countries is to pull the seedlings, tie them into bundles of convenient size for handling, the roots being rinsed in water to remove soil, and the top few inches of leaves cut off to reduce evaporation and give rigidity to the plants, so that when transplanted the leaves do not bend over into the water. In parts of Malabar[511] a ripening process of seedlings for the second crop is usual. Seedling bundles are arranged in a circular heap with the roots exposed for three or four days, the heap being watered should it show signs of drying out. The bundles are then left in water for a night before being planted. The object is to destroy by fermentation eggs and insect pests to which the second crop is usually subject in this region. Seedlings treated in this way are said to regain their green colour quickly and to grow better and be more free from insect pests than are untreated seedlings.

About 700 large bundles of seedlings are required to plant an acre and this quantity may weigh about two tons. Their transport to the field, therefore, merits consideration. In some regions seedlings are carried to the field in rattan baskets so designed that air circulates freely, thus preventing the seedlings from becoming over-heated before they are transplanted. Elsewhere, seedlings are loaded into small dug-out boats and carried on irrigation canals to the fields. In Burma, the bundles are conveyed either on sledges or by boat.

Whereas ploughing, raking and nursery work is usually done by men, it falls to the lot of women and children in most Asian countires to carry out transplanting, which is often done on a communal basis. A bunch of seedlings is held in the left hand, from two to six are transferred to the right hand and thrust into the mud, the distance between "hills" of plants being from four to twelve inches, depending on the variety, local conditions and custom. Experiments in India[265] showed that the number of fertile tillers was greater with three to four seedlings per "hill" and decreased with closer planting; length of panicle and yields increased with wider spacing. On first-class land in Malaya, a spacing of fifteen to seventeen inches is usual, using a seven months' variety of paddy. Jack[297] states that where the water in the field is deeper than one foot to fifteen inches it becomes necessary to space the plants somewhat closer than in shallow water, because deep water inhibits tillering considerably. In Burma, from one to four plants per "hill" are spaced from four to eight inches apart. The optimum spacing in Ceylon[474] is four to six inches, one seedling only being placed at each point, except where there is liability to crab damage, when two seedlings are planted. In view of this very close planting, it is not surprising to learn that it requires fifteen to twenty women to plant an acre a day, as compared with ten to twelve in other countries where wider spacing is usual and the number of seedlings per "hill" greater. In Japan, the so-called rectangular planting is often adopted in which the interval between "hills" in the row is narrowed. The object is to give the plants sufficient sunlight despite close planting. In contrast to this careful planting, in most parts of Bhandara and Balaghat in India the seedlings are simply thrown into the mud as the worker moves backwards.[129] In the Krian District of Perak, Malaya, the women usually employ a small two-pronged implement, known as *kuku kambing* (goat's hoof), to assist in transplanting. Seedlings are placed between the two prongs and thrust into the mud. It appears to be merely a "backache-saving" device. Transplanting is arduous work, but the women work with great speed and precision and can complete an acre in six to ten days per worker.

Shallow transplanting is recommended, for if the seedlings are planted deeply the roots fail to develop normally and a new system of roots must develop from the upper nodes. This delay in root formation retards plant growth.

Investigations in India[49] show that if seedlings are planted in a slanting position there is a setback in tillering, for the seedlings so planted develop at $1-1\frac{1}{2}$ inches below the surface a short rhizone sideways which delays the establishment of the plant and results in a reduction in the number of tillers.

AFTER-CULTIVATION

In most regions, little or no after-cultivation other than weeding is attempted with transplanted paddy. Weeding is easily performed by hand if done early when the weeds are but lightly rooted and can be drawn together and thrown on the bunds. In the extensive Central Plain of Thailand the land is so flat that bunds are rare. The weeder therefore squeezes the weeds into bundles and impales them on sticks which project above water level, where they are left to wither. In Japan[38] three or four inter-cultivations begin ten or twelve days after transplanting. As a result of the introduction of row planting, a hand-operated weeder has become widely used. It consists of two rolling steel wheels arranged one in front of the other with a U-shaped sled and wood handle. This rotary weeder stirs the soil and cultivates while weeding. Depth of cultivation can be adjusted by changing the angle between frame and handle and controlling the angle of sled. This implement can be used only in the early stages of growth; at later stages the crop is either hand-weeded or cultivated by means of a scraping weeder which has a number of short teeth fixed under the crosspiece of a curved and elliptically-shaped frame. When using weeding implements it is still necessary to hand-weed round the plants.

The herbicide 2,4-D has recently been introduced and is said to be effective in controlling weeds in Japan. In the warmer regions of that country, paddy may be weeded once by machine, followed by an application of 2,4-D some thirty days after transplanting. It is stated that this herbicide also prevents growth of non-effective tillering and lodging.[379]

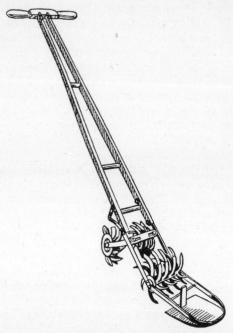

Fig. 6
Takakita conical weeder.   Manually operated

The practice called "Baido" in Japan consists in moving the soil around the plants during cultivation. It is claimed that this increases growth of stems and also the size and number of grains. Yamaguchi *et al.*[711] found that Baido on ill-drained land increased the absorption of minerals, particularly potassium, but that during periods of high temperature, rapid oxidation of organic matter caused sufficient reduction of intake of minerals to retard growth.

In certain valleys in south-west Kwangtung, China, the straw of the first crop of the year is twisted into bunches or hanks "forearm size" and trodden into the mud between the rows of young transplanted paddy of the second crop, planted in July.[485]   Trials in

38. Winnowing paddy, South India

39. Threshing grain in Egypt

40. Paddy awaiting sun-drying before storage, British Guiana

41. Drying paddy at the millyard. Labourers are raking the paddy to dry in the s
Malaya

Portugal[402] showed that ploughed-in straw at the rate of 9,000 lb. per acre gave highly significant increases in grain yield and no significant increase in straw yield.

As a preliminary to harrowing a broadcast crop when three to four weeks old in Ceylon, the field is drained overnight, leaving about three inches of water. A toothed harrow, yoked to a pair of buffaloes or cattle, is then drawn over the field, returning over the same strip in the opposite direction. This operation is then repeated in the crosswise direction. Thus, the harrow is drawn over the field four times. It is stated that three to four acres can be harrowed in a day. Any vacancies in the field are then supplied by transplanting from the more thickly sown patches and any weeds are removed by hand. It is held in Ceylon that harrowing the standing crop increases the yield by four to ten bushels an acre, the beneficial effect being due to stimulating tiller formation and root development caused by trampling and disturbance of the plants, the thinning out of excess plants and removal of weeds. On the day following harrowing, water in the field is reduced to about one inch, at which it is held for about five days, when the depth is increased and should be retained at about six inches.[474, 553]

PRUNING PADDY

As already stated, the usual practice is to cut off the top few inches of leaves of seedlings before transplanting, to assist handling the seedlings, reduce transpiration and give rigidity to the newly-transplanted seedlings. The leaves of transplanted seedlings die back in any case, and are replaced by new leaves, so there is no reason why the leaves should not be cut (or twisted), especially when growth in the nursery has been very luxuriant.

A practice prevalent in some Asian countries is to cut a foot or so of foliage from half-grown plants in the field; alternatively, cattle are allowed to graze the fields of paddy. West Pakistan experiments showed a beneficial effect of topping in cases of luxuriant growth. It has also been claimed that the practice encourages tillering. It is, indeed, possible that pruning will reduce tendency to lodge; it is also likely that it will increase tillering, but stimulation of tillering at this stage of growth is probably inadvisable, for late tillering causes uneven ripening.

It was found in the Philippines that when the leaves were cut at sixty-five days old, the flowering stage was prolonged, but it had little effect if the plants were younger. The age for cutting leaves that gave greatest yield was when the seedlings were thirty-seven days old.

The question of pruning paddy in the field, or grazing it is bound

M

up with the complex of carbohydrate production. On land rich in nitrogen and growing a paddy variety which tends to become too leafy—common amongst *indicas*—in such limited cases there may possibly be an advantage in pruning. There seems to have been no critical work on this subject and one cannot generalize because loss of leaf to a crop which has not too much could be harmful by reducing starch accumulation, but might do good to an over-lush crop. The section on Fertilizer Response on page 223 is relevant to this question.

HARVESTING

Methods of harvesting paddy in the East are simple, but entail much labour, especially if the crop has lodged. In Thailand, much paddy lodges because of wind squalls and light straw. In Thailand and also in Burma, the farmer therefore pushes all the crop down in one direction before it lodges and tangles. He uses a long bamboo with a short, heavy portion of bamboo slipped over the light end. With this pole he walks across the field, pushing down a strip, takes a few steps and leans forward pushing a second strip and so on across the field, back and forth, until the entire field has been pushed down. This operation also obtains in parts of Formosa, when winds are strong. The system is deprecated by Iso[293] because breaking the culms in the ripening stage adversely affects the crop.

Vast areas are reaped by hand, either with a sickle or with other hand-operated knives. The traditional, and probably the original, harvesting implement is still widely used. It is a small knife from two to six inches long, fastened crosswise on a short stick and so held that the blade is covered by the palm. The belief is still held in many parts that the spirit of the paddy crop is offended by the rough cutting of the sickle and will show displeasure in the following season by causing the crop to fail, but that it will imagine the small knife in the hand to be a bird, which in fact it is made to resemble, and will therefore not visit its wrath on the offenders. This implement is well known in Malaya as *pisau penuai*, in the Philippines as *yatab*, Sarawak as *ketap*, Java as *aniani*. It is also used in Panama, but its use in many countries is gradually giving way to the sickle.

Using the small knife, the harvester bends the finger round the stem of the plant and draws the ear on to the blade, which severs it from the stalk a few inches below the collar. When a few heads have been cut and retained in the cutting hand, they are transferred to the left hand, until a large bunch is obtained. This is then placed in a basket for removal from the field. The chief advantage of this laborious method is that the maximum crop is obtained from badly lodged or very unevenly ripe areas. The task of harvesting falls to the lot of the women, who work with great speed. Freeman[201] timed Iban women harvesting in Sarawak; prolific and upstanding paddy was plucked at the rate of forty heads in thirty seconds. From further observations he estimated that, working ten hours a day, a woman could harvest an acre in seventeen days.

The Hanunóo, a small pagan tribe living by subsistence agriculture in the mountains of the Philippine island of Mindoro, know and use metal blades, but usually harvest the crop without the aid of a knife. The *yatab* has been known to them for several generations, but is still regarded as a foreign implement, and for this reason is considered less suited than the bare hands for the intimate and direct contact of the respectful harvester with the "sacred" paddy plants. The harvester therefore breaks off the panicles one at a time by hand, using any one of several fingers and thumb techniques in which the thumb nail most often acts as a blade.[134]

Where the *yatab* is not used—and this includes all India, Burma, Indo-China and Japan—the sickle is employed, and this implement appears to be gradually replacing the *yatab* in Malaya and Java. Wijewardene[701] has remarked upon the fact that the Japanese farmer uses a sickle to harvest paddy and a scythe for harvesting wheat, although the latter is preferable both as regards ease of operation and output per man-day for harvesting paddy. The sickle varies in shape in different countries, but it is essentially the same, being the familiar shape and usually having a serrated, self-sharpening cutting edge. The crop is cut with some of the straw, dried on racks or poles and then taken to the threshing floor. Occasionally it is cut with the sickle about six inches from the ground and when dry is made into small round stacks, usually built on old ant hills or other situations which are unlikely to flood. The stack may have a diameter of about nine feet and a similar height. Stacks are protected from rain by a thatch of sago palm leaves. Paddy remains in the stack for two or three months. Stacking paddy is common in Java and may be seen occasionally in some other countries, including Malaya, Japan and Sierra Leone. Maturing grain in stacks facilitates threshing. In Peru the crop is retained in large stacks some fifty feet across and twelve to fifteen feet high.

DRYING

Weather conditions in the tropics are not conducive to uniform drying of grain in the field. If the harvested crop is shocked (stooked) the top grain gets more heat and air than the bottom; if the paddy is delivered to the mill when the top grain is at the right moisture, the bottom grain may still be wet and cause the whole lot to turn a brown colour (stack burn). Conversely, if the grain is allowed to dry until the bottom grain is at the correct moisture for milling, the top grain will be over-dried, sun-cracked and will therefore tend to break in. the mill. Should rain occur shortly before the grain is dry, the crop cannot be removed from the field until the moisture has again dried off; this also results in sun-crack and poor milling.

When drying is carried out on open-air concrete (or hard earth), as is customary in Asia, sun-crack (known as sun-checking in the United States) results. The paddy is spread on the concrete, being occasionally stirred. At night or when rain or heavy dew occurs, it is heaped and covered. Where climatic conditions are such that long dry spells may confidently be expected, in Burma for instance, sun-drying and open-air storage for a considerable period is customary.

Alternate loss and absorption of moisture by the grain causes development of internal cracks in the grain. Stahel[629] showed that a moisture content of 15 per cent is critical for crack formation, drying or absorption which passes this point increasing the internal cracks. Grain at reaping usually contains about 23 per cent moisture. By the end of a hot day it may be reduced to 14 per cent, to rise again at night with dew. Interruptions in drying during the day by rain may also be experienced.

Because wetting and drying cause crack formation the crop should be reaped before it is fully ripe, cracks being formed more readily when the grain is quite hard. Slow drying gives a higher percentage of whole grains and the moisture content at milling is less critical. Sun-checking is immaterial if the paddy is to be parboiled, provided that it is dried slowly after parboiling.[150]

In large-scale paddy production, if the crop is reaped with a binder, the paddy must be properly shocked in such a manner that the grain is adequately protected from sun and rain. In the southern United States the shock consists of about ten bundles of sheaves, capped with a bundle placed upright on the top with the heads downwards and in contact with the heads of the bundles in the shock. The straw of the capping bundle is pulled down and spread evenly so that it covers and protects the heads of the cap bundle as well as the underlying bundles. After about ten days in the shocks, the grain is considered to be cured and the milling quality of the paddy thereby improved.

Crauford has studied sun-checking in West Africa.[149] He found that it was caused by atmospheric conditions associated with the dry, harmattan wind. The cracking is caused by early morning mists resulting in water condensing on the panicles. Changes in moisture content of the grain associated with changes in relative humidity do not lead to cracking provided the panicles are not in contact with liquid water. He suggests that the way to avoid sun-check is to harvest before the grain moisture falls below 15 per cent. This may be done by following the daily change in grain moisture and to harvest the day before it reaches 16 per cent.

With almost daily rainfall and heavy night dew it is almost impossible to obtain satisfactory drying in the field. The alternative is, as is usual with small farmers, immediate threshing after harvest and subsequent sun-drying under conditions which permit adequate protection of the grain. For large-scale production the solution of the problem is found in artificial drying.

THRESHING

Threshing paddy separates the grain with its adhering husk or glumes from the stalk. Generally throughout the East the paddy crop is threshed as soon as it is harvested, occasionally, as condition of the crop demands, after a short period of sun-drying.

In Burma, British Guiana and some other countries, the sheaves are brought to threshing floors where they are laid in the sun to dry. Sheaves are laid two or three deep round a stake with the heads towards the stake. Buffaloes or cows are then driven slowly round to trample out the grain. Less commonly, threshing is done by beating sheaves against a block of wood.[528] Threshing combs are said to have been invented in Japan about the year 1700. Several makers in that country now produce both pedal and power-driven machines of this description which are widely used throughout the country. The former have an output of about 220 lb. paddy per hour, or double this amount with a two-man tread, while 1 h.p. power threshers worked on this principle have a capacity of about 600 lb. paddy per hour.

In many countries, sheaves are threshed on or adjacent to paddy-fields. A tub about the size of a half-barrel is used. Inside the tub rests a ladder with rungs about four inches apart. Sheaves are beaten two or three times against the ladder, thereby removing the grain from the ears and collecting it in the tub. A screen is placed round the tub to prevent grain from scattering. Much paddy is also threshed by foot. When this is done, the worker prefers the ears to be slightly damp as it is less injurious to the feet. Awned paddy is distinctly unpopular if it is to be threshed in this way.

Awners (*ebarbenses*) are used in Italy to remove awns. The machine is described[648] as consisting of two metal cylinders on the same axis (generally vertical, but sometimes horizontal). The inner cylinder rotates around the fixed outer cylinder. Both cylinders carry metal tines which cross each other, one set with the points inwards,

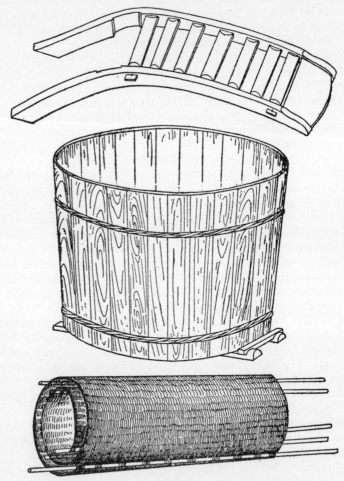

Fig. 7

Implements used in Hong Kong in threshing paddy.

1. Threshing ladder   2. Threshing tub   3. Threshing mat

the other with points outwards. The distance between the two sets of teeth is sufficient to permit passage of grains downwards while the inner cylinder is rotating, the awns being removed by impact without

FIG. 8
Minoru pedal thresher

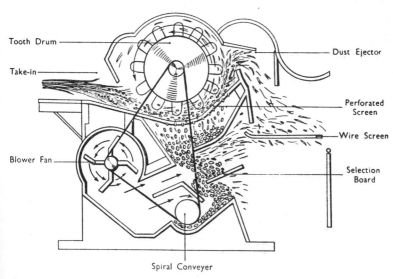

Tooth Drum

Take-in

Blower Fan

Dust Ejector

Perforated Screen

Wire Screen

Selection Board

Spiral Conveyer

FIG. 9
Sectional drawing showing construction of Minoru thresher

the ends of grains being damaged. The awns are then removed by a fan or aspirator.

Copeland[135] gives the following technique for threshing awnless paddy as practised in Leyte in the Philippines. "A platform, eight or ten feet high, with bamboo floor with cracks between the slats, is erected. A rope is stretched above the platform; to this the workers hold with their hands while they work the rice with their feet. The grain falls through the cracks, is winnowed by the wind, and collects, clean, on a mat on the ground. An efficient worker separates as much as fifty *cavanes* (about 5,000 lb.) a day in this way. The remarkable feature of this method is the removal of the grain as fast as it is separated from the straw, so that the worker sees constantly what remains to be separated."

WINNOWING

The native method of winnowing is of the simplest. It is performed by shaking backwards and forwards paddy placed on a flat tray of plaited bamboo or rotan finished off with a lip about an inch high. The paddy is shaken and tossed with a twist of the wrists, which has the effect of working the empty husks, light grain and chaff to the edge of the tray furthest removed from the worker. As a result of long practice, the worker is able to throw over the edge of the tray the outer portion, which consists of chaff and dust. Then, standing at the windward edge of the mat, the worker holds the tray above the head, gently shaking the paddy from the tray, so that the good seed falls on the mat and the husk and chaff are carried away by the wind. Women generally perform this task and they may frequently be heard calling the wind by a kind of yodel, or calling the spirit of the wind by name.

Paddy is also winnowed by suspending a bamboo sieve of one-half inch mesh from a tripod about six feet high. Paddy is placed on the sieve, which is then gently rocked. The wind carries away dust and husk and the cleaned grain falls on a mat placed below the sieve.

Hand-winnowing machines are coming into favour in some areas. In these machines a draught is created by turning a handle which operates a fan. Paddy is fed into a hopper from which it falls into a draught created by the fan. The rate of feeding the grain is regulated by a wooden shutter. The draught carries off the chaff and the clean grain falls and is collected separately.

Winnowing paddy before sale to mills is insufficient to meet the requirements of the miller. On arrival at the mill the paddy is subjected to further sieving and winnowing to remove immature grain and extraneous matter such as sticks, straw, sand, stones and pellets of mud. Even in a consignment of fair average quality the matter removed may amount to 2 to 5 per cent by weight of the total.

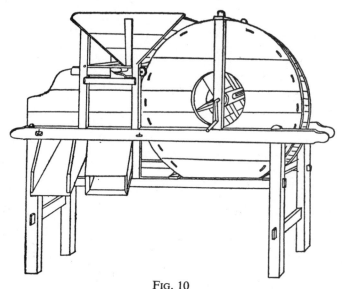

Fig. 10

A hand-winnowing machine used in Hong Kong

Shakers or shaking riddles remove the larger impurities and the grain passes over aspirators consisting of fans so arranged as to draw air through a thin curtain of paddy, thus carrying away the lighter deleterious matter.

MULTIPLE-CROPPING SYSTEMS

In many parts of China, Japan, Ceylon, parts of India and elsewhere, two or even three crops of paddy are removed from the land annually. Because there are two monsoons during the year, many paddy areas in Ceylon are cropped twice annually. In hilly regions such as Priangan and Kedu in Java, where much water is available throughout the year and paddy cultivation is therefore less dependent on the season, three harvests in two years, or two harvests in one year, are obtained. Trials in India have proved that it is possible to grow three crops of paddy annually—two crops of short duration interposed by one crop of moderately long duration. By this method a combined yield of 9,574 lb. per acre was obtained on an area of 50 acres.

The Food and Agriculture Organization reported in 1960:[551]

A substantial increase in the area harvesting two rice crops a year (currently some four million hectares excluding India) is technically possible by means of a fuller development of irrigation potentialities and proper drainage, and there are plans to extend the double-cropped area in a number of countries, notably Ceylon, India, Pakistan and Thailand. Double-cropping balances the labour load and it is often considerably cheaper to provide perennial irrigation (so there is sufficient water in the off-season) than to reclaim waste land. But there may be limiting factors. On well-drained land other products may already be grown as a second crop, as wheat and barley are on one-half of the rice land in Japan, and climatic conditions preclude double-cropping in the rest of the country. In Malaya, the irrigation system in some areas is based on long-maturing varieties and where it is practicable double-cropping is discouraged by a general tendency for rents to rise following its introduction. Poor drainage often makes a long-maturing period necessary for paddy, and it is sometimes found that two crops of short-term varieties produce a smaller combined yield than one long-term crop.

Writing of the double-cropping paddy areas of China, Buck[94] states that the larger cultivated areas are in flat irrigable valleys, scattered from Lungchow, Nanning and Ishan eastwards at an elevation of 500 to 1,000 metres above sea-level. The Canton Delta, about 7,000 square miles, is considered the most important and prosperous in the whole area and the most intensely cultivated. The area is practically frostless, the mean temperature being 57° in February, the coldest month, and 84° F. in July, the hottest month. A well-distributed rainfall of about 69 inches is experienced, with rather high humidity.

Soils of the area he describes as being chiefly of the laterite type, podzolized Old and Young Red Earths on the eastern two-thirds of the area, and Older Red Earths on the western part. Both types of soil erode easily, are badly leached and require heavy fertilization, for which reason large areas remain uncultivated. In the valleys modification has occurred through centuries of paddy cultivation, resulting in a podzolized soil of a different and more productive character. The yield of rice in this double-cropping area of China is said to be low.

Gourley states[221] that from Manchuria to south of Shanghai only one crop is grown per annum. From this point to Foochow two crops are grown by interplanting, and south of Foochow and in central China two consecutive crops are grown. When two crops are obtained by interplanting, this is achieved by means of one early and one late variety of paddy. Both varieties are sown in the seed bed at the same time, about the middle of April. The early variety is transplanted in the middle of May in rows eighteen inches apart and a fortnight later the late variety is interplanted between the rows. The early crop is harvested by the end of July; the second crop, the growth of which has been retarded by the shade of the first, is then able to develop rapidly and is harvested at the end of October.

In Hong Kong[269] there is a choice of five varieties of paddy for the first crop, the maturation period varying from 95 to 125 days, and six varieties for the second crop, with maturation periods varying from 100 to 125 days. Seedlings are retained in the nursery for 15 to 40 days for varieties cultivated for the first crop, the length of time in the nursery depending on variety. For the second-crop varieties the seedlings are in the nursery from 25 to 30 days.

To obtain two harvests a year there must be strict observance of the time-table for planting and cultivation. In Hong Kong, for the first crop, the nursery is planted from March to early June and the crop harvested about mid-July. For the second crop the nursery is planted at the end of June or early July and the crop reaped in November. In this way advantage is taken of the rainy months, which are from May to September. During this period between sixty and seventy inches of rain may be expected out of a total annual rainfall of between eighty and ninety inches. Between November and March the land is frequently utilized for cultivating crops other than paddy.

A top dressing of fertilizer, weeding and cultivation are usually carried out together about a month after transplanting, when the more prosperous cultivator will broadcast about 75 to 100 lb. groundnut powder and 25 lb. ammonium sulphate per acre. The less well-to-do cultivator will be content to use about 600 lb. per acre of dried dung instead. Before broadcasting the fertilizer, the field is drained and immediately after its application the weeds are trampled into the mud and the paddy roots pressed deeply into the mud at the same time. In some districts a wooden board with nails protruding on the lower surface is pushed in between the rows of plants to assist in packing mud around the seedlings. The field is left to dry for three to five days, the belief being that this enables more effective absorption of nutrients when irrigation is resumed. Sometimes weeding is carried out twice during the growing period and two applications of fertilizer are given. From the time when the lower part of the stem begins to swell, walking in the field is not permitted for fear of interfering with the formation of grain. The average yield of paddy is stated to be about 1,600 lb. per acre for the first crop and 2,000 lb. for the second crop.

Double cropping is quite common in Japan, chiefly on the island of Shikoku, the shores of Kinki and Tokai districts and Okinawa. In the Kochi Prefecture the first crop is sown in the nursery in late March and transplanted thirty days later, the harvest being reaped early in August. The second crop is sown in the nursery in July, transplanted as soon as the first crop is reaped, and ripens in about ninety days. Early-maturing varieties of low photoperiod response are planted for the first crop and medium-maturing varieties of high photoperiodic response for the second crop.[379] The yield of the second crop is stated to be about 60 to 70 per cent of the first crop.

In the two northern provinces of Formosa—Taihoku and Shinchiku—where rainfall is fairly evenly distributed and irrigation facilities are ample, about 80 per cent of the fields grow two paddy crops a year. For the first paddy crop a 4 to 5 months' variety is grown, for the second crop a 3 to 3½ months' variety. There is thus about one-third of the year in which to grow other crops, such as wheat, flax, sweet potato, green manure and sugar cane. Where sugar cane is included in the rotation, a 16 to 19 months' variety is grown and paddy becomes the catch crop. The rapid succession of crops is achieved by the *kao* method of interplanting in which crops are planted on ridges during growth of the paddy crop. Thus sweet potato cuttings are planted in the paddy before the soil dries out and are ridged as soon as the paddy crop is harvested. In south Formosa, rainfall is insufficient to allow two crops annually, the single crop of paddy being planted about May and harvested in November.

In the double-crop areas of Madras State in India the first crop is grown from May to September, a 95- to 110-day paddy being cultivated; the second crop is planted in September and harvested in February. The long-duration crop may yield 2,700 lb. of paddy, but the second crop, which is not manured, may yield about 1,500 lb. On Government farms the yield of the second crop was raised to 3,000 to 4,000 lb. with the aid of green manure.[121] Double cropping is now advocated in Malaya,[14] provided that the crops are manured and that full irrigation can be maintained for both crops. Yields for the main crop are about 1,600 lb. and for the off-season crop over 1,000 lb.

The main limitations to an extension of double cropping are availability of water, temperature and a suitably dry season for harvesting. Under monsoon conditions common over most of the paddy-growing areas of south-east Asia, water is not available to permit the cultivation of paddy beyond the period of about seven months in the year; consequently, economic production must depend on a single crop of a long-term maturation variety to cover the period rather than the employment of two short-term maturation crops. Burgess[97] writing of the Central Plain of Thailand, states that the inter-season rainfall in that country is scanty so that a second crop cannot be grown. He adds that some of the more recently completed irrigation schemes are designed to supply water independently of rainfall, the ability to do so depending on the level of water in the stream across which the barrage has been erected, which in turn is governed by the amount of rainfall in the catchment area. The authorities are hopeful that in the area served, two crops of paddy per annum may be realized.

Experimental data are far from complete concerning the relative merits of a single long-maturation crop per annum or two crops of shorter maturation period. It is common experience that the longer the maturation period the heavier the crop. Whether two crops of shorter duration will produce a heavier crop than one crop of long maturation period probably depends on local conditions. From the economic standpoint, one must remember the very much greater cost of producing two crops per annum as compared with one crop. It is possible that as irrigation schemes are improved and perfected in south-east Asia, reconsideration may be given to the economics of producing two or more crops a year. Where double-cropping is noi possible, the best course would appear to be the planting of paddy varieties with the longest maturation period possible in conformity with the expectation of sufficient water to irrigate the crop during its period of growth.

Double cropping tends towards a build-up of pests and the encouragement of diseases; it is, in fact, a denial of an elementary principle of agriculture. Before further extension of the double-cropping system it should be carefully compared with the rotational system. Improved control of irrigation should greatly facilitate the introduction of rotations on paddy lands, for it makes possible the cultivation of a number of crops on land which formerly was considered useless for any crop except rice.

RATOON PADDY CROPS

In some areas it is customary to obtain a ratoon crop of paddy. Certain varieties are suitable for this purpose, ratooning being very largely a varietal character. Gupta and Mitra, for instance, found[235] that of 170 varieties tested in the Upper Provinces of India, only sixteen were capable of giving a ratoon crop; the remainder either did not produce ratoon shoots, or formed sterile spikelets. The first crop is usually cut about a foot from the ground before all the green has left the straw, the land again irrigated, when axillary buds develop at the lower nodes. In exceptional cases a satisfactory crop is obtained, but usually it is light. Despite the fact that this system is not generally recommended as it greatly increases the incidence of insect pests, it is becoming increasingly popular in many countries.

Iso[293] points out that ratooning in Formosa has increased appreciably in the past few years. He appreciates its advantages in some areas if it is practised rationally. Evans[193] has described the system developed in the Swaziland Irrigation Scheme. Difficulty was found in weed control when a ratoon crop was grown in the same year as the main crop. Consequently, a system was adopted whereby the ratoon crop follows the main crop after an interval of about six months. The main crop is planted in October/November after the fields have been flooded to promote weed growth and then disc-harrowed or ploughed to turn in the weeds. The main crop is harvested in January/March after which the fields are allowed to remain in stubble, without irrigation, until the temperature rises in August/September when the stubble is irrigated and the ratoon crop grows, to be harvested in January. Under this system only two crops of paddy are obtained in two years, but there is a considerable saving in cost of cultivation and planting, economy in use of machinery and a saving of about 20 per cent in water requirement for the ratoon crop. The ratoon crop appears to be relatively free from weeds and self-sown paddy. Yields of the main crop are about 2,700 to 3,000 lb. paddy and of the ratoon crop 2,300 to 2,400 lb. per acre. The danger of build up of pest population is, however, recognized and is, indeed, inseparable with any system of continuous paddy cultivation.

In some countries more than one consecutive ratoon crop is obtained. In some regions of Colombia two or three ratoon crops are obtained and in parts of the Causa Valley in that country up to six consecutive ratoon crops are harvested. Experiments showed[205] that the first and second ratoon crops were 54 and 59 per cent less, respectively, than that of the sown crop. Although production costs per acre of ratooned paddy were lower, the cost per lb. of rice was higher than that of the sown crop.

DROP SEED CROPS

Under suitable climatic and soil conditions, and with adequate water, a second crop may be obtained from seed dropped during harvesting the paddy crop. This system is largely adopted in British Guiana. This method cannot be recommended as subsequent paddy crops are likely to be adversely affected as a result, owing to the delay in preparation of the land, to a marked increase in weed growth and the greater incidence of insect pests. Drop-seed cropping in British Guiana is largely responsible for the high proportion of red rice in the main crop throughout the territory. In British Guiana, 2,4-D applied before germination at the rate of 4 lb. per acre, gave reasonably good control of drop seed.

ROTATIONS

The subject of rotational cultivation of paddy is intimately connected with soils and manuring. It is an accepted principle of agricultural practice that an annual crop cannot be produced economically continuously on the same land. But such is the nature of the paddy crop that continuous cultivation is possible, and has in fact been in vogue for centuries in parts of Asia, usually without systematic manuring. Crops have reached a low level of production, but at still an economic level. In certain parts of Asia, notably in China and Japan, continuous cropping with paddy is not usually practised, two crops being obtained in the summer months, followed by winter crops, such as sweet potatoes, tomatoes and green vegetables. Lord[366] observed in the neighbourhood of Saigon in Indo-China that many fields from which the paddy crop had been removed about two months previously were being cultivated with tobacco. This catch-crop was being irrigated from wells situated in the fields.

In well-drained, terraced fields in Ceylon, where soils are of a light texture, vegetables are grown for one season and, since these rotations commenced, the paddy crops have shown marked increases in yield. From the Malayan state of Kelantan[12] it is stated that as a direct result of an off-season crop of vegetables there was a 45 per cent increase in yield of the subsequent paddy crop.

In many parts of Asia, however, the semi-aquatic conditions which prevail throughout the year, or the nature of the soil when it dries out, preclude the cultivation of any crop other than paddy. Most of the paddy land of Lower Burma, for instance, is unsuited to any other crop than paddy. The possibility of establishing a rotation of crops on such lands as these must therefore be ruled out, and one comes to the alternative—the simplest form of rotation—a crop of paddy followed by a fallow, or two or three crops of paddy followed by a fallow period. This system is not unusual in the East and is also seen in the United States. In the wet tropics uncultivated land does not remain bare for long. Weeds, grasses and frequently secondary jungle take possession and soon cover the land. While this system appears to serve its purpose, it cannot be considered as ideal, for it does little to increase the manurial content of the soil and it encourages noxious weeds and insect pests. Where possible, it might be better to water-fallow the land, as is done in British Guiana (see page 21).

Paddy cultivation in the United States has been able to develop unhampered by the traditions and prejudices inseparable from attempts to institute innovations in Asian countries. In some Californian[310] districts a rotation of three crops of paddy is usual, followed by spring or summer ploughed fallow on which wheat or barley is sown in the autumn, after which paddy is grown for one year. Another method used is to alternate a paddy crop with a fallow. Some growers do not fallow but leave the land uncropped and uncultivated until it is prepared for paddy in the following spring, and such land is frequently pastured. Experiments in Louisiana[301] showed that in a four-year rotation, fertilizing cotton or stubble pasture did not increase the yield of the following paddy crop, but paddy after stubble pasture yielded 7·4 bushels per acre more than after cotton. Rice yields on a ten-year rotation of paddy followed by cotton averaged 32·1 bushels per acre, following native pasture 47·1, following maize and soya beans 45·6 and following improved pasture 48·7 bushels per acre. On land continuously in paddy for forty-nine years, the yields were 24·5 to 32 bushels per acre, depending on climatic variations rather than on fertility.

In Texas, the rotation of paddy with *Sesbania* gave the highest yield. But cultivated crops in rotation with paddy are often unprofitable in the United States. In Louisiana and Texas it is usual to grow one or two paddy crops and then pasture the land for one to three years before planting paddy once more, cattle being put on the pasture. By this method rice yields have been much increased, the incidence of red rice reduced and it has been possible to increase the rate of stocking.

In the Murrumbidgee Irrigation Area of New South Wales, a three-, four-, or even six- to seven-year rotation has been developed for paddy, with cereal crops such as wheat and oats, and with temporary pastures on which fat lambs are successfully raised. Under this system, the soil has yielded prolific paddy crops, with an average of 1·8 tons of paddy per acre.[281] Heavy dressings of artificials are no longer supplied under these conditions. In earlier years, 2 cwt. per acre of sulphate of ammonia were usual on this area, but with the adoption of clover-rye-grass pastures in wide rotation, the use of sulphate of ammonia is considered not only superfluous but dangerous.[492] It is, however, applied to the pasture at the rate of 1 cwt. per acre annually. Wimmera rye grass (*Lolium rigidum*) and mid-season subterranean clover (*Trifolium subterraneum*) may be established in paddy stubble or under a cover crop of winter cereals. Subterranean

42. Building a levee or bund with a checker, California

43. Contour ploughing with a tractor, India

44. A D.4 tractor towing a Mitchell seed-drill with the rear-gangs of a Martins disc-harrow hitched on behind as a covering harrow

45. The Endgate Broadca seeder

46. A.—Paddy field being sown by an aeroplane which is seen approaching a flagman. B.—Seed rice dropping on the water from an aeroplane, U.S.A.

clover will regenerate after each rice crop from hard seed carried over from the previous pasture. Hard seed of West Australian blue lupin (*Lupinus varius*), Strawberry clover (*Trifolium fragiferum*) and Bokhara clover (*Melilotus alba*) sown with paddy will withstand submergence during the paddy season and germinate after the paddy has been harvested, but in the case of the last two only after the paddy straw is removed.[603]

In Indonesia, satisfactory control of water and a suitable soil for dry-land crops favour rotation of paddy with dry-land crops, and on much of the land paddy is rotated with such crops as maize, soya beans and groundnuts. In sugar-producing areas, conditions of land tenure under Dutch rule compelled a rotation of paddy with sugar-cane.[366] In parts of the Philippines also, paddy is successfully grown in rotation with sugar-cane.

Rotation of crops with paddy is more usual in countries where there is a winter season, paddy being grown in the summer months and other crops—usually food crops—in the winter. In Italy rotations are usually practised. Around Vercelli, one crop of cereal such as wheat or oats is followed by one or two years pasture, after which paddy is grown for three or four years. In regions where clay predominates and drainage facilities are lacking, as in Bologna and Montana, paddy is grown but once in the rotation. It is now considered that the continuous cultivation of paddy reduces yield owing to defective soil aeration and consequent disturbance of the micro-biological balance of the soil. A further objection to continuous cropping is that it is said to result in an increase of malaria. The rotation in Italy provides for maize, hemp or beetroot in the first year, followed by wheat in the second year, pasture in the third year and paddy in the fourth year. Rotations of longer duration usually allow for two or three years in pasture, while an eight-year rotation may be: first year, wheat, rye or maize; second to fourth year, pasture; fifth year, wheat, rye or maize; followed by three annual crops of paddy.[649]

It has been observed that the advantages of a rotation of a grass ley with dry cereals is now widely accepted in principle and its extension to include paddy may hold out great possibilities as it may enable animal husbandry to be incorporated into a rice economy under tropical conditions. It is uncertain how far this is practical in un-regulated peasant agriculture, although controlled rotation of rice with sugar cane, pulses and dry grains on communally-owned peasant land has long been a feature of the system devised many years ago by the Dutch in Java, while in north Malaya cattle and buffaloes are pastured in rice-fields during the interval between two crops.

N

Rotation of paddy with other crops implies adequate control
of irrigation and drainage throughout the year. This control is
obtained in Spain, Italy and New South Wales, where rotation of
paddy with temporary pasture and dry-land crops is successfully
operated and the yields of paddy are high. Before 1877 the rice
yields in Italy were little if any higher than those in tropical countries. It was the influence of the Cavour Canal resulting in the
introduction of rotations that went far to increase paddy yields in
that region.

In arid regions, such as West Pakistan, the rotation decided upon
must necessarily depend on the quantity of water available and the
months in which irrigation facilities can be counted on. Obviously,
a rotation in an area provided with perennial irrigation may be more
comprehensive than is possible in regions depending upon seasonal
irrigation. In the former case it should be possible to ensure that
the land is almost continuously under a crop; in the latter instance
periods of fallow are inevitable.

The following rotational systems have been suggested as a useful
guide for conditions such as exist in West Pakistan.

Type of Soil	*Rotation*
Fertile; light textured, well drained land	Paddy—Grams—Paddy
Wet heavy soil	Paddy—Pulses—Paddy
Fertile land; medium texture	Paddy—Wheat—Paddy
Poor soil	Paddy—Wheat—Paddy —Grams—Paddy
Good soil; winter water available	Paddy—Fallow—Sugar- cane—Fallow—Paddy
Saline soil, or lack of water	Paddy—Fallow—Paddy.

The inadequate control of irrigation in most parts of the paddy
belt of Asia coupled, in many cases, with the very stiff clay soil, mili-
tate against the development of crop rotation. Where control of
water is possible and the soil is not too heavy, rotations are possible
and are sometimes practised. In the Jaffna District of Ceylon, for
instance, tobacco, chillies, green gram, gingelly, vegetables and sunn
hemp are rotated with paddy, the crops being irrigated from wells
situated in the fields. It would appear, therefore, that the development of rotations in Asia might be advantageous, but the system
is unlikely to make much headway in the absence of good water
control.

Experiments in Madras State[500] over a number of years proved
that cotton planted after paddy gave good yields without prejudice
to the subsequent paddy crop, provided the latter was given normal
fertilizing. The cultivation of cotton in paddy fallows, however, has
not made much progress.

Chapter IX

CULTIVATION OF DRY-LAND PADDY

ADVANTAGES OF DRY-LAND SYSTEM

DESPITE the fact that it is the oldest form of paddy cultivation, non-irrigated or "dry" paddy appears to have received less attention than it deserves both from cultivators and investigators.

The potential value of dry-land paddy cultivation does not depend on the fact that it is the original method of cultivation of the crop. Maybe man discovered that higher yields could be obtained under irrigation; far more likely he discovered that the crop could be obtained with more certainty and less expenditure of energy when grown in water. Possibly he realized that, whereas cultivating dry-land paddy necessitated heavy manuring or constantly shifting the cultivated area, involving much hard work in felling and clearing forest, "wet" paddy could be grown annually on the same land without manuring.

In modern times, dry-land paddy cultivation has been neglected, except in times of economic depression or failure of the irrigated crop, and it has been frowned on by responsible governments because of soil erosion danger resulting from "shifting" cultivation, with which dry-land paddy has been so closely connected. Dry-land paddy cultivation, however, need not be a shifting cultivation and the dangers of soil erosion may be guarded against. The investigator has usually ignored the possibilities of dry-land paddy in favour of the already established irrigated system. The possibilities of increasing the yield of dry-land paddy merits attention and in many countries a survey might usefully be made of land considered suitable for this form of cultivation. It may be argued that vast areas of swamp land await development for wet paddy; it is possible, however, that the cost of reclamation may be excessive, but that areas elsewhere may be suitable for development with dry paddy at a much lower cost.

Burkill[98] has rightly observed: "Though it is customary to speak of dry-land rices it must be remembered that they require a humid atmosphere and endure no desiccation. As a result of their demand for moisture, the area of the whole world in which dry-land cultivation is practised is limited. They demand an assured rainfall over three or four months, and this greatly limits their cultivation." He might have added that the dry crop requires a more fertile soil than irrigated paddy and the maintenance of fertility is difficult under tropical conditions.

Under modern methods of cultivation, irrigation water is the most expensive item in wet-paddy cultivation. One may visualize, however, the cultivation of dry-land paddy unrestricted by the vagaries of the weather on areas supplied with water under controlled irrigation. The amount of water required is much less than for wet paddy and irrigation would be required for a shorter period. Conservation of water for dry-land paddy cultivation would in many areas of low rainfall enable the crop to be grown profitably, whereas the water supply might prove inadequate or too costly for growing wet paddy.

PRIMITIVE METHODS OF CULTIVATION

In Burma, dry-land paddy is grown in the thickly wooded hills in regions having an annual rainfall of fifty inches or more. The area is felled and burnt in the dry season, and with the advent of rain is given a rough cultivation to work the ashes into the soil. On this the paddy is broadcast, either alone or with cotton. Little or no weeding is given to the growing crop. The paddy crop is harvested in September–October and the cotton picked from January to March. The area may produce a ratoon crop of cotton the following year, and is then abandoned to grow secondary jungle for a period of seven to ten years. The paddy crop is all consumed locally.[525]

A somewhat similar system obtains in Thailand and the Philippines where it is known as *Caingin*, and in Malaya under the name *Padi huma*, commonly grown by the aborigine tribes. In Malaya, maize (*Zea mays*) or Job's Tears (*Coix lacryma-jobi*) is frequently grown with the paddy. Paddy seed, either alone or with an admixture of maize or Job's Tears, is broadcast, or more usually dibbled in by the simple process of scraping a depression with a stick, dropping the seed in the depression, and covering it with soil by the foot. The initial crop is usually heavy—if birds and rodents have been kept from it—while each succeeding crop, and usually two or three annual crops are taken, is lighter.

It must be emphasized that this simplest form of cultivation entails the wanton destruction of forest, practically all the trees being felled and burnt. Necessarily, responsible governments look with disfavour on this destruction and have attempted to suppress it, for apart from the wastage of timber, the abandoned clearings frequently fail to revert to forest, but become poor grassland, often after serious erosion by reason of the torrential rains experienced in the tropics.

Under good conditions in Malaya, that is, the use of virgin land and comparative freedom from pests, a yield of 1,500 to 2,000 lb. per acre of paddy can be produced from the first crop, the two succeeding crops giving perhaps 1,200 and 800 lb. of paddy respectively.

The primitive methods described above should not be permitted in any future development of dry-land paddy cultivation.

JAPANESE METHODS

Dry-land paddy (usually the *indica* type) is well known in Japan, where the annual area under this form of cultivation is about 350,000 acres, or 5 per cent of the total area planted with paddy in that country. It is grown in rotation—barley, paddy, wheat, soya beans —mainly in the Kanto district and on volcanic soils in Kyushu. Elsewhere it may be grown on the same land for two or three years, after which, on account of diminished yields, the fields are planted with other crops. Frequently paddy is interplanted with wheat, barley or cotton. The paddy is usually drilled, in rows about twenty-two inches apart, and the inter-crop fertilized with dung, ammonium sulphate, soya bean cake, superphosphate and ashes. It is recommended that fertilizers should supply about 80 lb. nitrogen, 67 lb. phosphoric acid and 62 lb. potash per acre. After-cultivation consists mainly in cultivating and weeding two or three times, the plants being thinned to about four inches at the first cultivation, some of the seedlings removed being used to supply areas where the stand is unsatisfactory. Yields are about 60 per cent of wet paddy.

DRY PADDY IN KELANTAN

Both in the Philippines and Malaya, other systems of dry-land cultivation are customary, some of which are of only local interest. The State of Kelantan, on the north-east of the Malay Peninsula, provides an example of extensively-planted dry-land paddy, there being in that region about 45,000 acres under this system. The following account of a system known as *Padi Tugalan* is summarized from Craig's description.[142]

Dry-land paddy cultivation in Kelantan falls under two groups; that habitually planted with dry paddy, and that which can be used for either dry or irrigated paddy. The second group comprises but a small proportion, being in the lower-lying dry paddy-lands, the choice of wet or dry paddy depending, usually, on the inclination of the cultivator.

The soil throughout this dry-paddy area is markedly homogeneous and though occasional ridges of slightly sandy soil are found, a heavy clay predominates. Only twelve distinct varieties are cultivated, the maturation period of which varies from 173 to 197 days. The success of dry paddy depends on a favourable monsoon. Kelantan suffers from a markedly dry season which may extend from the middle of February to the end of May, but which varies from year to year in duration and severity. During this dry season the land becomes so baked that the local plough is barely able to penetrate the soil and the small local cattle, which have to live on the sparse grazing provided by the baked paddy-fields, are unable to drag the implement effectively. Ploughing commences at the end of June or early July when the land has been softened by rain, but has not dried out sufficiently to prevent puddling.

The land is ploughed to a depth of about two inches and harrowed in the subsequent dry weather. Should rain fall after ploughing, harrowing becomes necessary. These operations are repeated twice with appropriate intervals, in order to kill weeds and cultivate to a depth of about three and a half inches. Finally, the land is ploughed and harrowed a fourth time and the seed planted in rough lines by dibbling. Subsequent cultivation is confined to weeding at intervals by cutting down the grass with a short knife. Throughout these proceedings the utmost care is taken to avoid puddling or packing the soil unduly.[57]

For a successful crop the plants must become established and twelve to eighteen inches high before the land becomes waterlogged. If the dry season has been severe and protracted, cultivation retards planting, until by the time the crop is ready for weeding, rain is of daily occurrence and weeding is ineffectual.

This system demands a large amount of labour and care which all cultivators are not prepared to give, and which greatly exceeds the labour required for wet-paddy cultivation.

Another dry-land system practised in north-east and east Malaya is known as *Padi Taburan*. In this system the land is ploughed and harrowed and the seed then broadcast and harrowed in. No after-cultivation is done and the crop becomes choked by weeds. Craig[142] truly remarks that the system is exceedingly wasteful, for not only is the crop small, but the land is fallowed for one or two seasons after the removal of two annual crops.

PHILIPPINE SYSTEMS

In the Philippines[135] two dry-land systems are recognized, viz. upland or *secano* and *sabog* or broadcast. In the first-named system the land is ploughed and the seed either broadcast or sown in drills.

While crops by this method do not compare favourably with wet-paddy cultivation, pure-line selection from good varieties has yielded surprisingly good results.

Sabog cultivation is intermediate between upland and wet paddy. The land is bunded and graded and prepared as for transplanting, and the seed is then broadcast on the field. This practice is confined to a rather limited territory and is used only for a second crop where the supply of water for irrigation is or may be inadequate. The crops obtained by this method are smaller than by transplanting. Its advantages are some saving of time and labour, and the possibility of maturing a crop with less water than transplanted paddy. Of the four varieties most favoured, three are typical upland varieties but will also grow in wet conditions. All mature in about 125 days. Seed is sown at the rate of 200 lb. per acre.

The College of Agriculture in the Philippines recommend application of 2,4-D in conjunction with hoeing for the control of weeds. They also found that this herbicide should be used sparingly because it has an adverse effect on the yield of some paddy varieties.

DRY-LAND PADDY IN JAMAICA

In Jamaica,[385] a fairly large amount of dry-land paddy was sown during the 1914–18 war. Planting took place at the beginning of the rainy season and the crop was reaped six months later. Yields of about 1,800 lb. paddy per acre were recorded, with an average of about 1,000 to 1,400 lb. per acre. No account is given of the method of cultivation, from which it may be presumed that cultivation was reduced to a minimum. Hanson,[246] however, gives the following account of the method used by East Indian tenants on certain estates in Jamaica. A dry nursery was used. The land was ploughed and harrowed and seedlings transplanted in furrows, three feet apart and six inches deep, "hills" of seedlings being spaced six inches apart in the furrows. The plants were mounded when they started to grow. No record of yield is stated.

SOUTH AMERICA

Dry-land paddy cultivation has made considerable headway in South America. Brazil is the largest producer of dry paddy in the world, about 80 per cent, or 3 million acres of the total area under paddy in that country being cropped under this system. Efferson[190] states that the extension of dry-land paddy cultivation in Brazil has been brought about by high rice prices, causing this crop to replace cotton as a catch crop on many farms. He adds that additional areas are being cleared for cotton and coffee on which dry-land paddy is usually the initial crop. For this reason he concludes that dry-land paddy production will probably decrease.

Cultivation methods in Brazil are primitive: virgin forest is cut and burnt in the dry season and a paddy crop dibbled in with the advent of rain. Weeds are hoed during crop growth. Under these conditions it is not surprising to learn that yields are only half those obtained in the irrigated regions of Southern Brazil where cultivation is highly mechanized.

Venezuela has about 35,000 acres under paddy, most of which is dry-land. In many parts of the South American paddy areas, particularly in Colombia, climatic conditions make it possible to plant and harvest at any time of the year. Given adequate water, therefore, the extension of dry-land paddy in South America should be possible.

CULTIVATION ELSEWHERE

A system of dry-land paddy cultivation was investigated[232] some years ago in Malaya. Under this system, four successive crops are grown followed by fallowing for four to six years, during which period the land reverts to grassland or secondary jungle, or a mixture of both, and the fields then become grazing ground for buffaloes. The land is low-lying and situated on the banks of a river, the fields being liable to occasional flooding. As a preliminary to cultivation, the secondary jungle is felled and all stumps and wood removed or burnt. The land is ploughed to a depth of two or three inches with a wooden plough. Should the field have been newly opened after a period of fallow, an interval of about a month is allowed to elapse between the first and second ploughing to give the land time to "weather" and permit the grass thus turned in to rot. It is then cross-ploughed, and again ploughed in the same direction as the second ploughing. Finally, the land is harrowed once.

Seed paddy is steeped in water or in a weak solution of salt, only the seed that sinks being used for planting. While still wet, the seed is retained in a cool place for a day and night, and is then broadcast at the rate of about 60 lb. per acre and covered by a single ploughing or by raking. Should weeds subsequently become numerous the land is weeded with a short-handled hoe some six to eight weeks after planting. Yields of paddy are in some cases 1,800 lb. per acre. Normal yields are below this figure, owing largely to the use of inferior varieties of paddy. Under this system the land is not manured, so that crops rapidly diminish in yield with successive planting.

There is a considerable area of dry-land paddy production in Ceylon and a dry-farming research station has been established at

47. Self-propelled combine harvesting paddy, U.S.A.

48. Under-water cultivation, British Guiana

49. Extension wheel fitted to tractor, Malaya

50. D.4 "Drum" type roller, Malaya

51. A toothed harrow, bogey mounted, for the Trusty Tractor, Malaya

52. Double "Kedah" type roller, Malaya

53. The Howard Rotovator Gem pumping water from paddy field in preparatio[n] for cultivation, Thailand

54. The Howard Rotoho Gem, British Guiana

which paddy growing is being studied. The system is practised in Ceylon mainly on undulating land dependent on rainfall and underground seepage, where a light soil overlies rock. Under these conditions seepage zones are formed in which the soil is waterlogged during the rainy seasons. Paddy growing in these zones is a new development of much promise, although a number of problems remain to be solved, particularly the control of weeds.

Considerable areas of dry-land paddy are grown in Indonesia,[395] although the area is decreasing. In 1940 the planted area was about 800,000 acres, or about 10 per cent of the total area under paddy. Areas under this form of cultivation are, in fact, to be found in almost all countries in the East. An interesting account of primitive dry-land paddy cultivation together with the ceremonies, ritual and customs practised by the Iban of Sarawak has been published.[201] Ritualistic customs of this nature are common in many Asian countries.

Dry-land paddy is grown in Papua and New Guinea, despite the suitability of the country for extensive cultivation of irrigated paddy and also in the very extensive Japanese wartime flooded paddy culture areas in New Guinea and New Britain.[491]

Trials carried out in Fiji[558] have indicated that crop rotation and adequate cultivation are necessary to maintain weed control in dryland paddy production. The seed should be drilled as soon as possible after preparation of the land to give the crop a good start over the weeds. Horse-hoeing with a row spacing of 18 inches was considered better than the use of weedicides. The first hoeing should be done about five weeks after drilling, subsequent cultivation depending on weed growth. The following table shows the yield of paddy under different treatments.

TABLE 9

FIJI: YIELD OF PADDY WITH DRYLAND CULTIVATION
lb. per acre

Treatment	1958–59 Variety B.G. 75	1959–60 Variety Patarka	Average Yield
Control	2,500	1,962	2,231
Cultivation only	2,750	2,640	2,695
Spraying (MCPA) plus cultivation	2,692	2,301	2,496
Spraying (MCPA) only	2,395	2,086	2,240
M.S.D. 5 per cent	314	157	

Dry-land paddy has been grown for many years in the tropical regions of Africa. Irvine states[290] that a considerable quantity is produced in Northern Nigeria, where good crops are grown in open country of the savannah-forest type with rainfall between thirty and fifty inches a year. Mention is made of considerable areas under these conditions in Togoland and also on steep stony slopes of the hills in that country, where paddy forms the main food of the people throughout the year. It is also cultivated in Ghana and in parts of Sierra Leone. The methods of cultivation do not greatly differ from those in Asia, and here again it is noted that paddy is usually interplanted with other crops, such as maize, pumpkins, tomatoes, taro and cassava.

In Senegal,[371] under the direction of a semi-government company in conjunction with farmers, a crop rotation of green manure—groundnuts—dry-land paddy—groundnuts is maintained. Yields of paddy are about 1,100 lb. per acre. Selection and breeding are being pursued to obtain earlier and disease resistant varieties. Higher applications of fertilizers are expected to increase yields.

ROTATIONS

Discussing the potentialities of dry-land paddy, a F.A.O. publication summarizes information on rotations in Japan and Indonesia.[41] Experiments in Japan compared the cultivation of dry-land

TABLE 10
DRY-LAND ROTATIONS IN JAPAN

Type	First Year	Second Year	Third Year
Two-year rotation	Paddy—barley or wheat	Soya bean—barley	—
	Ditto	Sweet potato—wheat or barley	—
Three-year rotation	Rice—barley	Soya bean—barley or wheat	Taro—barley or wheat
	Rice—barley or wheat	Hercules' club—barley or wheat	Ditto
	Rice—wheat	Sweet potato—naked barley	Soya bean—millet—naked barley
	Rice—barley	Soya bean or red bean—millet—rape	Sweet potato—wheat

paddy under continuous cropping with a rotation of crops. Average yield per acre of paddy for seven years was 15·9 bushels where paddy was rotated with soyabeans and 12 bushels where paddy was grown every year.

In Japan it is customary to grow dry-land paddy every two, three or four years. Table 10 shows typical rotations in that country.

In Indonesia, the general rotation scheme for dry-land paddy is as follows:

First year: Wet season, paddy; dry season, fallow.

Second year: Wet season, various crops such as maize, manioc (tapioca), peanuts, legumes, vegetables. If soil fertility is reasonably good, another crop, such as cowpeas or other legumes, is sown before the dry season. If the soil is poor, no crop is grown in the second year.

VARIETIES

There are a large number of varieties of dry-land paddy, and many others that will grow under either dry or wet conditions. Hitherto, research work on these varieties has been neglected in favour of selection and breeding wet-land types. There is no doubt that had the same amount of attention been given to dry-land varieties, the results would have placed this method of cultivation in a more favourable position than it at present occupies. Research work on problems connected with dry-land paddy cultivation has been started at a few centres, including Formosa, Ceylon and the Philippines.

Pawar records[477] that local varieties in the Punjab have red kernels, are awned and shatter easily. A number of *japonicas* have been tested and two—Norin 18 and Asaki—proved successful. On one estate yields of around 8,000 lb. paddy were obtained when fertilized with 10 tons farmyard manure, plus 60 lb. nitrogen and 30 lb. phosphoric acid per acre.

PESTS

Dry-land paddy suffers from many of the diseases and pests that affect wet-land paddy. According to Tsutsui,[669] the main injurious insects are paddy borers, army worms and rice bugs. Larvae of the seed corn maggot, *Hylemyia platura* Meigen consume newly sown seed and the mole cricket, *Gryllotalpa africana* Palisot de Beauvois, attacks seedlings and roots of established plants. The dry-land rice root aphid, *Rhophalosiphum prunifoliae* Fitch, the ribes root aphid, *Tetraneura ulmi* Linné and the Japanese dogwood aphid, *Anoecia corni* Fab., swarm over the roots of young seedlings, retarding their growth. Excellent control is obtained by the application of aldrin or heptachlor dust mixed in the soil.

Army worms cause much damage to dry-land paddy crops in Venezuela[92] unless control measures are taken immediately the presence of the pest is discovered. The use of insecticides, combined with pre-emergent weed killers or alone at the first appearance of the pest, provide good control.

Chapter X

MECHANIZED CULTIVATION

OBJECTIVES

FARM mechanization owes its inception to growing labour difficulties and steadily increasing wage rates. The use of machinery has raised output per man and in some cases per unit of area and has been achieved mainly by combining several operations in one machine, thus enabling one man to control both tractor and implement.[250] While manpower difficulties do not arise in many regions of paddy production, in some areas of sparse population, development of extensive areas under the crop must depend to a great extent on mechanization. At the present time manpower requirements for the crop vary enormously—from two days per acre for well-mechanized areas in the United States to 400 men-hours in some small holdings in Asia.[110] The urgent need to increase world rice production at the end of the second world war directed renewed attention to the possibility of rapidly extending the area under the crop by mechanizing the various field operations.

Mechanized paddy production is not a new venture; it has been in existence in the United States for many years, it is practised in Australia, while isolated examples of large-scale production have proved successful in Asia, for instance in Thailand as well as in Indo-China. These adventures are or were concerned with large-scale production; post-war conception was for both large- and small-scale production. In fact, it would appear that in the enthusiasm to solve agronomic problems in connection with mechanization there was much uncertainty regarding the ultimate goal of the investigations and failure to relate it to the individual requirements of a locality, to the nature of its soil, water supply, land tenure system, economic conditions of the inhabitants, density of population, social and religious customs of the people.

Some of these difficulties have been discussed by Vaugh Mason,[681] who points out that mechanization has three objectives, viz. increase in production, reduction in cost of production and reduction of human drudgery. Increase in production, he states, may be sharply differentiated into two phases—increase in production per worker and increase in production per acre. In many cases very large

173

increases per worker may be achieved by accepting methods which involve cultivating large areas at a reduced yield per acre; in other cases very large increases per acre may be secured by methods which result in less production per worker, that is, by expenditure of much more labour on each cultivated acre.

While considerable progress has been made to solve the physical problems related to mechanization of paddy cultivation, perhaps insufficient attention has been directed to the adaptation of mechanization to the particular needs of the smallholder. The matter is of great importance because the great bulk of production is and will remain in the hands of small producers, while the land available for large-scale production is limited and in very many cases the capital cost of development prohibitive.

One of the problems in many Asian countries is to maintain paddy production in face of less laborious means of gaining a livelihood. Paddy growing is indeed arduous and generally not particularly remunerative; not the least of the advantages of mechanization is to lighten the work of the cultivator, thus making it a more attractive pursuit. Difficulties in mechanizing field operations on small holdings are numerous, but are not insuperable. If the large amount of money being spent on investigations is to be justified, machines and techniques suitable for small-scale production must be forthcoming in addition to more ambitious machines for large-scale farming.

SOILS IN RELATION TO MECHANIZATION

Paddy is cultivated on three main types of soil, viz. clays in which a firm bottom is found within a few inches of the surface; silts and clays which are very soft and have no firm bottom although they become hard when dry; peats, "mucks" and peaty soils some of which may be used for paddy cultivation provided that the depth of peat is not excessive. They have no firm bottom and therefore are difficult to cultivate with standard machinery.

Machinery must be supported either by penetration, in which tractor wheels gain adhesion on the hard bottom, or flotation in which the wheels are kept near the surface by using tracks, wide wheels, large diameter wheels or floats in order to distribute the weight of the machine over as great an area as possible.

Where land can be cultivated during the dry season and flooded in the wet season, or where a firm bottom or pan provided by heavy clay soil exists and water control is good, the machines and system of cultivation for paddy differ but little from those employed in cultivating a dry-land cereal such as wheat, although the technique must be adjusted to conditions arising from imperfect water control.

Soils of this description are found in the paddy areas of the United States, the Guianas, Australia, and parts of Europe and Africa. It is in these countries, therefore, that paddy cultivation is so highly mechanized.

A great deal of paddy-land in Asia is in deltas, coastal strips and along the banks of rivers; much of it is swamp and consists of clay silts, silts and silty sands—providing a deep "mud" in which machine wheels cannot find adhesion, so that the flotation method appears to be the only one for heavy implements. The peats vary greatly, but usually have a surface mat of organic matter which, if unbroken, can bear a considerable weight. Bates[71] adds that in such circumstances the best tractive effort is likely to be obtained by using very long crawler tracks laid evenly over the peat surface. He continues:

> There are, however, four big problems connected with peat cultivation: (1) once the surface skin of a virgin peat bog has been broken by implements behind the tractor it may be unable to support any more equipment until either it has drained or it has had time to regenerate a skin; (2) many of the tropical peat soils do not have a satisfactory skin; (3) it may be found that after a year or two of cultivation the peat soil becomes toxic to plant growth and satisfactory yields can be obtained only by excavating the peat and cultivating the subsoil; and (4) peat swamps are frequently endowed with submerged timbers and soft spots, both of which are serious hazards to mechanical cultivation.

It is, in fact, extremely unlikely that surface "skin" on peat land can be relied upon to provide the constant conditions of firmness that are essential for successful use of machines. The depth of peat in most cases precludes the possibility of its complete removal to allow cultivation of the subsoil, while submerged timbers, which with drainage and cultivation come to the surface, are a continual menace to machines. It is very doubtful, therefore, whether deep peats are, or ever will be, suitable for mechanized paddy cultivation.

It is obvious that no one standard set of implements is adequate to contend with the varying types of soil on which paddy is grown. It therefore becomes necessary to devise new or adapt existing machines to the conditions of each type of soil. Further, implements suitable for service on a large development scheme will probably be unsuitable for use by owners of small areas. Perhaps the most important point of all: successful mechanization demands efficient control of an adequate supply of irrigation water and comparatively level land.

CULTIVATION ON HARD CLAYS

Clay soils which have a firm pan within a few inches of the surface provide the ideal condition for completely mechanized paddy cultivation. Such conditions obtain in a number of countries, in the United States, the Guianas, Australia and parts of Asia and southern Europe. Paddy had been grown in Louisiana for many years by primitive methods until about 1885, when farmers from the wheat-growing areas settled and adopted their methods of wheat culture to the cultivation of paddy. The success of this venture resulted in the development of the industry in other States where land was found to be equally suitable for the crop. Thus, in the United States paddy cultivation follows closely the methods used for other cereals.

Somewhat similar conditions are found in the coastal areas of British Guiana, where however, tillage operations are dissimilar to those in the United States because water control is less perfect. In the neighbouring Dutch territory of Surinam mechanized cultivation is being developed under somewhat similar conditions, but here the soil is a "difficult" clay over about a foot of organic matter known as *pegasse*. On the Murrumbidgee Irrigation Area in New South Wales mechanized methods have been successfully practised for some years on a medium-heavy clay overlying a stiff clay subsoil. The rice production scheme in Northern Australia is on shallow, hard and intractable soil. Mechanization methods are also associated with paddy cultivation in some parts of South America and in southern Europe.

MODIFICATIONS OF TRACKS AND WHEELS

Flotation methods are essential when using machinery on swamps and bottomless soils. Considerable attention has been given to tractor stability in Malaya. Allen and Haynes[13] have succinctly stated Malayan experience as follows:

> On bottomless mineral soils, track layers with wide plates or swamp blocks are successful but wide wheels are less satisfactory.
>
> Where there is a hard pan near the soil surface standard wheels are good, especially with wheel strakes. Pneumatic tyres are also successful, but there is great variation in the tread pattern of different makes and careful selection is necessary. Wide drum or lattice wheels are not normally used since they make ploughing difficult. However, narrow-rimmed, large-diameter wheels are very effective under certain conditions, but the performance of oversized tyres with rice treads has been disappointing. Bombardier half-tracks are of outstanding value under bad conditions; they may permit work to extend both earlier and later in the season and so increase tractor utilization. Under all conditions mounted implements are favoured, especially on small plots.

Elsewhere the same workers report improved performance with standard wheeled tractors fitted with larger diameter rear wheels or by using outsize "rice" tyres on standard size wheels. They also found Darvill wheel strakes a valuable aid to traction, especially as they can be brought into operation very easily and do not have to be removed for road travel.

Mayne[382] states that a new commercial development has been described which gives stability and flotation by cage extensions to the standard pneumatic tyre equipment. The extensions are about twelve inches wide and slightly less in diameter than the tyres so that road travelling is not affected. The tractor can be fitted with a hydraulic depth-controlled mounted disc harrow and levelling board combination. Reports received from India have justified production of a large consignment of this equipment.

CULTIVATION OF "BOTTOMLESS" LAND*

Despite the realization that development of bottomless land must make use of the flotation method, little progress has been made in devising suitable wheels or tracks to render this possible. The matter is important since most of the best land suitable for cultivation by penetration is already under cultivation and future developments may have to depend almost entirely on the reclamation of swamps, silts, silty soils, and peat lands into which almost any kind of wheel or track sinks. Attention has been drawn to certain sugar estates in British Guiana where cable-operated equipment is used, powered from two barges on irrigation canals, and to Bologna, Italy, where cable traction is operated from bunds for paddy cultivation.

The Brunei Government were interested in introducing methods of cultivation which would make better use of the extensive areas of soft "muck" soils which were either giving very low paddy yields or were unproductive. This deep muck soil overlying soft clay, or a soft clay with no accessible underpan or hard sub-soil, consists chiefly of decayed vegetation but is much less matured than a true peat soil. It is usually badly drained and remains waterlogged in many places throughout the year.

Muck soil has a very low bearing capacity when wet and will not support more than $1\frac{1}{2}$ lb. per square inch. When flooded and puddled it will not support more than 1 lb. per square inch; even the

---

* The following information is drawn from a confidential report, the property of the Brunei Government. This brief abstract is published by kind permission of the Brunei Government and of Messrs Sir Bruce White, Wolfe Barry and Partners, Consulting Engineers, London. Mr L. Carpenter was the resident agricultural engineer. He carried out all the tests and was responsible for incorporating a number of modifications to the implements.

soft clays will not carry 3 lb. when wet. A man has a ground pressure of about 5 lb. per square inch, when his weight is on one foot so that, when walking on this land, he sinks in at each step at least up to his knees.

It was proposed to position powered winches on the field boundaries with cables as the source of motive power for traversing the implements across the fields. Cable traction has been used in the past only for ploughs; it was now intended to apply it to all the field implements and, as the soil was too soft to use wheels and tracks, they were to be carried on sledges.

Tractors and Winches. The two tractors to carry the power-driven wire rope winches for cable traction were the Fordson County Major and the Platypus Bogmaster. The former was a standard 40·5 b.h.p. diesel engine, full track model with extended tracks. A Broughton standard model rope was mounted on one side of the tractor and a hydraulically-operated lifting boom with a cargo hook on the other. The tractor had a fully hydraulic system worked by the standard tractor pump.

The Platypus Bogmaster tractor was a standard model with a 34 b.h.p. Perkins P and diesel engine and tracks extended. A 2-speed power-driven winch for ½-inch diameter flexible steel wire rope was mounted between the track runs on one side and a hydraulically operated lifting boom with a rope sheave at the head on the other side.

Sledges and Steering. Designing suitable sledges to carry mounted implements presented many difficulties. Eventually they were built of 2-inch mild steel angle covered with one-sixteenth-inch mild steel plate which would carry the necessary machinery as well as the mounted implement hanging clear of the rear. To give better lateral stability and greater buoyancy, two feet wide extensions were built on each side of the original frame, covered with plate and sealed to form flotation tanks and to increase the ground bearing area; and two long-stroke hydraulic rams were set up on the top of and along the outer edge at the front of the extensions for steering control.

It was necessary to devise positive steering control on the pontoon, otherwise it yawed and, if deflected in its course, there was no means of getting it back in line. This difficulty was solved by providing a triangular hitch of wire rope, so that one member was adjusted for length and the other fixed as shown diagrammatically on page 179, where AB is the adjustable length and BC fixed or equal to the length of the sledge. Altering the length of AB varies the angle between the longitudinal axis of the sledge and the direction of pull,

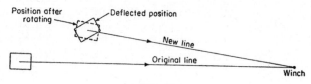

Fig. 11

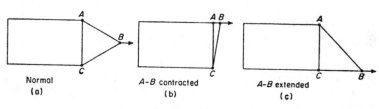

Fig. 12

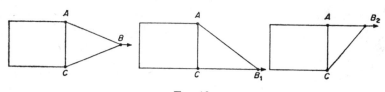

Fig. 13

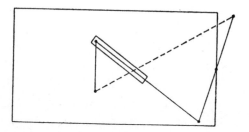

Fig. 14

Figs. 11–14. Explanation of sled steering

so steering the sledge. The length of AB is controlled by a hydraulic ram pulling on a hitch made up from wire rope or galvanized chain. A later type of hitch, used on the harvester with success, incorporated a long-stroke, power contracting ram for AB and a rigid bar for BC. A, B and C were all pin joints. BC was increased in length and AB allowed to contract to only half of its fully-extended length: Fig. 13 on page 179 in which $AB_2 = \frac{1}{2}AB_1$ shows this.

Earth Levelling. A frame was made of three-inch mild steel angle and covered with three-sixteenth mild steel plates to form a scoop eight feet in diameter, and four feet wide. Galvanized chains and shackles were used to make the operating hitches. The scoop worked well but would have been more effective if the scoop had been twice as wide.

Roller Cultivation. Cultivation by roller proved impracticable because it did not control weed growth effectively. Furthermore, the heavy rollers sank in places too deeply, causing the surface soil to be so displaced that, on subsequent runs, it was difficult to pull the roller on an adjacent line without its slipping into an old run or leaving a high ridge between it and the new run.

Ploughing. Ploughs included the Ferguson single-furrow mould-board 16-inch semi-digger; the double-furrow mouldboard 12-inch general purpose—both with disc coulters—and a double-furrow disc plough; an Australian-made Buncle, mounted, one-way, turn-over, double-furrow disc plough and a Fordson mounted, single gang, heavy duty, disc harrow with eight large diameter cut-away discs.

The Ferguson heavy duty disc harrow proved to be a good implement both for primary cultivation of virgin land and for puddling before planting. Two passes were the minimum required for preliminary cultivation of weed-covered land, while a third pass gave a more satisfactory finish. On muck soils with surface water which had been cultivated with the Ferguson heavy disc harrow, a 12-feet wide harrow was successfully used.

It was possible to plough satisfactorily with a standard mounted turnover plough fitted on a three-point linkage set up on the rear of a narrow pontoon sledge. It took $5\frac{1}{2}$ hours to plough an acre with a two-furrow plough, but a four-furrow plough could have been used.

Puddling. Puddling was quickly and effectively carried out on previously ploughed muck or clay soil under water, using a 12-feet wide single gang harrow mounted on the three-point linkage fitted on the rear of a wide pontoon sledge which had "built in" flotation tanks. It is possible that a 12-feet wide "Kedah" type roller might be used to perform this operation in the same time and at a saving in labour.

Rotary Cultivation. A Rotovator was successfully fitted to the rear of the County tractor with the hydraulic ram, which operated the side-mounted lifting boom on the tractor, removed from there and fitted to work the raising and lowering of the Rotovator. The machine successfully cultivated the dry clay and peaty clay areas. The implement was very satisfactory for primary cultivation on clay soil, but on muck soils it broke down what little soil structure there was and produced such a fine tilth that when water was added the soil became a liquid slurry. This bad effect was still clearly evident 18 months later. Rotary cultivation should not, therefore, be attempted on muck soils.

Planting. Broadcasting seed presented no difficulties, but was not advisable because of subsequent competition between the newly-emerged seedlings and weeds. Transplanting with the ILCMA transplanter was not successful because it is impossible to bring muck soil to the correct condition for this operation.

Weeding. A small sledge was made of three pontoons designed to pass between the rows of plants. The implement worked correctly, but it caused so much disturbance that the plants were no longer in straight lines after its passage and therefore the implement could not be used a second time.

Harvesting. The harvester thresher unit was made by M. B. Wild and Co. It was mounted on a turntable carried on a pontoon sledge, the thresher being placed to one side so that the centre of the rotor was 20 inches to the right of the centre line of the pontoon sledge and turntable when facing in the direction of travel. This positioning solved the difficulty of laying out slack cable, but it necessitated extending the pontoon by 12 inches on each side and also extending the engine mounting to enable the weight of the engine to make better balance with the thresher. Various other modifications were found necessary to improve the performance of the unit and further improvements are possible. It was proved that a combine harvester could be operated successfully on sledges and was capable of producing a good sample of paddy.

Many possible improvements became evident in the progress of this investigation. For instance, a capstan type winch would solve all problems found in the direct drum spooling type of winch which was used, and hydraulic accumulators for powering the hydraulic controls on the pontoon sledges carrying implements would eliminate the need for a small engine driven by hydraulic pump to give power for sledge control. However, the main difficulties in mechanizing paddy production on this type of soil have been solved, and it has been proved that cable-operated equipment carried on sledges enable "bottomless" soil to be cultivated mechanically for paddy.

MECHANIZED TRANSPLANTING

Hand transplanting is a slow process, consuming more labour than any other operation in paddy planting (see page 454). The agronomic advantage to be derived from transplanting, however, at least under Asian conditions, is so well established that mechanization of this operation merits close attention by agricultural engineers.

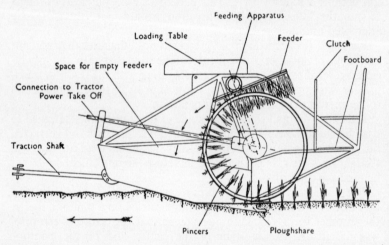

FIG. 15

Sectional drawing of ILCMA rice transplanter

Italy and China are the only countries that have sustained effort to produce a satisfactory machine for the purpose. It is stated that machines have been under development and test in Italy for fifty years. The fact that competitions for newly-invented transplanters are held in Italy shows that there is room for improvement in these machines. This is not to say that certain of the present machines are inadequate; their effective performance, however, depends on producing the correct texture of the muddy surface on which to plant. One machine which has been successfully developed and is in commercial production is the ILCMA transplanter.

Preparatory to using the ILCMA transplanter in the Po Valley of Italy, the soil is ploughed and all stubble and straw from the previous crop completely turned under to avoid clogging the ridgers underneath the transplanter. Immediately after ploughing the field is flooded and the soil well puddled and carefully levelled. The soil is ready for transplanting when there is a layer of puddled mud at least 10 cm. deep, perfectly levelled and without a trace of trash. The mud must not be watery and large puddles should be avoided, otherwise the wave caused by the movement of the transplanter may uproot or bury the newly-planted seedlings. As mechanized transplanting is done without water on the field, it is important to complete transplanting and to flood the field before the first plants put in die for lack of water. Another point for consideration is that with too large a field the mud may be perfectly suited to transplanting in the morning, while in the afternoon of a hot day it may become too dry. In the north of Italy, a field of about five to eight acres is dealt with by a transplanter without difficulty.

The ILCMA transplanter (type TR52) has been developed for power take off for which purpose a Ferguson tractor is considered suitable. Crawler tractors, or tractors with large wheels are unsuitable as they make deep ruts in the mud, spoiling the surface for planting. The best results are obtained with tractors of about 1½ tons in weight equipped with steel wheels having a width of 65 mm. and provided with spikes. If there is a hard pan a few inches below the surface, the wheels of the machine sink down to this while the belly of the machine lies on the surface. If the pan is non-existent the wheels are removed and the machine is towed like a pontoon over the surface of the mud. Removable pneumatic wheels are provided for transport to and from the site.

Seedlings from the nursery are arranged in magazines which are fed into the transplanter by two operators. Each operator feeds three rows and also makes minor adjustments to the machine by means of conveniently located levers. When the magazine is fed into the machine, the seedlings are gripped between the internal surfaces of revolving pincers which pull the seedlings from the magazine, take them down into the soil and leave them planted in the furrow. The number of plants in a given surface is governed by the speed of the tractor and power take off and the number of seedlings contained in the magazine. It is possible to regulate the density of plants by various adjustments. Spacing of rows is fixed by the dimensions of the selector units located at the top of the machine. The operation of planting absorbs 2 to 3 h.p.

In connection with mechanized transplanting, the question has been raised whether plants would suffer if deprived of their roots in the process of transplanting. In a trial, roots of plants 60 days old and 40 cm. high, were removed before transplanting. Although new roots formed rapidly these plants yielded 17 per cent less grain, 13 per cent less straw and tillered 15 per cent less than plants not deprived of their roots.[29]

China has been active in experimenting with new designs of transplanting machines suitable for use on small paddy areas. It is reported[32] that the first transplanter was made at the East China Agricultural Research Institute at Nanking in 1956. Since then improvements have been effected and in 1959 seven models were selected as suitable for extensive use. Five are hand-operated, one is drawn by an animal and one either by animal or tractor. Another type under trial is cable-drawn. Even the simplest is said to work three times faster than by hand transplanting. The simplest machine is made chiefly of wood and bamboo. It consists of a box containing the seedlings set in a smooth base which glides on the muddy surface of the field; a pincer grasps and plants along seven rows with every step taken by the operator and can plant about half an acre in ten hours. It is understood that a number of Chinese transplanters are being tested in Ceylon. The opinion has been expressed that operating the transplanter requires considerable skill. This opinion may, however, be somewhat premature for skill in its use may require practice (see Appendix VII).

CULTIVATION METHODS IN THE UNITED STATES*

Bunding. Contours are determined by a competent surveyor and the various points on the contour line marked by a plough, the ploughed furrow indicating the base of the bund, known as a levee. A tractor drawing ten or twelve furrows then makes a round, back-furrowing to the furrow made by the team. Loose soil is thus drawn to the centre to provide material for building the bund. A disadvantage of this system of bund construction is that the richer top soil is removed for bund construction. Outside bunds which are to serve as one bank of the supply or drainage ditch are often built by a Fresno scraper, while the interior or field bunds are usually made with a home-made checker drawn by one or two tractors. Bunds on small fields may be built with a ditcher or V-crowder.

The checker is made in various sizes. Runners for the sides are usually made of 3-inch by 12-inch plank 16 to 24 feet long and are lined with steel. The front end is 10 to 18 feet wide and the rear end 3 to 6 feet wide on the bottom. The sides are 2 to 3 feet high and are set on a slant of $\frac{1}{4}$ to 1, the tops sloping outward. The checker

* Largely drawn from the following publications of the U.S.A. Department of Agriculture: *Rice*, Misc. Pub. No. 615; *Rice Culture in the Southern States*, Farmers' Bul. No. 1808; *How to Grow Rice in the Sacramento Valley*, Farmers' Bul. No. 1240; together with information supplied by the U.S.A. Department of Agriculture by correspondence.

is pulled with the wide end forward, the loose surface soil being drawn through the small end. This makes a bund of twelve to twenty-four inches high and four to six feet at the base. The implement is usually equipped with a device for raising and lowering the rear end, enabling the operator to lift it from bund to bund and to control the size of bund. It can construct ten to fifteen miles of bund a day. Newly constructed bunds must be made twice as high as required to allow for settling. Outside bunds are made higher than field bunds and must be well constructed to avoid seepage and loss by overflowing.

Field bunds are made with gently sloping sides and high enough to hold a depth of about six inches of water. Machinery can pass over the bunds without damage to machinery or bund. The bunds are sown with paddy at the same time as the field and often produce a good crop. Well-constructed bunds with gently-sloping sides therefore reduce operational costs and, being planted with paddy, occasion less trouble with weeds. Preparation and repair of bunds is usually done in the winter so that they have time to settle before irrigation begins.

Preparation of the Land. In Louisiana and Texas the land is ploughed in the autumn and cultivated in the spring; in Arkansas and California ploughing, harrowing and preparation for sowing are usually done just before seeding time in the spring. The aim is to plough as soon after harvest as local circumstances permit and to leave the land in this condition for as long as possible to permit frost, rain and sun to break down the land, thus enabling a good seed bed to be prepared with the minimum of cultivation. The choice between mouldboard and disc ploughs depends on the nature of the soil; the former are preferred for a hard, dry soil. The land is sometimes flooded before discing to break down clods and fill holes. To prepare the seed bed, which should be slightly rough because a finely pulverized seed bed has a tendency to run together and remain cold and unfavourable for germination, the land is disc-harrowed and harrowed, the amount of harrowing depending on drainage and soil condition. Heavy soils, when spring-ploughed, usually require more subsequent tillage to obtain a good seed bed than when ploughed in the winter, but light soils are prepared easily after either winter or spring ploughing. The final condition of the land for broadcast paddy should be such that there is no danger of seed being buried by breaking clods. The bed should, therefore, be fine unless the seed is to be broadcast in water; in the latter case the water will break down the clods. Winter ploughing is often followed by a light spring ploughing to kill all weeds before the paddy is planted.

Levelling.[573] Land levelling preparatory for irrigation is done with great care. The object is to remove the slightest differences in level which might have resulted from ploughing or cultivation, or may exist naturally. The ordinary scraper pulled by a caterpillar tractor may be used on very uneven land. Subsequently, a land plane is used, consisting of a Fresno-type scraper, one edge of which is in contact with the ground. This drum is fixed at the middle of a long frame some fifty feet long, supported at the four corners by wheels. When working, the cutting edge of the scraper is level and "planes" off high spots in the soil. Surplus earth accumulates in (and in front of) the scraper and is deposited in low places. Variations in level of the soil over which the wheels of this implement have to pass cause only slight changes in the position of the scraper, because of the length of the frame. Levelling is finished off with a sort of sledge called a float. It consists of a frame $3\frac{1}{2}$ yards wide and 7 to $9\frac{1}{2}$ yards long. The sides of the frame rest on the ground like sledge runners and are joined by two or three horizontal "beams" or scraper bars.

Recent experiments[196, 351] have shown that levelling under water results in the elimination of many levees and makes for easier working. The danger, however, is that this operation will break down soil structure, which in a rotational system should be avoided.

Bunding. Bunds or levees are necessary in paddy cultivation to maintain a uniform depth of water over the field. Hitherto, they have been made of soil. The major disadvantages of earth levees are that they are a constant source of weed infestation, occupy much space, interfere with cultivation and harvest operations, and harbour pests and diseases.

The possibilities of using plastic levees, first explored in 1958 and still in the experimental stage, has much to recommend it, for it overcomes most of the disadvantages of earth levees.

The plastic levee consists of a film of plastic fastened to stakes following the contour, the top of the plastic being about 14 inches above soil level. An apron about a foot long extends underground to anchor the levee so that water does not flow underneath. It is considered that, despite the rather high cost of plastic, an appreciable saving in costs may result from their use.[200, 360]

The method of laying plastic levee has been described in *The Rice Journal*, October 1961, as follows:

First a furrow of uniform depth with smooth, clod-free bottom was made, 6 inches deep and 6 inches base width. Then, $1 \times 2 \times 30$ inch Douglas fir stakes with rounded corners were driven into the downward edge of the furrow with 14 inches above grade. Two-foot-wide black polyethylene film was unrolled along the furrow, positioned and pulled tight, and fastened at the top of the stake. The fastener was a 3-inch piece of lath or garden label held with two nails or two staples, respectively. A 4-inch apron spread flat in the furrow was anchored with a shovelful of soil every 5 feet. The furrow was then back-filled using two blades which form a V and move soil right up to the plastic simultaneously on both sides. The backfill was raised 5 to 9 inches above grade to allow for settling and to give additional support to the plastic between stakes.

Sowing. A feature of paddy cultivation in the United States, especially in California, is sowing seed by aeroplane, by which method about 400 acres per day may be sown as compared with 15 to 40 acres by seeders or drills, the cost of seeding by air being no greater per acre than by other methods, provided that large areas are to be seeded. More recently, aerial seeding and fertilizing have been combined. Nelson[430] states that even distribution of seed and granular fertilizer can be obtained, but adds that the characteristic deposit patterns should be studied before the initial use of new or modified distributors. From the deposit patterns optimum flagging intervals can be determined that will allow a sufficient overlap to maintain a uniform application rate.

The system of broadcasting seed in water was first attempted in 1930 with the object of controlling weed growth. So successful did this prove to be that the system became generally accepted, until today about 90 per cent of the acreage under paddy in California is planted by this method. The operation is described[310] as follows:

A hopper that will hold about 600 lb. of seed rice or enough to sow five or six acres is built in the plane in front of and below the pilot's seat. The bottom of the hopper slants downward to an adjustable opening which runs out on to a sloping baffleboard, where it is caught by the draught from the airplane propeller and scattered over the field. The seed is sown quite evenly over the strip thirty to fifty feet wide for each trip of the plane across the field. To obtain uniform coverage and to prevent overlapping of the seeded area or missing some of the land, the pilot is guided by a flagman at each end of the field and by one in the middle if the field is large.

Broadcasting, whether by airplane or other method, is almost always on land submerged to a depth of two or three inches. It is claimed that sowing paddy on water not only protects the seed from birds, but entails less labour in seed bed preparation because the water breaks down the clods. Furthermore, it reduces trouble from growth of early and mid-season types of water grass. Less seed is required when paddy is sown in water than if sown on the soil surface, while the possibilities of getting good stands of paddy are better from seedlings in water than from seeding on the soil surface.

As an alternative to seeding by aeroplane, sowing with a grain drill or broadcasting with an end-gate seeder is practised. Broadcasting in water is usual on old paddy land but on new land, or on land that is known to be free of water grass, seed may be drilled before the land is flooded. If broadcast, the land should not be subsequently harrowed, for seed on land to be continuously submerged should never be covered with soil.

The broadcast sower consists of a small hopper under which are one or two horizontal discs fitted with ribs. A chain worked from the back axle makes the horizontal discs rotate at great speed, causing paddy to be thrown over a width of about fifty feet. About 100 acres can be sown in a day.

Seeding rate depends on a number of factors: variety of paddy, quality of seed, soil fertility, condition of seed bed, method of irrigation, date and method of planting, drainage and whether the land is new or old. The seeding rate may thus vary from 90 to 160 lb. per acre. It is held that the rate of seeding should be sufficient to produce stands that are dense enough to check weed growth and prevent excessive tillering, which might result in irregular ripening and reduced yields of inferior quality.[311] This effort to prevent or limit tillering will appear revolutionary to those accustomed to the transplanting method, but it is the fundamental difference between the two systems.

Depth of seeding depends on the character of the soil, condition of the seed bed and on drainage. Paddy can be sown deeper on a light warm soil than on a heavy cold one; on a poorly prepared seed bed the seed must be sown shallower than on a well-prepared one, while seed should be lightly covered on land that cannot be adequately drained. Paddy will germinate through water, or through soil, but not through both. Nore and Theoan found[440] that paddy is adversely affected by covering the seed with soil, by stagnant water (as opposed to running water) and by the application of ammonium sulphate immediately before sowing. These effects are associated with restricted aeration and/or accumulation of toxic gases in the soil.

Irrigation and Drainage. The subject of irrigation and drainage is treated in greater detail in another chapter; suffice here to record, in outline, the manipulation of water considered necessary under the American system of cultivation.

On heavy soils in California, irrigation practice appears to vary somewhat from that employed elsewhere in the United States. In California the land is frequently irrigated and drained to germinate the seed. This is continued for about thirty days, when the land is irrigated once a week or ten days until the paddy is submerged. At the last irrigation preceding submergence, the water is drained off slowly. The land remains submerged for 90 to 140 days. Elsewhere in the United States, when seedlings reach a height of about six to eight inches, the land is submerged to a depth of one to two inches; as the plants grow, the depth of water is gradually increased until it is held at about five inches.

Fields must be drained and dried before harvest to permit the use of heavy machinery. As a rule, heavy soils dry slowly, but their surface soon becomes baked and hard. Light soils should therefore be drained earlier than heavier soils because on such soils more time is required to form a crust to support machinery. Water is usually held on the land until the heads turn down and begin to show early signs of ripening. This is usually about two weeks before maturity. If drainage is too early the yield is reduced and some kernels are immature; if too long delayed there will be a loss of crop due to overripeness, resulting in shattering during harvest and possible loss of quality caused by sun-cracking. No water should be allowed to enter fields for about a week before final drainage. In this way, the water will be gradually lowered and lodging obviated.

Harvesting. The crop is harvested either with a combine or binder-thresher. With the combine harvester-thresher the paddy may be cut with swathers and the swaths allowed to dry in the windrows for three or four days; a combine with a pick-up attachment is then used to thresh the paddy. The crop may, however, be combined direct. Swathing part of a crop may enable a combine to do more in a season by cutting a standing crop whenever possible and picking up swaths when the standing crop is too damp. If paddy is left until it is thoroughly ripe and dry before combining, the straw will be brittle and break, while the grain will be liable to shatter. It is thought that very dry rice grains may be liable to internal damage during mechanical threshing, the effects not becoming evident until milling is in progress. Stiff, short-strawed, non-shattering varieties of paddy are being developed to obviate such damage. Investigations in several of the States[611] indicate that when the crop is harvested at the stage of maturity at which the grain contains 23–28 per cent moisture, good yields of high-milling quality and a high percentage germination will be produced.

When the combine-harvester is used, it is essential that driers be employed to reduce the moisture content of the grain to about 14 per cent, so that there is no deterioration during storage before milling. Harvesting by the combine-harvester has been more cautiously adopted in the southern States than in California because of the difficulty in pulling the machines across bunds and low wet spots. Power for running the cutting and threshing units is supplied by a petrol or diesel engine mounted on the frame of the combine. A self-propelled combine is also powered by a petrol or a diesel engine which supplies power both for propelling the machine and operating the threshing unit. Some combines are equipped with dual engines, one for propelling the combine and one for operating the cutting and threshing mechanism. The self-propelled reaper-thresher is becoming more general in paddy harvesting.

As an alternative to the combine-harvester, the crop is reaped by the reaper-binder. The grain is cut with the grain binder and promptly shocked in such a manner that the grain is protected as far as possible from sun and rain. Careless shocking results in more breakage in milling. In the southern States a shock consists of about ten bundles and is capped with a bundle placed upright on the top with the heads downwards and in contact with the heads of the bundles in the shock. The straw of the capping bundle is then pulled down and spread evenly so that it covers and protects the heads of the cap bundle and underlying bundles. After about ten days in the shocks the grain is considered cured and the milling quality of the paddy thereby improved. There are five types of binder: (i) the conventional trailed machine whose moving parts are driven by a large land wheel (the "bull" wheel), (ii) trailed, but driven by power take-off from the tractor, (iii) trailed, but driven by an auxiliary engine, (iv) semi-mounted on the tractor and cutting to one side, (v) front mounted, or push type. Official publications of the United States state that some binders are equipped with small auxiliary engines, so that they will continue to cut even though the driving wheel slides in wet or muddy ground. A binder drawn by a tractor and operated with a power take-off attachment is said to give much less trouble than the auxiliary engine. Power take-off rice binders are usually eight- or ten-foot cuts, whereas a six-foot binder was formerly the most common size. Most binders are drawn by tractors. Push binders, i.e. binders mounted on a frame and carried in front of a tractor, are sometimes used in opening up or cutting the first swath against the bunds. Small tractors, however, with power take-off attachments, if run on the bunds, can open up a field without loss of paddy. Experiments in Malaya have indicated that in certain conditions paddy can be successfully and economically harvested from small fields with a "set" of equipment consisting of a Ferguson tractor, a Bisset semi-mounted binder and a semi-mounted thresher.

Threshing. Paddy harvested with the combine is threshed as it is cut. The paddy is carried by a conveyor-belt to the threshing part of the machine, which is similar to a stationary thresher. It consists essentially of a revolving cylinder and a concave with heavy metal teeth which strip the grain from the straw, shaker screens to separate paddy from straw, and aspirators or fans, to draw out or blow out weed seeds, chaff, dirt and other foreign matter. Threshing is best carried out when the grain is reasonably dry, otherwise there may be poor separation and loss of grain. Paddy from the combine-harvester usually requires drying before storage, the moisture content therefore must be reduced to 14 per cent.

Rossin[573] has summed up the method of paddy cultivation in the United States by stating that as soon as threshed, the paddy is transported to a mill, there to be dried, stored and milled. This, he states, is the characteristic of American paddy cultivation; the farm is reduced to its simplest form, while in California it may be reduced to nothing, for the farmer lives in the town and enters into contracts for labour, sowing and other operations. He merely owns the land but possesses no equipment or buildings on his farm. In the States of the south-east, however, the farmer carries out cultivation personally. Nevertheless, farm buildings consist of a residence and sometimes rough shelters for the plant, with neither barns, cowsheds, nor storage sheds for the grain. As soon as the paddy is harvested it is taken from the farm and the farmer's rôle is ended.

PRE-HARVEST DESICCATION

Pre-harvest drying of paddy, particularly when the weather is humid and wet, makes it possible to replace two-stage harvesting by direct combining, thus increasing the harvested crop. In the U.S.S.R.[498] the following desiccants have proved successful: 1 : 5 mixture of endothal and ammonium sulphate (0.5–1 per cent solution), magnesium chloride (1.3–3 per cent solution) and sodium monochloracetate (1.5–3 per cent solution). In all cases the OP–7 surface active compound was added. The plants were sprinkled at the rate of 90 gallons per acre. With this treatment standing paddy dries within 4 to 6 days.

Work at Stuttgart, Arkansas,[610] showed that using sodium chlorate and magnesium chlorate as desiccant on grain with a moisture content of 24–26 per cent, the moisture content was reduced by about 1 per cent a day. Yield was reduced but bushel weight was not affected.

Tests conducted at California[46] showed that pre-harvest sprays lower milling quality if improperly used, so that the technique should not be used if high milling quality is desired. Under good drying conditions, paddy could be combined six days after treatment. Endothal and sodium monochloracetate increase drying but are not acceptable because they reduce yields and quality.

DEVELOPMENTS IN BRITISH GUIANA

A mechanized pilot scheme, known as the Mahaicony/Abary Scheme,[539] covering between 4,000 and 5,000 acres, was inaugurated in 1942 as a war-time production effort. On this area much useful work was carried out in adapting agricultural machinery for paddy cultivation. From the experience gained it has been possible to devise a sequence of operations suitable for average field conditions in British Guiana.

The aim is to cultivate when the land is dry and to drain off the water so that the crop is harvested on dry land. Straw left by the combine is burnt as soon as possible after harvest, as it is stated that it has an adverse effect on drying out the fields. Ploughing-in stubble and straw is therefore not practised. Mouldboard ploughs are unable to turn in stubble and loose straw, although disc ploughs prove successful in performing this work. The land is usually ploughed with a polydisc plough. Two- or three-disc harrowing usually breaks down the land sufficiently to obtain a satisfactory seed bed for drilling or broadcasting seed.

A system of underwater cultivation has been adopted and is successful provided that there is a sufficient depth of water on the land, for it was found that tractors and harrows could travel through flooded fields and effectively destroy vegetation. The operation is carried out by steel-wheel tractors of the 45 to 50 drawbar horsepower class pulling the front section of a medium to light double disc harrow. With 4 to 6 inches of water on the field, harrowing is done first in one direction and then in another, each tractor following the preceding tractor with either right or left wheel between the tracks made by the one in front. This overlapping is adopted because tractor wheels make greater marks than harrows. Usually four to six passes are necessary to reduce the top 4 to 6 inches of soil to a soft creamy puddle. Levelling pipes are attached to the rear of the harrow to remove wheel marks. Adequate water control is essential for this method of cultivation. Too much water hinders incorporation of vegetable growth with the soil by allowing it to float, while too little water causes clogging of wheels and harrow discs, making free movement difficult.

Giglioli adds that prolonged wet cultivation under field conditions in British Guiana has led to very serious drops in yield (from 2,800 lb. in the first year to 1,000 lb. in the fourth year). This fall in yield is not caused by a decrease in the inherent yielding ability of the land through prolonged use of the technique but by the breakdown of the cultivation method when faced with ever-deteriorating soil-water conditions. Wet cultivation on land that has been so treated in the previous year is very difficult; by the fourth year the tractors can hardly move through the field, with the result that the quality of the seedbed bears no relation to that achieved in the first year. Harvesting troubles also result from this method of cultivation.[212]

Reaper-binders and threshers proved unsatisfactory; they were inefficient with a crop that tends to lodge, and handling the crop was also expensive, and usually resulted in much loss of grain on account of shattering. Windrowing was attempted, but was unsuccessful because the swather gave trouble and there was apt to be insufficient stubble on which to lay the windrow. Massey-Harris self-propelled combines with a cutting width of fourteen to nine feet, mounted on tracks, proved successful, as did the tractor-drawn Case combine with a six-foot cut. The former did excellent work in opening a field and with a short standing crop; the latter proved more satisfactory in dealing with a lodged crop.

Harvesting in flooded fields has been possible; in fact, it is claimed that when soil conditions are, in themselves, too sticky and muddy for even the track-laying machines, the addition of free water over the surface of the mud improves the working conditions for machines. This is because the water washes the tracks (or wheels) and frequently keeps them free from mud, thus preventing them from "balling up." When a wheel or track becomes "balled up" it presents a smooth mud surface to the ground and adhesion is lost. Transport of paddy from field to dumps is effected with rubber-tyred, steel-framed ox-carts, and from dumps to warehouse with rubber-tyred, tractor-drawn trailers.

Emphasis has already been made on the necessity of adequate water control for successful mechanized cultivation of paddy. Under-water cultivation is no substitute for water control; in fact, to permit under-water cultivation water conditions have to be correct. To obtain these conditions, therefore, water control is essential. Furthermore, under-water cultivation is more expensive and depreciation of machinery greater than in dry-land cultivation; it should therefore be considered as an expedient rather than a system.

Mechanized cultivation in British Guiana is successful largely because the underlying clay is firm; this supports machinery and prevents it from bogging down.

P

The success of the Mahaicony/Abary Scheme as a pilot scheme is undoubted, even though the scheme may continue to operate at a loss. Farmers throughout the country have purchased mechanical equipment for cultivating their areas and for operating contract services. In no other tropical country has mechanized paddy production been so widely or rapidly adopted as in British Guiana, where its influence is already reflected in the extended area under the crop and larger units cultivated under one ownership. Forty Massey-Harris Super 92 self-propelled rice combines were imported at one time in 1960 and sold to individual farmers, and one firm had sold more than 1,500 tractors.

MECHANIZATION IN AUSTRALIA

On the Murrumbidgee Irrigation Area in New South Wales, mechanized methods have been successfully practised for some years. The land is cultivated by plough, fertilizers applied with a drill and seed subsequently broadcast after germination. Recently, tests showed that aerial sowing is feasible. The crop is harvested with a rice-header of Australian manufacture. This is a sidecut auxiliary-driven tractor or horse-drawn header with eight- to ten-feet cut, which cuts, threshes, winnows and cleans paddy in one operation. The machine is fitted with a large grain box and bagging platform so that grain can be bagged as the header moves through the field. Fore-cut automatic headers on crawler tractors are increasingly employed. They cut the headlands without damage to the crop; for this reason many growers employ contractors with fore-cut headers to cut tracks around each bay. Tractor units collect the bagged grain for transport to local mills and railhead.[281] Mechanization in this area appears to present no problems, probably because the soil has a firm bottom and because irrigation control is good. It is of interest to note that 64 per cent of farmers still use horses for harvesting their crops.[545]

SOD-SEEDING IN AUSTRALIA

Sod-seeding of various crops and pasture species has been proved economic and practical in Australia. The first attempt to sod-seed paddy into an established subterranean and rye pasture was undertaken by Hood[278] in 1955. In this technique the paddy seed is placed in a narrow slit in the soil which falls back over the seed immediately following the operation, leaving the surface otherwise undisturbed. The sod-seeded crop yielded little less than was obtained by conventional methods of cultivation.

The advantages of sod-seeding are stated to be: costly cultivation is eliminated; less frequent irrigation is required; harvest is earlier; the soil drains out quickly and remains firm, allowing harvesting machinery on the land without bogging—thus, harvest costs are reduced and there is speedier harvest. The grazing land remains in production until a week after sod-seeding, in fact, it is advantageous to the sod-seeded crop if the pasture is grazed until the paddy emerges.

In all sod-seeded demonstrations, invasion of the crop by barnyard grass has been greatly reduced—a factor of extreme economic importance. A possible inference is that conventional cultivation brings barnyard grass seed close to the surface so that it germinates with the paddy; sod-seeding avoids this and weed seeds remain buried.

THE WAGENINGEN RICE PROJECT[703]

The Wageningen Rice Project is an estate of about 15,000 acres developed by the Dutch Government on the fertile and largely un-inhabited coastal plain of Surinam. Reclamation of this area was effected by polders and irrigation by pumping from the Nickerie River. The pumping station was built with a reversible direction of rotation of pumps, so that it could be used for both irrigation and drainage.

The soil consists of impermeable, marine-fluvistile, heavy clay, deposited without lime and covered with a layer of organic matter, called *pegasse*, which may be anything up to a foot or more thick.

Highly mechanized paddy cultivation is employed on the Project. Tillage is by machine, seed is sown direct (i.e. is not transplanted), weeds are controlled by sowing the paddy in water and by use of herbicides, harvesting is by combine and the produce is removed in bulk.

An initial difficulty was that the pegasse surface layer with the young paddy seedlings was apt to float when the land was irrigated, thereby severing the plants from the clay soil under the pegasse. Also the pegasse fields were difficult to harvest by combine because the clay soil under the pegasse remained wet and soft. Consequently, as much pegasse as possible was burnt and the remainder ploughed under.

Tillage. The following implements were used for tillage. Solotrac: Ransoms TS.1K, single-furrow plough, fitted with International cut-out disc coulter. Disc plough—International No. 98–53, five discs (cut-out or smooth). The plough can also be used with four or three discs. Spade plough—an experimental machine which may be compared with a slow-running mounted p.t.-o.-driven rotary cultivator in which the cultivator blades are replaced by spades which perform a digging movement. The Rome plough—which is not actually a plough but a heavy reclamation disc harrow. Three disc harrows were employed, i.e. the Ransome Baronet, with 24 smooth discs in two sections turning like the Rome plough; Ransomes Baron, with 36 smooth discs in two sections and the Ransomes offset disc harrow, of which three models were investigated. The Marden T5 weed cutter was employed. Normally this machine is supplied in three sections, although for wet cultivation under difficult soil conditions one section can be used separately. The Landplane was the Marvin Junior 94 and the Marvin Standard 86. A mud roller with plank was an open roller in a draught frame, consisting of two iron wheels connected by welding-on iron bars in such a way that an open cylinder shape was obtained. The plank, of varying dimensions, is dragged on a steel cable behind the roller.

Depending on moisture conditions and the carrying capacity of the fields, the operations were selected as shown in Table 11.

TABLE 11

PLAN OF TILLAGE OPERATIONS ACCORDING TO CARRYING CAPACITY
OF THE FIELD

Field condition	Ploughing	Rough seedbed preparation	Fine seedbed preparation	
			dry (levelling)	*wet (puddling)*
Dry and firm reclamation land	Solotrac	Rome plough	Landplane	Mud roller + plank
Dry and firm cropped land	Disc plough	Disc harrow	Landplane	Mud roller + plank
Wet and firm reclamation land	Solotrac	None	None	Mud roller and /or plank
Wet and firm cropped land	None or spade plough	Weed-cutter	None	ditto
Wet and soft reclamation land	None	None	No sowing	No sowing
Wet and soft cropped land	None	None	None	Tractor alone or mud roller + plank

Crawler or Wheeled Tractors. Crawler tractors of approximately 45 d.b.h.p. have been used almost exclusively for tillage operations. On the basis of experience gained the International TD9 and Caterpillar D4 crawler tractors with broad tracks (45–50 cm.) but with an extended track frame which increased by a further 20 cm. the length of the track resting on the ground proved most successful. On newly reclaimed soft land the tracks were always fitted with wooden extension blocks which give a smaller ground pressure and a better grip. Wheel tractors at Wageningen have proved entirely unsatisfactory. Apart from a surface crust the soil has the consistency of putty. Because of the small pressure distribution of wheeled tractors as compared with crawlers, the rear wheels easily sink through this crust, after which slip and bogging may result. A further disadvantage of wheels is the deep track they leave in a wet field. It is possible that eventually the firmness of fields will increase to such an extent that some tillage can be done by wheeled tractors. This is of some importance because work can be done more cheaply with wheeled tractors than with tracks.

Ploughing. Conditions for ploughing on cropped land are better than on reclaimed land because the soil has become firmer and the problem of turning the pegasse mat under no longer occurs. Before ploughing, which is usually done directly after harvest, the paddy-stubble is flattened with weedcutters and if possible then burnt.

Levelling. After reclamation differences in levels still occur owing to decomposition of organic matter and soil stabilization. Mechanized cultivation also disturbs the level of the fields every year and if this is not corrected, the unevenness may become serious.

Preparation of Seedbed. A carefully-prepared seedbed is necessary to ensure good emergence after sowing. For successful emergence, the seedbed should have no large clods, no weeds or germination of weed seed, no remains of straw or weeds on the surface of the bed, and no substantial quantities of pegasse on the surface.

Harvesting. A great deal of investigation proved necessary to find the right combine for work under difficult soil conditions. With the standard types, bogging down was frequent. Massey Harris Super No. 27 12-ft., on tracks, Massey Harris No. 90 Rice special 14-ft. on tracks and Claeys M.Z. 14-ft. for rice, on tracks were used. The Claeys M.Z. was found to have better floating capacity and weight distribution than the Massey Harris models. Another important difference was that the Claeys machine was equipped with a diesel engine and the Massey Harris with a petrol engine, so that fuel costs per working hour for the Claeys were lower. The Massey Harris No. 90 and Claeys combines were about equal as regards performance and cost. The advantages of the Claeys were balanced by the better quality of construction of the Massey Harris No. 90. However, from the experience gained on the Project, the Massey Harris No. 92 machine which came on the market later, proved superior to both the others, provided that it is equipped with 5-roller tracks and large rear wheels.

PROBLEMS IN ASIA

Mechanization methods so successfully applied in the United States, British Guiana and Australia are not directly applicable to most paddy-growing regions in Asia. The crux of the problem is water control. In the above-mentioned countries rainfall is less and the seasons more defined than is usual in Asian paddy regions. Furthermore, heavy precipitations experienced make it very difficult to devise irrigation and drainage works that will effectively and quickly cope with the excess water. Cultivation, therefore, may have to be carried out on wet or flooded land.

Beachell and Brown[72] point out that the smallholder is usually able to produce satisfactory crops under poor drainage conditions and with limited irrigation supplies and it is not uncommon for him to carry out all production operations under flooded conditions. Before mechanized methods can be operated successfully, however, drainage must be satisfactory and the cost of improved drainage will be prohibitive unless the maximum efficiency of drainage systems is utilized. Maximum efficiency depends on carefully laid-out plans, taking full advantage of all natural drainage conditions. The above opinions were expressed with special reference to British Guiana, but they apply with equal force to the problems in Asia.

Allen and Haynes[12] have emphasized that type of machine and implement, and timing of cultivations, depend on the soil-water relationship of paddy land in the cultivation season. They conclude that with a hard pan there are four alternative cultivation methods, viz. dry cultivation followed by drilling or seeding in dry soil with subsequent irrigation; dry cultivation followed by normal transplanting; dry cultivation followed by flooding and seeding in shallow water; and wet cultivation followed by transplanting. Their investigations in Kelantan, Malaya showed that wet cultivation followed by transplanting gave higher yields, while dry cultivation followed by flooding and seeding in shallow water also gives good results provided that accurate water control is possible.

The condition of the land, however, is but one of the difficulties encountered in Asia; another is the very small field divisions rendered necessary to ensure even distribution of water over an area which is not flat. Breaking down and subsequent reconstruction of bunds is out of the question in such areas; the alternative must be the use of implements which can be manœuvred—a matter of extreme difficulty when cultivating heavy land with perhaps two or three inches of water lying on it. Mention must also be made of the present system of ownership of land usual in Asia; most of the land is worked in units of under five acres. Some of these difficulties are not applicable to all areas in the East. Many of the large regions of production are situated on practically flat land, thereby reducing the number of bunds necessary, while co-operative arrangements should not be impossible to overcome the problem arising from the multiplicity of owners. There remains the difficulty of cultivating soft boggy land and land that may be inundated at the time when cultivation becomes imperative. These circumstances impose severe limitations to improvement in monsoon rainfall areas.

IMPROVED IMPLEMENTS FOR SMALL HOLDINGS

Progress has been made in devising better implements suitable for use on small holdings. Wan Mohd. Din describes[179] the prototype of an improved animal-drawn plough in Malaya. The implement gave a good performance with regard to penetration and inversion. The draught was appreciably less than that of the Japanese six-inch plough. Working to a depth of six inches in coastal clay soil draught was 200 lb. as compared with 300 lb. with the Japanese plough. The plough weighs 25 lb. and is therefore easy to carry on the shoulder from field to field.

Westgate reported[696] that Chinese engineers have been developing special tractors for use on paddy fields and two have been selected for mass production; one is a 35 h.p. machine and the other a 27 h.p. type. Both have bladed wheels and are light in weight, have good traction, adequate power and manœuvrability. They can plough deep and are adapted for operation on small plots. Kiangsi Province has also developed the use of ploughs and harrows, mounted on tractors, for small paddy areas and is now producing implements for transplanting and harvesting.

The Thailand government is working towards the improvement of light multi-purpose mechanical equipment at a cost that Thai farmers can afford. A small tractor, adapted to local conditions has been designed. It is equipped with a five to six h.p. diesel engine and can be used for ploughing, harrowing and hauling. The motor may be used as power for pumping, threshing and even for propelling a boat.[549]

A new and cheap locally made machine for puddling paddy fields has been tried at the Central Rice Research Institute at Cuttack, India. It has several rotating blades and shares with which it cuts and churns the soil. It can be easily drawn by a pair of bullocks. About three acres can be puddled in eight hours.

In England, the Midget Rice Thresher was designed by the National Institute of Agricultural Engineering (N.I.A.E.) and tested in Malaya. This 12-inch diameter steel rasp bar machine powered by a 150 c.c. four-stroke, air-cooled engine was found capable of producing over 1,600 lb. threshed grain per hour. It was used on small holdings and fitted into normal harvesting methods, including head stripping, and was readily accepted by smallholders.

The above examples of endeavours to design new and improved implements for smallholders provide evidence of a growing awareness amongst agricultural engineers that simple small machines are required, and one is glad to notice that considerable progress is being made to provide such machines. If the implements and methods of cultivation recommended by the Departments of Agriculture were accepted by the cultivators yields would be much higher. It appears fantastic that millions of pounds should be poured into countries to provide irrigation and other facilities and that at the same time the cultivators should continue to cultivate the land with the inadequate implements of thirty centuries ago.

INVESTIGATIONS IN MALAYA

Investigations into the mechanical cultivation and harvesting of paddy have been carried out in Malaya over the past decade. Initially, these trials were conducted on bog, "bottomless" and hard-pan areas. Earlier reports on the progress of the work left one under the impression that once bog soils are cleared and tree stumps removed, little difficulty is experienced in cultivating the land with tractors fitted with special wheels to prevent the machines from bogging down. It now appears that attempts to introduce mechanized cultivation on bog soils have been abandoned[27] in favour of investigations within the hard-pan zones of coastal and inland alluvial areas, much of which is already cultivated by traditional methods. Since much of the potential paddy-land is bog or "bottomless" swamp, success in mechanization on hard-pan areas is unlikely to increase the total area under the crop, although it may have other advantages.

Coulter[140] states that it may never be economic or indeed possible to grow good paddy crops on peats, while Allen and Haynes[12] consider that only dry cultivation is possible on bottomless soils, success depending on the use of low-pressure tractors. Such soils, they point out, usually have a high water-table in the cultivation season, consequently the season for dry cultivation is restricted. Under these conditions, they add, tractor cultivation becomes increasingly difficult after the first cultivation, so that a tractor-mounted or tractor-drawn hoe, which produces a tilth in one operation, has advantages over ploughs and harrows.

Increased cost of labour and the serious shortage of rice in the early post-war period encouraged mechanization investigations in which emphasis was laid on agronomic aspects since it was hoped that more thorough cultivation made possible by applying greater power to implements would raise yields, thus increasing production per acre and allowing two crops per annum to be grown in certain areas. This work was not very successful for it was found that there were formidable technical problems to be overcome before mechanization could be introduced into existing areas, while it was realized that immediate benefits would be small. Subsequent endeavours, therefore, have been mainly directed to solving the technical problems for mechanizing all operations necessary for growing paddy, with the final objective of opening a pilot scheme where new techniques can be tested, costs determined under actual working conditions and the optimum size for a mechanized family farm determined.[258]

Cultivation. Where there are no underground timbers, mouldboard ploughs are preferred, but where timber is present disc-ploughs are used. The Rotoplough has shown promise especially on swampy, bottomless soils. Where there is heavy growth, a disc-harrow is used. A Tillmore was modified by enclosing the wheels using light-gauge sheet steel, to prevent clogging. Coleman[132] stated that the implement was first tried on land in a dry state and worked very well to a depth of three or four inches, but below that the tractor laboured badly and tended to stall. On sticky land it proved useless as the draught was so great that the tractor had insufficient power to overcome rolling resistance and operate the power take-off, and the rotary augers clogged up. In wet conditions, however, the machine worked well and was self-cleaning as it worked. The depth of work was four inches. Of other tractors that have been tried, the Platypus Bogmaster deserves notice, although its cost would probably render it uneconomic on an individual holding or as a contractor's machine. It might, however, be justified in an area where the holding had been laid out for mechanical work and where considerable work could be obtained within a short distance of the contractor's base.[258] Preliminary trials on mineral soils indicate that the implement is particularly suitable for after-cultivation on flooded land. One cannot escape the suspicion that much of the cultivation work has aimed at a depth unnecessary for paddy. It is probable that on most soils depth of cultivation sufficient to smother weeds and to work up a fine but not necessarily a deep seed bed is all that is necessary.

Type of Power Unit.[13] Several makes of wheeled tractors have proved satisfactory including various Ferguson models, the diesel-powered Fordson Major and the Farmall H, but the Farmall A is underpowered and has wheels that are too small. Of track-tractors, the International-Harvester TD.6, the Bristol 20, the Caterpillar D.2 and D.4 and the David Brown Trackmaster have been used satisfactorily on wet land, especially for after-cultivation.

After-cultivation. A series of implements are in use to work the land into a proper state for planting. The amount of cultivation and type of implement used must, of course, depend on the type and condition of the soil.

Disc harrows have proved successful in wet land; care has to be taken, however, to set the discs so that the drag is not too great, as this may bog the tractor. A locally-made tooth harrow, bogie mounted, for the Trusty tractor, has proved a useful implement for after-cultivation of wet paddy-land. Light disc-harrows break down clods provided that the land is either dry or flooded, but they are useless when the land is merely wet.

The "Kedah-type" roller, designed on the hand-operated wood roller traditionally used in many countries, has proved successful. It is constructed of steel, having a width of five feet and an overall diameter of one foot, and weighs 475 lb. with two rolls or 323 lb. with the rear roll removed. This double roller has recently been largely superseded by a ten-inch roller. The latter is said to be better in most cases than the drum roller. The drum roller was devised for deep and very wet land. It consists of two forty-five-gallon fuel drums mounted end to end on a long shaft and fitted longitudinally with wooden slats three inches high, the whole being mounted on a light steel frame and directly attached to the hydraulic power-lift. The weight can be varied by filling with water through the screw-on caps.

Planting. Transplanting machines have not been used in Malaya. Seed drills have been tried, but are unsatisfactory because of the difficulty in controlling sowing depth in soft mud and also because mud chokes the seed tubes. Bow-operated hand fiddles have proved fairly satisfactory, using seed soaked for 48 hours and germinated for 36 to 48 hours before sowing. Width of spread depends on the height of the operator and softness of mud. An average working rate is about three acres per hour.

Transplanting is such an important factor in maintaining or achieving a high yield per acre of paddy that investigators cannot afford to relax efforts to invent a satisfactory transplanting machine. There appears no reason why the problem cannot be solved.

Harvesting. Mechanized harvesting is important in the main rice areas of Malaya because labour requirements are difficult to meet at this season.[259] A number of machines have been tested under varying conditions,[12] but no outstanding success appears to have been achieved. Even where reasonably successful, loss of time for various reasons has been great and the acreage covered far below an economic level.

Threshing. A number of threshers have been tried with varying results. A Danish thresher (the "Rajah" thresher) especially designed for paddy has been developed in collaboration with the Department of Agriculture, Malaya. It is semi-mounted on a Ferguson tractor and driven by power take-off. It therefore requires no lining up before work and can run about the field, or up and down a wide bund to thresh small patches of paddy here and there. Winnowing machines sufficiently large to cope with the crop from mechanized harvesting are necessary. It should not be difficult to devise a machine for such a simple operation. Small balers have been found economical for handling paddy straw for mulching, bedding and perhaps cattle food.[260] The demand for baled paddy straw in Malaya, and in most other countries in Asia, must be small.

Allen and Haynes have summed up the results of the Malayan investigations as follows:

(*a*) Areas cultivated "in the wet" have given significantly higher yields than those cultivated "in the dry" and subsequently flooded.

(*b*) Tractor ploughing in the wet has tended to give better yields than ploughing with the local buffalo-drawn plough—apparently owing to better weed control.

(*c*) Deep ploughing (8 to 9 inches) and rotary cultivation do not give such high yields as shallow ploughing (4 to 5 inches), but sub-soiling does not reduce yields.

(*d*) Superficial cultivation (e.g. surface puddling) appears to give yields comparable with shallow ploughing.

(*e*) Following shallow ploughing, the less soil is worked in order to create good conditions for transplanting the better.

(*f*) Tractor ploughing four to six weeks before transplanting gives higher yields than either very early or later ploughing.

MECHANIZATION IN CEYLON

Investigations in mechanizing agriculture have engaged attention for some time past. The Engineering Division of the Department of Agriculture has demonstrated the economics of tractor use under proper management for primary tillage of paddy-land by establishing six tractor units. The demand for tractor units has consequently increased rapidly, especially in areas where cattle and labour are insufficient. It is estimated that about one-quarter of Ceylon's million acres under paddy is suitable for mechanization. There are about a thousand tractors in the country, including a gift of about 200 by the Australian Government under the Colombo Plan.[173]

The results to date of mechanization in Ceylon have been summed up[541] as follows:

> Mechanization has reached a stage when preparatory tillage can be completely mechanized on the larger farms which have been laid out with this object in view. Seed-drilling seems feasible and may have advantages for inter-cultivation over broadcasting. Deeper seed placement gives greater initial weed control and inter-cultivation will enable crops to be kept in a weed-free condition. Smaller units could make more use of the Planet Junior type of inter-cultivator, row-spacing being accordingly adjusted. Tractor units exist at a number of places and demand for their services to undertake preparatory tillage exceeds their capacity.
>
> Mechanization has been little used in connection with colonization schemes in the dry zone. Some effort has been made to encourage the use of tractors, mainly through Government tractor pools, and considerable use has been made of the facilities thus made available. It appears, therefore, that ploughing is becoming more popular, perhaps because of the saving in personal effort.

On the other hand, Farmer,[195] writing of the development in the Dry Zone of Ceylon, doubts whether mechanization is really economic, either in the general sense of its utility in an economy in which labour is superabundant, or in the particular sense because tractors are used almost exclusively for ploughing and lie idle when there is no ploughing to be done, and are inefficiently maintained. In fact, he concludes: "under present circumstances it appears that mechanization may only function where land is farmed in large units. ... Mechanization within the existing framework of peasant colonization is another matter, a matter of untried agronomic experiment. Work should proceed with caution; the Government and the peasant must beware of the pushful commercial pedlars of the apparent panacea of mechanization, and even look in the mouth of gift-horses which arrive under the Colombo Plan."

MECHANIZATION IN AFRICA

Much of the paddy development in West Africa is in inland swamps and natural flood plains without means of water control, mechanical operations being directed to both small- and large-scale ploughing; possibly also seed drilling. At the Gambia Rice Farm paddy-growing techniques are being investigated with an extensive irrigation system, while other investigations are also in progress in Sierra Leone. Mayne concludes that there will be little expansion of agricultural mechanization in the Gambia for several years. Sierra Leone may develop ambitious plans for rice production on coastal swamps and riverine grasslands, while in Ghana, despite considerable difficulties, there is much interest in mechanization and the subject is being investigated by the Government and the University. In Nigeria interest is concentrated on rice production and general tractor ploughing and progress is being made at the engineering headquarters in the Northern Region.[382]

The 1955 Annual Report of the Gambia Rice Farm mentions that field operations depend primarily for motive power on Massey-Harris 744D wheeled tractors, a Ferguson petrol tractor has been in use for six years, while a David Brown 50 crawler tractor proves its worth during the sowing period when the land is very wet in places. To enable wheeled tractors to operate in wet conditions half-tracks have proved useful, but demand care in driving. It is thought that the operating hours of a wheeled tractor can be materially increased in the wet season by fitting some sort of half-track. A serious disadvantage of wheeled tractors on swamp soil is that the small diameter front wheels experience difficulty in riding over the uneven surface left after ploughing, while the strain placed on the steering mechanism and front axle mounting is considerable. This has been overcome by a home-made invention—the rhum palm sledge—which consists of two whole rhum palm runners with split palms bolted across. When hauled across the land it exerts a rubbing and rolling effect which breaks down clods and flattens the surface thus enabling wheeled tractors to work better.

Giglioli, reporting on the Mwea Irrigation Settlement, Kenya, stated that in 1960 an area of 1,572 acres was cultivated mechanically with great success and in the following year, mechanized cultivation was adopted throughout the Settlement (about 5,000 acres). Land preparation was carried out by flooding the fields to a depth of four inches and then cultivating underwater with a 52-inch Rotovator hydraulically mounted on a Massey-Ferguson 35 tractor, equipped with 13-inch by 24-inch tyres. A fleet of eleven tractors dealt with the entire acreage in 85 days, with a daily rate of 5·31 acres per tractor.

MECHANIZED CULTIVATION IN SWAZILAND

On their Swaziland Irrigation Scheme the Commonwealth Development Corporation have successfully cultivated by mechanical means some 1,000 to 1,500 acres of paddy annually for the past eight years. The virgin bush is cleared with Caterpillar D6 and D7 tractors. The trees are burned and the land, after ripping, is ploughed with a Davies plough pulled by a TD 14 tractor. This is followed by a heavy discing with Rome discs.

The fields are constructed with road scrapers pulled by TD 14's in conjunction with Warco and Caterpillar motor graders. Final levelling is done with Murray scrapers and Ferguson trip dump scrapers levelling to plus or minus three inches, the topsoil being replaced as far as is economically possible. Sizes of individual fields differ according to gradient, but where possible they are one or two acres.

The first agricultural operation on new land is ripping with a Caterpillar D4 with five chisels. The land may then be disced with Caterpillar D4 using double Goble discs or ploughed with two-furrow Ferguson disc ploughs.

Seed beds are prepared first with Goble discs, the Ferguson offset discs if required and then with light Ransome discs followed, if necessary, with Ferguson peg-tooth harrows. Some of these operations may be omitted or may be repeated according to the physical nature of the soil. If the land is prepared well in advance of planting time, it is left to weather after the initial ripping until about three weeks before planting. On land which has already grown paddy and on which a ratoon crop is not required, the normal procedure is to disc in the stubble as soon as possible after harvest. The land is then left from March until July or August before being either ploughed, using Ferguson mould board or disc ploughs, or disced with D4's, using Goble discs. Fields are then flooded to germinate drop seed paddy and weed seeds. It is possible at this stage to pick out high and low spots and level them under water with Ferguson scrapers or trip dump scrapers, or to mark the spots for attention later when the land is dry. Resultant weed and volunteer paddy growth is disced in. It is often necessary to flood more than once to free the land from weeds. At this stage the type of cultivation must depend very much on the weather. If little rain is experienced, the small weeds can be disced in with Ferguson offset discs, but if rain prevents tractors from operating at the early weed stage it may become necessary to use Goble discs. Pre-planting operations are thereafter the same as for new land. Bunds are raised with Ferguson side disc terracers; fertilizers are applied with distributors and subsequently disced in.

The seed is sown on dry land with Case seed drills, which can sow up to 40 acres each per day. A light harrowing and rolling follows. The rate of seeding varies according to the time of sowing, but the basic rate for early sowing in August is 100 lb. of Blue Bonnet per acre, rising to 130 to 140 lb. per acre in the middle of November. Yields drop significantly if planting is delayed after this date. Flooding, then quickly draining, is practised immediately after planting. It is most essential that the flooding be quick and the draining thorough, otherwise a poor, uneven stand is obtained. Broadcasting pre-germinated seed in water has been tried, but unless the land is very level it is not very successful. Ducks cause considerable damage to the crop when sown this way.

The crop, about one ton of paddy per acre, is harvested with Massey-Harris combine harvesters with either tracks or rubber wheels and the grain is mechanically dried.

MECHANICAL CULTIVATION WITH "MARKET-GARDEN" TRACTORS

One would expect that the light "market-garden" tractor would prove ideal for cultivating paddy on small areas by reason of its convenient size, ease of manœuvre and comparatively low initial cost. In Thailand, the Howard Rotavator Gem provided with a power take-off pulley has been used to pump water from each small division of the field in turn, the area from which water has been pumped being then cultivated with the same Rotavator. The machine is provided with extra large wheels which penetrate the mud and find the bottom.

Tests of several makes of market-garden tractors have been made in Malaya.[57] All the machines performed reasonably well in the initial ploughing or cultivation in a moist soil. Subsequent disc harrowing in sticky ground proved difficult. A second ploughing was possible but exhausting to the operator. Second harrowing on flooded land proved impossible, discs could not be used as they penetrated into the mud and built up a wall of mud in front. A locally constructed tined harrow attached worked well, but a Cambridge roll used after ploughing clogged up and sank into the mud. The conclusion was reached[57] that in their present form none of the machines and standard equipment is suited to wet-paddy cultivation. All were comparatively expensive to run and most of them required a disproportionate amount of manual labour to operate. Ashby concludes that "small engines operating under difficult conditions are more prone to stoppages from minor mechanical faults than are larger ones, nor do they require less frequent or less skilled servicing. There are many grounds for thinking that the small horticultural type of tractor, of which some are capable of good and efficient work on dry land, is not likely to be of much value to the smallholder for wet cultivation."

This opinion is supported by the National Institute of Agricultural Engineering, for Hawkins[257] states that on dry land most machines of this type suffer from lack of wheel grip on heavy operations such as ploughing, and modifications to aid traction in wet fields have been unable to overcome this. He adds that it is just possible that the two-wheeled rotary cultivator may prove satisfactory for its engine power is used mainly to drive the rotor, not to provide traction.

One cannot regard this opinion as representing the last word on small tractors for paddy cultivation. Indeed, a more recent report from Malaya states that pedestrian tractors are gaining in popularity. Rotary cultivators have been introduced into British Guiana where the writer saw (and personally worked) a 6 h.p. Rotoho Gem rotary hoe on land with about four inches of standing water. Under these conditions it was easy to operate and appeared to do satisfactory work. Its performance was said to be about one acre a day and its petrol consumption about four gallons per acre. Mayne[383] mentions that the Department of Agriculture in Sarawak has gained experience with small walking tractors and has demonstrated that, properly selected and operated, such machines need not be too exhausting to drive in the tropics. In the past few years automatic cultivators and garden tractors have become very popular in Japan.[379]

JAPANESE CONTRIBUTION TO MECHANIZATION

Japan appears to be leading the world in the application of small tractors for paddy cultivation. These tractors first attracted attention about 1952, when several thousand were put into service. In 1955, over 30,000 were manufactured and found their way to rural communities. The number in operation at the end of 1955 was estimated to be about 90,000. Mechanization in Japan, however, is still in its infancy, for one is told[421] that the use of agricultural machinery and implements is relatively unimportant and farmers buy machines and implements at random.

The rotary type has been the most popular and accounts for 50 per cent of all small tractors under operation. It is rather heavy, weighing around 400 lb. and is powered by water-cooled kerosene or diesel engine of 4 to 6 h.p. This tractor is single purpose; i.e. it is used once or twice a year for land preparation—about 100 to 300 hours per annum. More than half of these machines are under co-ownership because of their high cost. Other types, such as crank and screw types are used, but have lost in popularity because of their liability to mechanical troubles during operation. The screw type is used under certain soil conditions and its popularity is confined to certain localities. A garden type exists, but is not used to any extent because of its high cost.

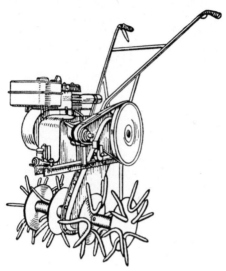

FIG. 16
Merry tiller—Japan

A recent innovation is a tiller weighing about 100 lb., powered by a 2½ h.p. air-cooled engine and supplied with various attachments. It is designed for small holdings of about two to four acres and is said to perform practically all phases of paddy cultivation, while seedling, transplanting and harvesting attachments are contemplated.*

Reverting to the 4 to 6 h.p. power tiller, mentioned above, a wheel type is used in dry paddy regions and a crawler type in semi-wet regions. Ploughing and harrowing are done at the same time, thus easing labour requirements during rush periods of work. For after-cultivation, a rotary cut-away disc harrow, animal-drawn, is used, but these are gradually being replaced by power tillers with rotary or screw tines.[38]

In Formosa,[369] seven models of garden tractor, ranging from 10 h.p., were introduced from the United States but were found to

* Private communication.

be too heavy for paddy fields, the chassis were too high for Orientals and the prices were too high. Japanese power tillers, especially the rotary models, have proved acceptable because they are light in weight, compact, easy to operate, cheap, have great manœuvrability in small fields and are able to perform other kinds of work around the farm. The 2·5 h.p. machine is considered suitable for light soil, 3·5 h.p. for heavy soil and 5 h.p. for farms wishing to use them for other jobs requiring greater power. Power tillers of this type can also be used for inter-row tillage, weeding, ridging, propelling power sprayers, threshing and winnowing. Attached to a trailer, the power tiller can serve as a transport vehicle for a load of 1,200 lb. at 12 miles an hour.

COMBINES

It is obvious that although a measure of success has been achieved in mechanized cultivation of paddy under some soil and water conditions, nowhere in Asia has the mechanization of harvesting proved an outstanding success, although in the United States and Australia it is standard practice. The reason for this failure is probably that the land is not in a suitable condition to carry the equipment. The solution of the problem is not to be found in adapting present machinery to the wet conditions in which it is expected to work, but to obtain better water control, so that the land may be dry at harvest time.

In order to be economical, a combine must harvest about 150 acres in a season. Morning work cannot commence until the dew has dried off the grain and work must cease as soon as evening dew falls. To harvest paddy at the optimum stage and avoid loss through shattering of late-harvested crops, the harvesting period should not extend more than twenty-four days. Usually, therefore, a combine cannot harvest more than 120 acres per year unless early-, medium- and late-maturing varieties are grown so that harvest may be more protracted.

HIRE SERVICE

The cost of machines for paddy cultivation is usually beyond the means of the individual cultivator; in fact, the small use he would make of an implement in a year might not justify its purchase. The alternatives to personal or private ownership is either communal or government hire service. Machinery cannot be employed economically unless it finds full employment. In fixing their rates of hire, the Agricultural Machinery Pools in England found it necessary to allow for their machines being idle for two-thirds of the time during which they might normally be expected to be in use. The allowance is almost certainly higher in the tropics. In operating a hire service, much difficulty may be encountered, time and money wasted and damage occasioned in moving from one job to another. Machine performance is usually underestimated and its performance overestimated; few appreciate, for instance, that 25 to 30 per cent of the tractors in a scheme are likely to be out of action at one time because of breakdown and shortage of spare parts, while the high rate of depreciation, breakage and the expense of repairs are usually more costly than anticipated. Shortage of skilled mechanics is a factor of great significance when estimating costs.

Government-sponsored hire service may be justified for propaganda purposes during the initial stage of a campaign to introduce mechanization, but even then, cultivators should not be encouraged to imagine that mechanization is cheap, an idea they will certainly gain should hire charges be below the actual cost. Co-operative ownership of a contract service, group ownership or commercial enterprise should ultimately undertake such services. Recent information shows that contracting services are increasing in numbers, especially in British Guiana and Malaya.

COSTS

A recent publication[546] has restated the theory that if machinery on a farm is to replace or supplement labour, it must so reduce production costs by saving man- or beast-hours that its cost can be more than recovered within a reasonable time. Otherwise, it must perform a task which is beyond the capacity of the labour force. In the latter case, the service would either be profitable or be of such value to the farmer or the community that it is acceptable as a financial burden on other farming operations or on the state.

In Asia and Africa mechanized paddy cultivation is slowly emerging from its adolescent stage: the agronomic and technical problems are fairly appreciated, though not all of them are solved, but there exists very considerable uncertainty as to whether mechanization can be integrated into peasant agriculture. Furthermore, much has yet to be learned regarding the economics of mechanized paddy production. The inconclusiveness and some of the inconsistencies of many estimates of costs have not infrequently been the result of lack of appreciation of the influence of local social conditions. Inefficient costing and record keeping in some regions have resulted in waste of time and money, but it would appear that investigations at present in progress are likely to produce more positive results, for the reason that they are in the hands of trained personnel.

In the main, costs per acre of paddy cultivation show no increase

TABLE 12

HARVESTING BY DIFFERENT METHODS IN MALAYA

METHODS	Capital cost of Equipment	LABOUR			Estimated acreage per gang per year	Average cost per acre	Remarks
		man hours per acre	woman hours per acre	optimum size of gang			
	$					$	
Hand reaping with sickle and hand threshing	120	43·2	83·8	3 men 6 women	10	40·65	Average of 4 trials
Hand reaping with sickle and threshing with small thresher driven by stationary engine	1,200	12·0	102·9	4 men 30 women	50	45·88	Average of 3 trials Thresher moved around field
Hand reaping with sickle and threshing with large thresher driven by tractor	8,350	21·0	104·1	3 men 15 women	50	47·10	Average of 4 trials Thresher on band
Reaping with semi-mounted binder and threshing with large semi-mounted thresher	10,900	16·0	20·0	4 men 6 women	60	46·04	One trial of 12 acres only Thresher moved round field
Trailer combine pulled by modified tracked tractor	23,945	8·4	—	2 men	100	31·94	One trial only
Self-propelled combine on tracks	23,044	3·6	—	2 men	190	39·76	Average of 16 trials

$1 Malayan = 2s. 4d.

with mechanization, but there is a marked reduction of labour and a considerable increased area that can be cultivated in the season. Table 8, prepared by Haynes[546] in his very objective article, clearly indicated this trend.

Concerning labour utilization of tractors and combine harvesters during a period of twelve months, a report* on tractor operations, Gambia Rice Farm, shows that 46 per cent of the time was unproductive, consisting of hours spent travelling out to fields and back at the beginning and ending of each day's work, idle time caused by breakdowns or lack of work.

The following table, compiled from more elaborate tables in the Report, shows details of cost and output of tractors, and costs allocated to operations on the basis of productive hours. The main agricultural operations were not necessarily performed on all land under cultivation and, conversely, some operations were performed twice on the same land. This is the reason for the different acreages given for each operation. The total area cultivated was all ploughed once so that the acreage shown for ploughing is also the total area cultivated.

TABLE 13

COSTS AND OUTPUTS OF TRACTORS

Operation	Acres	Total hours worked	Rates per acre					
			Fuel	Engine oil	Spares	Fitter's wages	Driver's wages	Total
			s. d.	s. g.	s. d.	s. d.	s. d.	s. d.
Plough	664	1715	6 9	1 0	6 8	1 6	1 9	17 8
Disc harrow	1121	1032	2 4	4	1 9	6	7	5 6
Drill	552	268	1 3	2	1 1	3	4	3 1
Spike harrow	541	148½	7	1	3	1	2	1 2
Roll	648	321	1 1	2	5	4	5	2 5
Spray	475	205	1 0	2	3	2	4	1 11
Total		3689½	12 0	1 11	10 8	2 10	3 7	31 9

In addition, rice carrying took 453 hours of tractor time, rice milling 612½ hours and miscellaneous 961 hours, at a cost of £89 7s. 5d., £118 10s. 10d. and £207 1s. 9d. respectively.

An attempt is being made on the Swaziland Irrigation Scheme to cost each operation for labour, stores and tractors—a long process

* Quoted in this book by kind permission of the Gambia Government and *The Farm Manager.*

but one which should provide valuable information. Operating costs vary considerably from place to place, depending on the basis of cost analysis, whether full overhead costs are included, allowances made for future repairs etc. The true cost also depends on the skill of operators, soil and climatic conditions. The following tables of operations and rates of work on three blocks of land in Swaziland—A being old land, B and C new land—show the possibilities of mechanized cultivation and provide a basis on which costs may be estimated.

TABLE 14

A. TRACTOR OPERATIONS ON A BLOCK OF 179 ACRES OF ESTABLISHED PADDY LAND

Tractor and implements	*No. of hours*	*Acre/hour*
D4's with double Goble discs, discing in paddy stubble	136	1·31
Ploughing with Ferguson disc ploughs and mouldboard ploughs	335	0·53
Levelling with Fordson front-mounted scraper (spot levelling, no definite acreage)	16	—
Discing with D4 prior to planting	226	0·79
Preparing seed bed with Ferguson tractors using offset discs, light Ransome disc and harrows	232	0·77
Planting with Ferguson tractors using Case seed drills	54	3·32
Rolling after planting with Ferguson tractors using Cambridge roller	28	6·39

TABLE 15

B. TRACTOR OPERATIONS ON A BLOCK OF 132 ACRES OF NEW LAND

Tractor and implements	*No. of hours*	*Acre/hour*
Discing land with Caterpillar D4 using double Goble discs	52	2·54
Ripping land with Caterpillar D4 using five chisels on tool bar	130½	1·01
Preparing seed bed with Ferguson tractors using offset discs, light Ransome discs and harrows	186	0·71
Planting with Ferguson tractors using Case seed drills	45	2·90
Rolling after planting with Ferguson tractors using Cambridge rollers	27	4·90

TABLE 16

C. TRACTOR OPERATIONS ON A BLOCK OF 201 ACRES OF NEW LAND

Tractor and implements	No. of hours	Acre/hour
Ripping land with D5 chisels on bar—100 acres	102	0·98
Discing with Caterpillar D4 using double Goble discs	282	0·72
Ploughing with Ferguson tractors using two furrows and three-furrow disc ploughs—102 acres	189	0·54
Preparing seed bed with Ferguson tractors using offset discs, light Ransome discs and harrows	294	0·68
Planting with Ferguson tractors using Case seed drills	60	3·35
Rolling after planting with Ferguson tractors using Cambridge rollers	40	5·03

MECHANIZATION AND THE SMALLHOLDER

In terms of man-hours, the cost of paddy production on small holdings is so great that the economist assumes that mechanization must reduce cost of production, increase yields and enable the farmer to undertake cultivation of a larger area. To reason thus is to make an entirely wrong appreciation of the situation. The crux of the matter is that many holdings are so small that mechanization is quite impracticable. Furthermore, mechanized cultivation does not increase yield per acre, in fact, yields are less than on a carefully cultivated holding. It also does not follow that the cultivator will wish to tend a larger area, or even that a further area of suitable land is available for him to develop. Finally, where family work is involved, costs are not related to man-hours but only to actual out-of-pocket payments for services or materials. The smallholder may, however, welcome mechanization to obviate "bottle-necks" in the cultivation operations, or to allow him greater opportunities for pursuing other activities.

Efferson has observed[190] that if China or Japan mechanized along the United States plan, one-fourth to one-half of their populations would starve to death in less than two years; if India suddenly shifted from hand-harvesting to combining, the social upheaval caused by the displacement of millions of workers would cost much more than the saving in harvesting costs, while to discard the straw in Japan would eliminate one-third of the rural industry of the country and cause 10 million workers to become unemployed. Mechanization would also cause millions of Chinese to become homeless and cause thousands of livestock vital to the economy and well-being of the people to die of starvation each year in most countries of Asia, Latin America and the rice areas of Europe and Africa. Contrary to general belief, mechanization offers the least opportunity for increased production of rice in the deficit regions of Asia. He adds:

> Mechanization is profitable only when farm labour is scarce and expensive; these conditions do not exist in many regions. The most important piece of machinery needed in most of the deficit-regions of Asia is a good wheelbarrow, preferably one with a steel wheel and a rubber tyre. Gasoline-powered equipment is an interesting toy for the local politician in many under-developed areas; but it is too expensive to be practical under the existing conditions on most of the farms.

Mayne expresses much the same warning against the indiscriminate introduction of mechanization:

> In a sense it is spectacular to have mechanical power to ease labour and to speed operations, but less spectacular means of agricultural improvement are likely to be much more effective on most peasant holdings. Advice on the use of fertilizers, the selection and care of seed, the proper management of livestock and the correct use of animal-drawn implements should come long before advice on tractors.

While Mayne was referring to the small farm and not specifically to paddy cultivation, his views are generally applicable to paddy production. The Japanese approach to this subject has been realistic, for they have been concerned to cater for the needs of smallholders by improving existing machinery and introducing comparatively lightweight powered machines at a price reasonably within the means of groups of farmers.

As a result of an inquiry into mechanization of rice production, a FAO Report[37] states:

> ... perhaps the greatest improvement in mechanization can be brought about by picking out the best equipment already in use in the region and gradually bringing about its introduction into other countries where conditions are similar. ... The peasant working a small farm consisting of a number of fragmented holdings can have little use for powered equipment, even if he could afford it, which he cannot—often, in fact, he may be unable to afford even animal power. Moreover, where there is ample family labour, improvements in the immediate future will be best brought about by developing better hand-tools, simple animal-powered equipment, and actual methods of work. Only when there are good employment opportunities off the farm, which could absorb some of the labour force, will mechanization in the usual sense really be efficient.

55. Husking paddy with a pestle, Bengal

56. Husking paddy, Ceylon

57. Milling rice, Thailand

58. Hand-operated huller
(Messrs. John Gordon & Co.)

59. Rice huller with a single pulle
(Messrs. Lewis C. Grant Ltd.)

60. No. 7 Bon-Accord Combined Rice Huller and Polisher
(Messrs. William McKinnon & Co. Ltd.)

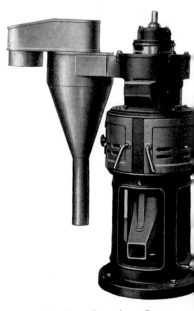

61. Rice Sampling Cone
(Messrs. Lewis C. Grant Ltd.)

62. Hand Trieur
(Messrs. Lewis C. Grant Ltd.)

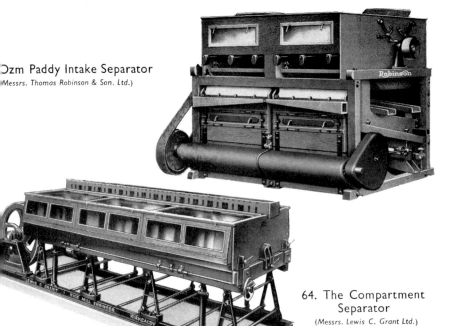

Ozm Paddy Intake Separator
(Messrs. Thomas Robinson & Son. Ltd.)

64. The Compartment Separator
(Messrs. Lewis C. Grant Ltd.)

65. High Capacity (Kapak) Separator
(Messrs. Lewis C. Grant Ltd.)

66. Pearling or Whitening Cone
(Messrs. Lewis C. Grant Ltd.)

67. Rice straw stored on a farm the Po Valley, Italy

68. Rice straw products of Japan

69. Earthenware grain stores in village, West Pakistan

70. A Chinese transplanting machi

A report[725] on problems of mechanization of native agriculture in tropical African Colonies expresses a somewhat similar view:

> The chances of being able to introduce tractors economically in some areas for the heavier tasks would probably be enhanced by the introduction of better tools and implements to make fuller use of hand and animal power in the lighter tasks. Studies of mechanization possibilities and economics should not neglect these simpler implements.

Further valuable information on the possibilities of mechanization was provided by the International Rice Commission in Calcutta in 1956. The Commission laid emphasis on the importance of developing better hand tools and simpler equipment. Not only is any more advanced form of mechanization far beyond the means of the grower, but there is also a more or less complete lack of trained maintenance staff required for even the simplest forms of power mechanization. Evidence was forthcoming that tractors and equipment, in many cases, are not used even when purchased, because of lack of facilities for maintenance and repairs.

From many points of view, therefore, progress in the mechanization of rice production will be slow, being intimately tied in with many other aspects of development of the region in which the crop is grown. This is not to preclude the possibility of mechanization on small holdings, but to counsel a policy of caution so that mechanization may be fully integrated with local conditions.

Chapter XI

FERTILIZERS AND MANURES

THE paddy plant requires mineral nutrients similar to other cereals but also demands silica, which is deposited in certain epidermal cells of the leaves and husk. Nutrients absorbed by the crop vary considerably but broadly, the straw and grain at maturity contain approximately 0·14 per cent nitrogen, 0·05 per cent phosphorus, 0·25 per cent potassium and 0·10 per cent calcium; in addition, there is a large amount of silica, some magnesium and sulphur with traces of other elements including boron, iron, manganese, zinc, copper and molybdenum. The most usual deficiencies encountered in paddy growing are nitrogen and phosphorus, with potassium and sulphur in limited areas, and sometimes silica on peaty soils. Responses to dressings of other elements have rarely been observed though calcium may be beneficial under very acid conditions.

The crop receives part of its nutrient requirements in irrigation water, either in solution or in suspended solids. The latter is particularly important on some river systems where the silt load is high, as in Thailand, Burma, Egypt and the Gangetic plains of India. Investigations in Indonesia[210] have shown that this applies especially to potash although phosphates may also be supplied in appreciable quantities. Der Berger[79] in Java concluded that all the nutritive elements, with the exception of nitrogen and phosphorus, are supplied by the water in sufficient quantity to replenish the losses of these elements absorbed by the plants. This applies to irrigation water obtained from rivers; the nutritive elements obtained from lakes, wells and artificial reservoirs are less. Not only may the paddy yield vary considerably on account of small soil differences, but varieties of paddy have different nutrient requirements.

VARIETAL RESPONSE TO FERTILIZERS

It is widely recognized that varieties of paddy differ in their response to fertilizers. In an experiment in West Pakistan, one variety gave an increase of 800 lb., another variety 300 lb., and a third variety 450 lb. over the control, as the result of the application of similar fertilizers under identical conditions. This differing response to fertilizers is most evident in comparing *indica* and

218

japonica sub-species of rice. *Indica* varieties are widely grown in the tropics, where they show great resistance to infertile soils and extreme tropical conditions. *Japonica* varieties, suited to cultivation in sub-tropical and warm-temperate latitudes, where they are capable of heavy yields, are strong-strawed, resistant to shattering and possess a great capacity for responding to fertilizers. Unfortunately, *japonica* varieties give a low yield when grown in the tropics, while *indica* varieties are equally unsuited to the sub-tropics and warm-temperate regions. The attempt is being made to obtain by crossing, varieties capable of growth in the tropics and possessing the high-yielding quality and good response to fertilizers possessed by *japonica* varieties, while retaining the hardiness and other good characters of *indica* varieties.

NITROGEN

It seems that the majority of *indica* varieties are adapted to relatively low dressings of nitrogen, in the region of 20 lb. nitrogen per acre. Higher quantities of nitrogen usually result in lodging and consequent loss of crop. On the other hand, *japonica* varieties respond to very heavy fertilization—100 lb. per acre and over. The process by which yield increase is obtained differs with variety. In some, it is caused by increase in number of panicles per hill (panicle-number type), in others increase in weight of the panicle (panicle-weight type).[708]

Tanaka, in his studies on paddy nutrition states[647] that the comparative efficiency of a short duration *indica* variety, in this case Ptb 10, and a *japonica* variety (Aikoku) showed that the *indica* variety thrives at 20 ppm of nitrogen, but at higher levels the grain yield decreases. The *japonica* variety grows well at a nitrogen level of 60 ppm, but at higher nitrogen levels yield is still maintained. The *japonica* variety gives a very poor yield at 20 ppm and less, the grain yield at this level being even poorer than that of the *indica* variety. The efficiency of nitrogen utilization by the two varieties was measured by the ratio of soluble to protein nitrogen in the plant both at vegetative and reproductive stages. At the reproductive stage the *indica* variety has a higher ratio of soluble to protein nitrogen both at 60 and 150 ppm nitrogen than that of the *japonica* variety, showing a disturbed nitrogen metabolism of *indica* under high manuring conditions. The depression of grain yield of *indica* at higher nitrogen levels is also seen to be due to decrease both in the number of filled grains per panicle and weight of 1,000 grains, factors which are mainly decided at the reproductive stage. It is concluded that the nitrogen metabolism of *indica* becomes disturbed at the reproductive stage due to excess nitrogen, and the variety is not able to utilize nitrogen efficiently for grain formation. The *japonica* variety utilizes nitrogen efficiently under high manuring conditions and gives greater yield.

Tanaka also shows[646] why nitrogen applications to *indica* varieties should be given in split applications. He found that when grown at low levels of nitrogen (10 ppm), *indica* varieties have two peak periods of partial nitrogen efficiency for grain production, viz.: the tillering stage, which determines the number of tillers and panicles, and the flowering stage between boot- and milk-stage, influencing grain weight per panicle. When grown at high levels of nitrogen (60 ppm), there is one peak period of partial efficiency, the tillering stage, by which time sufficient nitrogen is stored in the vegetative parts to supply the needs of the reproductive organs later on. Further nitrogen supplies reduce grain yield and render the plant susceptible to disease. Thus, *indica* varieties should be given split applications of nitrogen, the first as a basal dressing at an early stage of vegetative growth, the second as a top dressing at the reproductive stage.

The paddy plant depends mainly for its nitrogen upon the decomposition of organic matter under anaerobic conditions, and in the early stages of growth takes up its nitrogen in the form of ammonia and not as nitrates.[330] It also receives a small amount dissolved in rainwater.[293] Many experiments could be quoted to prove that the application of nitrogen as nitrates in the early stages of growth is without effect or is even deleterious to the plant. This may be because nitrates are easily leached and in solution are lost to the plant, while the deleterious effect may be due to the conversion of nitrates to nitrites. In the later stages of growth manuring with nitrates has sometimes proved to be advantageous. This lack of favourable response to sodium nitrate is not thought to be due to the effect on the physical condition of the soil.[392] The utilization by paddy of ammonia and nitric nitrogen is affected by the reaction of the medium, but plants supplied with ammonia make better growth at all reactions than those supplied with nitrate.[600] Bamji[65] found that there is no increase in inorganic nitrogen under field conditions with the addition of fertilizers. The ammoniacal nitrogen is higher than the nitrate nitrogen and while no relationship exists between nitrate nitrogen and organic nitrogen, the ratio between ammoniacal nitrogen and organic nitrogen is more or less constant. Geus[208] explains the relatively small response to nitrogenous fertilizers, which is experienced in some parts of south-east Asia, notably in Indonesia and the western side of the Malay peninsula, to the great activity of nitrogen-fixing organisms found in these areas, which seem able to supply practically all the nitrogen needed by the plant.

NITROGEN FIXATION IN PADDY SOILS

Most authorities are agreed that paddy soils have the power to fix nitrogen but are not agreed as to how this takes place. *Azotobacter* are always found in large numbers in paddy soils and these, in association with algae in the presence of growing paddy roots, may bring about fixation. Uppal[673] *et al.*, writing of the soils of Karjat, India, observe that *Azotobacter* has an important rôle in the nitrogen recuperation of paddy soils. The species is stimulated when associated with the growing roots of paddy, which seem to increase the efficacy of bacterial nitrogen fixation. They further state that there is a marked periodicity in the number of bacteria, and during the monsoon there is an increase in the nitrogen content of paddy soils. Fallow soils do not support a large population of *Azotobacter*. Ruinen[574] has found nitrogen-fixing bacteria in Indonesian water and soils, demonstrating that such bacteria are plentiful in both acid and alkaline soils. De[161] agrees that algae are the main agents of nitrogen fixation in paddy-fields, but denies the importance of bacteria. Writing at a later date, Sulaiman[637] remarks that the abundant growth of algae is common in submerged paddy-fields, but the dead algae do not provide a source of energy for *Azotobacter*. He suggests that algal growth in the fields does not assist growth of *Azotobacter* or nitrogen fixation. Dhar and Mukerjie[172] had previously asserted that nitrogen fixation can take place in the complete absence of bacteria provided energy is available from the photochemical or induced oxidation of sugars.

De[161] proved that a considerable amount of nitrogen is fixed in alkaline soils when they remain submerged and exposed to sunlight, the addition of calcium carbonate to acid soils stimulating both algal growth and nitrogen fixation. Four species of blue-green algae, three *Anabaenas* and one *Phoridium*, were shown to be responsible for this nitrogen fixation. Investigators in India have also isolated a more acid-tolerant *Azotobacter* (*Az. indicum*) capable of fixing nitrogen, while preliminary results are quoted by Sethi[597] showing that there are one or more nitrogen-fixing bacteria within the tissue of the leaves. From 643 samples of blue-green algae collected from paddy fields in east and south-east Asia, Watanabe *et al.*[692] found thirteen species able to fix atmospheric nitrogen. These species belong to the genera *Tolypothrix, Nostoc, Schizothrix, Calothrix, Anabaenopsis* and *Plectonema*, all of which are plentiful in tropical and semi-tropical regions but scanty in the more temperate parts of Japan,

North China, Manchuria, Korea and Sakhalin. As the result of experiment S. Nishigaki, in co-operation with Watanabe, concluded[692] that *Tolypothrix* had a definite effect on paddy plants while no such effect was found with *Anabaenopsis*. *Tolypothrix* fixed about 22·5 kg. of nitrogen per hectare and the paddy plants absorbed about 4·8 kg. of nitrogen more than the control, the unabsorbed nitrogen being absorbed the following year. De and Mandal[162] determined the amount of nitrogen fixed by algae in paddy soil under waterlogged condition by weekly analyses of the gases in the soil atmosphere. In cropped but unfertilized soils fixation varied from 13·4 to 44·4 lb. nitrogen per acre, more than 50 per cent of the fixation taking place in the first four weeks after transplantation. It is clear that, as most paddy soils devoid of these specific blue-green algae can support paddy plants and also maintain a more or less constant level of nitrogen, there must be other sources of nitrogen recuperation. Various authorities have shown that the presence of growing roots is concerned with nitrogen fixation. Chakraborty and Sen Guppa describe[109] experiments in culture solutions indicating that the plant is able to synthesize elementary nitrogen under conditions of nitrogen starvation, but this ability decreases with age of the paddy. Hart and Roberts, however, disprove this,[252] pointing out that the apparent nitrogen fixation by paddy grown in hydroponics is due to the fact that nitrate content of plants grown in solution is abnormally high when compared with paddy plants growing under natural conditions. Reliance on Kjeldahl nitrogen determinations, therefore, results in apparent decrease in "fixation" in older plants.

Harrison and Aiyer[251] have sought to explain how nitrogen fixation takes place and how the roots of the paddy plant—a dry-land root and not an aquatic—are provided with the necessary oxygen. They showed that the chief gases produced during fermentation are methane, hydrogen, carbon dioxide and nitrogen. These, on rising to the surface, encounter active aerobic bacteria which oxidize methane to carbon dioxide and hydrogen to water. Carbon dioxide is then taken up by the green algae present on the surface and oxygen is liberated. Thus the undesirable gases are removed and only oxygen and nitrogen are evolved for the root system. Evidence has also been adduced to show that plant roots assist in facilitating oxidation changes in the soil.

Many writers have endeavoured to discover the condition of nitrogen in the soil and its relationship with the paddy plant. Bhuigan[83] showed that the total nitrogen in the soil remains practically constant throughout the year. He found that the ammonia content reached a considerably higher level soon after waterlogging; it then decreased and remained at a low level. Nitrate was absent during the waterlogging period, but may accumulate after harvest. Hydrolysable nitrogen fluctuated irregularly. Soluble nitrogen was at its maximum in July and August. The results, on the whole, show that the two different conditions that exist in a paddy-field have little influence on the organic make-up of the soil. Barrera[67] determined the nitrogen content of the soil during the four stages in the growth of irrigated paddy. Generally he found that the nitrogen content during the last sampling was greater than that obtained when the soil was flooded and before the application of fertilizer. Aoki[52] showed that the reduction of nitrate attained a maximum on the seventh day after the soil became waterlogged. The reduction of nitrate increased with rise of temperature to 35° C. and with the lowering of the soil potential.

Sethi[597] summarizing the investigations on manuring paddy in India, states that where fermentation takes place under swampy conditions of an anaerobic nature, instead of nitric acid, ammonia is produced, which is readily assimilated by the paddy plant. The nitrates, on decomposition under this condition, liberate the nitrogen in the free state, in which it is of no use to the plant. Loss of ammonia will be slight for although it is soluble in water, the soil has such a great attraction for ammonia that it removes it from the solution and prevents its loss by leaching. Thus ammonium compounds or substances which yield ammonia under anaerobic conditions are more useful as manures than are nitrates.

RESPONSE TO NITROGENOUS FERTILIZERS

The effect on the plant of increasing the amount of nitrogen in the soil by the application of fertilizers has been studied in many countries. While field experiments have shown that there is no definite correlation between crop productivity and the C:N ratio of the soil,[294] and no significant correlation between soil nitrogen and the nitrogen percentage in the grain,[686] yet ammoniacal fertilizers alone and in combination with other artificials will result in an increase in the whole grain weight, mainly in the endosperm and not in the husk and bran.[674] Soriano[624] found that the leaves of plants fertilized with ammonium sulphate contained more chlorophyll and less ash than those receiving sodium nitrate, and by increasing the ratio of nitrogen application, the water content of the leaves was increased and the ash decreased. Libatique[362] found that the application of ammonium sulphate in moderate quantities tended to develop and in large quantities to retard root development of paddy. On the other hand, lack of nitrogen is considered[323] to be responsible for most of the abnormal growth and low yields.

In the first stages of growth, inorganic fertilizers, e.g. quick manures, are more effective in producing growth than organic manures, but the latter produce healthier plants.[324] Ammonium sulphate, or other fertilizers that supply nitrogen in the form of ammonia, are the most effective for paddy in its early stages, although Dennett[169] found that insoluble nitrogen was more effective than ammonium sulphate. There is, however, a considerable weight of evidence that, after the first few years of application when yields are considerably increased, the continued use of ammonium sulphate over a number of years causes deterioration of fertility and decline in yields. Chang[118] et al. have remarked on this decline, while Rhind and Tin,[556] growing paddy continuously on the same land for ten years, found that 100 lb. per acre per annum of ammonium sulphate gave yields always significantly higher than those not treated, but that after the first three years the increase in yield declined from the maximum of 1,062 lb. per acre to a minimum of 321 lb. per acre. These observations suggest that the balance between the nitrogen and other fertilizing elements required adjustment. Anderson[18] et al. have observed that, provided other nutrients are not the limiting factor, yields are substantially increased by the addition of a nitrogen fertilizer. They compare the efficacy of urea and ammonium nitrate with ammonium sulphate and conclude that ammonium sulphate is usually the most efficient nitrogen fertilizer, but that urea is often to be preferred. The Japanese Ministry of Agriculture concludes[47] that urea, when deeply placed, gives the highest yield, but the longer that irrigation is delayed after application, the lower the yield. This conclusion is contrary to usual expectation. The relative merits between top and basal dressings are not yet known. Tokuoka[664] is of opinion that urea-gypsum is equal or superior to ammonium sulphate.

A new fertilizer, Oxamide, is designed to regulate the supply of nitrogen to the plant. The fertilizer is obtained by mixing pure oxamide with superphosphate and potassium chloride, the mixture being then granulated. Its percentage composition is nitrogen 11·1, phosphoric acid 8·3 and potash 8·9. Having little solubility in water, the nitrogen is gradually decomposed into organic nitrogen by soil micro-organisms. It has no injurious effect on germination and growth of plants and it may be mixed with almost all materials for compounding fertilizers.

Trials in Japan showed that Oxamide fertilizer supplied but little nitrogen to paddy in the earlier stages of growth, when it is less necessary, but supplied a fair amount later, when nitrogen was especially necessary for the plant. Timely supply of nitrogen to the plant and less development of nitrite helped the fertilizer to raise the yield of paddy 24 to 45 per cent.

Investigators in India, as a result of a long series of experiments, have come to the conclusion that paddy in all circumstances responds to the application of nitrogen. Sethi[597] states that it is difficult to find an instance where the application of nitrogen failed to show a response, while Gushchin[236] states that nitrogen is found to be the most necessary fertilizer in the Soviet Union.

In many regions it has been found that while the young paddy plant responds to ammoniacal nitrogen and not to nitrate nitrogen, in the later stages of growth nitrate nitrogen is effective. Investigations in India, summarized by Sethi[597] showed that from a solution of ammonium sulphate the plant in all stages of growth absorbed a greater quantity of ammonium ions than of sulphate ions:

The absorption of ammonium ions decreased as the plants aged. The absorption of ammonium ion is independent of the presence or absence of nitrate ions or any other ion, as the same quantity of ammonium ions was absorbed from all solutions at a particular stage of growth. It was considered possible that the absorption of ammoniacal nitrogen in the early stages of growth of the rice plant and of nitrate ions in the later stages might be correlated to the iso-electric point of the proteins of the protoplasm of the tissues of the rice plant. The changes in the *p*H value of the soil, of rice plants treated respectively with ammonium sulphate, sodium nitrate and a mixture of the two salts on an equal nitrogen basis, and of untreated rice plants, were therefore determined. The *p*H value of the soil manured with sodium nitrate was always the highest, of the soil manured with ammonium sulphate lowest, while that of the soil manured with a mixture, midway between the two. It was found that the iso-electric point of the plant tissue lay between *p*H 4·1 and *p*H 4·4. At this hydrogen-ion concentration the proteins of the protoplasm will neither behave as acids nor bases, as the electric discharge on the proteins is neutral. The preferential absorption of ammoniacal ions in the earlier stages was thus found to be due to the electric charge on the proteins of the cells.

PHOSPHORUS

Apart from phosphates brought in solution or suspension in irrigation water, there is no natural means of increase of this element in the field, and as the plant removes considerable quantities from the soil, it may be anticipated that the crop will readily respond to applications of phosphate. Manuring with phosphates frequently gives increased yields, but in many cases it has failed to show any response. Phosphates tend to increase the yield of grain but not of straw,[118]

R

while from Greece it is reported[432] that in a loamy soil deficient in phosphate and rich in nitrogen and potash, the addition of phosphate not only increased yield but caused the crop to ripen earlier.

In sand cultures, Sircar and Sen[605] found that progressive phosphate deficiency led to progressive reduction in height and tillering. The intake of nitrogen was found to depend on the phosphorus concentration, and they concluded that phosphorus is not only useful in the early stages of growth, but may be utilized in the later stages of development. Phosphate and potash increase the growth of roots relative to tops, whereas nitrogen increases the growth of tops.[589] In Malaya it was found that the addition of phosphate had a more marked effect on light soils than on heavy soils, while from Japan it is reported[530] that larger quantities of phosphate are used on soils derived from volcanic ash than on sandy or alluvial soils. In Japan the amount of phosphoric acid applied is greater in the cold regions than in the warm regions.

There are often long-sustained residual effects from phosphate dressings on paddy soils, particularly those with a montmorillonite type of clay. Rhind and Tin[557] demonstrated residual effects in Lower Burma giving measurable increases in yield over ten years and, by extrapolation, probably much longer. This long persistence of phosphorus in the soil indicates the need for caution in laying down fertilizer trials involving phosphorus, since results may be vitiated by previous applications. In common with other soils those of paddy-fields fix phosphates in varying degrees and this fixation may be very great in acid soils containing large amounts of free iron and aluminium, such as occur under tidal conditions on old mangrove lands. Here the degree of phosphate fixation may be so great as to prevent response of the paddy to phosphate dressings unless accompanied by calcium. Phosphate availability is greatest above pH 6·5, becoming very low below pH 6·0 and, because of fixation, small dressings are sometimes quite ineffective, there being little or no response until a sufficient quantity has been applied to overcome the fixation inherent in the soil. Initial dressings, therefore, may have to be considerably higher than subsequent dressings. Moreover, it may be advantageous to make large applications at longer intervals, rather than to give small annual doses.

POTASSIUM

Potassium is less generally required on paddy soils, probably because such soils are usually of a heavy nature and contain adequate quantities of this element. Chang *et el.*[118] found that potash did not affect yields. Similar results are general, but on light soils potash frequently gives an increased yield. In Japan[530] the yield of irrigated paddy is not materially increased by applications of potash above 20 lb. per acre. While potash is generally ineffective in increasing yields, when used in conjunction with the application of nitrogen and phosphorus it frequently produces higher yields. On the upland areas of the Philippines, potash is found to be the soil base absorbed in greatest amount. The conclusions of Koyanagi[341] concerning the use of potash in Japan were that without potash plants had a higher percentage of sugar and a lower percentage of starch than those receiving potash: excess potash is to be avoided, but small additions of this element to the soil are beneficial.

Potassium is less fixed in soils than phosphorus but nevertheless is retained to a large extent. The availability is not markedly influenced by soil reaction but there is some falling off under very acid conditions (below pH 5). Some evidence exists that where there is no lack of potash, further additions may have a small negative effect on yields and too much potash in the nursery appears to have the delayed effect of reducing tillering. The inclusion of potash in fertilizer mixtures is not warranted merely on an "insurance" or "balancing" principle unless it is demonstrably in deficit.

CALCIUM

Paddy appears to flourish best in a slightly acid soil. It might reasonably be expected, therefore, that additions of calcium to the soil would be without effect on yield. While in most cases this is true, on some very heavy soils, or under very acid conditions, the application of calcium may exert a beneficial effect and may also stimulate nitrogen fixation. In some parts of India[597] the addition of calcium is only useful in large quantities and this is found to be uneconomic.

While lime may or may not affect yield, there is evidence that its application influences the composition of the rice grain. Deguchi found[165] that when applied to the soil at the time of panicle initiation, it increased the protein content and hardness of the grain, but when applied later, before heading, the content of calcium, reducing sugar and non-protein nitrogen in the grain increased.

SULPHUR

Lack of sulphur causes stunted growth with yellowing of the leaves.[8] Though seldom encountered in acute form it has been observed in some areas and a moderate deficiency may possibly be more widespread than is commonly thought.

In a series of papers published between 1956 and 1960, Tokunaga and Tokuoka reported[662] the results of their studies on the influence of sulphur on the growth of paddy. Among their findings, they show that sulphur applied to young plants increased growth, number of leaves and yield. When sulphur supply was cut off at the early stage of plant growth (about 30 days after transplanting) it caused disturbance in the sulphur and nitrogen metabolism of the plant, and growth and yield were depressed; by the fiftieth day however, the effect was small, while removal of sulphur on the seventieth and ninetieth day had no adverse effect on the plant. Both total and organic sulphur was most concentrated in the ears at the seventieth day from transplanting.

Improved yields have been obtained in a number of countries by treating alkaline soils with sulphur. Karim and Khan Majlis,[325] for instance, in Pakistan, applied six to 50 lb. sulphur per acre to soil containing 33 ppm sulphur. Plant height, earliness in attaining maximum height, leaf area and number of tillers were favourably affected. Yield of grain increased with application of sulphur up to 25 lb. per acre. In Arkansas,[31] alkaline soils treated with iron sulphate and top-dressed with nitrogen gave nearly double the originally very poor yields.

It has been suggested[9] that the absorption of iron and manganese by the paddy plant is related to the intake of sulphur. Sulphur deficiency may be corrected by the application of 10 lb. per acre of sulphur, or as pyrites, gypsum, manganese sulphate or other sulphates, nitrogenous or phosphatic fertilizers containing sulphur, but farmyard manure will not supply the necessary sulphur. Usually the sulphur contained in fertilizers, such as ammonium sulphate and single superphosphate, is adequate to overcome any sulphur deficiency. In fact, responses to these common fertilizers may not always be due to their nitrogen or phosphorus alone, but also to the sulphur they contain. Alleged residual effects from ammonium sulphate should be regarded as suspect unless a sulphur response is definitely excluded, and in basic studies of fertilizer requirements, it is desirable to regard sulphur as a major nutrient and to arrange for its observation separately from nitrogen, phosphorus or potassium.

BALANCE OF FERTILIZER ELEMENTS IN THE SOIL

Application of a single element to the soil is usually found to be beneficial only within fairly narrow limits. This is but to be expected, for such single additions, if applied in quantity, must upset the balance of fertilizer materials in the soil. The amount of any one element which the plant can absorb depends on this balance.

Shibuya and Saeki,[601] for instance, showed that the intake of ammonia nitrogen by paddy causes greater absorption of phosphoric acid than does the intake of nitric nitrogen, which contributes to greater absorption of potash; and Okada[448] states that the application of phosphorus increases the absorption of nitrogen by paddy and hastens maturity. On the light sandy and clay-loam soils in the Central Provinces of India, Dave[155] found that high and profitable yields were obtained only with phosphorus and nitrogen fertilizers, the most effective $N:P_2O_5$ ratio being 1:1. Ichikawa[285] in Japan concluded that a deficiency of phosphorus and nitrogen decreased yield, silica and nitrogen increased it, while those of phosphorus and calcium decreased the yield. General experience concerning the application of fertilizers on paddy-land has resulted in the accumulation of considerable knowledge on manuring the crop with mixtures containing varying amounts of nitrogen, phosphorus and potash, but with very little exact knowledge on the nutritional requirements of paddy. Necessarily, the most suitable proportions of the elements to apply will vary according to the nature of the soil, especially in view of the fact that in some instances no increase in yield results from the application of fertilizers. But to give a few typical instances one may quote the following: in Madras, the most remunerative application is stated to be 30 lb. nitrogen and 20 lb. phosphoric acid. In the Central Provinces of India 20 lb. nitrogen and 20 lb. phosphoric acid have been recommended.[155] In Japan[530] the optimum applications appear to range from about 50 to 90 lb. nitrogen, 35 to 70 lb. phosphoric acid and 18 to 50 lb. of potash. In Thailand, departmental recommendations are stated to be 44 lb. phosphoric acid and 22 lb. nitrogen, while in Indo-China the standard recommendation is 9 to 18 lb. nitrogen and 36 lb. phosphoric acid. In Bulgaria,[358] 58 lb. phosphoric acid, 30 lb. nitrogen and 30 lb. potash are recommended.

TRACE ELEMENTS

Knowledge of trace elements in relation to paddy growth is incomplete, but there is reason to believe that they play an important rôle in all stages of development of the plant. It is possible that the limiting factor of growth and yield is frequently to be found in the deficiency or excess of an element or elements in the soil other than nitrogen, phosphorus and potassium, although the plant requirements of such element or elements may be very small.

Iron and manganese are undoubtedly the two most important of these trace elements. An average crop removes about 1 lb. of iron from the soil and a similar quantity of manganese. Iron deficiency results in chlorosis and most commonly occurs in calcareous soils. Usually farmyard manure will serve to counteract any such deficiency and spraying with ferrous sulphate is also effective. In parts of Japan,[531] particularly on sandy soil, the iron content in paddy-fields has been so depleted that a condition of "iron-podzolization" has resulted. Paddy grown on such soil is particularly susceptible to brown spot disease, which it is found may be substantially reduced if "iron-rich" soil, up to about 50 tons per acre, from Red Podzolic soils is added. The addition of this red silty clay also results in improving the growth of paddy. The beneficial factor is believed to be iron, but some investigations indicate that manganese and soluble silica are of importance in reducing brown spot disease and in the improvement of growth and yield. Iron deficiency is frequently associated with calcareous soils where it is overcome by spraying or applications of iron sulphate.

When Red Podzolic soil is not available, the addition of iron filings is recommended by Japanese authorities, while in some districts mud balls, made of iron-rich subsoil and ammonium sulphate, are placed between the rows of paddy plants.

Deficiency of manganese may occur in neutral calcareous or very sandy soils, but is not common. Excess of manganese, however, is quite common and may exert a toxic effect through suppression of iron availability. Paddy in flooded soil[634] will tolerate large quantities of soluble iron and manganese if the soil is supplied with actively decomposing matter.

Symptoms of boron, copper and zinc deficiency have been obtained in cultural solutions, but field evidence is incomplete. Tokuoka and Mooruka[665] showed that a small amount of boron added to the soil increased germination and yield, but had no effect on the straw or roots. Tokuoka[663] also states that traces of boron were almost without influence on increase in dry weight, though within defined limits it may increase yield of grain, or accelerate leaf growth, while reducing nitrogen intake.

A minute trace of zinc is said to speed up growth of the plant and to increase grain yield, but in cultural solution it is toxic beyond 1 p.p.m. It is suggested that up to this limit zinc favourably affects nitrogen intake, the C/N ratio of the plant being proportional to the amount of zinc added.

Minute traces of copper have a favourable effect on growth, maturation and yield, but larger amounts are toxic. There is evidence that progressive traces of copper increase the amount of nitrogen in the stem and root. The copper content of the paddy plant shows regular fluctuations in the course of development, absorption being at the maximum during the period of rapid growth and at the time of seed production.[587]

In water cultures, the addition of silicon to the solution proves beneficial, an effect which is more marked the greater the amount of nitrogen given. The absence of silicon in nutrients reduces the amount of nitrogen, phosphorus and potassium absorbed and translocated by the plant. To promote efficiency of nitrogen, lime silicate has given good results. The consumption of lime silicate in Japan increases annually; in 1957 over 476,000 tons were applied to more than a million acres. Increase of grain and straw is due to added silica, decrease to increasing doses of phosphorus.

Resistance to blast disease is stated to increase with silica supply and to decrease with the amount of fertilizer given when the soil moisture is sufficient. There also appears to be a relationship between silica content of the plant and resistance to certain insect pests, particularly stem borers.

In pot cultures, increases of yield beyond those derived from ammonium sulphate alone were obtained by the addition of manganese, zinc and copper, singly or in combination. Japanese work has also shown the stimulating effect of sodium fluoride on the growth of paddy, but quantities over 1 lb. per acre were toxic.

Pot experiments with vanadium additions showed that this element stimulated tiller development and increased yield of straw and grain, though at first the growth of straw was retarded. Vanadium may have some stimulating effect on *Azotobacter*.[601]

The above evidence concerning the importance of trace elements to paddy growth is sufficient to show that there are a number of elements whose presence is essential in available form to enable the plant to absorb nitrogen, phosphate and potassium, and these trace elements may profoundly affect the growth and development of the plant at all stages. Undoubtedly, large quantities of most of these trace elements are extremely toxic, and until their functions are better understood the practical application of much of this investigation must be postponed. It appears possible, however, that in many cases the absence or insufficiency of certain of these trace elements in the soil, or lack of balance between them and the nitrogen, phosphorus and potassium, may account for the fact that in certain areas of low yield the application of the usual fertilizers is followed by no significant increase of crop. Furthermore, resistance of the plant to certain diseases has been noted by several authorities; it may well be that increased knowledge of the ideal balance of certain trace elements in the soil may lead to developments in methods of disease control.

Russell[575] sums up the practical aspect of trace elements in the soil as follows:

Deficiencies of the trace elements need not be made good by adding the deficient element to the soil: it is often more economical either to spray it on the leaves of the plant or, if it is a tree, to insert pellets containing it under the bark in the trunk. Further, trace element deficiencies often occur in soils which contain adequate quantities of the element, but in a form unavailable to the plant. Under these conditions the deficiency cannot usually be made good by adding some of the element to the soil. In general, increasing the acidity of the soil by any means, such as placement of sulphur near the plant, for example, will increase the availability of all the trace elements except molybdenum. As a corollary, if an acid soil is suspected of having any trace element in minimal quantities, liming that soil may easily induce a deficiency of that element. Trace element deficiencies have the characteristic that their severity on a soil depends very strongly on the season, hence the climate affects either the trace element requirements of the crop or else the availability of their compounds in the soil to the crop.

AREAS WITHOUT MANURES

Manuring paddy is such a complicated problem and the evidence as to its efficacy is so conflicting, that it is unwise to be too dogmatic on the subject. Comparison with other cereals provides no guide to the manurial requirements of the crop, for whereas other cereals are grown on dry land, paddy is grown in water. Vast areas under paddy have been cultivated annually in Asia for centuries without manuring, yet the yield remains at a remunerative, although low, level. Historical records show that yields in India were about 50 per cent higher during the Mogul period than at present,[512] but this proves nothing since it is probable that, with the smaller population of that time, cultivators confined their energies to the more fertile lands.

It is argued that the consistant yields obtained under present conditions are invariably low and that when fertilizers are employed as in Japan, China and Europe, yields are high. It is probable, however, that these high yields are largely the result of latitude, longer sunshine, the effect of frost on the soil in the winter months, rotation of crops and to the fact that the varieties of paddy grown are usually the *japonica* type which respond to manures. It might reasonably be expected that if the manured paddy-lands of Asia were so deficient in plant food as to produce minimum crops, the application of almost any fertilizer would produce an immediate and great response, but this is by no means always the case.

Artificial manures have been applied with success in many countries, but in the East, although significantly increased yields have been recorded in numerous experiments, their use is by no means widespread, perhaps because of the widely divergent results obtained, but also in no small measure because the poverty of cultivators precludes them from purchasing such manures. Ignatieff[286] has deplored the fact that in some countries experiments with fertilizers have been postponed on the ground that their use would not be profitable to the cultivator. This, he points out, is unfortunate, because it takes many years for experimentation to develop sound recommendations for fertilizers. Further, technical advances have been made in the manufacture of fertilizers and it may well be that prices of these materials may eventually come within reach of cultivators who cannot afford them at present. In many countries increased agricultural production is of such importance that a subsidy on fertilizers is considered a national advantage. Ignatieff's statement concerning the postponement of fertilizer experiments is misleading. Experiments have been carried out in almost every country where paddy is grown, and although much of this experimental work cannot be statistically examined by modern methods, had the results been strikingly in favour of manuring (as might be expected with a crop grown on the same land yearly over a period of centuries) either experiments would have been continued or manuring would have become commonly employed. It is agreed, however, that the need for further experiments is most desirable.

Foliar analysis may assist in determining the fertilizer requirements of the crop. Go and Schuylenborgh have shown[213] that foliar analysis of paddy in an early stage of development is a good indicator. They state that a crop age of about 30 days is suitable for the analysis, because the plant is relatively small. The whole plant may be taken for analysis.

The paddy crop removes from the soil considerable quantities of plant food and no completely satisfactory explanation is forthcoming as to how soil fertility is maintained in the absence of manuring. The proportion of straw to grain and husk is roughly 5:4. According to Sampietro[580] this ratio depends on variety, manuring, climate, temperature of irrigation water, time of harvesting, soil, the ratio increasing with large fertilizer applications. On the other hand, Haigh[240] states that the relationship between the amount of grain and straw is not seriously affected by spacing or type of soil. That the amount of food removed by the crop varies widely under different conditions is shown by the figures given by the following three authorities. Jack[297] states that a crop of 2,800 lb. paddy removes (in lb.) the following: with the straw 24·5 lb. nitrogen, 2·5 lb. phosphoric acid and 60 lb. potash; with the paddy are 42 lb. nitrogen, 9·5 lb.

phosphoric acid and 10 lb. potash. According to Sahasrabuddhe[578] the paddy crop removes an average of 28 lb. nitrogen, 20 lb. phosphoric acid, 60 lb. potash and 28 lb. calcium. Camus[104] states that an average production of 1,550 lb. paddy per acre removes from the soil approximately 20 lb. nitrogen, 10 lb. phosphoric acid and 5 lb. potash, while a similar amount of straw contains about 11 lb. nitrogen, 2·5 lb. phosphoric acid and 28 lb. potash.

In the following table, Ochse *et al.* quoting Penders, show[444] that paddy straw removes nearly as much nitrogen and phosphoric acid as does the grain, but the roots contain little of either element. Straw, however, contains several times the quantity of potassium as other parts of the plant. The importance of silica will be noted.

TABLE 17

PLANT NUTRIENTS REMOVED BY A CROP OF PADDY

Lb. per acre, Percentage of Yield and Ratio Air-dried Crop

Part of Crop	Yield	N	P_2O_5	K_2O	CaO	MgO	Fe_2O_3	SiO_2
Paddy	2170	20·8	10·8	10·9	1·3	3·9	1·4	132·7
Straw	4400	19·6	10·2	46·0	12·0	5·0	38·1	83·8
Roots	1780	4·3	1·3	6·7	2·7	1·3	31·8	81·5
	Plant Nutrients as Percentage of Yield							
Paddy		0·96	0·498	0·527	0·062	0·181	0·058	6·13
Straw		0·45	0·231	1·050	0·272	0·113	0·864	1·90
Roots		0·24	0·076	0·378	0·152	0·071	1·803	4·62
	Ratio (N=1)							
Paddy		1	0·52	0·53	0·64	0·19	0·06	6·38
Straw		1	0·52	2·34	0·6	0·25	1·94	4·27
Roots		1	0·31	1·56	0·6	0·28	7·43	1·91

In many regions in Asia the straw is not removed from the fields, but in other cases it is removed and put to various uses. The removal of straw depletes the land of considerable quantities of plant food.

FERTILIZING THE NURSERY

In most countries experiments in fertilizing the nursery have shown that the practice does not result in higher yields of paddy. In India, Sethi[597] sums up the experimental work in that country by stating that at most centres no advantage was found as a result of the practice, although in a few places useful results were obtained by the production of healthier and more vigorous seedlings with better developed root systems, but the yield from manured and unmanured seedlings did not show significant difference except when some adverse climatic factors, such as drought, set in, when the crop raised from manured seed beds showed better performance. At Bogra (Bengal) manured seed beds showed better growth of seedlings than the unmanured beds and seedlings from the former beds were ten to fifteen days ahead of seedlings from the untreated plots. This result is considered of importance in places where the cultivators' seed beds are washed away by floods.

Experiments in the Philippines showed that, in general, plants fertilized in the field gave a higher yield than those unfertilized, or fertilized in the seed bed alone. They stress, however, the importance of fertilizing the nursery. In Spain the seed bed, which may be situated miles from the paddy-field, receives a heavy dressing of fertilizer. In Malaya[229] an experiment showed that the yield from seedlings grown in an unmanured nursery was higher than that from a manured nursery. Another report stated that the response to a nursery manuring in Malaya was spectacular, but no yield figures were given to support this claim.

While experiments have usually failed to show that there is any advantage in manuring the seed bed, the very great care taken in China and Japan in supplying the nursery with heavy applications of fertilizer must not be overlooked (see pages 131–32). In Japan,[531] ammonium sulphate and other fertilizers are mixed with the soil before the seed is sown. More nitrogen should be applied to the seed bed, it is claimed, in cold regions than in warm regions. The recommended amounts per square metre of seed bed are 22·5 grams or more in cold regions, 8 grams in temperate regions and 4·5 to 6 grams in warm regions. For all regions the phosphate application is about 12·5 grams of phosphoric acid per square metre and the potash about 13·5 grams (K_2O) per square metre. In Burma,[286] cultivators use cow dung at the rate of about 20 to 25 tons per acre in the nursery.

It would appear that many experimenters have missed the real implication of manuring the nursery. Plants raised in a manured nursery should be sufficiently large for transplanting earlier than those grown in an unmanured nursery. This should allow the manured plants a longer vegetative growth (i.e. tillering period) in the field, which should be reflected in increased yields (see page 71). Therefore, no advantage from a manured nursery is likely unless it results in a shorter period of growth in the nursery, and a correspondingly longer period in the field. One may conclude that, while fertilizing the nursery may give increased yields in some cases, particularly in cold regions, the increase is usually conditional on the plants being transplanted earlier than would otherwise be possible, while in any case the results are not comparable with manuring the crop in the field.

RESULTS OF EXPERIMENTS

A vast number of experiments have been carried out in many countries, most of which, unfortunately, appear to be unrelated to soil analysis, so that comparisons are difficult to make, while many were designed in such a way that they cannot be critically examined. Ignatieff,[286] however, has collected valuable information on the response of paddy to fertilizers together with notes on the soil types on which the trials were conducted. Many results have a local value and undoubtedly serve to stress the fact that practically throughout Asia manuring would materially increase yields.

BURMA

Experiments over a number of years showed that nitrogen and phosphates are the main constituents required. The addition of potash gives no increased yield. Results of manuring with different quantities of ammonium phosphate fertilizers containing about 20 per cent phosphoric acid are summarized as follows:

TABLE 18

RESULTS OF MANURING PADDY IN BURMA

Fertilizer lb. per acre	Increase in grain lb. per acre	Increase in grain per lb. of fertilizer applied
50	400	80
100	650	65
200	1,100	55
300	1,400	46
400	1,600	40

It was found that the best time to apply the fertilizer is just before the crop is sown or transplanted. Preparatory to the application, the water should be drained off of land and the fertilizer incorporated into the soil by going over the land with a harrow.

THAILAND

Phosphates appear to be the chief deficiency in Thailand, although small dressings of nitrogen also seem to be effective. The phosphate is usually applied in the form of superphosphate or ammophos and the nitrogen in ammoniacal form. It is said that the general increase in yield is about 15 per cent. The opinion is expressed that much of the low yield on the Central Plain is due to poor drainage and high soil acidity. Calcium, applied as a marl, seems to retard the early stages of paddy growth and makes no significant difference in the yield. Potassium is seldom effective.

INDONESIA

Phosphates on many soils give large increases of crop, the area deficient in this element being over a quarter of the total paddy area.

CEYLON

Phosphate is most needed on the average wet-zone paddy soils but nitrogen and potash are essential on the light and dry-zone soils. The quantity of nitrogen required is between 20 and 30 lb. per acre in the form of ammonium sulphate, applied at the final levelling before sowing, or preferably in two dressings, one at the final levelling and the second a month later. One hundredweight per acre of superphosphate should be applied with the nitrogenous fertilizer at the final levelling.

INDO-CHINA (Cambodia, Laos and Viet-Nam)

Potash alone or in combination with nitrogen has not been found very effective. Experiments conducted by Coyaud[141] showed that nitrogen increased yields over a wide range of conditions, phosphates increased yields on light soils, slightly on clay soils and invariably on alluvial soils, but only phosphates are profitable. The combination of phosphate and nitrogen gives large increases in yield, as much as 50 per cent in the initial season and 30 to 20 per cent in the subsequent two seasons. The Rice Bureau recommends the application of 9 to 18 lb. nitrogen as ammonium sulphate and 36 lb. phosphoric acid per acre.

PAKISTAN

Experiments show that the application of ammonium sulphate at 30 lb. nitrogen per acre gives a 10 to 20 per cent crop increase—provided that the crop does not lodge. Split applications have given the maximum response. Phosphoric acid, 30 lb. per acre as superphosphate to berseem clover and 30 lb. nitrogen as ammonium sulphate to the succeeding paddy crop, gave 11·4 per cent higher yield of paddy as compared with ammonium sulphate alone applied at 30 lb. nitrogen per acre. In another series of experiments, 40 lb. phosphoric acid as superphosphate applied before transplanting gave 450 lb. paddy per acre increase as compared with 40 lb. ammonium sulphate in two applications, while the application of this amount of phosphate with 40 lb. nitrogen gave no greater yield on one variety, although with another variety it gave 250 lb. more paddy.[59,60]

INDIA

The application of phosphate in the form of bone meal is particularly useful in the acid soils of Assam and has greatly helped the extension of the paddy area in the Khasi and Jainter hills,[597] but in a soil of pH 8 bone meal gave no significant increase of crop.[675] On light soils phosphorus is the limiting factor where there is no response to nitrogen alone.[155] Mineral phosphate, ground as finely as possible, is a suitable phosphatic manure when applied with decomposing matter.[607] Sethi,[597] in summing up the experimental work in India, states that both nitrogen and phosphorus tend to give increased yields, but the optimum rate of both manures seems to vary in different places, as might be expected in such a vast area. In Bihar, increased quantities of phosphoric acid are of no advantage to the crop unless the quantity of nitrogen is also increased considerably, the most favourable balance being in the ratio of 1:1. In the United Provinces, higher quantities of nitrogen in the presence of phosphoric acid are found effective. In Hyderabad the application of nitrogen and phosphoric acid in the ratio of $1:\frac{1}{2}$ is most suitable for the *kharif* crop. In another series of experiments nitrogen proved very successful in Bengal, the optimum dressing being 120 lb. ammonium sulphate applied at transplanting.

Recent reports state that experiments in cultivators' fields throughout India showed responses to potash in areas hitherto considered to be rich in this element. In Bihar, potash at 40 lb. per acre in combination with nitrogen and phosphorus can increase the yield of paddy by 160 to 240 lb. per acre. It is doubtful whether this increase is large enough to prove attractive to cultivators.

MALAYA

Experiments in Malaya showed that there appears to be a correlation between manuring and tillering, but none between tillering and yield, i.e. increases as a result of manuring have occurred in both tillering and yield but without causal connection. Except on very poor land, the response to artificials has been disappointing, usually insignificant or uneconomic. Exhaustive tests, carried out over a number of years and in different parts of the country, showed that for each area there is a maximum yield beyond which manuring gives no increase of crop. Were it not for the existence of small patches of land regularly giving yields of about 4,400 lb. per acre of paddy, it might be assumed that climatic conditions preclude yields of the order of those obtained in Japan, Spain and Italy.[77]

CHINA

The area over which paddy is grown in China is so great that no generalizations can be made regarding manuring. Manuring is intimately connected with the various operations of cultivation. The general practice is to manure the nursery and also the field. The manures used are generally those most easily obtained locally, such as dried cow dung, bone meal and peanut cake, while the well-to-do also employ ammonium sulphate. Gourley[221] states that there appears to be no exact relationship between yields and the amount of fertilizer used. He continues: "The most exhaustive use of fertilizers would certainly increase the production of rice in China but would not greatly affect the variations between different localities as in many cases there are limiting factors of greater importance than fertility. A district which produces heavy crops does not indicate a liberal use of fertilizers. It is often due to the suitability of conditions in general for rice growing."

JAPAN

The increase in yields of rice in Japan in recent years as a result of research work in various directions and in no small measure to intensive manuring, has been spectacular. In this connection, the value of research work on varieties should not be forgotten, while improved drainage and irrigation have contributed to these high yields. In support of this contention, the general use of large quantities of manures was practised in Japan before this striking increase in yield took place. Doubtless, subsequent investigations resulted in improvements in manurial practices, particularly in respect to time of application, but they have also been directed to greater knowledge of the economic use of artificials to supplement the natural manures already employed, rather than to replace them. The recent difficulty experienced in obtaining sufficient artificials has renewed interest in local sources of organic manures. The large amount of humus applied to the soil is to be noted, applied in the form of "natural" manures that are carefully collected and conserved, together with such by-products as fish waste and soya bean cake.

Nitrogen is by far the most important fertilizer influencing grain yield of both "wet" and "dry" paddy. Phosphorus and potash also have important influences on yield, especially on "dry" paddy. Optimum applications of these nutrients on "wet" paddy range from 55 to 110 lb. per acre, 20 to 55 lb. phosphoric acid and 35 to 70 lb. potash. Heavy application of nitrogen and potash has been found to cause an unequilibrium between organic and inorganic matter in the soil, resulting in an increase of worn out and low production areas. Experimental results obtained from ten stations throughout Japan show that yields from plots receiving no fertilizers averaged 54 per cent of the yields from plots receiving complete fertilizer (nitrogen, phosphates and potash). When phosphates and potash were added, but nitrogen omitted, yields were 59 per cent of those completely fertilized. Yields averaged 94 per cent when only potash was omitted from applied fertilizers.[530]

The effect on yields of "wet" paddy from varying amounts of nitrogenous fertilizers indicates only small yield increases when more than 100 lb. per acre is applied. Additions of increasing amounts of phosphorus have but little effect on raising yields above those obtained from the smallest application of about 18 lb. per acre of phosphoric acid. Further, yields are not materially raised by increasing applications of potash above 18 lb. per acre.

FORMOSA

Experiments show that the response of paddy to potassium in the red and yellow earths is generally higher than on the other soil groups. On the slate alluvial soils and acid sandstone and shale alluvial soils of the northern part of Formosa, the response is usually light and on alkaline soils no response is obtained.

THE NEAR EAST

Experiments on lateritic soils of the Yellow Earth type at Lenkoran in the province of Azerbaidjan on the Caspian Sea[413] showed that nitrogenous manures were the most important, ammonium sulphate, urea and calcium cyanamide being the best.

EGYPT

Paddy is grown on both light and heavy clay soils. Manurial experiments in the Sharqia Province, where the soil is of a sandy nature, showed that some of the delta soils are very deficient in phosphate, while increases from the addition of nitrogen are also found to be economic. Increases from phosphate application in one case was as much as 60 per cent.

ITALY

In Italy, very heavy manuring of paddy is usual. For example, for paddy-land planted for the first time after grass, 4 cwt. basic slag or superphosphate and 1 cwt. ammonium sulphate may be applied per acre: in addition, after the crop is established and after the first weeding, $2\frac{1}{2}$ cwt. per acre of superphosphate, $\frac{1}{2}$ cwt. sulphate of potash and 1 cwt. ammonium sulphate may be applied.[649]

UNITED STATES OF AMERICA

At the experimental stations in the southern States fertilizer experiments in which nitrogen, phosphate and potash have been applied singly and in combination at seeding time have not as a rule shown consistent or marked increases in yield. In the three most important States of the south, the results of applying fertilizers are so uncertain that it is recommended that preliminary tests should be carried out to determine whether nitrogen, phosphate, or both, are likely to be profitable. In California, fertilizers are widely used and experiments indicate that their use is justified. The application of ammonium sulphate at the rate of 100, 150 and 200 lb. per acre, of dried blood at 160 lb., of cotton seed meal at 280 lb. and dung at 1 ton per acre, applied just before seeding, gave increases of crop.

The official recommendation is that granular ammonium sulphate at 150 lb. per acre be applied at seeding time and many growers have found this practice profitable. Whitlow[697] reports that the fertilizer Aero-cyanamide, containing 20·6 per cent nitrogen, has been successfully applied by plane at 100 lb. per acre. He recommends that the application be made when the paddy is four to eight weeks old and when both ground and paddy are dry (no dew). The field should be flooded after the application.

FERTILIZER PRACTICES

Apart from Japan the results of experiments have found no wide application in Asia. In Burma and Thailand manuring paddy is unusual. In China some artificials are employed by those who can afford them, but the amount used is small in comparison with the total area cultivated. In Ceylon, Malaya, Indonesia and the Philippines, artificials are little employed. In Indo-China their use is well known and their employment extending. The country is fortunate in possessing local sources of supply. The use of fertilizers in Egypt is not common and where paddy is grown for reclaiming saline land no manuring is done. Most of the land in the Nile Delta is heavy clay and the value of manuring such land is becoming more widely recognized, as the old idea of the fertilizing value of Nile silt has been found to be much exaggerated.

In the United States there is no regular system of fertilizing paddy fields, reliance being placed on fallowing the land after a few crops of paddy have been removed. Interest in the subject, however, is increasing, since the farmer finds that while new fields are very productive, the yield of successive crops decreases to a marked degree, owing perhaps not to lack of plant food but to such causes as weed

S

increase, deterioration of physical condition, lack of humus, un-favourable conditions for the soil micro-organisms or to other causes.

Writing recently on fertilizing paddy in Louisiana, Patrick stated :[473]

The fertilizer recommendations for the rice area of South-west Louisiana call for the use of 40 to 80 pounds of nitrogen, 20 to 40 pounds of phosphate (P_2O_5) and 0 to 40 pounds of potash per acre. These recommendations are based on moderate production goals. . . . The use of fertilizers is now standard practice. This has not always been the case. Many of the early experiments in which nitrogen, phosphate and potash were tested showed that no increase or only a limited increase in yield could be expected from the use of fertilizer. . . . One reason why fertilizer usage has become a common practice is due to the fact that the soils of the rice area are generally poorer than they were in the past. Seventy years of growing rice has lowered the amounts of nitrogen, phosphorus and potassium that the soil can supply to the crop. Fertilizers are also essential at the present time because the higher yields of rice being produced as a result of the addition of certain plant nutrients having resulted in a drain on the native supplies of other nutrients. . . .

The most striking change in the soils of the rice area as a result of sixty to seventy years of rice growing has been the decline in organic matter and nitrogen and the deterioration of the soil properties that are dependent on organic matter. When the Coastal Prairie soils of Louisiana and Texas were first broken the organic matter content of the surface soil was in excess of 4 per cent. The surface 6 inches of virgin soil contained approximately 4,000 pounds of nitrogen per acre. The organic matter content of these soils has now fallen to around 1·5 per cent and the nitrogen content in the surface 6 inches is down to approximately 1,500 pounds per acre.

This most recently expressed opinion on manuring is quoted *in extenso* because it probably represents the situation in many regions of America and elsewhere.

The use of fertilizers in the U.S.A., states Beacher,[73] falls far short of minimum recommendations, which are 40 to 80 lb. nitrogen, with the addition on some soil types of 40 to 50 lb. phosphorus and 20 to 30 lb. potash per acre. This authority estimates that the average rice production of the United States of 42 bushels per acre is only 57 per cent of the potential production attainable by general use of fertilizer practices recommended by experimental stations. Since the above was written, heavier applications of fertilizers have become more usual in the United States and yields have increased in consequence.

In New South Wales heavy dressings of artificials are no longer applied to paddy. Formerly, 2 cwt. per acre of ammonium sulphate was usual on the Murrumbidgee Irrigation Area, but with the advent of clover-rye grass pastures in wide rotation the use of this fertilizer is superfluous. Superphosphate is applied to the pasture at the rate of 1 cwt. per acre annually.

There remains, therefore, Japan, Spain and Italy where heavy dressings of artificials are regularly applied. As producers, all these countries, except Japan, are relatively unimportant, the crop being grown in restricted favourable areas. The importance of Japan, however, lies in the fact that paddy is grown there on a large scale within a wide range of latitude, climate and soils. Leonard[356] states that much use is made of manures, both natural and artificial, the fields receiving 58 to 135 lb. per acre of nitrogen, 35 to 90 lb. phosphoric acid and 50 to 100 lb. potash—not, of course, all in the form of artificials. Ammonium sulphate, calcium cyanamide, superphosphate, potassium sulphate and potassium chloride are, however, in great demand.

In Formosa, the Japanese used great quantities of artificials, particularly ammonium sulphate, to overcome the exhaustive effects of double cropping on a naturally poor soil. Before the war, Formosa probably consumed more nitrogenous fertilizers per unit of area than any other country in the world. About 1 cwt. ammonium sulphate was usually applied to the nursery shortly before sowing the seed. In addition to natural manures, 1 to 2 cwt. per acre of ammonium sulphate and superphosphate, or mixed artificials, were usually broadcast just before transplanting, but often half or more of the ammonium sulphate was applied as a top-dressing two or three weeks before transplanting. The second paddy crop was less heavily manured and in some districts given nothing—with consequent smaller crops. Before the war, an annually increasing proportion of the fertilizer requirements of paddy was supplied as artificials; difficulties in obtaining supplies in post-war years has necessitated greater reliance on natural and local sources of organic manures.

Under the Japanese, rice production in Korea was greatly expanded by the use of fertilizers, mostly produced in North Korea, but also imported from Japan and used on the great paddy-growing areas of South Korea. Post-war reduction of fertilizer imports, coupled with inability to obtain supplies from North Korea, have seriously affected rice production. Imported fertilizers have been supplied to growers at subsidized prices in order to stimulate rice production. Before the war, ammonium sulphate was applied just before transplanting. At the end of the war no ammonium sulphate was available and imports were mainly ammonium nitrate. The advisers to the South Korean Government found that if ammonium nitrate is applied in three or four applications as top-dressing after transplantation, the increased yield, per unit of nitrogen, is equal to that obtained from ammonium sulphate. They proved this point to the Koreans and by 1948 ammonium nitrate was widely used on paddy-fields.[189]

In passing, it is noted that the countries that use the heaviest dressings of artificial manures are usually sub-tropical countries that either obtain more than one paddy crop a year or grow a rotation of annual crops in which paddy is included perhaps about one year in four. Most of the paddy varieties grown are *japonica*, which are recognized as responding to manuring. Caution is therefore necessary in comparing fertilizer practices in these countries with regions in the tropics where one paddy crop is grown annually, and *indica* varieties are cultivated.

TIME OF APPLICATION OF FERTILIZERS

In general, it would appear that when heavy dressings of fertilizers are applied, the most satisfactory results are obtained by applying part shortly before transplanting and part as a top-dressing about a month later. The top-dressing is usually applied after removing water from the land, the water being readmitted soon after the fertilizer is applied. This process implies a degree of water control rarely possible in most Asian paddy areas.

In India,[597] the most suitable time for application varies in different localities; while in some places the application at different times does not produce any effect, at others it shows a marked increase of crop. Also in some areas the total quantity applied at one time seems more satisfactory than its application at two or three times and *vice versa*.

Time of application has been closely studied in Japan. The following recommendations for various climates, soils and paddy varieties have been laid down in that country.[531] (See Table 19).

The first top dressing is made twelve days after transplanting, the second twenty-four days after transplanting and the third application forty-eight days after transplanting. Top-dressing with nitrogen fertilizers normally takes place twenty-four days before the paddy heads. On a fertile field the application is sometimes delayed until about a fortnight before heading. The beneficial effect of top-dressing paddy with nitrogen at the booting stage has been explained[374] by the increase in chlorophyll content of the leaves as a result of the fertilization, thus making them more efficient in photosynthesis. Late nitrogen application, however, stimulates production of late tillers, which should be avoided for they either do not head or they

TABLE 19

RECOMMENDATIONS OF TIME OF APPLICATION OF FERTILIZERS FOR VARIOUS
CLIMATES IN JAPAN

Climate	Soil	Paddy variety	Percentage of total nitrogen for crop			
			Basic application	Application of top-dressing		
				First	Second	Third
Cold Inter-	Clay	Early maturing	80	20	0	0
mediate	Loam	Intermediate	50	50	25	0
Warm	Sand	Late maturing	30	20	20	30

result in uneven ripening of the crop. When calcium cyanamide is used as a top-dressing about 50 to 100 parts of soil are mixed with one part of the fertilizer, piled into a heap and moistened with water. The mixture is applied after decomposition of calcium cyanamide, indicated by cessation of heat evolution, is completed. Alternatively, several parts of wet soil are mixed with one part of calcium cyanamide, the mixture being applied immediately between the plant rows, care being taken that none shall fall on the paddy leaves. The toxic effect of calcium cyanamide[7] on paddy results in decreased vegetative growth but increased yield.

Californian soils are said to utilize nitrogen most effectively when the fertilizer is placed 1 to 4 inches into a dry seed bed immediately before the seed is sown. This prevents nitrification after flooding and the nitrogen is therefore available to the plant throughout its growing period.

METHODS OF APPLYING FERTILIZERS

In addition to the conventional methods of application of fertilizers, i.e. broadcasting, drilling and from aeroplanes, more recently introduced methods include foliar application and the application of nitrogen in irrigation water.

Research has shown that major nutrients and trace elements can be absorbed by plant leaves. The method is of particular value in applying nitrogen at the booting stage of development of paddy. For application of phosphates the method is stated to be very efficient, because 95 per cent of the fertilizer is thereby utilized by the plant. For correction of deficiencies of minor elements, foliar application is probably superior to soil application.[15, 709] In Hungary[493] no difference was observed between spray fertilization applied before the formation of panicles and after flowering. In the latter case only sprays of 2·5 per cent should be used, but sprays used before panicle formation using solutions of ammonium sulphate, potassium sulphate and superphosphate with concentration of 20 to 25 per cent may be applied at a rate of 45 lb. per acre. This solution does not cause burning and can be applied safely from planes. It gave responses five times greater than fertilization by conventional means.

Foliar application, however, should not be considered a substitute for soil fertilization with major elements, for its primary value is to supplement supply of nutrients at a critical stage of growth. Experiments in India[429] showed positive effects with urea and magnesium sulphate, but if given more than once to paddy depressed yield more often than not.

Application of nitrogen in irrigation water has been known for some years. Van Dijk, for instance, reported[175] that ammonia dissolved in irrigation water gave an increased yield of paddy, but losses of ammonia by evaporation were high, reaching 66 per cent in laboratory experiments. The extra yields were smaller and more uncertain than those given by an equivalent ammonium sulphate. Ammonia also injured the fish fauna. However, it is stated[22] that application of nitrogen in irrigation water is now being used successfully in Louisiana, Arkansas and Texas.

FERTILIZER REQUIREMENTS OF ASIA

The Rice Study Group at the Baguio Rice Meeting in 1948 appears to have accepted the principle that the paddy crop in Asia is in need of increased quantities of fertilizers, although indeed they did recommend "that more experimental work be carried out by the rice-producing countries to determine the most efficient practices with respect to kinds of fertilizers, rates of application, time and method of application, and the use of chemical fertilizers in combination with organic manures." Further, the F.A.O. Report of the meeting states: "There is no doubt that fertilizers are not utilized as they could be in the rice-producing countries. Experimental data are still lacking in most of these countries with regard to the efficient use of the various nitrogenous fertilizers with the exception of ammonium sulphate. Nor has the question of phosphate fertilizer received the attention it deserves. Mere lack of response to phosphate, for example, should not be a deciding factor as to its value. More critical experiments are necessary with regard to methods of application when used with a pulse crop grown in rotation with rice. The application of a balanced fertilizer treatment with nitrogen, phosphoric acid and potash should receive more consideration."

It cannot be claimed that the position has been greatly clarified in the years since the above was written. It must be remembered that no complete answer is yet forthcoming as to how the plant obtains its requirements of nitrogen, phosphate and potash with continual cropping over a period of years. The question is not answered by assuming that a low level of productiveness has now been reached, "a level at which the plant food removed by the annual crop is made good by the natural breakdown of the soil." Response to manuring in countries of low yield is so conflicting that it is evident that before a further series of manurial trials are laid down, further research is indicated as necessary towards correlating soil types in relation to yield and a study of the reasons for the successful growth of paddy on the same land over a number of years.

The value of organic manures is apt to be overlooked because of the great increases in yields frequently recorded as a result of applying artificials. The Japanese, in particular, are firm believers in the use of all forms of organic matter for paddy cultivation, although they also apply heavy quantities of artificials. They have also developed the use of green manures for which appropriate nitrifying bacteria are cultivated and distributed to farmers. Pauli reminds one[476] that the problem of maintaining soil fertility is more than balancing the input and output of nutrient elements. In reviewing the work on humus he shows how the concept of the positive effect of water-soluble compounds from manures on plant growth came to be associated with the hormone-like effect of the free humic acid present. The physiological importance of humic acids was established when it was discovered that when humic acids are added to the soil nearly all inorganic elements are absorbed to a greater extent by the plant. He adds that future research work on the influence of well-defined humic compounds in the soil on the plasma of the plant, in combination with the study of the uptake of ions by the plant, offer great opportunity to elucidate the intimate relations between plant and soil.

It is noted that the most fertile soils contain more freshly-formed humic acids than those of lower fertility. It is therefore suggested that rather than trying to increase the total amount of humus in the soil in admittedly difficult circumstances, the aim should be to add to the soil, regularly, fresh starting material in order to animate the dynamics of the cycle—plant and soil—through the interaction of humus and plasma colloids. It is, however, necessary to counsel a policy of caution in advocating the addition of organic matter to soils used for growing wet paddy; breakdown of bulky manures under anaerobic conditions can have a marked reducing effect, with production of hydrogen sulphide, and resulting sometimes in *Akiochi* "disease".

ORGANIC MANURES

Cultivators in Asia, especially in China and Japan, have for long made use of waste products for manuring their paddy fields. In the United States also, organic manures are recognized as invaluable for paddy. This opinion is officially expressed as follows: "Usually the soil nitrogen can be maintained by turning under organic matter, such as rice stubble, green manure crops, weeds, and other organic materials. In soils well supplied with organic matter, the decomposition of this material under submerged conditions usually liberates sufficient nitrogen as ammonia to meet the requirements of the rice plants."[311]

In China use is made of every conceivable source of manure. Waste is not thrown on the land without treatment or discrimination, it is carefully matured before application. In north China, night soil is composted under anaerobic conditions in the process of which much nitrogen is lost; in western China the composting is carried out under aerobic conditions, with little loss of nitrogen. The north China method consists in composting in pits, into which all kinds of refuse material are thrown—human excreta, decayed vegetables, wood and straw ash, animal manure and the like. Pigs wallow in this mixture and add their excreta. Soil is added and after several months the resulting compost is ready for use. In the western China method, carried out under aerobic conditions, more waste matter is added, so that the carbon-nitrogen ratio is nearer the ideal of 30:1.

In Formosa[598] emphasis is placed on the use of compost and there are on the island some 36,000 compost houses. Production of compost is estimated at about 8 million metric tons a year, equivalent to 80,000 tons of ammonium sulphate, 40,000 tons of superphosphate and 56,000 tons of potassium sulphate. Production of compost is expected to increase to about 14 million tons annually. Iso[244] comments on the very low humus content of Formosa soils—averaging about 1·4 per cent as compared with 5 per cent in Japan and 2·4 per cent in Korea. He advocates application of abundant organics, accompanied by fertilizers, but states that the benefit of this treatment depends on increasing the depth of ploughing gradually till a deep (1 foot) cultivated soil has been built up.

Organic manures contribute largely to the success of paddy cultivation in Japan. Farmyard manure is usually applied before irrigating, compost before planting. The materials chiefly used in making compost are rice straw, barley straw, plant residues, grasses, sea-weed, night soil, farmyard manure, silkworm excrement and inorganic fertilizers may be added to provide additional nitrogen for micro-organisms. The recommended application is about 1,000 lb. per acre.

Night soil is also largely used in Japan. It is usually stored for varying periods of time, depending on the season. To hasten the breakdown of solids a few handfuls of powdered soya bean meal are sometimes added and the addition of 3 to 5 per cent of superphosphate is recommended to prevent loss of ammonia. When the ripened night soil is applied at planting time it is seldom diluted, but when applied as a top-dressing it is diluted by the addition of one to three parts of water.

Cattle manure is generally considered the most satisfactory form of organic matter for the paddy crop, but it is usually not available in sufficient quantities and more often than not, in the tropics, has been stored with so little regard for its fertilizing value that much of its nitrogen is lost. One is often surprised at the response of paddy to application of dried dung in arid countries, a response which appears to be far greater than would appear possible when one remembers that most of the nitrogen in the manure has been lost. On light loams in Ceylon, manurial trials pointed to the need of organic matter and in every instance where green manure or cattle manure was applied, significant increases of yield were obtained. It was found, however, that applications of cattle manure in excess of ten tons per acre were uneconomic.[475] Trials in Lower Burma[267] showed that cattle manure supplying 70 lb. nitrogen gave a five-year increase over controls of 68·7 per cent, while the residual value of the dressing was 37·7 per cent greater than the controls.

GREEN MANURES

Paddy soils are, as a rule, deficient in organic matter on account of the high temperatures and moisture causing rapid decomposition of organic matter in the soil. The addition of organic matter to paddy soils not only enriches by reason of added plant foods, but materially improves the physical condition of the soil.

The decomposition of green manures under anaerobic conditions such as obtains in inundated paddy fields, is brought about by micro-organisms (see page 221). Under submerged conditions ammonia and not nitrate is formed as the nitrogenous end-product. Joachim[304] summarizing his previous work[305] on the decomposition of green manures in paddy fields, states that as a result of incorporating green matter at time of puddling the land, i.e. *late*, large quantities of ammonia are made available to the soil at all stages of the decomposition process coinciding with the period of crop growth, the maximum being obtained in about four weeks from the time of planting.

By *early* green manuring, i.e. ploughing-in the green manures when the soil is semi-dry, large quantities of nitrates are formed. On subsequent flooding and puddling the soil these are lost as free nitrogen, leached in the drainage water, or reduced to nitrites which are injurious to paddy seedlings if present in excess. The amounts of ammonia found in *early* green-manured soils are very much less than those found in *late* green-manured soils. By *late* green manuring of paddy soils their nitrogen contents can be maintained or even increased. *Early* green manuring results in large losses of nitrogen. No nitrates are found in paddy soils after they have been puddled, nitrates present or added before puddling being denitrified or converted to nitrites.

Almost invariably, green manure applied to badly-drained and waterlogged soils depresses the yield of paddy.

Whenever possible, the organic matter should be added by cultivating and ploughing in a leguminous crop grown between the paddy seasons. Inoculation of the seed or soil with nodule organisms is usually necessary for satisfactory development of legumes on soils never previously planted to such crops. But however desirable it may be to plough in a cultivated crop, in many paddy areas the cultivation of such crops is impossible because of the nature of the soil, or of climatic conditions. Paddy harvesting usually coincides with the end of the rainy season; stiff clay soils, so characteristic of vast areas of paddy-land, dry out completely and crack, and are so hard that cultivation is impossible, while any green manure crop sown before this condition is reached would be unable to grow through lack of moisture and the impervious nature of the soil. This is the experience in Lower Burma and similar difficulties are experienced in other countries.

Experimental evidence supporting the practice of green manuring is considerable. In Louisiana[521] the addition of leguminous organic matter was found to be the most effective treatment for improving the physical condition of the soil. From the Soviet Union[126] it is reported that peas, ploughed in green in the spring at the rate of about five tons per acre, before the paddy was sown, increased yields by 23·65 per cent over the control. It was noted that tillering was increased on the green manure plots. In Indonesia[215] it was found that improvement in nutritive value and considerable increases in yield were obtained through green manuring, though the effect varied with the variety of paddy grown. The vegetative period of the paddy crop was shortened, indicating, it is suggested, that the green manure supplied nutrients other than nitrogen. *Crotalaria* spp. were the best as green manure. Soils with a deficiency of humus or containing insufficient nitrogen, gave the best results from green manuring. This is especially noticeable on the young volcanic ash and sandy soils and also on both young and old laterite soils. Lime marl soils, with a deficiency of phosphate, also respond favourably to green manuring. In Surinam *Crotalaria quinquefolia* is recommended as a green manure. Ten Have states[651] that when combine-harvested at 15 weeks it produces 18–17 tons per acre, replacing about 90 lb. per acre of nitrogen. Rice yield increases of 900 lb. per acre have been obtained with the use of this green manure, though in wet-growth conditions it may lead to rank growth and lodging. Ossewaarde[451] found that the green manure should be turned in about ten days before planting paddy; Van de Goor,[215] working with older, lignified material, found that the crop should be turned in about two to four weeks before planting paddy. In many of the experiments it appeared that green manure can be substituted for other fertilizers such as stable manure and artificials.

Mudalier[420] in India states that following the application of green manure to paddy annually for several years in Madras, the yield of paddy had risen to about 2,500 lb. per acre. Writing of agricultural developments in Madras State, Chari[121] states that *Tephrosia purpurea* is commonly intersown with paddy a week before harvest; it grows through the summer in the fallow fields and is "incorporated" when water is let into the fields about June. It supplies about one ton of green leaves. *Sesbania aculeata* seedlings are planted closely round the field borders of the first crop, simultaneously with planting the paddy. It grows to about eight feet in height and yields about a ton of green leaf when the fields are prepared for the second crop. *Sesbania* is also grown separately in fields for supplying green manure; one acre of *Sesbania* will supply about ten acres of paddy land with green manure at the rate of 5,000 to 6,000 lb. green leaf per acre. Leaves of wild rubber (*Manihot glaziovii*), commonly used as live fencing in parts of India, have been found to be as good as *Sesbania* for green manuring paddy land.

The practice of green manuring is carried out extensively in some Asian countries. In Japan Chinese vetch (*Astragalus sinicus*) and soya beans are most usually used for this purpose, the crop being cut and dried for two or three days before being ploughed in. Studies in California showed that greater yields are obtained when purple vetch is turned under four to six inches (in the reducing zone) than when placed at shallowed depths (oxidizing zone). Shortening the time interval between turning under the vetch and flooding and sowing paddy also increased yield. Californian investigators found that when properly incorporated, vetch green manure is equal to mineral sources of ammonium nitrogen in increasing paddy yields.

Matsuo[379] considers that green manures should be ploughed in two weeks before transplanting, not too deeply in heavy clay for this would delay decomposition owing to lack of oxygen. The field should be irrigated as soon as possible after application to prevent loss of nitrogen. Misu[729] found that green manures showed lower availability of nitrogen and lower yields than did soya bean cake and ammonium sulphate and that the availability of nitrogen was less in dried than in fresh green manure. When planted for the first time, the seed may be inoculated with nodule bacteria (*Rhizobium* sp.).[407] After planting, the fields are kept well drained and in cold regions about a ton of straw is scattered over the field as a protection for the young plants during winter. The crop is fertilized and yields usually range from about eleven to fifteen long tons per acre. The crop[356] is ploughed under one or two weeks before paddy seedlings are transplanted in the spring. As soon as the green manure crop has been ploughed in, irrigation water is run on the land to prevent loss of nitrogen through aerobic action.

In India and Ceylon, planting green manure crops has for long been practised where possible. Sunn hemp (*Crotalaria juncea*) and green gram (*Phaseolus aureus*) and wild indigo are also grown where circumstances permit. Lord has shown[522] in Ceylon that large increases in crop yield of both grain and straw have been obtained by incorporating green manures into the soil one or two weeks before puddling (under anaerobic conditions). He recommends that with large dressings 1 cwt. superphosphate and with small dressings $\frac{1}{2}$ to 1 cwt. ammonium sulphate be added. Further, where weed growth is poor, the application of inorganic manures should invariably be accompanied by at least a small dressing of green manure.

Paul[474] in Ceylon has suggested the possibility of planting the pith plant (*Aeschynomene aspera*) as a green manure as it can grow in standing water and, in fact, its economic value in the manufacture of pith hats depends on that part of the stem which is submerged. In India and Ceylon it is also customary to collect green-stuff from outside the paddy fields and apply it before planting. It would seem that this practice might be more widely adopted in countries where it is found impossible to cultivate green manures on paddy fields. In the Jaffna Peninsula in Ceylon, for instance, it is common practice to bring large quantities of green-stuff from jungles or wild trees growing on the small islands adjoining the Peninsula by train, cart and boat for manuring the paddy crop. Molegode states[414] that the leaves and twigs are carted to the fields in Ceylon before the second ploughing and allowed to decay before being ploughed in. Paul[474] recommends *Gliricidia maculata* for planting along the high-land boundaries of the fields, and for the low zone *Cerbera odollam* as it can stand wet conditions of the soil and makes a good fence. He also suggests *Tithonia diversifolia*, the wild sunflower, which produces much leaf and makes a good hedge. It was found that green manuring gave its maximum effect if applied under anaerobic conditions (i.e. after the land has been flooded) and within a few days of broadcasting or transplanting. An application of five tons an acre gave an increased yield of thirty bushels.

In the Philippines legumes are grown for this purpose. In Egypt berseem clover is sown while the paddy is ripening; after harvesting the paddy the clover is cropped, often more than once, and then cattle are allowed to feed on the clover. Burr clover is grown in California as a green manure. In one experiment, after ploughing in a crop of burr clover, the yield of rice was increased by about 38 per cent over that from fallowed land.

The choice of green crop must depend on local conditions, but it is suggested that very much greater use might be made of wild plants growing in the vicinity of paddy-lands.

Summarizing the results of investigations with green manure crops for increasing paddy yields in South-East Asia, Staker[630] states that green manures are important in India, Indonesia and Formosa, but in Burma, Thailand, the Philippines and Cambodia they are not generally used. For the region as a whole, crops which have proved successful include species of *Sesbania* and *Crotalaria*, peas, soya beans, mung and radish. In India, leaves from trees and shrubs are as effective as green manures grown *in situ*. In a trial in Formosa, the amount of nitrogen fixed by legumes varied from 23 lb. per acre for blue soya bean to 82 lb. per acre for *Sesbania*. In trials in India green manuring increased yields 2 to 114 per cent. In Java, *Crotalaria juncea*, grown normally before paddy for 10 years, increased yields by an average of 19 per cent. In Ceylon six tons of green manure per acre were more effective than 10 tons of farmyard manure or compost.

FERTILIZERS WITH ORGANIC MANURES

Desirable as is the increased use of artificial fertilizers, they are beyond the means of the majority of Asian cultivators, particularly if employed in quantities recommended to produce optimum crops. There remains, however, the possibility of using fertilizers in conjunction with such local organic matter as may be available. The evidence in favour of so using fertilizers should be considered the immediate objective of organizations investigating ways and means of rapidly increasing rice production in Asia.

This combination of inorganic and organic manures has been tested in many regions. At Karnal, India, Parr[471] showed the following increases of yield: 120 lb. bone meal, 10·5 per cent; bone meal and farmyard manure at 40 lb. nitrogen per acre, 21·6 per cent; ammonium sulphate at 40 lb. nitrogen per acre, 18·1 per cent; ammonium sulphate and bone meal, 29·0 per cent. Recommendations[591] in India are 5,000 lb. green manure, supplying 35 to 40 lb. nitrogen per acre ploughed in with superphosphate to supply 30 lb. phosphoric acid. In addition 100 lb. ammonium sulphate supplying 20 lb. nitrogen is recommended to be applied before transplanting and another 50 lb. 30 days after planting. In certain soils 30 lb. potash should be applied additional to the above. Chang *et al.* in Formosa[118] showed that stable manure, and to a less extent soya bean cake, maintained fertility and was more effective for the later than for the earlier crops over a twelve years' experiment. Green manure gave the highest yield during the first few years, but this effect was not maintained. A complete inorganic manure was inferior to green manure, but with the addition of lime the yield was greatly increased. Experiments in five centres in Thailand showed that the greatest increases of yield were obtained when fertilizers were applied in conjunction with green manuring: NPK gave a 11–14 per cent increase of crop; green manure 23–44 per cent and NPK plus green manure 37–91 per cent increase.

In Mysore[688] it is considered that artificial fertilizers are less efficient than green manures, while the efficacy of either class of manure can be considerably improved by combining them. Hwang and others[284] in China recommended compost, with a top-dressing of ammonium sulphate, the latter promoting decomposition of the compost and green manure. Richardson and his colleagues in China stated[560] that the fertility of the alluvial paddy soils, such as those of the Changto Plain, can be maintained or even increased by the use of compost, or green manure instead of compost, if supplemented by a moderate dressing of inorganic nitrogenous fertilizer.

In Ceylon[406] there was an improvement in yield from the application of small amounts of green organic matter in conjunction with bone meal. The free issue of bone meal in Ceylon was made conditional on the application by the cultivator of a stated amount of organic matter. Experimental work in India[597] has also demonstrated the useful results of combining organic forms of nitrogen such as green leaf, cakes and cattle manure with inorganic forms of nitrogen such as ammonium sulphate while the use of lime and bone meal proved to be useful adjuncts to green manuring in India.[602]

Yields in British Guiana are high, approaching those obtained in Japan, yet manuring is not usual. Experimental work in that country indicates that higher yields are possible and that the highest returns are obtained when green manuring is followed, seven months later, by the application of ammonium sulphate in conjunction with superphosphate.[527] While green manuring is not practised in Peru,[190] its place is taken by guano. About 450 lb. Peruvian guano per acre are applied to the crop. In addition, nitrate of soda is used as a top-dressing, while occasionally ammonium sulphate is applied just after planting or broadcasting.

Ramiah[512] recently summarizing replies to a questionnaire of the International Rice Commission sent to member governments confirms the opinion expressed above that artificials in conjunction with organic matter is usually the most satisfactory manure for paddy. He states that in all the paddy-growing countries of the warm temperate regions, intensive manuring with fertilizers or combination of fertilizers and organic manures is carried out, amounting to 60 to 130 lb. nitrogen, 35 to 90 lb. phosphoric acid and 50 to 100 lb. of potash (K_2O). Nowhere in the tropics, he observes, except in Formosa, are similar quantities used. Although heavy manuring has proved satisfactory in the tropics, it is found that where paddy is chiefly a monsoon crop, large quantities of nitrogen, above 30 to 40 lb. per acre, encourage vegetative development at the expense of grain. Occasionally there is no response to manuring. Experimental evidence emphasizes the necessity for nitrogen in some form and in addition, for phosphates in certain regions of India, Indonesia, Burma, Thailand and Malaya. In the last three countries, the most satisfactory results are obtained by the application of phosphates with or without nitrogen. Phosphates have also given satisfactory yields when combined with green manures. There appears to be no need for potash over large areas of the tropics but in the warm temperate regions the addition of potash together with nitrogen and phosphoric acid is a regular practice. The application of phosphatic fertilizers to legume green manures renders a large percentage of the fertilizer available as it is taken up by the legume instead of becoming an unavailable compound in the soil.[56] In this connection, on the Wageningen Project in Surinam, it was found that paddy did not respond to phosphatic fertilizers but *Crotalaria quinquefolia* did, so that in this way it was found possible to improve the phosphorus nutrition of the paddy crop.[703]

Nitrogen in an organic form gives the best results in almost every country. Since tropical soils are generally deficient in organic matter, there is a greater use of organic manures combined with inorganic fertilizers. In warm temperate regions the importance of organic manures is recognized. The United States is the only country which uses large quantities of inorganic fertilizers alone.

Green manuring has proved to be the cheapest method of manuring paddy and in India, Ceylon, Indo-China and Indonesia this method is recommended where conditions permit. Green manuring is also practised in Italy, Japan and Formosa.[512]

A most satisfactory treatment in paddy cultivation appears to be skilful combination of green manuring and fertilizer application. Experiments in Brazil have shown that paddy after paddy, treated with NPK gave the same yield as paddy after green manuring, but green manuring and an NPK fertilizer increased the yield of paddy by 81 per cent. This favourable result is probably due to the fact that green manuring improves the soil properties by bringing the C : N ratio nearer the optimum of 10 : 1, while the activity of nodule bacteria may be responsible for a considerable increase in nitrogen.

OXIDATION-REDUCTION ZONES IN WATERLOGGED SOILS

Instances may be multiplied of the varying response of soils to the application of fertilizers, the results being so conflicting as to offer no basis for a generalized statement of the manurial requirements of the crop. Admittedly, the difficulty may be accounted for, in part, by incomplete knowledge of the soils upon which the manures were applied.

A new scientific approach is needed to this problem and in this connection the work of Pearsall on oxidation-reduction zones in waterlogged soils provides a basis for study on the problem from an entirely new and more scientific angle than has hitherto been possible.

In brief, Pearsall and his co-workers found measurable differences in oxidation-reduction potential in waterlogged soils, oxidation taking place in the surface layer of the soil and reduction at lower levels. Pearsall and Mortimer have outlined[479] the concept of oxidation-reduction zones and the measurement of electrical potential in soils ranging from forest to waterlogged or submerged soils. At about 320 to 350 millivolts there is a change from oxidizing to reducing conditions in submerged soils. They suggest that a relatively low oxygen concentration suffices to maintain predominantly "oxidizing" conditions and state that it appears probable that organic matter, or some associated system present in the soil, may exert a "poising action" which assists the establishment of an approximate stable potential at the lower ranges. The chemical properties of soil organic matter (including base exchange properties) are much affected by oxidation or reduction, if not mainly determined by these conditions.

Appreciation of the existence of oxidation-reduction zones in paddy soils leads to the study of soil reaction from three points of view, viz. cultivation, manuring and plant growth.

CULTIVATION

The cultivation of seasonally waterlogged soils involves three principles—those controlling the seasonal development or reducing zones, the effect of these on mineral availability and the effect on biological systems in the soil. The rate of development of the reducing zone and the depth of the zone below the surface depends on the amount and type of organic matter and on the soil flora.

MANURING

The Japanese were quick to realize the implications of Pearsall's work on the action of manures applied to the paddy crop, for it explained why certain methods of application were practised, why fertilizers so frequently gave negative results and suggested new methods of applying fertilizers and the compounds of nitrogen most suitable for the crop. Pearsall has stated the position as follows:

During the periods when it is submerged or waterlogged a rice soil develops reducing conditions, even though the surface-layer remains oxidizing as long as it is in contact with air or oxygen-containing water. It is therefore common to see a rusty-coloured surface-layer and a blue or blue-mottled soil below whenever the lower layers are exposed. Japanese workers have experimentally confirmed the existence of oxidizing and reducing zones, the depth varying probably with the duration of flooding and other similar conditions.

When a fertilizer like ammonium sulphate is sprinkled on a rice-field, it is affected by the conditions present in the surface or oxidation layer, the sulphate radical remains unchanged and the ammonia is converted to nitrate as in a normal soil. If, however, any part of this nitrate should pass into the lower reducing zone, it is reduced to nitrite and thence to atmospheric nitrogen, which is lost. It has been stated that as much as 70 per cent of the nitrogen applied as ammonium sulphate may be lost in this way, not by leaching. The mechanisms by which the nitrogen is lost are almost certainly of microbiological origin.[68]

If in contrast, ammonium sulphate is trodden or worked into the lower zones of a wet rice soil, the ammonium ions remain unchanged in the reducing zone and are available to the growing crop. Marsh plants like rice have roots that are able to grow and function in reducing soils because they contain internal air-spaces, which carry oxygen internally

T

to the respiring cells and growing tissues. Roots of this type often have round them a red-brown oxidizing zone and in some cases traces of nitrates have been detected in this "rhizosphere." It may also be mentioned that rice roots raise the oxidation-reduction potential of un-aerated solutions.

It will be clear from the above that the success of any particular types of fertilizer will depend partly on the method and place of application. In general, nitrates should be applied only to the oxidizing zone at a time when immediate uptake by the crop is possible. Nitrate that penetrates to the reducing zone is generally lost. Ammonium nitrate has the particular theoretical disadvantage that in contact with reducing conditions it is readily reduced to ammonium nitrite, which may be converted microbiologically to gaseous nitrogen with great ease.[478] Calcium cyanamide has been tried as a source of nitrogen for rice. When it is applied to the surface-oxidizing soil it is acted on (presumably by micro-organisms) and is almost quantitatively converted to ammonia in from 5 to 7 days. It can then be mixed with all layers of soil. The best crop yields are obtained by this method. If the cyanamide is mixed with the deeper reducing layers at the time of application, it causes serious damage to the plants, so that it is not very effective in increasing the yield. Apparently the organisms converting it to ammonia require oxygen. An organic material like bean cake is, however, quite effective when applied in the deeper layers. Presumably it is partly broken down to ammonia by anaerobic organisms and retained in the reducing zone in this form.

It must be assumed that ammonium sulphate produces other effects besides those due to ammonia utilization. For example, when ammonium ions are absorbed, sulphuric acid is left and the soil solution may become extremely acid. This must accelerate leaching effects. When ammonium sulphate is added to the reducing zone the sulphate will be reduced to sulphide, which will combine with iron as long as that metal is available, but when iron becomes deficient, hydrogen sulphide or methyl sulphide will appear, both producing toxic effects on the crop-plant. It would appear that as long as the soil is saturated with calcium or iron the toxic effects are likely to be small.[480]

Work along these lines has produced favourable results in Japan. Japanese official recommendations now state "that the loss of ammonium-nitrogen through oxidation-reduction in paddy fields can be prevented largely if nitrogenous fertilizers are applied deep in the soil. Consequently, nitrogenous fertilizers should be thoroughly mixed with the soil and the field be irrigated within three or four days after application of fertilizers. If considerable time elapses between the time a fertilized field is irrigated and the time paddy seedlings are planted therein, the loss of nitrogen becomes serious. Farmers are cautioned not to let more than ten days elapse from the time a fertilized field is irrigated until the paddy plants are transplanted. Irrigated fields should be drained before fertilizers are applied."[531] But as early as 1920, long before Pearsall's work threw light on the subject—experiments in Japan[379] indicated that increasing applications of fertilizers is ineffective unless accompanied by deeper ploughing, an operation which, presumably, permitted the fertilizer to penetrate to a greater depth.

The effect of deeper application of fertilizer is worthy of intensive study in the light of Pearsall's work. While the practice of applying nitrogenous fertilizers well below the soil surface is already usual in some regions, the possibilities of improvement in this direction are by no means exhausted. For instance, ball-shaped lumps of peat with ammonium sulphate and superphosphate have been applied deeply in the soil, and larger lumps or crystals of ammonium sulphate or oil-covered ammonium sulphate crystals have been suggested. In Louisiana,[690] nitrogen, phosphorus and potash, each applied at the rate of 24 to 30 lb. per acre, increased yield by about twenty-five bushels per acre, but a top-dressing gave less consistent results than applications below the seed. In California,[399] experiments showed that when ammonium nitrogen is drilled at a depth of two to four inches before flooding, yields were increased 25 to 50 per cent as compared with similar fertilizer treatments broadcast.

The implications of the oxidation-reduction zone on plant growth must be taken into account. It is possible that further study may reveal the explanation of phenomena concerning plant growth which have hitherto remained unexplained.

Chapter XII

WEEDS

PADDY-LAND is particularly suitable for the development and spread of both aquatic and semi-aquatic weeds. Of these, perhaps the most universal are various species of *Cyperus*, or umbrella plants, commonly known as sedges, some of which are both annual and perennial. The weed flora depends largely on the length during which the land has been under cultivation, nature of the soil, effectiveness of irrigation and drainage and the method of cultivation.

The penalty for broadcasting paddy is the increase of weeds. In Asia, where paddy is usually transplanted, adequate opportunity occurs for suppression of weeds, the land receiving its final clearing just before transplanting. Seedlings at transplanting may be anything up to forty days old and they quickly become established in the field. The paddy is weeded by hand from time to time; it develops and tillers quickly and is therefore soon in advance of weed growth, so that the latter can no longer compete with the crop. Where paddy is drilled there is limited opportunity for weeding between the rows, with broadcasting none. It is to be noted that weeds assume increased importance in those parts of Asia, such as parts of Ceylon and India, where broadcasting is usual and in the United States as well as most of the regions where mechanical cultivation is carried out.

VARIETIES OF WEEDS

Various forms of *Cyperus* grow on bunds and poorly drained or abandoned land. Where they occur in the fields, improved drainage and good cultivation may rid the fields of them. Annual forms are found amongst standing paddy, especially where the stand of paddy is thin. It is common in California, especially in seasons preceded by wet spring weather. In Ceylon, *Cyperus iria* and *C. dehiscens* appear in most paddy fields soon after the crop is sown, they flower in about a month and may produce a second crop in one season, seeding being very prolific. The weed flourishes on insufficiently irrigated land.

Typha species, the cattails, are common in the paddy fields of Asia and the Western Hemisphere. The cattail is a perennial which spreads by seed and creeping root-stock. Seeding is prolific and is distributed by wind and water. In California, cattails growing in irrigation ditches have been destroyed by spraying, when the weed commences to head, 2 lb. of 50 per cent amino triazole in 100 gallons of water. To be effective the weeds must be thoroughly wetted with the spray. Cattails have been controlled by 2,4-D and MCPA, which are probably much cheaper than amino triazole.

Numerous species of water grasses, *Echinochloa*, are common to paddy fields everywhere and in the United States. *E. crus-galli* and *E. stagnina*, known as Barnyard grass are about the worst weeds in Texas. The seeds mature with the paddy and after threshing it is difficult to separate grass seeds from paddy by mechanical means. Varieties of *Echinochlea* are placed in four groups:[310]

(1) The early red varieties, which grow $1\frac{1}{2}$ to $2\frac{1}{2}$ feet high, stool heavily and have small stems. They mature and shed their seed before the paddy heads.

(2) Mid-season varieties, which grow 3 to 6 feet tall, stool heavily and have coarse stems. They mature and drop their seed before the paddy is fully headed.

(3) Late white varieties which grow 2 to 5 feet high, stool heavily and have rather coarse stems with comparatively large, compact heads. They usually mature before but often with the paddy crop.

(4) Other late varieties, which grow $2\frac{1}{2}$ to 4 feet tall and stool heavily, have mid-sized stems with compact heads and mid-sized to large seeds. They usually mature at the same time as the paddy crop.

The water grasses—or barnyard grasses—are annuals and most of them tiller abundantly and produce much seed. The white varieties do not shatter to the same extent as other forms and much of the seed may therefore be harvested with the paddy crop.

Where weeds are not numerous control may be effected by hand-weeding, a process which is usually too costly. Control by continuous submergence is now extensively accepted as the most effective method. In California it controls the early and mid-season types, but does not check growth of the white water grasses. Species of *Aeschynomene* and *Fimbristylis* appear to be common in paddy fields in various parts of the world. Among other weeds reported from California are the spike rush (*Eleocharis palustris*), a perennial which establishes itself in places where cultivation and drainage are poor; the water plantain (*Alisma plantago*), the presence of which has been on the increase during the past few years; arrowhead (*Sagittaria latifolia*) favours lower situations and thin stands of paddy and tends to increase as a serious pest, and *Leptochloa fascicularis* may also be found in low land, while *Ammannia coccinea*, or redstem, is found in shallow drainage ditches and often in paddy fields, especially where the stand is thin. The creeping perennial joint grass (*Paspalum distichum*), spreads rapidly by rooting at the nodes and is difficult to eradicate. When growing in ditches it tends to impede the flow of water unless the ditches are frequently cleaned. Water hyssop (*Bacopa rotundifolia*), bulrush (*Scirpus fluviatilis*), canary grass (*Phalaris paradoxa*) and *P. brachystachys*, crab grass (*Digitaria sanguinalis*), *Aster exilis* and *Bromus secalinus* are also mentioned in connection with paddy cultivation in California. To these may be added a number of varieties more commonly met with in the southern States, including *Caperonia palustris*, *Sesbania macrocarpa*, *Diodia teres*, *Sphaenoclea zeylanica*, *Commelina virginica* and *Polygonum acre*.

The beautiful water hyacinth (*Eichhornia crassipes*) is found in many parts of Asia, including Malaya, India, Ceylon, south China and Java, and also in America and Africa. It is often a troublesome weed, impeding the flow of water in rivers and irrigation channels and causing floods. It is a native of Brazil but has been introduced into many countries as an ornamental plant. It is used by the Chinese and others as pig food, as cigar wrapper in Thailand and can also be used for mushroom growing. The plant floats in deep water and roots in swamps. Propagation is by seed and by stolons. The latter arise from the plant base and bear suckers which become independent when the runners break. Swellings at the base of the leaves act as floats and the roots as ballast. In this way plants are carried long distances by wind and current, especially in times of flood. When the water subsides they settle down as dense carpets and root in the mud. The seed germinates only when desiccated and germination may therefore be delayed for many years. Parija,[466] for instance, proved that under natural conditions the seeds may be viable after at least seven years. This fact accounts for reinfestation in areas that have been cleared of the weed, so that long surveillance is essential to keep the weed in check. Mechanical methods of control have hitherto been considered essential but chemical control methods should prove successful. In East Pakistan, jute and *Sesbania* are sometimes cultivated on the river banks as barriers to check the entrance of water hyacinth into paddy fields.

Isachne australis is common in Eastern paddy fields, *Coix gigantea*, the giant adlay, is reported as a paddy weed in Ceylon as are also *Ischaemum rugosum*, *Asteracantha longifolia* and *Fimbristylis miliacea*. Failure to weed in Ceylon is said to cause an average loss of 20 to 25 per cent of the crop. Wild starch (*Heliconia* sp.) is common in British Guiana and Surinam. It is controlled by disc harrowing under water.

In most parts of the East, many wild varieties of paddy, e.g. *Oryza rufipogon*, are associated with paddy cultivation. In Thailand, *Ischaemum rugosum* is said to be the most noxious weed in paddy fields. Several of the Cyperaceae are troublesome in that country, including *Fimbristylis miliacea*, *Scirpus grossus* and *Fuirena glomerata*. On the other hand, many of the weeds commonly found in paddy are treated with some respect, either on account of their value in fish rearing, as an animal food or in medicine.[640] The land of the Central Plain of Thailand is baked hard and is cropless for most of the year, but it may be under a considerable depth of water during the paddy season. The weed flora is therefore sharply divided into dry- and wet-season phases, both being characterized by an abundance of annual weeds. During the dry season the land is covered with grasses, species of *Sporobolus* being dominant. Flood water destroys these and they are replaced by the aquatics, mainly annual and perennial sedges and rushes, and annual weeds the seeds of which lie dormant until the land becomes sufficiently wet. *Ottelia alismoides*, *Sagittaria latifolia* (arrowhead) and species of *Mimulus*, *Monochoria* and *Utricularia* are common. In the floating paddy regions especially, there is a floating *Ipomoea* with hollow stems which grows rankly with the paddy. It becomes a serious pest because weeding is difficult. Conditions in Burma are similar. Most of the paddy is transplanted and preliminary cultivation is sufficiently thorough to reduce the trouble from weeds.

Sands[581] reports that *Enhydrias angustipetala* Ridl., *Chara jymonopitys* Brann, and *Utricularia flexuosa* Vahl, are very troublesome in Kedah (Malaya). Local planters broadcast salt on fields after harvest as a means of control.

Hand-weeding is usual in the Philippines, the chief weeds being the perennial grass *Leersia hexandra*, various sedges—which are the worst weeds—and *Monochoria hastata*, which resembles water hyacinth but is always anchored. *Imperata cylindrica* is mentioned as a noxious weed in the Philippines. It is a serious weed on dry land and common in the tropics, but it does not stand inundation and is not therefore a danger in "wet" paddy fields, although it may be found on the bunds. In China and Korea, thorough preliminary cultivation and frequent weeding reduce weed trouble, while cleansing bunds and planting thereon soya beans also assist in reducing loss of crop by weeds.

Ischaemum rugosum is considered the most dangerous grass in Surinam.[176] Fields can become infested in a very short time by this weed, which in its early stages closely resembles paddy, as does *Echinochloa colonum*. These two grasses can completely suppress the paddy.

Transplanting paddy gives better weed control than is possible with broadcasting or drilling. In France, for example, where ten years ago transplanting was used in only 5 per cent of the fields, direct seeding increased rapidly until about 60 per cent of the acreage was transplanted in 1960.[10, 25]

Copeland[135] states that *Panicum phyllorhyzoide* and *P. crus-galli* (*Echinochloa crus-galli*) are the worst weeds in Italian paddy fields. Douglas[182] refers to ridge cultivation which has been adopted in parts of Italy. "In this system," he states, "rice seed is sown on the crest of the ridges under the least possible depth of water, while the greater depth of water in the furrows undoubtedly helps to drown the weeds. Moreover, by this method it is relatively simple to remove the weeds from the furrows without damage to the rice." The weeds that would be killed would probably be dry-land weeds which would, in any case, be destroyed by inundation. Ridging for cultivation of other crops between paddy seasons is common. Tidbury states[655] that results of experiments in Zanzibar indicated that increased yields of paddy were obtained if, after the paddy harvest, the land is thrown up in ridges and planted with other crops. He does not mention the effect, if any, on weed growth.

In Egypt, soils in the irrigation area are liable to become saline. When this is the case paddy is grown, the growing crop being treated with successive flooding and drainage to rid the soil of salinity (see page 51). The test crop for salinity after removal of the paddy is the weed *Echinochloa crus-galli*, which is deliberately planted with this object. If this weed will not grow the land must be subject to further washing. Needless to say, the weed is liable later to become an embarrassment.

In North Sind much damage is occasioned by a thick algal growth causing the water to become stagnant and partially strangling the paddy. It may be controlled by drawing a bag of copper sulphate through the water, using 16 to 20 lb. per acre. The scum dies off and settles, leaving clear water in three or four days. The scum does not reappear with subsequent irrigation.

In British Guiana, the aquatic animal, the manatee, is now being used for the control of weeds in canals. It was found that a manatee about 8·5 feet long could clear a canal at the rate of one acre in eight weeks. Legislation is therefore contemplated to prevent slaughter or capture of this animal.

RED RICE

In some countries, notably in both North and South America, wild red rice, *Oryza rufipogon*, is considered the most serious weed pest of paddy which, unless eradicated promptly, soon practically takes possession of the land. It is necessary to distinguish between wild red rice and the domesticated rices (*O. sativa*) which have red grains. The trouble in the Central American area and in parts of India and Ceylon is due to wild rices which have red grains and which readily shatter. They cannot be distinguished in the early stages of growth so weeding is difficult and they shed grain which re-infests the fields in the subsequent paddy crop. In point of fact, there is no character which distinguishes *O. rufipogon* Griff. from *O. sativa* except that of early and complete shedding of the grain even before it is fully ripe and dry. It bears red awns, but there are a few cultivated varieties which are also awned. Part of the grain is reaped with the cultivated crop and so contaminates the produce. The red testa character is common in domesticated rices and there is need for a great deal of care in keeping it from breeding plots and from the bulk crop except for those countries which prefer red rice, e.g. parts of Ceylon and India. A great number of local varieties in Ceylon are red. Red-grained wild plants usually have all the external characteristics of the white varieties amongst which they grow, while the fact that the grain is not dissimilar in size or shape to the white varieties makes it impossible to separate wild red from white paddy in the milling operation.

Official American publications point out that red rice may be the result of natural crossing, because all the plants of the first hybrid generation and three-fourths of the second generation have the red kernel coat. The proportion of red rice rapidly increases when crossing between red and white varieties takes place.

The incidence of red rice is less marked in areas where the paddy crop is transplanted from seedlings than where seed is broadcast or drilled. This is probably due to cultivation being more protracted and final preparation being completed just before transplanting. It is probable, therefore, that most of the drop seed has germinated and been destroyed before the paddy is planted out. Furthermore, taking a drop-seed crop is less frequently practised in areas where transplanting is the rule.

Red rice is considered a most important problem in many South American countries. It is looked upon as the most serious pest of paddy in British Guiana, while in Colombia,[190] where the practice of growing two paddy crops annually on the same land, without rotations, has continued without interruption for some years, red rice is responsible for contamination of 10 per cent for the whole country and as much as 30 per cent in some areas. In the Central Provinces of India, where wild rice is a serious problem, Dave[156] suggested the cultivation of purple-leaf hybrids which can be readily distinguished from the green wild plants. This practice has now been adopted in parts of India, red and green varieties being planted in alternate years, all red plants being rogued in years when green varieties are cultivated and *vice versa.*

The following cultural methods to control the incidence of red rice in the field may be usefully employed:

(*a*) Neither ratoon nor drop-seed crops should be allowed and where the crop is grown from broadcast or drilled seed only one crop per year should be taken.

(*b*) Only properly selected and rogued pure-line seed should be sown. It is, however, useless to use pure-line seed unless steps have been taken to eliminate red seed from the land.

(*c*) Early ploughing after harvest to encourage germination of drop seed which should then be controlled by grazing cattle.

(*d*) Deeper ploughing discourages development of red rice seed in the soil.

(*e*) Thorough cleaning of harvesting machines before entry into a field.

(*f*) It may be necessary to rest each field for one year in four; thus, the rotation might be three years paddy followed by one year fallow, during which cattle would be grazed on the land. Many American rice farms have adopted the practice of cropping one-third of the farm with rice and feeding beef cattle on two-thirds, thus providing for a three-year rotation.

(*g*) Early ploughing after harvest should be immediately followed by two or three weeks' flooding. Paddy seed rots if placed in the soil on flooded land.

Giglioli[211] found that excellent control was achieved by wet-cultivation but concluded that this technique has many disadvantages and is uneconomic.

Elimination of the red grain character from commercial crops is an altogether different matter from control of wild red rice. The red testa character is inherited as a simple dominant for all practical purposes though at least two genes are actually involved (see Chapter VI). White-grained varieties breed true for the white character, so that if all red grains can be eliminated from the sown seed a wholly white-grained crop will result (apart from any F_1 crossed seed which may be included). Careful attention to pure seed supply and replacement of farmers' mixed stocks when required should keep down red rice contamination. It is necessary, however, to bear in mind that seed for issue to farmers needs to be sampled for the presence of red grain on a scale sufficient to reveal its presence in low amounts.

In other words, the sample size must have regard to the degree of contamination which will be tolerated. The presence of 1 per cent red grains means some 8,000 red-grained seeds per bushel, but to be sure of detecting even this high degree of contamination a sample of about four ounces of seed must be examined. Rhind and Subramanian[731] give the statistical basis for detecting low amounts of contamination by sequential analysis, a method which reduces the labour of seed testing for red grain contamination. (See Appendix I.)

HORMONE WEEDKILLERS

Hormone weedkillers most generally used in paddy cultivation are based on:

(*a*) 2-methyl-4-chlorophenoxyacetic acid (MCPA);
(*b*) 2,4-dichlorophenoxyacetic acid (2,4-D);
(*c*) 2,4,5-trichlorophenoxyacetic acid (2,4,5-T).

(*a*) MCPA weedkillers are formulated as either the sodium or potassium amine salt, or ester, all of which have a similar action on weeds. They may be applied earlier than 2,4-D. The sooner weeds are removed from the crop the greater the crop increase resulting from weed control.

(*b*) Weedkillers contain 2,4-D as an amine or ester. The latter is generally more active than the former and is therefore used in smaller quantities. The esters are formulated as oil emulsions and give more consistent results under unfavourable weather conditions.

(*c*) In general, 2,4,5-T is less effective as a herbicide than (*a*) or (*b*), its principal use being as an arboricide. Both amine and ester derivatives are available commercially, the latter being the more important. The esters are applied as water emulsions for foliage sprays.

All the above herbicides are non-poisonous, non-staining and non-inflammable.* MCPA and 2,4-D are broken down in the soil within a few weeks of application, the rate depending on soil type, moisture and temperature, but 2,4,5-T persists for some time in the soil.[51] Mixtures of 2,4-D and 2,4,5-T esters are more economical to use and have a greater range of effectiveness than either used separately. While they are more effective than the salts, most of the esters are volatile and there is greater risk from spray and vapour drift, or "creep" when esters are used. This is so serious in the cotton areas

---

* Inflammability. The definitions of inflammability for transport purposes are: flash point over 150° F.—non-inflammable; flash point from 73 to 150° F.—inflammable; flash point below 73° F.—high inflammable. The formulated esters of 2,4-D and 2,4,5-T have flash points in the region of 110° F. on account of the oils in which the esters are dissolved. From an application point of view they are quite safe, but from the transport and storage angle are inflammable.

of the United States that spraying is prohibited after a certain date in the year. Low volatile esters are available but more expensive. In irrigated paddy, the main herbicides used are derivatives of phenoxyacetic acids.

It is possible to apply weedkillers in paddy cultivation at three stages: pre-planting, pre-emergence and post-emergence.

PRE-PLANTING TREATMENT

MCPA, TCA, 2,4-D/TCA mixture, 2,4,5-T/TCA mixture, and TCA + MCPA have been used with varying success. Application of weedkillers should be made while the weed seeds are germinating. In trials carried out in Italy,[106] for instance, pre-sowing treatment with TCA, 2,4-D/TCA and TCA/MCPA all gave some success against *Echinochloa crus-galli*, but had little or no permanent effect on other weeds. It was established that *Echinochloa crus-galli* was more susceptible at higher temperatures. The seeds were killed by 27 lb. per acre at 20° C., but at 10 to 15° between 50 and 80 lb. per acre were necessary. The best kill was obtained on moist soil, while flooding the field a day after application speeded up the herbicidal action.

In France,[691] TCA and TCA + MCPA were tried in 1952. TCA killed *Scirpus* spp. and *Alisma plantago* at 18 lb. per acre, while TCA 4½ lb. per acre MCPA 6 lb./acre were usually effective and also caused *Typha* spp. to rot at the base and die. Paddy seedlings were planted four weeks·later, but after a month the land was re-infested with weeds. In Brazil,[106] trials to control *Digitaria vaginata* in paddy fields with IPC at 10 to 12 lb. per acre and sodium chlorate at 170 lb. per acre gave apparent success, but the grass completely recovered within two months. In Texas[159] pre-planting treatment with a number of weedkillers suppressed weed growth, but usually had an adverse effect on the crop.

The results of pre-sowing treatment are very inconclusive and it is apparent that a great deal more research into this method is necessary before any conclusions can be drawn.

PRE-EMERGENCE TREATMENT

Control of weeds in the pre-emergent stage is still experimental. Investigations appear to have been confined to upland dry paddy in Venezuela (probably post-weed pre-crop emergence) and Texas paddy fields infested with a mixture of weeds. In the Texan experiments, weedkillers which successfully controlled weeds usually also proved toxic to the paddy, while when control of weeds was unsatisfactory little or no damage was done to the paddy. It is obvious that much work has yet to be done before this method of treatment is established.

POST-EMERGENCE TREATMENT

It is stated that most encouraging results have followed post-emergence application of weedkillers on paddy fields. It must be recognized, however, that hormone weedkillers have very little effect on grasses, whereas they readily kill broad-leaved plants. There-fore, application of a hormone weedkiller at a concentration strong enough to kill grass weeds would also kill or damage paddy. The safest time to apply weedkiller in a paddy crop is before tillering is finished. MCPA can be applied at early tillering and 2,4-D at late tillering. Earlier application coincides with the differentiation of the inflorescence at the growing point. It is generally found that the weedkiller acts more effectively if the irrigation water is withdrawn from the field one or two days before application so that the leaves of weeds are exposed to the spray; the field is re-flooded two days later.[159, 691]

For several years 2,4-D has been used satisfactorily for control of broad-leaved weeds and some sedges, the weedkiller being applied six to eight weeks after sowing. In some instances, while it controlled weeds it also resulted in development of abnormalities in the paddy. Kaufman,[328] and others,[254, 288] who studied these deformities, showed that they covered a wide range of symptoms, including forma-tion of "onion leaves," fusion of tillers, replacement of seminal roots with an excessive number of thick adventitious roots, trapping of heads and deformities of the panicle. He also showed that paddy may be highly susceptible to 2,4-D particularly in the early stages of development and during periods of high temperature. Early seed-ling, tillering, boot and panicle emergence stages were all shown to be susceptible to 2,4-D. Kaufman and Krafts[329] showed in subse-quent work that drilled paddy was less severely damaged than broad-cast paddy and injury greater when the stand was poor; also that absorption of 2,4-D by the roots caused more damage than when taken in by the leaves. MCPA should be applied at the rate of 10 to 25 oz. per acre, the higher rate being needed for sedges and cattails. Herbicides applied in pellet form tended to be more selective—the potassium salt being more effective in this form than the amine. A higher application rate was necessary for pelleted herbicides.

In large-scale field trials in California,[288] the yield of paddy was doubled from 2,200 lb. per acre to 4,450 lb./acre by applying 10 oz. MCPA in twenty-eight gallons of water per acre by ground machine, but experiments at the Biggs Research Station in California, spraying paddy with a low weed population forty-six days after sowing, 2,4-D reduced the yield to 56 per cent of the control, whereas MCPA increased it 12 per cent. Field experience in California has confirmed that MCPA increases yield more than 2,4-D if application is made earlier than fifty days after seeding or when the air temperature after spraying reaches 95° F. and over.

Kaufman concludes his excellent study of the morphological responses of paddy to 2,4-D spraying in California fields with the following suggestion for effective weed control with the least possible injury to the crop. These recommendations include:

(1) planting the rice as early as possible, (2) sowing seed evenly at heavy rates, (3) fertilizing the rice early to promote tillering and a dense stand (4) keeping the water level as high as possible just before and after spraying, (5) making the spray application just before the most extensive aquatic weeds in the field begin to flower (in other words to spray as late as possible and yet achieve satisfactory control), (6) spraying only where serious weed problems exist in the rice field and avoiding the spraying of thin stands of rice if a weed problem does not exist in such areas, (7) spraying during a cool period (this is not always possible to anticipate)if such a period is found to coincide with requisite (5) above, and (8) using a salt of 2-methyl-4-chloro-phenoxyacetic acid in preference to 2,4-D at as low a dosage as possible (15–25 ounces acid equivalent per acre).

Despite the very convincing evidence produced in California, MCPA has not been extensively used in Arkansas, Louisiana and Texas. Smith[609] has explained that this is due to the less satisfactory weed control obtained with MCPA on the weeds of the South which are different from those of California. He considers that weeds cause a greater loss of paddy yield in Arkansas than any other pest, averaging 15 to 20 per cent of the crop.

Comparisons of the herbicidal activity and crop phytotoxicity of 2,4-D, MCPA and 2,4,5-T have been carried out in many countries with variable results. In Egypt,[691] MCPA 1·3 lb./acre killed the sedge *Cyperus difformis* but did not control *Cyperus rotundus*. In India, no injury to six weeks' old paddy resulted from application of 1¼ lb./acre 2,4-D, but in the Philippines, abnormalities have resulted from spraying with 2,4-D between germination and the last stage of tillering, but not from this point till the end of the "dough" stage of the grain. After the seedling stage, paddy was not killed by spraying, but there was a reduction in yield attributed to inhibition of tillers. In Japan[54] and the Gambia little difference was found in weed control or crop yield between 2,4-D and MCPA, but in the

West Indies MCPA proved to be the safer herbicide. The Japanese are convinced that MCPA is safer than 2,4-D, particularly in cold weather: 2,4-D caused yield reduction when sprayed early, attributed to low temperature and lack of sunshine. A similar conclusion was reached in Madagascar.[288]

In Malaya,[691, 132] 2,4,5-T esters at 3 lb. per acre did not damage paddy two feet high, seven to eight weeks old, and gave excellent weed control; paddy should not, however, be sprayed at this advanced stage of development. Earlier experiments in Malaya[11] showed that while broad-leaved plants were killed and growth of sedges checked sufficiently to ensure some control during the remainder of the season, efficient water control and a close stand of paddy is the soundest method of reducing hand-weeding. Other experiments in Malaya established the fact that a 1/60 and a 1/100 emulsion of ethyl ester of 2,4-D used against water hyacinth in still water, applied at the rate of 160 gallons per acre, gave good control. The heavier dosage gave complete kill in three weeks, the 1/100 solution taking a month to kill, but spot spraying was required to kill individual plants. Based on results[275, 715] obtained in the joint operation organized by the Boyce Thompson Institute of Plant Research, Tulane University and the U.S. Corps of Engineers, New Orleans District, 2,4-D applied as a 0·7 per cent solution of the amine salt formulation at about 100 gallons per acre (equivalent to 8 lb. application of the free acid equivalent of 2,4-D per acre) has been successfully employed to eradicate water hyacinth in the Belgian Congo rivers.[336]

In Ceylon, three pints of Phenoxylene 30 applied in twenty gallons of water per acre of paddy three weeks old increased yield by 19 per cent. If spraying was delayed until the paddy was five weeks old, the weeds were too advanced. A tendency for grass weeds to increase was noted in dry-land paddy. Ten oz. of 2,4-D per acre caused damage and reduced yield.

De Wit in his account[703] of the mechanized rice farming project in Surinam, states that grassy weeds could not be controlled by chemical means but were controlled by sowing the paddy seed in water and maintaining permanently a substantial layer of water on the field. This confirms experience in the U.S.A., Italy and some other countries. De Wit goes further: he asserts that if sowing in water were always possible, virtually complete weed control would be obtained over both grasses and non-grassy weeds—with the exception of floating water plants and algae. With regards to non-grassy weeds he confirms earlier investigations which concluded that, except for *Aeschynomene* sp., *Sesbania* and *Sphaenoclea*, such weeds could be controlled with 1·7 to 1·8 kg. acid equivalents of MCPA and 2,4-D per hectare, the former being preferred as it does less damage to paddy and is more effective against *Thalia*. For control of *Aeschynomene* and *Sesbania*, 50/50 mixtures of 2,4-D and 2,4,5-T at rates of 0·9 to 1·2 kg. acid equivalent/ha., and for *Sphaenoclea* the same mixture but at 1·2 to 1·6 kg. acid equivalent per ha. These mixtures are also effective against the other weeds. In practice, the following materials and rates were used by de Wit: 3 litres MCPA (50 per cent NH_4 salt) or 1·8 kg. acid equivalent/ha., except for *Aeschynomene*, *Sphaenoclea* and *Sesbania*, 2 to 2·5 litres of Bush-murder (26·5 per cent isopropyl ester of 2,4-D and 26·5 per cent isopropyl ester of 2,4,5-T) or about 1·0 to 1·2 kg. acid equivalent/ha. where *Aeschynomene* and/or *Sesbania* occurred in considerable quantities; 2·5 to 3 litres Bushmurder if *Sphaenoclea* also occurred. It was found that the best time for application was when the paddy was between five and eight weeks old.

In the United States, Ryker[576] reported that Dinoseb or D.N.B.P. and 2,4-D controlled Mexican weed (*Caperonia castanaefolia* (L) St. Hil) when treated before flooding and when water coverage in the field after treatment was satisfactory. 2,4-D was superior to Dinoseb when applied one or two weeks before flooding, but neither was successful when treatments were made three weeks after flooding. Dinoseb was not as effective as 2,4-D in the control of indigo (*Sesbania macrocarpa* Muhl.) and curly indigo (*Aeschynomene virginica* (L) B.S.P.). Indigo was killed at an early stage of development by 2,4-D, but curly indigo was more resistant to the chemical and for satisfactory control two applications made three weeks apart were usually necessary. Dusting was as effective as spraying for control of Mexican weed and indigo and was more effective for control of curly indigo. Large increases in yield of paddy were obtained when weeds were thus controlled.

It is reported that in Texas aeroplane applications of 2,4-D as dusts and sprays, using water and oil solutions, gave effective control. Oil sprays caused slight temporary injury. The dusts, except isopropyl ester dust with oil, which gave effective control, were washed off by rain six hours after application and did not seriously damage Mexican weed (*Caperonia palustris*) and tall and curly indigo. Davis reports[159] that neither 2,4-D nor MCPA affect eight-week-old paddy and there was little difference in the control of Mexican weed. In field trials, the triethanolamine, ammonium and sodium salts and the butyl ester at rates up to 1 lb. per acre in fifty gallons of water, applied three weeks after emergence, gave good control. Yields were about the same as those of control plots except with ammonium salt and butyl ester at 1 lb. which depressed yields. All treatments six weeks after emergence gave good control, except with butyl ester at ¼ lb. per acre, and significantly increased yields, as did also the triethanolamine salt eight weeks after emergence.

Nester states[431] that broadleaf weeds have been controlled by 2,4-D amine in Arkansas, but 2,4,5-T is more effective in controlling curly indigo. He adds that depth of water at application of weed-killer is important, a light flood helping to keep injury to paddy at a minimum. Proper timing of herbicide application is also important. Herbicide treatment should be made seven to nine weeks after the paddy emerges, at which time the plants are past their sensitive growing stage. Injury is greatest when the herbicide is applied at jointing, booting, flowering or grain formation.

In this connection, Srivastava found[628] that amine, sodium salt and ester of 2,4-D and MCPB have adverse effects on growth, seed fertility and yield. Irrespective of the stage of treatment and the chemical used, reduction in the rate of growth and yield, and increase in the frequency of ear abnormalities are proportional to the con-centration of the herbicide. It was concluded that the safest stage for application of hormone herbicides is in the early stages of growth and that treatment in the pro-flowering stage should be avoided.

POST-EMERGENCE TREATMENT FOR CONTROL OF GRASSES

While it is shown that hormone weedkillers used in post-emergence treatments control some sedges and most of the broad-leaved weeds at certain stages of growth, they are not effective against grasses. Continuous submergence for two to three weeks will sometimes eradi-cate some grasses which are not well adapted to aquatic conditions.

In Louisiana, serious weeds are *Echinochloa* spp. and *Brachiaria* spp., especially when rains occur soon after planting. Under such conditions, grasses emerge at the same time as the paddy and con-trol by early flooding does not produce satisfactory results. Plots were sprayed seven days after planting paddy, when shoots were one or two inches high and grasses just appearing. TCA treatment resulted in death of most of the grasses, the remainder being killed when the field was flooded fourteen days later. Paddy was unaffected until flooding when some plants died and others became dark green and dwarfed, eventually recovering and heading normally. In plots treated with Dinoseb and PCP, tops of both grasses and paddy were immediately killed. Much of the grass failed to recover but the paddy, with its protected growing point, soon recovered with no apparent reduction in yield.

U

Stam F-34 (3,4-dichloropropionanilide) is now widely recommended in the U.S.A. for control of grass weeds. The general recommendation is to use 3 lb. per acre for grass in 2 to 3 and early 4 to 6 leaf or very early tillering stage. Plants should not be treated later than six weeks after planting to avoid herbicide residues at harvest.

In Texas, a trial was carried out on paddy land heavily infested with *Echinochloa crus-galli* Beauv, but Dinoseb reduced neither the grasses nor paddy. In the Philippines, certain sedges and broad-leaved weeds were controlled by different concentrations of herbicides, but amongst the grasses the following results were reported: *Echinochloa crus-galli* was killed by two applications of 0·08, 0·10 and 0·12 per cent 2,4-D amine, 2,4-D ester or 80 per cent sodium salt of 2,4-D. Concentrations of 0·25, 0·50 and 1 per cent injured the weed slightly but recovery was complete in three weeks. *Echinochloa colonum* (L) Link was resistant to 2,4-D treatment.

METHODS OF APPLICATION OF WEEDKILLERS

Usually, hormone weedkillers act most efficiently if water is withdrawn from the field one or two days before application, the field being flooded again two days later. In California, irrigation water is allowed to remain on the field to a depth of about six inches and spraying is done from the air when paddy and weeds have emerged above water level. In Japan, a 2,4-D wettable powder has been formulated for use where irrigation facilities are not available for withdrawing water before treatment. This formulation is only slightly soluble in water and the grains are said to adhere to the leaf surfaces and the chemical is absorbed slowly. Weeds die about a month after application.

The weedkiller may be applied from knapsack sprayers, aeroplanes or tractor-drawn sprayers. Knapsack sprayers may be difficult to use where the field is very swampy. Where, however, there is heavy clay with a firm bottom a few inches down, spraying by this means offers no difficulty.

Aerial spraying is now usual in the United States, notably in California and Texas. This system is practical and economic where a large and continuous tract of paddy is to be treated. The opinion has been expressed that much time is saved by quick turn-rounds, there is more accurate coverage and less drift by using helicopters for spraying, as compared with fast-flying aeroplanes. Under ideal conditions, fixed wing aircraft are 20 to 25 per cent cheaper to operate. Where the surface permits, tractor-drawn sprayers are convenient for distributing the spray. In Italy, tractor-drawn sprayers are used, but more commonly hand-operated sprayers with boom extensions are carried by men walking along the bunds.

In selecting spraying equipment, size of area to be treated and type of equipment most suitable must be considered. The spraying equipment should ensure a complete coverage of the weeds and maximum penetration of foliage without operating at unduly high pressure. High pressures tend to result in fine mist-type sprays which drift in the lightest breeze. Nozzles giving flat, fan-shaped sprays provide more uniform coverage and greater penetration than nozzles delivering a cone-shaped spray. Correct calibration of spraying equipment, obtained by adjusting the speed over the ground and operating pressure, is necessary to ensure even distribution of the spray pattern.

Chapter XIII

FISH PRODUCTION IN PADDY FIELDS

Since fish production is intimately connected with paddy cultivation in both the Eastern and Western Hemispheres, no apology is needed for introducing this subject in a book on rice. It is probable that the paddy planter has always utilized indigenous fish found in the paddy fields to supplement his rice diet, although (with notable exceptions) he usually does little or nothing to increase their number, feed them, or protect the better species from their predators. Even in Japan, where carp culture in paddy fields is carried out with skill and success, it is estimated that less than 1 per cent.[343] of the fields are used for this purpose. The fish harvest in some regions is as important as the paddy harvest, for it provides the cultivator with a welcome addition to his income and the villagers with much-needed protein, vitamins and calcium in their diet. In fact, in many countries, fish is the only source of protein which can be produced in sufficient quantity and cheaply enough to constitute, after rice, the most important item of food. It is, as Schuster reminds one,[593] particularly in isolated villages, far removed from the sea, that fish culture assumes an importance which finds no parallel elsewhere; to people in such villages, the social importance of fish culture is closely related to their economic standards and practices.

The connection between paddy and fish culture is obvious, but the technical and economic aspects require much further study. A distinction must be made between the natural wild crop of fish and the deliberate culture of fish in paddy fields. The former appears more suitable for coastal swamps and low-lying paddy fields, the latter for fields above an altitude of about 1,000 feet. The technique of fish culture at the higher elevation has received some attention and future prospects appear promising. But the conditions are so different at coastal level as to constitute an entirely different set of problems. Encouragement of fish production is most desirable in the interests of the diet of rice-eating people, but caution in propaganda is advisable until such time as it is certain that the knowledge and technique is applicable to the area in which it is desired to develop fish production.

276

FISHPONDS

Pond cultivation of fish is important in many rice-producing countries and is usually more remunerative than fish production in paddy fields, for the latter is often carried out in a rather haphazard manner. It is estimated that in the Far East there are one million acres of ponds, producing some 1,100 million lb. fish at an average rate of 960 lb. per acre per annum.[33] Not infrequently fish pond culture is carried out in conjunction with fish culture on paddy fields, the fish being retained in ponds during the winter and at certain stages of development and released in paddy fields during the summer months when paddy is growing. In China fish ponds are drained dry about once in two or three years and planted either with aquatic plants or paddy. Thus one sees an overlapping of pond culture of fish, paddy cultivation, fish culture on paddy fields, and the peoples' diet in rural areas. Both Hickling[271] and Hoffman[277] draw attention to the regular alternation of paddy and fish crops in the Kwangtung Province of South China, the paddy crop being taken in the fish ponds from February to June and the fish crop from July to January. Hoffman adds that even when the pond is full and raising a crop of fish, paddy may be sown along the banks a few inches above the water level. Nair[428] describes the technique used in rearing fish in bunded areas alternated with paddy crops on the Calcutta sewage irrigation fisheries. Fingerlings of *Labeo rohita*, *Catla catla* and *Cirrhina mringala* are stocked in February and supplied with sewage from the Calcutta sewage canal. Sale of fish commences in June and continues till September. The remaining fish are then placed in another area, the bunded area dried, ploughed and planted with paddy.

Concerning the food available for fish in paddy fields, Hickling remarks that on and around the root-systems of paddy plants there is usually a rich growth of filamentous algae, as well as epiphytic algae and diatoms upon which fish thrive and one often sees traps placed in gaps in the low bunds which surround the paddy fields to catch fish moving out after a period of growth.

VARIETIES OF FISH

Carp are the most important fish for culture in paddy fields or ponds. The Asian stock of *Cyprinus carpio*, the scaleless Common carp, known in Asia as German carp, mirror carp, edelkerper etc., are merely offspring of the stock originating in Europe mixed with scale carp of Asian origin.[593]

Tilapia species, of which *T. mossambica* Peters is the most suitable, are well known in most Asian countries. *Tilapia* is a hardy fish which reproduces everywhere without special care and may be grown in fresh or brackish water in ponds, fields, lakes and reservoirs. It is not invariably successful in paddy fields chiefly because of destruction by predatory fish and shortage of water in certain seasons.[111]

In parts of Malaya and in Thailand *Trichogaster pectoralis* Regan, known locally as Sepat Siam, is important in paddy-growing areas. Indigenous to Thailand, it is a fish with no high gastronomic value, but it is most prolific and hence an important factor in the economic life of the peasant. It is found all the year round in irrigation canals and drains, but thrives best in paddy fields and marshes where, being a vegetarian, it finds abundant algae on which to feed. Looked upon as a bony and muddy fish, it is nevertheless "enthroned in the hearts of the poor."[622] In addition, Catfish *Clarias batrachus* Linnaeus,[621] Serpent-head fish *Ophiocephalus striatus* Bloch,[619] *Trichogaster trichopterus* Pallus and *Anabas testudineus* Bloch[620] are normally found wild in Malayan paddy fields and command a ready sale. Kissing Gouramy (*Helostroma temmincki*), found in many tropical regions, is also suitable for paddy fields.[50] This by no means exhausts the list of fish normally found or suitable for paddy fields. For instance, Peneid prawns are obtained in the brackish paddy fields of Malabar and Travancore,[391] mullets are reared on paddy fields in Bengal and *Puntius javicus* in the brackish delta fields of the Beganwan River in Java.

ECOLOGICAL CONSIDERATIONS

The main fish culture region of the tropics lies between altitudes 1,000 and 1,600 feet in the zone 20° north and south of the Equator. In this zone, writes Schuster,[593] practically every well-irrigated paddy field can be stocked with fish. Below 1,000 feet, controlled stocking of paddy fields can be replaced by release of cultivated species.

Soong[623] examines conditions which determine the well-being of fish under three headings: physical, chemical and biological. He reminds one that fish, in general, have a wide range of toleration to natural, physical and chemical factors of the environment and that while the first two of these factors determine the suitability of water for fish, the fish themselves directly and indirectly through their action on other forms of life, exert a great influence on the environment.

PHYSICAL FACTORS

Lowland tropical streams have a temperature around 25°C., while stagnant swamps are around 34° C. with a fluctuation of about 10° C. These warm temperatures are mainly responsible for the rapid growth of many species of fish. While the Asian varieties of Common carp tolerate temperatures as high as 34°C., provided the oxygen content of the water is sufficient, the optimum temperature for them seems to be from 22° to 28° C., while *Tilapia* thrives at about 20° C. High temperature, however, influences the amount of dissolved oxygen in the water and hence the rate of consumption of oxygen by fish and other organisms, the rate of breakdown of organic substances and consequent release of nutrients.

Turbid water reduces light penetration and hence slows down photosynthesis; it also discourages the presence of fish that are unable to adapt themselves to this condition. While tropical fish, in general, are able to tolerate wide ranges of turbidity, extremes and prolonged turbid conditions favour development of the cat fish type of fauna similar to *Pangasius*, *Wallagonia* and *Clarias*, with diminutive eyes and barbels to aid them in search for food as they grub along the bottom.

CHEMICAL FACTORS

Consumption of oxygen by fish varies with the temperature and environment. An excessive amount of dissolved oxygen has no ill effects and the minimum toleration varies with the fish. Dissolved oxygen which will maintain freshwater fish in good condition is in the region of 5 p.p.m. if the water temperature is 20° C. or over. The dissolved oxygen content in most tropical inland waters is well over 70 per cent saturation and therefore presents no hazard to fish. If, however, there is active organic pollution or decomposition, the dissolved oxygen may drop to dangerously low levels. This condition is a frequent hazard in tropical swamps and has given rise to the evolution of a very successful group of fishes with accessory air-breathing organs—the *Anabantids*, *Heteropneustids* and *Clarids*.

Although most fish can tolerate a wide range of hydrogen-ion concentration, there is considerable evidence to show that *p*H 5·0 is the lower limit critical for the survival of most freshwater fish, with an upper limit of *p*H 9·5. Under natural conditions, therefore, hydrogen-ion concentration is usually considered an unimportant ecological character. Soong,[623] however, emphasizes that hydrogen-ion concentration is a good, rough guide to the degree of fertility and hence the potential productivity of the water. Since water derives its dissolved substances from the soil, substances contributing to the *p*H of soil will themselves influence the *p*H of waters. While fish tolerate wide differences in *p*H, hydrogen-ion concentration is important because it influences soil fertility and hence the potential fish productivity of the water. Soong found a fairly definite relation between pH of the water and the yield of fish, fish yield being greater as the pH increased to the optimum of 7·0 to 8·0.

The difference in yield of fish between a rich coastal soil in Malaya and an inland acid soil was quite startling. The former yielded 200–400 kilograms per hectare, while the inland acid area gave 10 to 50 kilograms per hectare of *Trichogaster pectoralis*. Comparing the fish from the area of high pH value with those from a low pH value, Soong found that the former were in finer condition, grew faster and were more prolific. Comparing Sepat Siam grown in a sump pond with those grown in a paddy field, the former were thinner, indicating that it might be possible to increase the yield in the field by fertilizing the sump pond. Manuring experiments with cow-dung will give instant impetus to algal growth, lime has a more lasting beneficial effect.

Free carbon dioxide is usually present in water as a result of organic decomposition and the respiration of aquatic organisms. It would appear that only in swamps is the carbon dioxide content of water likely to rise to levels dangerous to fish. The determination of the ammoniacal nitrogen content of water gives a good indication of the extent of likely organic polution. Natural, unpolluted water generally does not contain more than 0·5 p.p.m. of ammoniacal nitrogen. Toxic effects are seldom met except in extreme cases of pollution.

Summing up the above, Soong writes:[623]

> Fish differ in their toleration to various physical and chemical factors. The swamp fish, of the genera *Ophicephalus*, *Clarias* and *Trichogaster* are able to withstand high temperatures, low pH and low dissolved oxygen content better than most riverine fish. The common carp, *C. carpio* is so hardy that its distribution is world-wide. Similarly, fish of the cat-fish type are more adapted to extreme turbid conditions. The choice of a suitable fish should therefore be related to the physical and chemical conditions of the water; in addition, its inter-relationship with other fish, either as prey or as predator, should also be considered.

> Of all the physical and chemical factors affecting the viability of fish in their natural environment, oxygen concentration is the major limiting factor. Certain tropical fish have anatomical adaptation to air-breathing which gives them a wider range of tolerance to oxygen concentration than fish that solely depend on dissolved oxygen.

FISH FOR LOWLAND SWAMPS

At the higher altitudes in tropical paddy areas it is possible to introduce and cultivate selected varieties of fish. For this purpose spawning ponds will be necessary, the fish being released in the flooded paddy-fields when they have attained sufficient growth. This fish farming is outside the scope of the present book. Considerable information on this subject is contained in a paper by Schuster[593] entitled Fish Culture in Conjunction with Rice Cultivation and by Kuronuma[343] on carp culture in paddy fields in Japan. At lower elevations probably the most that can be done is to introduce fish which can fend for themselves and spawn in and around the fields.

The opportunities for stocking paddy fields in lowland areas are restricted by the difficulty in protecting the selected fish from predatory species, in making provision for the fish population when the land is dry, and the often extreme acid reaction of the water. Despite these set-backs, such areas can be made productive by careful selection of the fish to be introduced. Reference has already been made to certain fish which are suitable for such an environment, in particular, the Common carp, *Tilapia*, *Trichogaster pectoralis* and in brackish water such species as mullets and prawns. In many areas, predatory fish such as serpent-head fish (*Ophiocephalus* spp.) and cat-fish (*Clarias* spp.) are highly thought of and find a ready market.

For *Tilapia* shallow ditches are dug to provide spawning places and shelter for the fish. The stocking rate is 10 to 100 fish of 1 to 3 cm. length per 100 metres and in addition some big fish to serve as spawners. Where predatory fish can be controlled the growth and yield are good, but it is usually found almost impossible to eliminate such fish as snake-heads. Attempts to introduce *Tilapia* into Malaya[620] have failed for this reason.[355]

Tilapia melanopleura is valuable in controlling weeds in irrigation channels; van der Lingen and colleagues state[363] that this fish gives good control of *Nymphaea* spp. if they are cut first. For rapid results 500 fingerlings per acre are needed, but 50 to 100 will ensure control within a year provided that conditions for their survival are good.

A large quantity of Sepat Siam (*Triochogaster pectoralis*) is obtained from paddy fields in Malaya[618] and Thailand. For this purpose a pond is dug at the lower end of a field of two or three acres, bunded on three sides, the open side facing the field to be drained. Coconut palms and bananas are usually grown on the bunds to provide shade for the pond. The fish live and develop in the paddy field from the time it is inundated for paddy cultivation until it is drained for harvest. As the water is drained off the field the fish move to the pond, where they are collected. A few fish find their way to drains and water courses and form the nucleus for the succeeding season's catch.

The commercially important predatory fish *Ophiocephalus* (serpent-heads) and *Clarias* (cat-fish) have a wide range of distribution in swamps and lowland paddy areas. In Malaya these fish are caught in large numbers in traps or by hook and line, and transported alive to markets often situated hundreds of miles away.[593, 619] Where facilities do not exist for rapid marketing, fish are cleaned, gutted and sundried.

PRAWNS

Hickling[724] draws attention to and comments on Menon's account[728] of prawn fishing in paddy fields during the fallow season in the coastal region of Travancore-Cochin State, India. About 11,000 acres are said to be used for raising prawns for market in this region. The Penaeid prawns breed in the sea and make their way up the canals to the paddy fields.

When the paddy crop has been harvested, the field bunds are strengthened and supplied with temporary wooden sluice gates—through which water is admitted to the fields when the tide has raised the water in the canal to its highest level. This ensures that the water flows with maximum force, since the number of young prawns entering the field with the water largely depends on the force and duration of the current. At low tide, much of the water is allowed to flow out to permit entry of more water—and prawns—at high tide. When water is admitted at night, a light may be hung at the mouth of the sluice to attract the prawns.

Fishing for marketable prawns in the paddy field usually starts with the neap tides four or five days before every new and full moon, and is continued for seven or eight days. A net, about 20 feet long and mounted on a wooden frame fitting into the sluice gate, is put into position when the water level in the canal is at its lowest. The sluice is then opened and the water rushing through it, carries some of the prawns, which collect at the narrow and closed end of the net.

Menon adds that, some twenty-five to thirty years ago, when the fields had been stocked with young prawns, the fields were kept under water for two or three months, thus allowing the prawns to grow. Rice stubble appears to be a good fertilizer, giving rise to a dense growth of algae, upon the detritus of which the prawns fatten. He states that the yield of fresh prawns is 700 to 1,900 lb. per acre per season. The prawns are usually marketed in the dried condition, so that the rate of production per acre is 106 to 295 lb. dried prawns.

CRAYFISH

Recently, crayfish growing in the Louisiana paddy fields has attracted attention, for crops of about 500 lb. of crayfish per acre in a season are reported. The crayfish find their way into the fields, being attracted by the duck potato weed, which is their natural food.[617]

YIELDS

Yields of fish vary enormously according to nature and quantity of food, water supply, control of predatory fish and care in stocking. Yields of *Tilapia* in Formosa in 1952 gave an average of 245 lb. per acre. A recent estimate of fish production in some 442,000 acres of paddy land in Malaya was 7,500 metric tons, excluding local consumption. *Trichogaster pectoralis* is now established as the most important single species economically, comprising about 60 per cent by weight of total production from the deep paddy areas of the west coast. The remainder consists of about 20 per cent. *C. batrachus*, 9 per cent *O. striatus* and 1 per cent *Trichogaster trichopterus* and *Anabas testudineus*. The fertile coastal areas are the most productive, giving yields of between 180 and 360 lb. *T. pectoralis* per acre, while production from the acid inland areas may be as low as 20 to 40 lb. per acre. In Indonesia, with a paddy crop in which water can be impounded for 40 to 60 days, yields of 30 to 50 lb. of fish can be obtained. In Japan, yields of 2,000 lb. have been obtained, in Malaya 120 lb., and in Tanganyika 100 lb. per acre.

EFFECT OF FISH ON PADDY CROP

The consensus of opinion, in many cases based on experiments, is that fish in paddy fields result in an increased yield of paddy varying from four to 10 per cent. The Russians have reported a seven per cent increase of paddy where fish are grown and China a 10 per cent increase. It has been found that fish help to control growth of algae and other weeds. While a possible disadvantage of fish production is that water must be maintained to a depth of at least 10 inches, which may lead to a loss of water by seepage, the advantages will generally outweigh any possible disadvantages. Fish eat large quantities of weeds, worms, insect larvae and algae which are either directly or indirectly injurious to paddy. Common carp are known to eat mosquito larvae and so may assist in controlling malaria. Fish also probably assist in making fertilizing material more readily available to paddy.

THE RISK OF PESTICIDES TO FISH*

A number of new and potent insecticides are being tested in many countries for use on paddy fields. Many of these are highly toxic to

* By Dr E. F. Edson, Medical Department of Chesterfield Park Research Station (the Research Centre of Fisons Pest Control Ltd.).

fish at the normal rates of application, as has been shown in Malaya where Wyatt[705] found that both endrin and dieldrin were toxic to fish although DDT and BHC would normally be safe to use. Fertilizers applied as top-dressing during the growth of paddy are unfavourable to fish. Weeding during the growth of paddy is good for fish as it assists in aerating the water.

In view of the desirability of encouraging fish production as a means of improving the peasants' diet, it would be folly also to advocate the use of chemicals which may benefit the paddy crop at the expense of the fish population.

Pesticidal chemicals may find their way into fish-bearing waters either accidentally as by sprays, spills, washing used containers from adjacent ground or air-spraying operations, or deliberately, as when they are used for the control of aquatic weeds, vectors of disease or pests of irrigated crops. The latter operations are far more likely to present risk to fish populations than accidental contamination from nearby spraying. The increasing use of pesticides in weed, insect and disease vector control in waters of tropical countries may, unless care is taken, produce an unacceptable fish mortality, with consequent reduction in protein supplies for the population. The avoidance of risks to fish is especially important in areas where inland fishing or fish cultivation make a valuable contribution to the country's diet or resources, e.g. in Indonesia, China, Japan and south-east Asia generally.

The harmful effects of such chemicals may be either direct, by chemical poisoning of fish; or indirect, as in the production of toxic waters by decomposition of killed weeds, or harmful effects on food supplies, shade plants, protective vegetation or other environmental features. Although such effects are more likely to be due to the active ingredient in the product used, it is at times possible for injury to be caused or increased by the solvent or manufacturing additives present in the formulation, especially when using undiluted oil-based concentrates.

The possibility of many fish being killed in any specific operation with a toxic pesticide is influenced by such factors as the numbers and sensitivity of fish species, the opportunity for the fish to move readily to unsprayed water, dilution of the chemical in flowing waters, temperature, oxygenation and depth of the water, frequency and method of application and other variables. Some of these aspects are discussed in more detail later.

From such considerations, it is clear that no prophesy of risk or safety to fish could hope to be very accurate, except under very extreme conditions, as when the proposed chemical application rate greatly exceeds the safe limit for fish. It is equally clear that many details have to be considered when estimating possible risk to fish from a proposed operation. It is often wiser to carry out a small-scale experimental treatment in fish-bearing waters then to attempt full-scale operations without sound evidence on safety to fish.

During recent years the widespread use of persistent insecticides in U.S.A. has been watched with great concern by biologists. From their studies it has become clear that prolonged exposure of fish to sublethal concentrations of DDT, dieldrin and probably other similarly persistent chemicals may cause tremendous accumulations of these materials in predominantly fatty organs in the fish. The biological consequences of such effects are not known; it is improbable that they are of negligible consequence in terms of fish breeding and survival. The general reaction to this finding is to try to limit the use of such materials to those purposes which are either essential, or which cause no subsequent exposure of important fish species or supplies.

THE MAIN FACTORS

Although the most important single factor may be the innate toxicity of the proposed chemical to fish species, there are other factors which will materially influence risks. For example, the use of a chemical in moving waters will usually involve speedy dilution of the contaminant and reduction of the concentrations to which the fish are exposed. Thus, the risks of application to still waters such as ditches, canals, ponds or lakes, are usually greater than from moving waters, streams, rivers or estuaries. However, in extensive operations on flowing waters, a wide zone of comparatively high concentration may steadily move downstream and may be lengthy enough to cause fish deaths several miles below the point of application. Similarly, where rivers expand into lakes, or where stagnant backwaters occur downstream, pools of chemical contamination may remain for many days or weeks, with little dilution. Even direct application to flowing rivers may therefore cause fish deaths some distance from the scene of application, days or weeks later.

The deeper the water, the less the final concentration after mixing or diffusion is complete. The ten-fold decrease in final concentration due to ten-fold increase in depth may not produce fish safety if the initial concentration was excessively high. Furthermore, a chemical may passively or actively incorporate itself with the bottom mud of still deep waters, where bottom-feeding fish may undergo prolonged exposure during feeding.

Sometimes external factors intrude to increase the hazards of pesticides to fish. For example, the use of pentachlorphenol as a weedkiller in rice in Japan normally carries a known but acceptable degree of risk to fish. When heavy rainfall overfloods the irrigation bunds, more widespread contamination follows, and heavy and quite unacceptable fish mortality can occur. Similar but smaller-scale problems have been observed in Europe during wide-scale use of copper fungicides to control potato blight during periods of persistent and heavy rainfall.

Most chemicals cause some sensory or repellent effect in fish, which may therefore try to swim to clear waters, away from the areas of highest concentration and irritancy. Large-scale treatments, as by air-spraying, massive application equipment, or large labour forces, may give fish little chance of successfully vacating contaminated areas and thus increase the risks. *Per contra*, small-scale treatments, or deliberate intervals between spraying separate "plots" on the area, may allow fish to escape to safer waters.

Repeated applications to water, or the use of concentrated chemical deposits which diffuse slowly, will prolong the exposure period to fish and may eventually produce a serious delayed mortality. Chemicals which are stable in aqueous solution are more likely to cause such effects than those which are unstable in water, e.g. TEPP.

The toxic action of most chemicals is increased by raised water temperature, which also increases the solubility of the applied chemical. Thus, application to warm waters in tropical areas may cause more fish deaths than similar operations in colder waters. In stagnant waters already partially deficient in oxygen, mortality may be greater than in fully oxygenated waters.

Although concentrate-spraying of oil-based pesticides may cause fish deaths due to the oily vehicle, this is less likely to be a significant risk than the deliberate use of aromatic solvents, such as naphtha, fuel oils, to destroy larvae or vegetation. With oily solutions of water-insoluble materials, there is a tendency for accumulation of surface oil and chemical to occur at the downward margins of the waters, with higher mortality as a result.

Field evidence strongly suggests that "miscible oil" formulations of pesticides ("emulsifiable concentrates") are much more likely to cause fish deaths than the same chemicals as wettable powders or dusts. Destruction of fish food supplies, such as aquatic insects and other arthopoda, e.g. crustacea and copepods, may often occur at concentrations not themselves injurious to fish and this is especially likely with insecticidal chemicals. Mortality may then be delayed and due to starvation. More severe effects may be found among eggs and young fish than among adults; therefore, known spawning, breeding and nursery areas may require specially cautious treatment. When disturbed, fish tend to seek protective cover amongst vegetation; the spraying of densely-weedy waters may therefore lead to heavy fish mortality, especially where application is by hand and involves disturbance by boats and wading. It is then important to treat, whenever possible, the total area in separate small plots.

TOXICITY OF PESTICIDES TO FISH

Increasing awareness of the need for fish conservation has intensified laboratory research and field studies on pesticide toxicity to fish. Indeed, fish toxicity data by chemical firms during the development stages of a new product is often a Government requirement. Extensive research has also been carried out in Government laboratories, particularly in the U.S.A. This work is making it obvious that the mammalian and fish toxicity of chemicals bear no consistent relationship and must always be specifically investigated before conclusions can be drawn. Tests on different fish species have made it clear that the response of one species may differ significantly from another, even under standardized conditions, thus emphasizing the desirability of small-scale field trials of a chemical before it is put on the market.

The toxicity of pesticidal chemicals to fish greatly varies. Study of the literature, mainly from North America, permits the compilation of a series of tentative figures for maximum safe initial concentrations of the more important pesticides. Few, if any, fish deaths would be expected if initial concentrations remained below these safe maxima, although the most sensitive species or individuals may die or show toxic effects. The figures suggested in this list are based upon the results of laboratory aquarium studies, but are modified, wherever possible, to take account of field observations with the chemicals.

In general, the existing herbicidal chemicals (weedkillers) are much safer for fish-bearing waters than the present insecticides. There is a general correlation, but not a precise one, between toxicity to fish and to mammals, usually influenced by the water-stability of the chemical. However, some chemicals, e.g. DDT, gamma-BHC, toxaphene and copper compounds, have a much higher toxicity to fish than their oral toxicity to mammals would indicate. Therefore, it cannot be presumed that a new pesticide of low mammalian toxicity is necessarily non-hazardous to fish-cultivation.

The use of figures in the list below may be aided if it is remembered that an application of 1 lb. per acre, when evenly distributed, will cause approximately the following initial concentrations in waters of different depths:

>1 foot   0·3 p.p.m.
>3 feet   0·1 p.p.m.
>10 feet 0·03 p.p.m.

TABLE 20

APPROXIMATE MAXIMUM SAFE UPPER LIMIT FOR INITIAL
CONCENTRATIONS FOR PESTICIDES APPLIED TO FISH-BEARING WATERS
(in p.p.m.)

Insecticides		*Herbicides*	
Endrin	0·0005	Pentachlorphenol ..	3
Toxaphene	0·005	Arsenites.. ..	10
*Guthion	0·005	Monuron (CMU) ..	20
Dieldrin	0·008	Simazine, atrazine ..	5–20
Aldrin	0·01	DNC, DNBP	10–100
DDT	0·02	Hormone-type weed-	
*Delnav	0·04	killers, (2,4-D, MCPA,	
Chlordane	0·04	2,4,5-T, etc.)	50–500
Heptachlor	0·05	Dalapon	1000
Methoxychlor ..	0·06	Chlorate	2000
*Disyston	0·07	Borate	2000
Lindane	0·08		
*Malathion	0·1		
*Diazinon	0·5		
BHC	1·0		
*TEPP	1·0		
*Methyl parathion ..	2·0		
*Dipterex	4·0		
*Dimethoate	5·0		

Fungicides	
Mercury compounds	0·001
Soluble copper compounds ..	3·0

It is thus evident that significant risks to fish in irrigation, fish-cultivation or natural waters may arise from the direct application of the insecticides endrin, toxaphene, DDT, gamma-BHC, dieldrin, aldrin and heptachlor. Among the other compounds, somewhat similar but smaller risks may arise from deliberate use of the herbicides pentachlorphenol and arsenites, and the fungicidal mercurial compounds. As a general rule, therefore, the ten materials mentioned above should not be directly applied to natural or irrigated waters in which fish are an important "crop". Irrigated crops should preferably be treated only after draining the fields or at least after lowering

* OP insecticides.

the water level to an adequate minimum. Water from treated fields should be held back from flowing into adjacent pure waters for at least one week and preferably for two weeks. Otherwise, most of the modern pesticides have only limited toxicity to fish, and at their application rates and normal methods of use are unlikely to cause adverse effects, even when deliberately used in fish-bearing waters. Application of knowledge of the factors here described as increasing risks to fish would go far towards making even the more dangerous pesticides free from effects on fish populations.

SELECTED REFERENCES ON RISKS OF PESTICIDES TO FISH

1. Fielding, J. R. and Baldwin, W. P. (1955). *Effects of some new Insecticides on Fish and Wildlife.* Pesticides Handbook, 1955.
2. Humphries, Miss (1957). *The Control of Aquatic Weeds.* Agric. Res. Council Unit, Oxford; revision of M.A.F.F. Fisheries Notice No. 28 of Jan. 1949.
3. Rudd, R. L. and Gennelly, R. E. (1955). *Contamination of Irrigation Waters by Agricultural Chemicals.* Amer. Chem. Soc. Abs. Papers 1955 Meeting.
4. Rudd, R. L. and Gennelly, R. E. (1956). *Pesticides; their Use and Toxicity in Relation to Wildlife.* Dept. of Fish and Game, Games Management Branch, State of California, Game Bul. No. 7.
5. Springer, P. F. (1955). *Pesticides as Pollutants of Streams and Ponds.* Amer. Chem. Soc. Abs. Papers, 1955 Meeting.
6. Springer, P. F. (1955). *Plant Pesticides (Herbicides) and Wild Life.* Pesticides Handbook, 1955.
7. Springer, P. F. (1956). "Insecticides; Boon or Bane?" *Audubon Magazine*, May–June and July–Aug. 1956.

NOTE ON PESTICIDES

The extent to which aldrin, dieldrin and other persistent organo-chloride pesticides contaminate the general environment and some birds is causing anxiety. In the United Kingdom their use in agricultural, horticultural, garden and food storage is now strongly discouraged.

If used, the detailed instructions supplied with these pesticides should be closely followed, but other less dangerous substances should be used in their place wherever possible.

Chapter XIV

PESTS

IMPORTANCE OF PESTS

THE worst paddy pests are plant bugs, stem borers, army worms and grasshoppers, of which each country has representative species. The greatest total damage is probably caused by paddy bugs, but the worst individual pest is frequently a stem borer or an army worm. The importance of pests, however, is frequently local as is only to be expected with a crop such as paddy, which is grown over a wide range of climatic conditions and under various cultural methods. Further, many pests attack sporadically, so that an insignificant one may suddenly become important, or a once injurious insect may disappear.

The vast majority of paddy pests belong to the Orders: Orthoptera (grasshoppers and locusts, which include the mole cricket), Hemiptera (plant bugs) which suck the sap, Lepidoptera (butterflies and moths) which include stem borers, leaf rollers, case worms, cut worms and army worms, and the Coleoptera (beetles) of which probably root weevils occasion most damage to the crop. There are a few Diptera (true flies) of importance, mainly gallflies and frit flies, and a very few Trichoptera (caddis flies) and Thysanoptera (thrips).

The varied habits of paddy pests are such that the plant can be attacked at every stage of growth—seedlings in the nursery bed by army worms, root caterpillars and grasshoppers; young plants in the field by leaf-eating beetles, leafhopper bugs, leaf rollers and case worms; stems by stem-boring caterpillars; flowers by gallflies and blister beetles which feed on pollen; and developing grain by earhead bugs.

But alarming as is this array of potential enemies—and several hundred species are known—most paddy-growing countries have only a few troublesome pests, though the damage occasioned by these may be considerable. It is comforting, too, to read the following opinion:*

---

* E. J. McNaughton,[389] *World Paddy Pests* (prelim. Report Commonwealth Institute of Entomology, Ref. C.1846, January 1946), to whom the author is indebted for much information in this chapter.

Although heavy damage can be done by insect pests and continuous cultivation of rice over wide areas seems to provide ideal conditions for their accumulation, no species is likely to become a serious threat to the existence of the rice industry in any land. Strongly acting against this are such factors as the hazards to insect life of alternate flooding and drying; the break in pest life histories caused by transplanting; pest dependence on special seasonal or other conditions for their most successful development and attack (e.g. early lack of rain for army worms and grasshoppers, proximity of shelter and alternate hosts for paddy bugs); high mortality amongst hibernating pests, including stem borers, by routine field cultural practices, and the high degree of hand control on the small paddy farms.

Plant bugs are probably the most widespread of all paddy pests; in Malaya, the Philippines, United States of America, British Guiana and Japan they are reported to be most serious. The genera *Leptocorisa, Scotinophara, Nezara* and *Mormidea* appear in swarms and suck the sap from the developing grain. *Leptocorisa acuta* Thünb. and *L. varicornis* F. are regarded throughout Asia as the most serious plant bug pests of paddy. Copeland[135] states that the damage occasioned by *L. acuta* varies from insignificant to complete destruction and the loss of 5 to 25 per cent of the local crop is no rarity. Leafhoppers of *Nephotettix* and other genera also do great harm and transmit the causal virus of dwarf disease. Attack by plant bugs is sporadic but can be devastating.

Among Lepidoptera, stem borers are major pests in each main paddy-growing area. In the old world, *Schoenobius incertulas* (Wlk.), the yellow stem borer, is probably the most important single pest of paddy, with *Chilo suppressalis* (Wlk.), the striped stem borer, running second. *Scirpophaga innotata* (Wlk.), the white rice borer, is the worst pest in Indonesia. *Chilotraea* spp. are among the chief borers in Malaya and in certain other regions in Asia.[705] The damage caused by borers tends to be overestimated owing to the confusion of plant injury with crop yield, but can be very severe in sub-tropical and tropical areas where there is a build-up to five or six generations and there is overlapping of paddy crops throughout the year. It would not, perhaps, be an overstatement to say that borers annually cause about 2 per cent loss of rice yield in the main old-world rice regions. It would appear, therefore, that although other pests may be severe locally, stem borers are the most consistently serious throughout all the important rice-producing regions of the world.

Among sporadic pests army worms rank high. *Spodoptera mauritia*, for instance, is stated to be the worst pest in south India and is serious elsewhere. Other important genera are *Borolia, Laphygma, Prodenia* and *Mocis*.

Case worms, i.e. caterpillars which make protective casings from leaves, do much damage by eating the foliage in nearly every paddy area. Cut worms are also destructive; they feed on the lower leaves and cut off plant stems at night, hiding in the soil by day. Ordinary leaf eaters, army worms and leaf folders may also cause much damage. The principal genera are *Nymphula*, a case worm; the leaf folder *Cnaphalocrocis*; and the army worm *Cirphis*.

Of Coleoptera, leaf-mining weevils are serious in Asia. Occasional damage is caused by various root grubs, flea beetles, water weevils and *Hispa*, a Chrysomelid beetle, but these are normally minor pests. In Arkansas water weevils in the larval stage have been known to reduce yields by as much as 30 per cent.

It is beyond the scope of this book to discuss the life histories of paddy pests exhaustively. The more important and universal pests will, however, be briefly described in the following pages.

STEM BORERS

Stem borers are moth larvae which bore into paddy stems shortly after hatching, and for most of their life remain in the stem, feeding on the tissues and either killing or so injuring the plant that it produces little or no crop. These pests are mainly small moths of the family Pyralidae belonging to the genera *Schoenobius*, *Chilo*, *Scirpophaga* and *Chilotraea*.

The damage they do may be illustrated by the following examples. In Japan, *Schoenobius* is said to have caused a 2 per cent loss of the crop in 1933. In some districts of Kyushu (south Japan) there is reported to be a crop destruction of 50 to 60 per cent in four or five years out of ten and of 20 to 40 per cent in the remaining five or six years, necessitating a reduction in land tax and sometimes driving farmers from home. The annual average loss in Formosa is estimated at 2 to 3 per cent of the crop; damage to the second crop is very severe and in some districts infestation may reach 100 per cent and over half the crop be lost. In China, *Schoenobius* and *Chilo* are said to have caused an annual loss of 10 to 20 per cent. In India, *Schoenobius* in Konkan (Bombay) is said to cause a loss of crop rarely less than 10 per cent and sometimes as large as 60 per cent. In the Philippines, *Scirpophaga innotata* (Wlk.) destroyed or severely damaged 285,000 acres in 1927 and the 1935 attack was described as catastrophic. Manickavasagar and Miyashita consider[372] *Schoenobius incertulas* to be the most destructive of paddy pests because it occasions severe damage from seedling to maturity, season after season, especially where paddy is grown on an extensive scale and double cropping is practised. The borer inflicts great damage to the

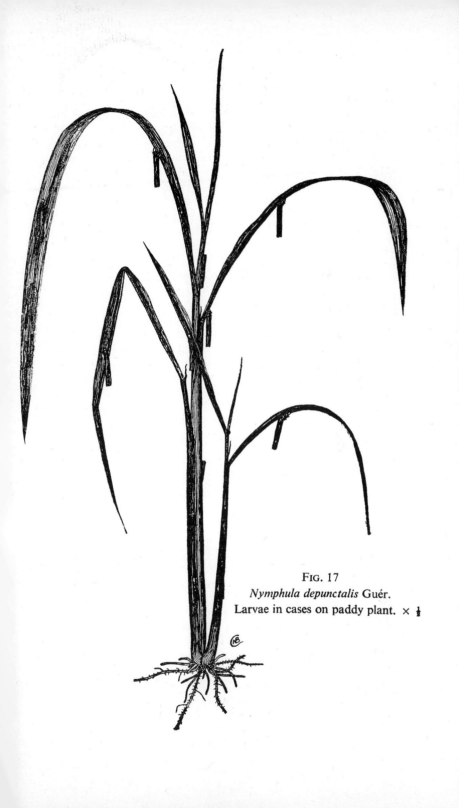

Fig. 17
Nymphula depunctalis Guér.
Larvae in cases on paddy plant. × ½

late crop. In Japan damage is less severe in areas when delayed planting is practised with single cropping.

McNaughton considers[389] that estimates of damage should be treated with reserve, for the proportion of injured stems is not that of grain loss, as plants may recover owing to tillering, and furthermore, because damage is subject to such wide local variations that estimates for large areas are often guesswork. This view may be true, but the extensive damage is so evident that these and similar reports should not be underestimated. The subject is given prominence in this place because it points to the fact that the most severe damage appears to occur in areas where more than one annual crop of paddy is reaped, or where overlapping of paddy crops permits the build-up of several generations of the pest in a year—a subject to which reference is made elsewhere in this book.

FIG. 18
Schoenobius incertulas (Wlk.).
Egg mass on leaf.
× 5

Schoenobius incertulas (Wlk.), the Yellow Stem Borer. The moths are nocturnal, hiding during the day under the upper leaf-sheaths. They become most active between 8 and 9 p.m., when they mate. The average length of life of the moth is five to seven days. No parasites of the moth are known, but they are preyed on by dragonflies, spiders, birds and bats.

The eggs are laid in clusters on the underside of young paddy leaves about one to three inches from the tips and touching the mid-ribs. Each female may deposit 120 to 150 eggs and is responsible for two to five clusters. Large numbers of eggs are lost by natural enemies and dislodged by storms.

Three species of Hymenoptera, notably *Trichogramma* sp., a minute wasp, are said to parasitize from 20 to 60 per cent of the eggs in Formosa and 40 to 70 per cent in Japan. In Malaya, efforts were made to control the pest by liberating *Trichogramma*[401] which also attacks *Chilotraea* (*Proceras*) *polychrysa* (Meyr.) and *Sesamia inferens* (Wlk.), but after two years' work[137] it was considered to be an ineffective parasite even when liberated at the high rate of 1,300,000 per acre daily throughout the paddy season. Further, only *Chilotraea* was attacked to any extent, *Schoenobius* being immune owing to the hairy covering of the egg masses.

Normal incubation period is from six to seven days. The newly hatched larvae wander about for a time and feed by scarifying the epidermis of the undersides of leaves, but soon make their way down to bore into the stems. Several larvae may enter the plant they are on, the others scatter to search for suitable hosts. This they do by suspending themselves from fine threads emitted from their mouths; they are also blown by wind, often for long distances, until another suitable plant is encountered. Some fall into the irrigation water and are thus carried for long distances before they find a host. At this scattering stage only 10 to 25 per cent of the larvae succeed in finding a host, the remainder perish.

If the larvae hatch on stemless seedlings in the nursery they soon run out of food and are forced to emerge and seek other host plants. They may find larger plants, but where it is customary to cut off the tops of seedlings before conveying them to the field for transplanting, and where injured plants are discarded, there is little danger of transferring the pest from the nursery bed to the field.

The larvae enter the stem immediately above the point where the leaf blade diverges from the leaf sheath. After eating the stem tissue of the uppermost internode the larva bores though the node to the internode below. When the stem is exhausted, the caterpillar migrates to another by

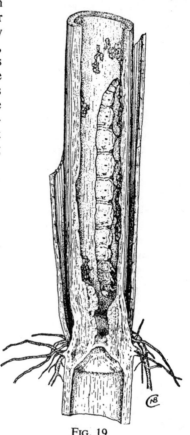

FIG. 19
Schoenobius incertulas (Wlk.).
Larva in stem. × 2½

floating in the water. A larva about to leave a stem crawls up to the leaf tip, bends the leaf margin with a thread and makes a rolled portion into which it crawls and then severs it to fit the body length. In this protective covering, with head and thorax protruding, it either attacks a suitable stem on the same plant or, suspending itself from the plant by a thread till it reaches the water surface, drifts about until it contacts a stem. In the course of its life each larva injures two or three stems.

As maturity approaches, the larva bores to the base of the stem where it pupates. When larvae pupate in flooded paddy fields, emergence holes are just above water level. Many larvae are not ready for pupation when the crop is harvested and may therefore be removed in the cut stems and die on drying out the straw. Other larvae reach stem bases but do not prepare for pupation and will pass through the dry season. This has been observed in Japan and China. Such hibernating larvae and pupae are liable to destruction by ploughing and irrigation for the next paddy crop. Larvae are well equipped for protection under all conditions and parasitism is therefore small.

The pupal stage may last from six to fourteen days, when the moths emerge without difficulty. In irrigated fields they can emerge successfully through four or five inches of water, and submerged land can give rise to many moths unless flooding has been sufficiently prolonged to rot the stubble and destroy hibernating larvae. If stubble has merely been ploughed in, the moths can often break through the earth, though with difficulty. Ploughing plus submergence effectively prevents exit.

The number of generations per year depends on climate and the continued presence of host plants. Where, as in parts of Japan, a single paddy crop is the rule, there are two generations in the north and three in the south. In Formosa, where double cropping is the normal practice, there are four generations in the cooler northern half of the island and five or six in the tropical south. Probably two generations are characteristic in the northern limit of the pest's distribution and six in the tropics.

Recent investigations in Malaya[705] show that, contrary to general belief, borers rely on volunteer paddy during the off-season and but little on other grasses and sedges. It is also shown that a large off-season population of borers is unnecessary to provide for a serious infestation by harvest time. The writer concludes that any attempt to control stem borers in the off-season will be unsuccessful since the high reproductive rate makes it possible for borers to increase out of all proportion to their initial population.

Perhaps the most effective method of controlling this pest is by ploughing immediately after reaping the crop, followed by submergence for as long a period as possible up to three months, thus avoiding any overlapping of paddy crops that would provide a continuity of host plants for the pest. It is appreciated that this is a counsel of perfection and in many areas other, possibly less effective, means must suffice. The moths are intensely phototropic and light traps are still widely used, though Japanese experience has shown that the proportion of moths caught is too small to reduce pest damage appreciably in the succeeding generation. Pagden[460] observed in Malaya that males of *Schoenobius* are attracted to light more than females in the proportion of about 2 : 1; with *Chilotraea* the reverse is the case. On the other hand, Rao *et al.*[519] and Wyatt[705] in Malaya found that more females than males are attracted to light. In explanation of this anomaly Wyatt suggests that such differences do not necessarily indicate variations in actual sex ratio, but may be reactions of the two sexes to light, or varying responses to the wavelengths or intensity of light from different sources. Hand collection of eggs and of injured plants can be effective, but is slow and costly.

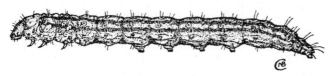

FIG. 20
Chilo suppressalis (Wlk.). × 4

Herding young ducks in the affected fields is a useful method of mopping up exposed larvae, but there is some risk of damaging the crop. Burning the stubble is of little use as the larvae are below ground. The use of resistant paddy varieties has met with no success, but work in this connection is being continued. Dry-land paddy is not attacked because the stems are too hard for the pest to penetrate. In China, steeping tobacco stems in water at 132 to 264 lb. of stems per acre and keeping one or two inches of water in the field for two weeks afterwards is said to kill young larvae. In the Krian District of Perak, Malaya,[705] where loss of crop from this pest is stated to be at least 30 per cent and can reach 70 per cent or more in limited areas, investigations show promise of control by spraying with suitable insecticides at the critical period, about three or four weeks before flowering.[302] Frequent dusting with 5 per cent DDT or BHC has been tried in Malaya with some success but with doubtful profit. Parathion has also given some control, but its toxicity is a serious disadvantage. Under conditions existing in south India, endrin sprayed at 0·13 to 0·19 lb. per acre twice on the main planted crop and once on the nursery, protected the crop from *Schoenobius incertulas* (Wlk.), but the higher dosage was required for green capsid control. Further studies by Sengapta and Rout[594] in India confirm this result: they add, however, that the most important factor in obtaining good control of stem borer is correct timing of the applications. In Formosa,[518] endrin and Guthion were found superior to other insecticides tested. It has been found in most countries that at least two sprayings of endrin gives the most satisfactory control of this pest.

Chilo suppressalis (Wlk.). *Chilo* is considered the most serious borer in the northern paddy areas of Asia and is met with elsewhere in this continent. It is said to be the worst individual pest in Japan, is very serious in Korea and is found as far north as Manchuria.

In Japan the moths emerge mostly from mid-June and July for the first brood and from mid to late August for the second. Adult moths fly around seed beds until the seedlings are large enough for concealment. Oviposition begins within two or three days of emergence. Spring-brood eggs are usually laid in the seed bed near the borders, on the upper sides of leaves and from one to two inches from the tip. Summer-brood eggs are laid on the leaf-sheaths. Egg clusters are about five to six per moth with an average of fifty or sixty eggs per cluster. In four to twelve days the eggs hatch. The larval life is about thirty-six days for the first generation and 350 to 300 days for the hibernating generation. Pupation of the spring generation lasts two weeks and the summer generation about one week. Larvae of the spring generation disperse by silk threads. Young leaves are often injured at the top of the sheaths, break off and float on the water, especially after strong winds. A single larva will destroy ten or more plants as against only two or three by *Schoenobius*. Pupation occurs in the stem just above water level.

Summer larvae do not scatter after hatching but feed for about ten days on the plant upon which the eggs were laid. When the plant is dying they migrate to neighbouring plants and usually one or two larvae enter each stem. They seldom migrate further than five feet. Attacked stems die without heading and new heads die or, if attacked later, bear inferior grain.

At harvest, larvae are usually found four to seven inches above the soil surface and as many as 80 per cent may be removed in the cut straw, though proportions vary greatly with conditions and as many may be left in the stubble. The larvae usually hibernate in stubble but, unlike *Schoenobius*, also migrate to the stems of various natural and cultivated grasses. Those removed in the cut paddy do not die but feed on the withered stems and when the paddy is stacked or stored after harvest, leave the straw to enter grass stems. They migrate extensively in late spring to pupate among straw, rubbish and in crevices, holes of about four millimetres diameter being preferred. Many form cocoons about four inches from the ends of cut straw. Those in stubble emerge and enter straw more exposed to the air.

Various methods of control have been used with success. Collecting eggs in the seed bed is important because the larvae can migrate to the field through host plants. Light trapping helps to reduce numbers, although the pest is less phototropic than *Schoenobius*. Cutting out infested stems before the larvae have scattered gives marked control of the summer generation. Flooding young paddy to a depth of four to six inches for a day is effective and complete submergence by bending the plants and forcing them under water gives 80 to 90 per cent kill. Stubble submergence for three weeks gives excellent control in Java. In China, an oil film on the water is recommended to destroy larvae of *Chilo* and *Sesamia*. Other control measures are adopted as described for *Schoenobius*. As paddy straw is used in sericulture in Japan BHC cannot be used to control *Chilo* because it results in injured cocoons. It is desirable to destroy the pest removed in the straw. The larvae can be trapped by mixing with the paddy straw strong stems of maize or sorghum into which they migrate. The introduced stems should then be burnt. Fumigation of straw with carbon bisulphide is effective, but chloropicrin is said to be better for the purpose, using 1 lb. to 1,000 cu. ft. exposed for two days. Tsutsui[669] in Japan concludes that EPN and BHC will prevent the attack of first and second generation stem borers. Endrin is as effective as parathion but in Japan is not allowed in field use.

Chilotraea polychrysa (Meyr.). This is a most serious pest of paddy in Malaya, particularly as no really effective method of control has yet been discovered.

The moth lays eggs on both the upper and under sides of leaves, an average of 400 eggs being laid per female. Eggs hatch in four to seven days and the larva enters the top of the leaf sheath and works towards the base, boring into the stem. Larvae may be found in stems up to one foot above water level; they can live in damp stubble and have alternative hosts in grasses. The larva reaches maturity in about one month when it pupates inside the stem and sometimes between the leaf-sheath and the stem. The pupal stage lasts from four to twelve days, when the moth emerges and may live for three to twelve days.

Light trapping for the control of this pest is unsatisfactory, and liberating predators in large numbers in affected areas has also proved to be unsatisfactory.

Control measures appear to be equally ineffective against *Sesamia inferns* Wlk., the Violet Stem Borer, a Noctuid moth common throughout Asian paddy areas, the larvae of which bore into stems. The pest is particularly difficult to control because it has a large number of alternative host plants. The eggs, being laid where the encircling margins of the leaf-sheath meet, are thereby well protected and the larvae can live within submerged stems.

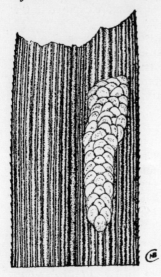

FIG. 21
Chilotraea polychrysa
(Meyr.).

Egg mass on leaf. × 5

Scirpophaga innotata Wlk., the White Stem Borer, is by far the worst paddy pest in Indonesia but is unimportant elsewhere. Adjustment of sowing and transplanting times, flooding and crop rotation are standard control measures. Van der Laan[345] indicated the possibilities of control by spraying seed beds with 0·04 per cent DDT emulsion at thirteen to twenty days after sowing. This resulted in a reduction of 25 to 30 per cent. He used a power-driven mist blower. Other insecticides were also tried, including toxaphene, parathion and derris.

Elasmopalpus lignosellus (Zell.) is a Brazilian pest of dry-land paddy. Its larvae bore into stems at or below ground level, each destroying about four plants. From Swaziland, McKinley[386] has reported the borer *Maliarpha separatella* (= *Ampycodes pallidicosta*), a Pyralid larva, as causing appreciable damage to paddy. Endrin at ¼ lb. actual per acre gave good control, but time of application was

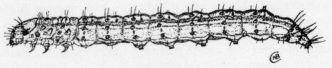

FIG. 22
Chilotraea polychrysa (Meyr.). Larva × 3

important. Hely reports[266] that in the Murrumbidgee Irrigation Area of New South Wales, *Phragmatiphila* sp., a Noctuid moth, causes

njury in some seasons by boring into paddy stems. Barnyard millet
Echinochloa sp.) and Cumbungi (*Typha* sp.) act as alternate hosts.
The pest, he states, is kept under natural control by two parasitic wasps
not named by him) which prey as external parasites in the larval
tage. In some instances up to 90 per cent of larvae have been found
o be parasitized and up to five wasp larvae may be found feeding on
a single host.

A critical review of world literature on the Lepidopterous stalk
borers of tropical Graminaceous crops has been written by Jepson.[302]

EFFECT OF SILICA ON BORER ATTACK

A series of papers by Sasamoto,[586] published between 1957 and
1960, records the results of his studies on the relation between the
silica content of the paddy plant and the incidence of borer attack.
He found that the mandibles of larvae feeding on silicated paddy
became worn and that the insects showed a preference to plants
cultured in nitrogen-rich manure. Damage to plants by *Chilo
suppressalis* Wlk. decreased when slag containing available silica
was applied to the soil. Silicated plants are resistant also to *Nephotettix bipunctatus cincticeps* Uhler., *Chlorops oryzae* Matsumura, but
it increases injury by the rice stem skipper *Parnara guttata* Bremer
and Grey.

CHEMICAL CONTROL OF STEM BORERS

A study of the life histories of the various borers indicates three
possible courses of action in attempting control by insecticides:

(*a*) by applying an insecticidal deposit to the plant to kill the
young larvae as they emerge from the eggs;

(*b*) by systemic action against the larvae in the plant;

(*c*) by adding insecticides to the water on the field to kill emerging
moths and migrating larvae.

Of these, the first is most widely practised, although it is possible
that insecticides such as BHC and parathion, applied to kill emerging
larvae, may have some action against the larvae in the plant. Attempts at control by killing the larvae within the plant by the exclu-
sive use of conventional systemic insecticides have so far proved
ineffective.

For several years after their introduction, the chlorinated hydro-
carbon insecticides were tested against stem borers, but the general
conclusion reached was that, owing to the long larval emergence
period and the number of generations in a year, several insecticidal
applications were necessary and in prevailing conditions the method
was uneconomic. Pressure on food supplies in Asia, however, has

become so acute that in many of the more advanced countries chemical control of stem borers is now recommended and practised

In China, and especially in Kwangtung, BHC has been extensively used in the past three years against *Chilo simplex* and *Schoenobius incertulas*. A 0·5 per cent gamma-BHC formulation is dusted on the nursery beds at the rate of 37·5 kg./ha. In transplanted paddy BHC dust of the same concentration is used at about 22 to 30 kg./ha. Alternatively, a 6 per cent gamma-BHC wettable powder diluted 100 to 200 times may be applied at 2,250 kg./ha. or 0·675 kg gamma-BHC per ha. Two to four applications a year are required for effective control. In Kwangsi, BHC is added direct to the irrigation water at the rate of 1·35 kg. gamma-BHC per hectare.

In Japan, tests have shown that 0·047 per cent parathion emulsion spray at 400 gallons per ha., 1·5 per cent parathion dust or 3 per cent gamma-BHC dust at 30 kg./ha. give adequate control. Numerous other materials have been tested but proved less effective. Large quantities of parathion and gamma-BHC are used in Japan for stem borer control. Official recommendations specify two applications against *Chilo simplex* and four to six applications against *Schoenobius incertulas*. Other countries have been reluctant to follow the example of Japan in recommending parathion for stem borer, because of the health hazards involved.

The principal borer in Formosa is *Schoenobius incertulas* but *Chilo simplex* and *Sesamia inferens* also occasion damage at the tillering and heading stages. Field control by insecticides was first practised in 1953 and has since considerably increased. Five hundred cc. 50 per cent parathion miscible liquid is diluted with 1,000 litres of water and sprayed on the crop at 1,000 litres per acre. Recently, endrin 19·5 per cent emulsion diluted at 1:400 has been introduced. One to three applications are needed per season.

Aldrin and dieldrin seed dressings are valuable for protecting seed and seedlings from insect attack, particularly when the crop is planted in land to which insecticide has not been applied. In several countries dressings containing a fungicide and aldrin or dieldrin are obtainable, but if an alternative to formulated dual-purpose products is required, wettable powders or dusts, based on insecticide alone, can be used. To obtain the required degree of protection the dressing must be applied to cover the seed evenly; 1 to 2 oz. of active ingredient per 100 lb. seed is the usual dosage. If dry formulations are used and no seed-dressing machinery is available, small quantities of seed can be shaken up with the dressing in a convenient tin, but for greater amounts a larger container (such as an oil drum) can be used. When wet treatments are preferred, wettable powder formulations can be used to make up slurries, but these must be applied in specially designed containers.

LEAF CATERPILLARS

Compared with stem borers and paddy bugs, leaf caterpillars are not of great importance, although sporadic attacks of army worms can entirely destroy nurseries and fields of paddy.

The most widely spread army worm is probably *Spodoptera mauritia*, which appears when the paddy seed is germinating. It is found in south India, Ceylon, Java, Malaya and the Oriental tropic and Pacific area generally, and is said to be the most important pest of south India, where broadcasting in place of transplanting is very common.

Seedlings in wet nurseries up to about twenty days old and broadcast sowing in ill-drained places are selected for oviposition. Plants over twenty days old and dry fields are not attacked. It is characteristic of moths to appear in large numbers leading to heavy infestation of extensive areas of newly-sown paddy.

Fig. 23
Spodoptera mauritia (Boisd.). Larva × 2½

The eggs are laid on leaves and hatch in four to five days. Newly hatched larvae scrape green matter from leaf tips and rest within the rolled edges of tender shoots. They let themselves down by silken threads and are thus wafted to other plants, but they can crawl to plants should they fall to the ground. As the larvae develop they feed only at night unless the weather is cloudy, hiding in cracks in the soil by day. They migrate from field to field doing extensive damage to the crop. In about four weeks' time, when fully grown, they pupate in damp or moist soil.

The larvae thrive on various grasses. They suffer severely from heavy rain at all stages, are prone to bacterial disease, are attacked by several parasites and are eaten by birds.

So sudden and unexpected are attacks of army caterpillars, as a rule, that the cultivator is usually unaware of the danger before his crop is entirely destroyed. Where this happens to the nursery, it entails replanting with a variety of paddy of shorter maturation period to make up for the delay. Control measures include flooding the nursery for two or three days where this is practicable. Attack is said to be less severe if the land is kept dry for a fortnight after sowing, but this procedure militates against a good crop. Standing water kills the larvae and a film of kerosene on the flooded field hastens their death. Moving swarms can be kept away from fields by trenching. Ducks rapidly clear up any larvae. Dusting with a

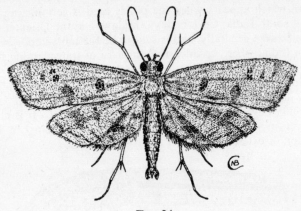

FIG. 24

Nymphula depunctalis Guér. Adult. × 7

1 : 8 calcium arsenate and lime dust has been successful in India. An arsenical bait is used in Fiji.[443] A 5 per cent DDT dust is said to be completely successful.

Several army worms are important. *Borolia venalba* is common in Ceylon and India. The larvae web two or three leaves together to make a shelter within which they spin cocoons and pupate. Control measures are similar to those described for *Spodoptera*, but collecting and destroying cocoons is also useful. Fernando *et al.*[199] claim that this pest is easily controlled by DDT; a 15 to 25 per cent DDT emulsified concentrate at the rate of two fluid ounces per gallon of water and sprayed at ten to fifteen gallons per acre with a double knapsack boom sprayer gives complete control. Similarly, for mist blower application they suggest two pints 15 to 25 DDT emulsifiable concentrate diluted to make 1½ gallons spray which is sufficient for an acre. According to Fernando,[198] fifteen to twenty acres can be covered in a day by one operator using a mist blower. Dusting with 5 per cent BHC dust at 15 lb. per acre on field edges and bunds in the early stages is recommended in India. For full-grown adult army worms a 10 per cent dust is suggested. The Malayan Department of Agriculture recommend 2½ per cent DDT dust or 0·65 per cent gamma-BHC spray for control on nursery beds.

Laphygma frugiperda is a serious pest in British Guiana and is also known in the United States and the Far East. Flooding the nursery beds is recommended, but is not always possible. Unpublished information suggests that a 2½ per cent BHC dust, applied at 20 lb. per acre, is effective for control in paddy.

In Formosa, the cut worm, *Prodenia litura* is controlled by lead arsenate, but derris and contact sprays are ineffective. In Brazil, *Mocis (Remigia) repanda* sometimes appears in large numbers in rain after a long dry spell and completely destroys whole fields. Collection of larvae and dusting with lead arsenate are methods used for its control.

Naranga aenescens Moore is a more serious pest in parts of China, and in Korea there are outbreaks every four or five years. The larvae feed voraciously and build cases which, when cut from the plant, fall in the water and float. Four or five broods are produced in the year, and pupation is completed by early October. Spraying with lead arsenate is employed in Korea, and in China tobacco dust is said to be effective. *Nymphula depunctalis* Guér, the Paddy Casebearer, is important in Malaya, the Philippines and Lower Burma, attacking seed beds and young plants in the field. Its larvae are semi-aquatic and can withstand prolonged immersion. They depend entirely on water for their oxygen supply. They carry their water supply and when the dissolved oxygen has been used up they descend to the surface of the water and, by violent contraction and elongation of the body, plus lateral flexure when fully distended, expel the water from their cases and draw in a new supply. If the water can be drained off for a period they die from lack of oxygen. Therefore, they cannot attack nurseries unless these are in water. In the case of *N. depunctalis* Guér, the larvae, at least in confinement, feed on the lower side of paddy leaves which are lying flat on the water or on submerged portions of a leaf, for the first week to ten days. Only then do they make their cases. Pupation may take place below water, but more usually above water. Moths emerge with ease from below water. In the case of *N. fluctuosalis* Zell. the young larvae move about quite actively about 1½ inches below the surface, crawling on the bottom, on the base of paddy stems, and they also drift freely, but always below water.* Control is by dislodging leaf cases by means of ropes, draining off the water and collecting the cases. A kerosene film on the water helps to kill, and in India a 1:3

* From a private communication from Mr H. T. Pagden.

Y

dust of paris green and wood ash has been used. *Nymphula vittalis*, a pest in Japan and Korea, has been controlled by dusting calcium cyanamide and by destroying the stubble in which the larvae hibernate.

Of leaf folders, a Pyralid moth, *Cnaphalocrocis medinalis* Guér., is said to cause over 5 per cent loss in Tonkin, 10 per cent loss in South Travancore and up to 60 per cent loss in dry seasons in Madagascar. The larvae cut and fold leaves and also bore stems. Deep flooding is recommended to combat the pest. In India, fertilizers are said to help the plants to recover. In Korea, lead arsenate is recommended. *Parnara guttatus* Bremer and Grey, syn. *P. bada* Moore, is a leaf folder serious in Kwangsi. It is controlled by the use of special combs for gathering larvae from the leaves, by knocking larvae into oiled irrigation water, and by the application of tobacco-lime dust. In Japan, lead arsenate-Bordeaux mixture is found effective. *Pelopidas mathian* (F) is equally common as *P. guttatus* in Malaya and has similar habits.

Cut worms include *Crambus malacellus* in Mauritius and the army worm *Cirphis unipuncta* Haw., an almost universal pest. The former has been controlled by watering Cyanogas on to the soil in the proportion of 2 grams Cyanogas to 1 litre of water and applying six litres of the solution per 10 sq. ft. The latter pest has been controlled with poison baits. In Hong Kong, Hall[244] reports that an infestation on some 500 acres was brought under control by a film of kerosene on the irrigation water and by spraying the crop, preferably at night, with one pint of 24 per cent DDT emulsion in 200 parts of water. Hely reports[266] that the cut worm *Pseudaletia australia* Francl. sometimes attacks paddy plants in the flowering stage. They feed on all parts of the plant above water. Pupation takes place in the leaf sheaths and in debris at the bases of stools just above the water line. Infestation is usually confined to individual sections of the crop and generally is observed too late to justify control measures. A DDT dust or spray at the rate of 1 lb. per acre of the active ingredient is effective to control the pest.

The main criterion for successfully controlling foliage pests is thorough coverage of the plants with the correct amount of insecticide. Timing the application may be important, particularly when an insecticide of short persistence is used. Endrin and dieldrin possess good residual properties and can therefore be applied some days before the critical stage in the pest life history, thus giving flexibility to the spraying programme. When the time of insect damage can be forecast fairly accurately, as for stem borers in south India, it has been found convenient to treat the crop with endrin according to the following schedule:

1st application—0·24 lb. endrin per acre, 1 week before transplanting.
2nd application—0·32 lb. endrin per acre, 2 weeks after transplanting.
3rd application—if necessary, three weeks after the second
   application, using 0·32 lb. endrin per acre.

A variation of this is to keep the seedlings in the nursery for longer than is normal and to apply two endrin treatments before transplanting.

When pest attacks cannot be anticipated so readily, it is usual to apply the insecticide when damage is noticed or egg masses found. Retreatment should be given if necessary. In the case of endrin or dieldrin the interval between treatments is often 10 to 20 days or more. Aldrin is not effective for so long.

In some instances it is an advantage to use the technique described as "preflooding treatment". This consists of lowering the water level to a depth of about two inches and then applying the insecticide, subsequently flooding the field. This method is used to control water-inhabiting species such as *Lissorhoptrus* spp. and *Chironomus* spp. If the volume of water in the field is not reduced in this way, the insecticide is very greatly diluted and its activity lessened. For some insects, for example *Hydrellia* spp., lowering the water level causes the larvae to leave their mines so that they become exposed to the action of the insecticide subsequently applied.

PADDY BUGS

Paddy bugs are serious pests in most countries, some attacking grain during development, others feeding on young leaves. They are capable of producing many generations in a season and under favourable conditions can therefore do extensive damage.

COREID BUGS

Leptocorisa acuta Thünb. and *L. varicornis* F. are widely distributed throughout the East and are generally recognized as the most serious of bug pests of paddy. They live and breed on various grasses, but appear to prefer paddy, for they attack the crop in swarms, sucking the sap from the developing grain. Awned varieties of paddy are less attacked. Attack continues until the rice grain hardens; the bugs then migrate to shady places and remain inactive throughout the dry months.

The female of *Leptocorisa* lays about 200 eggs at a rate of about twenty a day, glueing them in regular rows usually on the upper side of paddy leaves close to the mid-rib. Larvae emerge in about a week and, after sucking the leaf sap for about two days, climb into the panicles and feed on the milk-ripe grain. The bugs feed all day but are particularly active in the morning and evening. If disturbed, the adults fly (the young are wingless) for short distances and again settle on the developing panicles. They are easily caught in the early morning when their wings are damp.

Various methods are employed to keep the pest in check. The best precaution is to keep bunds and banks in the vicinity of fields as clean as possible between growing seasons in order to deny to the pest the wild grasses which are its alternative hosts when no growing paddy is at hand. This measure applies also to most other paddy bugs. Uniformity of planting to avoid extending the growing season is strongly recommended—but how difficult to put into practice! In Malaya, large bags, coated on the inside with crude oil emulsion, are swept over the growing crop. Netting the insects is also employed and carrion bait is used. In India and Ceylon, the inside of rice winnow baskets is smeared with a sticky preparation made by heating a mixture of breadfruit latex, coconut oil and a small quantity of powdered resin. Egg collection and shaking the nymphs into water on which there is a film of kerosene are also useful methods of control. Both BHC and DDT applied as dusts or sprays are very effective at doses of about 10 lb. per acre of 5 per cent dust. The Department of Agriculture, Malaya recommends[177] fogging with a mixture of 25 per cent DDT in oil (one part) to Sovacide (three parts). This method is said to be more effective than spraying or dusting with small machines which disturb the adults and cause them to move away before they receive a dose of insecticide. In India, dusting with 5 per cent BHC dust at 10 lb. per acre is recommended for this pest and also for *L. varicornis*. Insecticides should be applied as soon as the crop begins to flower. The pest has no serious natural enemies, but about 25 per cent of the eggs are infected by parasites.

Against *Leptocorisa varicornis* the Ceylon Department of Agriculture recommends[108] dusting with 0·5 to 1·5 per cent gamma-BHC at 10 to 15 lb. per acre and to ensure speed of application suggests using small power-driven dusters which cover 50 to 75 acres a day. Fernando *et al.* state[199] that aldrin 2½ per cent dust gives good and immediate control of this pest but reinfestation soon takes place. Two pints of a 15 to 25 per cent DDT emulsified concentrate made up to 1½ gallons with water and applied to one acre by mist blower is also said to give good control. Alternatively, using a double knapsack boom sprayer, two fluid ounces of the DDT emulsified concentrate is diluted with one gallon of water and applied at the rate of ten gallons per acre.

PENTATOMID BUGS (Shield Bugs)

The life history of these pests and methods of control are similar to those of *Leptocorisa*. *Scotinophara lurida* Burm. is controlled in China by flooding to a depth of five inches every fourth day, allowing the water to stand for one day. In Ceylon, the bugs are shaken into a film of kerosene oil, the water being run off after three to five hours. Dusts have been found rather ineffective in Ceylon,[199] but quick and economical control combined with good residual action has been obtained with dieldrin, using one fluid ounce dieldrin 20 per cent emulsified concentrate in two gallons of water, one fluid ounce 20 per cent gamma-BHC or endrin emulsifiable concentrate in $7\frac{1}{2}$ gallons of water. The diluted material is applied at ten to twenty gallons per acre, depending on the growth of the crop. In Japan, 3 per cent gamma-BHC dust applied at 12 kg. per acre is recommended. In Formosa, $1\frac{1}{2}$ per cent BHC is extensively used against this pest.

Scotinophara coarctata F., the Black Bug of paddy, does considerable damage in Malaya[136] by sucking sap from the stems, as a result of which the panicles fail to develop. In severe attacks the plants are stunted, the leaves become reddish-brown and few plants form panicles. The nymphs and adults seem free from natural enemies, probably on account of their "stink" glands. The eggs, when not protected by the body of the female, are attacked by a Chalcidoid parasite. Control as for *Leptocorisa*. When irrigation is practised, the affected area may be flooded and the larvae and adults skimmed off. Spraying with kerosene emulsion or derris has proved successful, but may be uneconomic. DDT and BHC dusts are very effective, particularly applied from a power duster, and insecticidal fogs containing these may be useful. The Department of Agriculture, Malaya recommends[177] dusting with equal quantities of 0·65 per cent gamma-BHC and 5 per cent DDT dusts, applied separately.

Solubea poecila Dall. is well known in British Guiana and a *Moridea* sp. in Uruguay; the latter is controlled by means of a 1·6 per cent nicotine sulphate spray and kerosene emulsion. In India, Gammalin 20 is recommended by the government to control *S. poecila*, at the rate of 5 oz. in 10 gallons of water per acre, with a second application if necessary, and dieldrin 19 per cent emulsion concentrate at 10 oz. in 10 gallons of water. Parathion has also been used to control this pest. In Brazil, adequate control is claimed using a 2 per cent BHC dust applied at 20 to 30 kg./ha. The following two preparations have also been recommended:[338] rhodiagama 2 (benzene hexachloride) and Rhodiatoz 1 per cent type BCL (1 per cent parathion). These insecticidal dusts should be applied at the rate of 9 to 13 lb. per acre.

Nezara viridula L. is almost cosmopolitan and may be controlled with pyrethrum dust alone or in equal parts with 2·5 per cent nicotine dust applied with a dust gun. *Solubea pugnax* F. is a pest in the United States. The bugs may consume the entire contents of kernels in the milk stage, so that no grain is produced. When kernels in the dough stage are attacked, portions of the contents are extracted leaving a chalky discoloured area. Kernels so affected are called "pecky rice." Moulds often enter the punctures causing black specks and consequent grain breakage in milling. Cold winters cause a high mortality and limit pest incidence. No chemical control measures are taken, but a trial by Bowling[87,88] indicates that economic control may be obtained with $\frac{1}{4}$ lb. dieldrin, $\frac{1}{2}$ lb. aldrin or $1\frac{1}{2}$ lb. toxaphene per acre.

JASSID BUGS (Leaf Hoppers)

Nephotettix spp. are serious and widespread in Asia, East Africa and Europe. In Japan, Malaya and Ceylon, *N. bipunctatus* F. is occasionally a serious pest and in Japan and the Philippines has proved to be a vector of the virus causing dwarf disease of rice. In India, *N. bipunctatus* is said to have caused damage amounting to one million pounds in one division of the Central Provinces. The pest may appear in swarms—as many as 150 hoppers may be seen on one leaf. The adults feed on leaves by night and hide by day. Control measures include early planting, sweeping seed beds, and shaking the pest into water covered with a kerosene film. In the Philippines, control has been gained by weekly applications of a solution of 2 lb. soft soap in 25 gallons of water; light traps are carried through the fields while a second man beats; weeding and use of fertilizers to stimulate growth are useful. In Viet-Nam, *Nephotettix bipunctatus cincticeps* and *Sogata furcifera* have been controlled by application of Malathion (5 per cent) dust at 27 lb. per acre.

FULGORID BUGS

Sogata furcifera (Horv.), which is severe in Japan, Formosa, Malaya and Fiji, can be controlled by a derris spray or with BHC and DDT. The pest has been known in Fiji since 1907, but it did not become serious until 1938. An attack in 1959 caught growers short of both insecticides and equipment for application; in consequence the damage was so severe that subsequent control measures were not worth while.[359]

In Japan, 225 grams 22 per cent DDT emulsion per 100 litres applied at 120 gallons (550 litres) per acre is recommended. In Fiji, an experiment by O'Conner[443] showed that a 2 per cent DDT dust or a 20 per cent DDT emulsion diluted 1 : 100 with water can com-

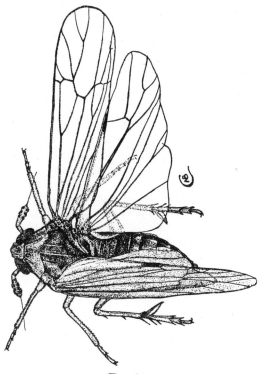

Fig. 25
Sogata furcifera (Horv.). Adult female. × 7

pletely eliminate the bug in twenty-four hours and prevent reinfestation for two weeks. The best time to spray appeared to be about five weeks after transplanting. In Formosa a 1 per cent BHC dust is used.

Nilaparvata oryzae Mats., which is one of the worst bugs in Formosa, attacks the lower part of the plant, nymphs and adults boring into leaf-sheaths. Good results have been obtained by spraying with petroleum oil with or without pyrethrum and by pyrethrum-soap sprays or, if there is no irrigation, by the use of tobacco dust or synthetic insecticides. *N. lugens* Stål. is sometimes damaging in Malaya and Ceylon. *Nisia atrovenosa* Leth. is prevalent in the Far East. It over-winters in the egg state on paddy and grasses and is controlled by flooding, ploughing and grass burning to destroy the hibernating egg masses. Tobacco dust kills the pest.

Coccid Bugs

Ripersia oryzae sucks the stem sap. In south India the pest can be so numerous that the ears are smothered and unable to emerge from the leaf-sheaths. Alternative hosts are grasses and sedges. Resistant varieties of paddy have been found which suffer 70 to 80 per cent less infestation than other varieties.

LEAF BEETLES

Hispa armigera Oliv. is a Chrysomelid beetle common in India and south-east Asia. The young larvae mine leaves, four to seven in a leaf, eating the green matter and causing the foliage to wither. The pest multiplies rapidly and may cause considerable damage to the crop. It also breeds on grasses, which makes control difficult. Netting the beetles is useful. In Formosa it has been found that the larvae emerge from the leaf mines between 4 and 6 p.m. and crawl to other parts of the leaf or to fresh leaves. During this period netting is most effective. Adults can be collected in the evening or sprayed with nicotine sulphate. Pyrethrum dusts and sprays are effective. Fields may also be drained and the adults sprayed with kerosene emulsion containing pyrethrum extract. Work by Agarwala[6] suggests that 0·25 per cent BHC spray at 100 gallons per acre can substantially reduce the pest population and increase crop yield. Spraying with 1 lb. BHC as a water dispersible powder per 100 gallons water per acre and dusting with 5 per cent BHC dust at 10 to 30 lb. per acre is recommended.

In California,[228] the rice leaf miner. *Hydrellia griseola* Fallen is present in the spring, but damage occasioned by it depends on weather conditions, cool temperatures that check seedling growth favouring increased populations of the pest. To control, dieldrin at 4 oz. of active ingredient per acre is applied by aeroplane.

Hispa aenescens destroys seedlings and young paddy plants in India. Some control is possible by light trapping. *Hispa similis* is peculiar to Formosa. The pest is controlled by burning grass where it hibernates, by hand collection and by spraying nicotine sulphate or pyrethrum with soap. Large-scale field control has been practised with 10 per cent DDT and 1 per cent BHC dusts.

Lema oryzae, the Rice Leaf beetle, damages crops in Japan and

Formosa. In the latter country it is controlled with 10 per cent **BHC** dust. In Japan, this leaf beetle is attacked by nine parasites. Farmers attempt control by early morning sweeping with a large box on a handle. Spraying 100 grams of 22 per cent emulsion per 100 litres

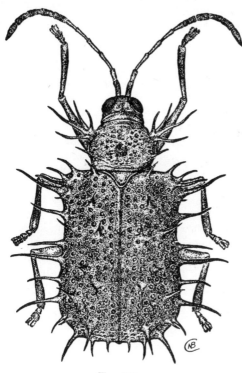

FIG. 26

Hispa armigera (Oliv.). Adult. × 17

is applied at rates up to 600 gallons (2,727 litres) per acre, or a 2½ per cent dust at 12 to 16 kg. per acre. *Lema flaviceps* causes severe damage to paddy leaves in Korea. Control by hand-collection of eggs and adults and spraying with DDT or BHC. *Trichispa sericea* is controlled in Madagascar by immersing seedling tops for fifteen or twenty seconds in boiling water before transplanting. This treatment does not harm the plants. In Swaziland, where paddy is broadcast, McKinley[386] recommends a spray of 1 lb. actual malathion per acre. Dieldrin at 1 lb. per acre, applied in 24 gallons of water, was also effective.

Dicranolaius bellulus (Guér) is a Malachiid beetle which in New South Wales[266] sometimes causes damage ranging up to 25 per cent in some bays. The beetles may attack the anthers and flowering organs but they mainly feed on the newly set grain. Damage is almost always confined to the margins of bays but may extend some distance into the crop. Arsenical or barium fluosilicate dusting of crop margins or DDT dusting are suggested for control.

WATER WEEVILS

The rice water weevil (*Lissorhoptrus orizophilus* Ksl.) sometimes causes considerable damage to paddy. The pest seems to be more prevalent and to cause more damage in North and South America than elsewhere. It is said[88] to be one of the most important pests in the Southern United States and in British Guiana to be more prevalent and serious in dry-sown paddy than in either wet-sown or transplanted areas.

The larva of this beetle is milk-white in colour and from a quarter to half an inch long. The adult is about one-eighth inch long, greyish-brown in colour with a darker area on the back.

In Arkansas[291] the adult beetles hibernate under cover in and around the fields. They begin to emerge from hibernation and feed on leaves of various grasses in late April. Adult feeding may occur in young unflooded paddy, the weevils being most active and numerous following the application of the first water. Eggs are deposited under the epidermis of roots and larvae appear in about eight days, pupating about three weeks later, the adults emerging after about a week. There are two generations a year in the Southern United States.

The beetles feed on the leaves, but the most serious damage is caused by the larvae, which feed on paddy roots, pruning them off close to the crown.

There are three methods by which the pest may be controlled. Bowling[87] found that the best control was obtained from treating the seed with aldrin or heptachlor mixed with fertilizer or from 4 oz. of the insecticide per 100 lb. seed applied as a seed dressing. Seed treatment, however, will not control the adult water weevil.[88] Spray applications with aldrin or dieldrin,[570] using about one pint of 20 per cent dieldrin in 20 to 30 gallons of water for every acre, will destroy larvae. Spraying should be done about two weeks after the seed has germinated and whilst the land is still dry.

Giglioli[212] states that in British Guiana water movement through the fields twice a month between June and August when the pest is most likely to be present has proved satisfactory with the dry-sown crop; with wet-sown or transplanted paddy the water need only be moved once a month. In severe cases of attack, the water should be drained off before again irrigating.

GRASSHOPPERS

Many species of grasshopper attack paddy, as well as grasses and other plants, but are not usually very serious.

Hieroglyphus banian (F) is injurious to paddy in India. Control is by ploughing and harrowing after harvest and by hand-digging bunds to destroy the eggs. Hoppers in young paddy are netted and half-grown and adults driven into a corner of the field and beaten to death. Dusting the young hoppers with 5 per cent BHC dust at 15 to 25 lb. per acre has been recommended. *Colemania sphenaroides* is also common on paddy in certain parts of India, the damage usually being most severe in July. BHC 10 per cent dust at 15 to 25 lb. per acre is recommended for its control. *Oxya velox* can cause severe damage to the crop in Korea when the pest is favoured with high temperature and little rain. It is also reported from the Solomons and Malaya. In the last-named region the commonest species on paddy is *O. chinensis* Thünb. In Japan, when the fields are flooded to prepare for transplanting, eggs of *O. velox* float and are collected. In dry fields a tobacco-lime dust is used. Grasshoppers may be controlled by spraying or dusting the crop with aldrin or dieldrin. The preferred insecticide is dieldrin used at a rate of $\frac{3}{4}$ to $1\frac{1}{2}$ oz. active ingredient per acre. Good control can also be obtained with applications of 2 to 4 oz. aldrin per acre. With dieldrin 15 to 30 days' protection can be obtained but aldrin is usually less persistent. The insecticide should be applied so that the crop is thoroughly covered. If the bunds are also well treated the adults, which sometimes congregate there, and the hoppers, which emerge from eggs laid therein, can also be destroyed. Endrin also kills grasshoppers. When endrin has been used against the paddy insect complex no special treatments for grasshopper control are necessary. Migratory locusts rarely cause total destruction of the paddy crop. Trouble of this nature was experienced in Malaya for two or three years about 1914. The swarms were wiped out by systematic poisoning of grass eaten by the pest in the hopper stage, aided by the nature of the country, which was unsuitable for swarming.

ROOT AND MISCELLANEOUS INSECT PESTS

Tipula spp. Leather Jackets. In Japan, *T. aino* is important, frequenting wet places, where it lays eggs on moist soil rich in organic matter. The larvae feed on decayed vegetable matter and in the roots of paddy and weeds. Control methods consist in attracting adults to lamps and by killing the larvae by spraying the soil surface with petroleum emulsion with or without pyrethrum *T. conjugata* causes serious damage in the Russian Far East. Over-wintering larvae migrate from the peat bogs to paddy fields and eat both roots and stems. Control measures are to drain the swamps, if possible; larvae are killed by applying to paddy fields sodium arsenate or tobacco extract, using 1 oz. of the former or 4 oz. of the latter in 25 gallons of water.

Gryllotalpa spp., the Mole Cricket, is controlled in some regions by burying poison bait containing paris green or barium fluosilicate, or by BHC, chlordane and similar materials at approximately ½ per cent. A gall midge, *Pachydiplosis oryzae*, attacks the growing portions of young plants, causing "silvery shoots." The irritation results in the formation of galls instead of ear-bearing stems. Control is by use of early varieties, early transplanting and fertilizer application to stimulate tillering. Light traps are useful. This gall midge is a serious pest in Thailand[452] where it sometimes causes a 50 per cent loss of yield. Experiments have shown that three applications of malathion with the copper fungicide Cuprwet doubled the yield of paddy. One glutinous variety of paddy, Muey Nawang, is found to be highly resistant to the gall midge. This variety may therefore prove useful for breeding purposes. *Cecidomyia oryzae*, another gall midge, is similar and can cause up to 50 per cent loss of crop in India. In Bihar,[540] control is obtained with 5 per cent BHC applied at 25 lb. per acre to wild grasses and weeds or by spraying early summer paddy with 0·15 per cent DDT two or three times. *Atherigona oryzae* Mall., a paddy seedling fly common in dry-paddy cultivation in Ceylon, Malaya, Indonesia and some other parts of Asia, lays its eggs under leaves. Maggots penetrate the leaf-sheath and bore down, killing the central shoot. It is controlled in Java by flooding. *Chironomus oryzae* Mats. is common in Japan. It is found on seedlings grown in a "wet" nursery in Malaya. The larvae is bright red in colour and when fully developed is 1 to 1·5 cm. long. It lives hidden in the soil and may be detected by the characteristic hole it makes.

A broadcast application of aldrin or dieldrin to nurseries and fields will control such pests as mole crickets, root flies, white grubs and wire worms. The treatment, using spray or dust, should take place shortly before the final cultivation is carried out and the insecticide should be thoroughly incorporated into the top three to six inches of the soil within two or three days of application, because aldrin is relatively volatile and part may be lost if it is not worked into the soil soon after being applied. Where aldrin-fertilizer mixtures are available, they may be used instead of sprays or dusts. For general soil insect pest control, 2 to 3 lb. aldrin is used per acre.

Thrips oryzae, Rice Thrips, is a sporadic pest, injuring seedlings in Italy, India and south Asia. It sucks sap from the leaves, causing wilting and often death of the plant. The pest appears only when rains are delayed and is quickly checked when they come. Control by flooding for a few hours with a film of oil on the water, and knocking the pests into the water by dragging a rope. Use may be made of petroleum or nicotine emulsions. In south India good results have been obtained by applying to seed beds a spray made by steeping 5 lb. tobacco for twenty-five hours in five gallons of water, diluted to 1:6 for spraying. In Ceylon,[108] dusting the crop with 0·5 per cent gamma-BHC at 10 to 20 lb. per acre or spraying with DDT as for *Spodoptera mauritia* is recommended.

OTHER PESTS

CRABS

In most tropical countries sea and land crabs are responsible for much damage to paddy by feeding on seedlings and burrowing into bunds, thereby interfering with irrigation.

Sea crabs, which breed in the sea, frequent paddy fields of coastal areas. In Burma, the adults go down to the sea, never to return, about the end of July, so that in areas where they are common, transplanting is postponed till their departure. A fresh lot of young crabs comes from the sea about the end of August, but the paddy plants are too large by this time for crabs to damage.

Triops longicaudatus (le Conte), the tadpole shrimp, periodically reduces paddy stands in some areas of California by feeding on and uprooting small seedlings. The pest may be controlled by copper sulphate crystals at 10 lb. per acre, and by DDT or Sevin, both at 2 lb. active ingredient per acre.[228]

Land crabs are more destructive, because there is no migration, and they are liable to attack paddy in the nursery and newly-transplanted paddy. They feed mostly by night and move more freely in water than on land. A common method of control adopted throughout the East is by trapping in wide-mouthed earthenware pots, known as *chattis*. The pots are buried with their rims at about water level and baited with well-fried bran, moistened and made into large lumps. The bait remains effective for about two or three days, even if the pot becomes filled with water. Four or five pots are said to be effective in controlling a small holding in a few days. Another method of control consists in mixing 3 to 4 lb. slaked lime with 3 to 4 gallons of water, adding $\frac{1}{2}$ to 1 pint of crude oil and 1 oz. arsenical "white ant" powder, and pouring one or two cigarette tins of this mixture down each active crab hole, which is then blocked. The treatment is repeated at least once a month and if persisted in, can almost clear an area of the pest. Natural enemies of land crabs are rats, various birds of prey and water fowl. Ducks are useful in helping to effect control. Jordan[314] found in Sierra Leone that a spray with a 10 per cent suspension of 50 per cent BHC wettable powder (containing 6·5 per cent gamma-BHC) kills the crab *Sesarma huzardi*. To protect seedlings in nurseries, treatment with $\frac{1}{2}$ oz. of 50 per cent technical BHC wettable powder (containing 6·5 per cent gamma-isomer) per square yard is being adopted. Baiting with cassava or sugar cane impregnated with insecticide was found less satisfactory than spraying and technical BHC (as distinct from the pure gamma-isomer) was slightly repellent to crabs. DDT was also effective for killing crabs. These treatments did not appear to affect fish. In Ceylon, it is recommended that the bunds and especially the breeding holes be sprayed with one fluid ounce of endrin emulsion concentrate in two gallons of water.

In India, Abraham[2] found that parathion 0·025 per cent spray (as 1 oz. folidol in 12·5 gallons of water) was most successful, killing 84 per cent of the crab population in 72 hours. Endrin 0·01 per cent spray and toxaphene 20 per cent dust killed 72 and 71 per cent respectively. In Viet-Nam, rice crabs (*Sarpatum* spp.) were controlled with malathion EC (0·1 per cent), endrin EC (0·05 per cent) or Sevin WP (0·1 per cent).

BIRDS

Birds are a serious problem in paddy fields, causing heavy loss of grain, especially where the crop is confined to a strip, e.g. along the banks of a river where there is plenty of adjacent cover. They are reported to be a great nuisance in many parts of South America. For instance, the bird *Agelaius ruficapillus ruficapillus*, known as Varillero or Congo, is a plague of paddy fields in Santa Fe, Argentina. Partial control is obtained by netting.[164]

Bird control on one farm in Venezuela was stated to cost $24 per acre, and still there was loss of crop.[190] Birds in Venezuela probably cause greater losses in paddy areas than any other pest. The main types are the migratory birds which pass south during September and October and return north in March. In irrigated areas sowing can take place so that harvest occurs before the passage of migratory birds. But where sowing is subject to rainfall, any delay in the onset of rains in the May–June period results in harvesting during the danger period. Owing to the vast numbers of birds involved, there are no effective control measures other than production of ultra-short term paddy varieties for use when the normal sowing date has been postponed.[92]

Sparrows, which are almost everywhere common, and in the East the rice bird (Munia) with its conspicuous white head, take their toll of the crop. In California, large flocks of blackbirds pick up the broadcast seed before it is irrigated and wild duck also cause serious damage. Mud hens alight on the open water after seeding and feed on the soaked paddy seed. Migratory ducks are reported to swarm at times in paddy fields, where they do much damage. It is reported that thousands of geese eat the paddy crop in the Northern Territory of Australia almost as quickly as the seed is sown. Control is attempted by early morning shooting, use of lanterns and flares around the fields at night and by firing cannon from time to time.

Measures to combat the birds vary according to the species. The present method of scaring the smaller birds is largely ineffective; it merely drives them from one field to another. Ingenious scares are devised by Asians, the aim being to protect the greatest possible area with the least possible trouble. Many of these scares are automatic, making use of water and wind power. Netting is sometimes used against swarming birds. Pieces of bright tin, flashing in the sunlight, undoubtedly scare birds for a time: thin tin is best as it rattles in the wind.

RATS

Rats are very destructive both to paddy and rice; they gnaw the stems, eat the standing grain and ravage the rice store. The damage they do has been variously estimated at 5 to 10 per cent of the crop—pure guesswork—but whatever the figure may be, the outstanding fact remains that they are a serious pest.

Once the crop is stored it ought to be safe, for rat-proofing a building is simple. But how few stores does one find that are proofed! Rats in the field, however, are more difficult to control, in fact, any relaxation of effort leads to immediate increase in their number. Individual losses are less if dates of cultivation are so arranged that all the crop is ripe at about the same time. The rat population depends on the amount of food available; therefore, the longer the period over which the harvest extends, the greater the rat population. It is generally recommended that waste land in the vicinity of the fields should be kept clear of undergrowth which provides refuge for rodents. Desirable as this may be, it is unlikely to be widely practised. One must, therefore, rely on direct methods of dealing with

the pest and of these poison baits are the most successful. But even
with poison baits it is essential that the campaign should cover as
wide an area as possible, otherwise the rat population merely
migrates from the untreated to the treated area where there is less
rat competition for the available food.

It has been found that if a poisoned bait is offered to rats, they
are suspicious and nibble it first. They therefore eat a sub-lethal
dose of the poison, enough to make them avoid the bait in future.
It is therefore necessary to offer them an unpoisoned bait in the first
instance and when they have confidence to consume the bait, the
poison is introduced. Changes of bait must be made from time to
time, as rats learn to avoid a bait that contains poison.

Several poisons are suitable for rat baits. The three standard
poisons[398] are zinc phosphide, the most deadly and the most popular because it kills very quickly and leaves many dead rats in the
open; finely powdered arsenic (arsenious oxide) and thirdly, red
squill, prepared from a large bulb (*Urginea maritima*) grown in North
Africa and the Mediterranean area.

Sodium arsenate and barium carbonate have both been used for
systematic destruction of rats in paddy fields. A most successful
bait consists of sodium arsenate one part by volume, rice polishings
four parts and dried fish or prawn "dust" one part by volume.
Coconut or palm oil is used to bind the mixture into small balls.
The balls are easily dissolved in rain and are therefore placed in
small lengths of bamboo for protection. This also makes them
inaccessible to most domestic animals and to children. Inserting
this poison into the body of a grasshopper or dragonfly makes the
bait irresistible to rats. Barium carbonate baits can be prepared in
the same way.

Other poisons have been recommended[66] for rat destruction:
arsenious oxide in the proportion of 10 per cent by weight, or 15 per
cent in the dry base; alpha-naphthyl-thio-urea (ANTU) in the proportion of 2 per cent by weight; red squill powder. Red squill is,
however, uncertain in its action and ANTU kills the brown rat but
not the black rat. The American material "Warfarin" (3(α-ace-
tonyl-benzyl)-4-hydroxycoumarin) is a most effective rat-killer.

In Surinam,[703] considerable success has been obtained with
cumarin. The bait is paddy which, after being sprinkled with water
is mixed in the ratio of 1 : 10 to 1 : 20 with cumarin poison. The
bait is placed at intervals along the bunds, each under a small
wooden shelter.

Much has been heard from time to time on the use of bacteria
cultures for rat destruction. Results have been variable and there

is no evidence that these cultures have given any reasonable measure of success.

SNAILS

The most costly pests of paddy in Surinam are the water snails *Pomacea lineata* Spix and *P. glauca* L. which destroy young seedlings over large areas of newly-sown paddy. *P. lineata* appears to be the dominant type in this region. Control with HCN and copper sulphate is effective. In Lower Burma, *Globa pilosa* is sometimes destructive. Copper sulphate (at about 5 ppm in the water) is a well-known mullusicide and a number of new synthetic chemicals has been developed for snail control, chiefly in connection with bilharzia eradication.

MILLIPEDES

In Formosa,[598] the salt-water millipede *Tyorphynchus chiensis* Crude., originating from the sea, migrates to paddy-lands where they eat all the organic matter and roots of paddy, thus rendering the land useless. They are controlled by application of about 500 lb. per acre of tobacco waste.

BLOODWORMS

In the Murrumbidgee Irrigation Area of Australia bloodworms (*Chironomidae*) may occur in enormous numbers in the mud of fields where considerable quantities of decomposing vegetable matter are present and their presence has been associated with failure of seedling development. Damage is usually more marked in pasture rotation than in arable rotation. Chironomid larvae are reported as injuring paddy in Japan and Portugal by burying the seed, feeding on germinating seed and very young roots and in some cases causing seedlings to be uprooted.

Control measures adopted in Australia consisted either in draining affected bays and allowing the ground to become dry or else application of DDT or dieldrin after draining off most of the water and then allowing the insecticide to drip into the head ditch on re-applying the water and aiming to put two to three inches of water over the bay. Approximately ten gallons of 25 per cent DDT emulsion or six gallons of 20 per cent dieldrin were sufficient for 100 acres.[266]

z

Chapter XV

DISEASES*

IMPORTANCE OF DISEASES

THE importance of insect pests is generally recognized; the damage they do is widespread and very evident, but the loss of crop caused by diseases is often overlooked or considered negligible. In many countries this may be true, but it is also true that the crop is liable to many diseases any one of which may suddenly occasion widespread damage. Padwick[457] states that it is difficult to estimate the part that disease plays in the economy of rice production, but points to the fact that diseases such as blast, brown leaf spot, "ufra," seedling blight and dwarf disease, to mention but a few, have from time to time caused great damage. "The most serious form of loss," he continues, "is the epiphytotic, even though on the average it may cause losses of only 5 or 10 per cent in yield." Brown spot disease was held to have been the major factor contributing to the Bengal famine in 1942 and a blast epidemic was responsible for famine conditions in parts of Japan in 1941. Padwick estimates[458] that paddy diseases result in a 6·7 per cent loss of production in British colonies. The urgent necessity of increasing the production of rice by all means, which has been emphasized by the Food and Agriculture Organization of the United Nations, directs attention anew to the part played by diseases in lowering yield. Knowledge of the diseases and early diagnosis may obviate preventable losses, while in the early treatment of disease and indeed in its prevention, improved cultural methods and better water control will be found to be of paramount importance.

About forty diseases attack paddy in the field and of these the most prevalent and important are "blast" (*Piricularia oryzae* Cav.), foot rot or "bakanae" disease (*Gibberella fujikuroi*) and seedling blight (mainly *Helminthosporium oryzae*). The severity of these diseases from year to year is unpredictable since environmental factors such as soil temperature, soil moisture, infestation of seed by fungi and depth of sowing influence disease incidence.

* In the preparation of this chapter free use has been made, by permission, of information and illustrations contained in Dr Padwick's book *Manual of Rice Diseases*[457] and also of *Diseases of Field Crops* by J. G. Dickson.[174]

DISEASES OF THE FOLIAGE

BLAST. Rotten Neck, "Brusone," *Piricularia oryzae* Cav.

The name Brusone has been applied to a number of damaging influences of quite different character which cause outwardly similar

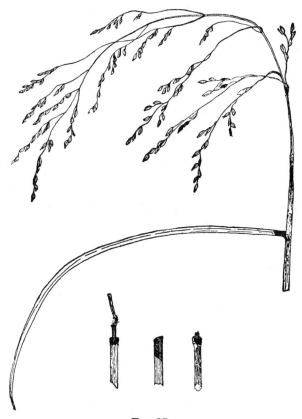

FIG. 27

Blast, *Piricularia oryzae*

Above: Spore masses at the base of the leaf, on the culm, rachids and glumes.
Below: Nodes blackened by the fungus. × ½

symptoms. The many different phenomena of the disease have led to a great number of names for it, and the fungi which are said to be connected with the disease are probably for the greater part only different stages of the development of one large polymorphous class which include *Piricularia oryzae, P. grisea, Helminthosporium oryzae, Cladosporium* sp., and others. The fungus *Piricularia oryzae* Cavara has come to be accepted as the cause of "blast," or rotten-neck disease of paddy, which many workers, rather uncritically, accepted as being synonymous with "brusone."

The disease has long been known and feared, and is widely distributed. Spore germination and conidial production are dependent upon high relative humidity; it is therefore more serious in most of the humid paddy areas of the world; paddy grown under irrigation in regions of low relative humidity, as in California, is not damaged by the disease.

The symptoms of the disease are usually found on the leaves, but also occur on the culms, branches of the panicle and floral structures. On the leaves the disease is first seen as small, bluish flecks which develop to brown spots with ash-grey centres. The spots increase and merge until the leaf is brown and shrivelled. Spots on the leaf-sheath resemble those on the leaf. "Rotten neck," i.e. lesions on the neck of the culm and on the panicle branches near the base of the panicle, is a conspicuous symptom. If the plants are attacked early the grains do not fill out and the panicle therefore remains erect, but if the infection occurs when some of the grains have already filled, the panicles drop over, giving rise to the name "rotten neck." In very severe attacks the heads may emerge from the sheaths, but become completely whitened long before the normal time of ripening. Externally, the appearance may be indistinguishable from borer attack, but instead of the reddish-brown discoloration of the enclosed culm, a grey, fluffy mycelium will be found, and the stem is shrivelled.

The disease may be carried in infected seed, and the fungus has been found within the tissues of the embryo, endosperm, bran layers and glumes, and between the glume and the kernel. It may also be spread by airborne spores, and can over-winter as conidia or mycelium.

There are considerable differences in the susceptibility of paddy varieties to the disease, as well as of paddy growing under varying soil conditions. The disease is said to be worst on land newly planted to paddy, and seedlings grown in a wet nursery are more resistant than are those raised in a dry nursery. Susceptibility also varies in inverse ratio to the amount of water contained in the soil; green manures favour development, whereas superphosphate is beneficial. Excessive applications of nitrogen intensify blast, but potash may partly counteract this excessive nitrogen effect. Early-maturing varieties tend to have a lower infection. Mechanical injury, such, for instance, as may result from high winds, favours infection.

Vamos contends that in Hungary *Piricularia oryzae* and *Helmin-*

thosporium are not primarily pathogenic, for attempts to produce the diseases failed. The fungi may appear with deficiency disease and subsequent metabolic disturbances.[676] He shows that a heavy, sticky, limeless clay soil produces a root rot attributable primarily to the toxic effect of hydrogen sulphide formed in the soil and the products of the butyric acid fermentation which kills the roots. The deep soil roots of healthy plants are replaced by adventitious roots developed from the nodes which can utilize only the nutrients dissolved in the water. The root rot, the subsequent deficiency diseases and the metabolic disturbances and fungi appearing on the affected plants give the symptoms known as brusone.[678] Sunless, cool weather conditions prevent the plant from overcoming the toxic substances in the soil and from replacing the destroyed roots.[679] It is also noted[677] that the total nitrogen is high in soils liable to brusone. Excessive nitrogen prolongs the developmental stage of the plant, enhances the energy of vegetative processes, formation of seed is delayed and the plant is exposed to injuries due to the low temperature in August. The excessive nitrogen is not the cause of the disease however, but rather a stimulatory factor of it.[676]

While no variety of paddy appears to be immune to blast, many show a high degree of resistance, although, in some cases, resistant varieties may deteriorate in this respect. The most resistant are those having a reclining shot-blade, long ear emergence and a spreading panicle. The resistance of varieties is found to be associated with cell-wall composition and tissue anatomy.

It has for long been thought that resistance to blast is in some way related to silica content of the plant. Early investigations by Hazime[261] established the fact that there is no relationship between toughness of the leaf blade and blast resistance but that susceptibility to blast infection is directly proportional to the nitrogen content and inversely proportional to the silica content of the leaf. Venkatachalam[687] then discovered that at the times when the leaf and stem respectively, were most susceptible to attack, they absorbed more silica in the resistant than in the susceptible variety. These findings seem to have been confirmed by Volk[689] who hypothesized that the silicon combines with one or more components of the cell wall to form a complex relatively resistant to attack by the extracellular enzymes of *Piricularia* and so diminishes hyphal penetration into the leaf.

No one method of control will ensure freedom from the disease. It is suggested that growing seedlings in a wet nursery, flooding the land and maintaining the irrigation water on the land as soon as the disease is discovered, may prove effective. Straw and stubble from a diseased crop should be burnt. The use of seed from a diseased crop should be avoided, and suspected seed treated with mercurial seed dressing. Manurial and cultural practices likely to result in excessive vegetative growth should be avoided. Matsuo[379] states that compost and barnyard manures are effective in increasing resistance of paddy to blast and other diseases by supplying them with silicic acid. Resistant varieties should be grown or those that mature early, varieties selected having a reclining shot-blade, long ear emergence and a spreading panicle. It is claimed that the fungus may be controlled by spraying with Bordeaux mixture just before emergence of the earheads. In Japan, a study of the relationship between weather conditions, spore counts and disease outbreaks has enabled a warning system to be set up to tell farmers when to dust their crops with organo-mercurials. It is usually necessary to apply 27 to 36 lb. per acre twice in the season. The dust contains 0·15 to 0·25 per cent mercury. In 1954 about 31,000 tons of organo-mercurial dusts, some 5,000 tons of which contained added fixed copper, were used in Japan, chiefly against blast. It is claimed that no serious ill effects have resulted from their use.[459]

Fig. 28

Brown spot,
Cochliobolus miyabeanus.
Kernels and leaf spotted
and blackened with conidiospores and spores. × ½

BROWN SPOT (Sesame leaf spot).
Cochliobolus miyabeanus = *Helminthosporium oryzae* Breda de Haan.

Brown spot disease is world-wide in distribution and may cause considerable damage to paddy in the nursery, to plants in the field, or in the quality and yield of grain. Losses in the nursery, probably the result of planting infected seed, may cause irregular germination, but the greatest damage is usually when the seedling leaves and culms are infected. The plants may survive, but in a weakened condition, resulting in shrivelling and poor setting of grain. Kernel infection may amount to blackening of small areas of the glumes or may affect the entire glume.

The symptoms of the disease occur in the coleoptile, leaf, leaf-sheath and glume. On the coleoptile the spots are brown, small and circular to oval. On leaves and leaf-sheath they vary in size and shape from minute dots to circular, eye-shaped, or oval spots. On the glumes, the disease appears as black spots, or in a severe attack the entire surface of glumes may be coated with a dark brown, velvety mat of sporophores and spores.

FIG. 29

Brown spot, *Cochliobolus miyabeanus.* Kernels showing stains, spots with margins, and black masses of conidio-spores and spores. × 2

Knowledge of control measures is incomplete and inadequate to ensure freedom. Stubble of infected crops should be burnt, as should also possible alternative hosts, and the passage of irrigation water from an infected to a healthy crop should, if possible, be avoided. The seed should be grown in a "wet" nursery, for plants in the dry nursery are more susceptible to the disease. Kosakuro Ono[340] states that this disease and also stem rot disease are suppressed by potassium. The most promising line of control appears to be in the selection of resistant or less susceptible varieties for planting, especially in areas liable to severe attack.

NARROW BROWN LEAF SPOT. *Cercospora oryzae* Miyake.

This fungus has been recorded in most of the important paddy-growing countries, but has hitherto attracted little attention. The disease may be found on leaves, sheaths, peduncles and glumes. It is suggested that by causing premature killing of leaves and sheaths the disease predisposes the plant to lodging.

The symptoms appear as narrow reddish-brown to dark reddish-brown linear spots. Dickson[174] states that on susceptible varieties the lesion fades to a lighter brown along the margins and is light grey-brown in the older centres, but on more resistant varieties the lesions are smaller and uniform in colour. The lesions are usually more abundant on the leaves, although spots on the sheath, culm and floral bracts are present in heavy infections. The spots on the floral bracts spread laterally to form oblong lesions.

Varieties of paddy vary considerably in their resistance to the disease. It is suggested that resistant varieties be grown, and that when infection is very severe and lodging is likely to result, the crop be harvested before fully mature.

STACKBURN DISEASE AND SEEDLING BLIGHT AND LEAF SPOT. *Trichoconis padwickii* Ganguly.

This disease has been reported from the United States as causing damage to grain before and during storage and from India as a disease of the grain in the ear.

It attacks both the roots and coleoptile of seedlings, and occasionally also the leaves, but more generally the grain. Padwick[457] describes the symptoms as dark brown to black spots. As the decay proceeds, discrete, black bodies, more or less spherical in shape, are to be observed lying superficially on the darkened areas. The coleoptile also becomes stained, with brown patches and streaks which become almost black and bearing on their surface scattered, black, minute spherical bodies. Heavily infected seedlings wither and die, but the less severely affected appear to recover. Glumes of attacked grains show pale brown to almost white, or occasionally faintly pink to reddish-brown discoloured spots of considerable size, usually bounded by a darker ring, and carrying a few to numerous black spots. In severe attack the fungus penetrates the glumes and discolours the kernel.

Little is known regarding control of the fungus. It is suggested, however, that burning the stubble and old straw should reduce the amount of infective material.

DOWNY MILDEW. *Sclerospora oryzae* Brizi.

This disease does not appear to have assumed great importance. The symptoms seen at time of flowering and formation of the panicle take the form of contorted, sometimes spiral spikes. The leaf-sheath may also be spirally twisted. The panicle is reduced in size and remains green for some time. Occasionally the main rachis is reduced, bearing only a few tufts of hairs in place of rachillae and flowers. On such portions the mycelium may be seen. The stamens and ovaries are completely abortive.

Control of the disease is uncertain. Stubble and straw from an infected crop should be burnt. It is stated that in Japan, growing the transplanted seedlings under dry or semi-dry conditions controls the disease.

LEAF SMUT. *Entyloma oryzae* H. & P. Sydow.

This is an unimportant disease found in many paddy-growing regions. It is one of the most widespread and consistently prevalent rice diseases in Arkansas. Templeton *et al.*[650] have studied the resistance to the disease of new varieties grown in this State. The symptoms are linear, rectangular, or angular-elliptical spots on the leaves. They are leaden-black in colour, covered by the epidermis. On soaking in water for a few minutes the epidermis ruptures, revealing a black mass of spores beneath. It is reported that crop rotation and use of cleaned seed are the only control methods for this disease.

BACTERIAL LEAF BLIGHT. *Pseudomonas oryzae* Uyeda & Ishiyama.

This leaf disease has been recorded in the Philippines and Japan, but does not appear to cause serious damage to the crop. It is caused by bacteria. The symptoms are described as stripes seen between the larger veins of the leaves, running lengthwise, and having a watery dark green, translucent appearance. These spots enlarge lengthwise and may produce a blotch. Amber-coloured droplets of bacteria ooze from the diseased portions. As the leaf dries out, the droplets harden, producing small, roundish, amber-coloured beads.

Control measures are unknown, but as the disease is most prevalent on succulent plants, it is suggested that suitable fertilizers may be effective, while it is possible that resistant varieties may be found.

DISEASES OF THE STEM AND LEAF-SHEATH

STEM ROT. "Sclerotial Disease," "Tiem." *Leptosphaeria salvinii* Catt. = *Sclerotium oryzae* Catt. = *Helminthosporium sigmoideum* Cav.

Stem rot has been recorded in practically every paddy-growing country in the world and is said to have increased in severity in recent years. By reason of the obscurity of the symptoms and their variations in different countries the disease is often overlooked, or the damage occasioned by it is not fully appreciated. One of the most commonly observed symptoms is excessive late tillering, but while the disease is usually seen on maturing plants in the field, it is also recorded as attacking plants in the nursery. In severely infested areas there is not only loss of grain, but the grain may have inferior milling qualities owing to its light, chalky character.

In some instances, infected plants show no definite symptoms other

than light ears and a tendency to tiller when the crop is ripening
Butler,[102] describing the disease in India, states that on splitting the
stem a dark greyish weft of hyphae may be found within the hollow
stem, and small, round, black, shining bodies (sclerotia) can be seen
dotted all over the inner surface. He adds that sometimes the base
of the culm is quite free from the fungus and the attack begins at a
node some distance up the stem, and that the lower leaf-sheaths are
also often attacked. When plants are grown in water, heavy infection is not unusual, and under such conditions the plants may fall
to the ground.

Sclerotia will survive in the ground and old stubble for a considerable period, and will also float from field to field in irrigation
water.

The effect of nutrition in relation to the disease was studied by
Cralley.[144] He found that excessive nitrogen applications to the soil
tended to increase both yields and disease incidence. Excessive
phosphorus applications produced the same result, but much less
marked. Nitrogen and phosphorus applied together tended to produce higher yields and severer infections than either alone. Potassium applications alone slightly increased yields and had no effect
on disease severity, but when applied with nitrogen and phosphorus in sufficient quantities, potassium maintained the severity of
infection as low as the controls or even lower. In fields subject to
stem rot, therefore, applications of nitrogen and phosphorus should
be well balanced by applications of potassium.

From the foregoing, possible methods of controlling the disease
suggest themselves. Where possible, stubble and straw should be
burnt, and irrigation water should not flow from an infected area to
a non-infected area. In some cases, draining away the water and
allowing the soil to bake before again irrigating has been found
useful. The inclusion of potash in the manuring programme to offset
the adverse effect of applications of nitrogen and phosphates appears
to be a most useful line of control. Many varieties of paddy have
been found to be resistant to the disease; the cultivation of such
varieties is recommended.

IRREGULAR STEM ROT, OR SCLEROTIAL DISEASE. *Helminthosporium
sigmoideum* Cav. var. *irregulare* Cralley & Tullis.

This disease closely resembles the stem rot described above under
the name *Leptosphaeria salvinii* Catt. It has been recorded as occur-
ing in the United States, Japan, the Philippines and Ceylon.
Ceylon,[468] on fully grown infected plants, pale olive-brown patches
occur at the first and second internodes from the roots. The disease

culms are hollow and amber-coloured, and small, black sclerotia are seen lining their anterior walls even before the plants are split open. Adventitious roots are produced from the first and second nodes of many of the plants. The culms are found to contain a dark weft of mycelium, and numerous black sclerotia are found embedded in the tissue of the inner surface of the stem. Sclerotia are rarely found on the outer surface of stems, as distinct from *H. sigmoideum*, which produces them readily externally. The sclerotia are smaller than those of *H. sigmoideum*, less regular in shape, and dull instead of shiny.

In the case of infected seedlings the leaves rapidly wither and turn yellow, and the plants die; with older plants, death, if it occurs, is slower.

It is assumed that control methods are similar to those recommended for controlling stem rot caused by *H. sigmoideum*.

ORIENTAL SHEATH AND LEAF SPOT. *Corticium sasakii* (Sharai) (Matsumoto)

This stem rot has been found in many countries, and may cause considerable damage. It also attacks a large number of other plants, including groundnuts, sweet potatoes and water hyacinth. The last-named is very susceptible to the disease and may serve as an important source of infection.

FIG. 30

Oriental sheath spot, *Corticium sasakii*. The sheath has been opened out and spread flat, and the outer surface is depicted. The spots consist of pallid, brittle zones which shed away in the larger spots, surrounded by a thin, dark brown ring which fades away to the straw colour of the non-infected portion. × ½

The disease may attack the plant in the seedling stage, in which case considerable loss may occur; if older plants are attacked the loss is less marked, for the outer leaves only are diseased.

The symptom of the disease is discoloration at the base of the culm at water level or higher on the leaf-sheath and leaves. The spots are large and may be at first greenish-grey and ellipsoid, gradually enlarging and becoming greyish-green with a blackish-brown margin. Oval, spherical, or cushiony sclerotia, brown in colour, frequently covered with brown hyphae, are found on the discoloured areas of leaf and stem, or between the leaf-sheaths.

For controlling this and other stem diseases Ceresan-lime mixture is satisfactory and Bordeaux mixture moderately so.[459] Burning infected material as far as is possible may assist in controlling the disease. The destruction of alternative host plants in the vicinity is an obvious precaution against spread of the disease.

RHIZOCTONIA SHEATH SPOT. *Rhizoctonia oryzae* Ryker & Gooch

This disease, which is of no great importance, is found in the United States, attacks being usually more severe on the bunds and in other places where paddy growth is dense. It has a great resemblance to Oriental Sheath and Spot Disease, but is usually restricted to the leaf-sheaths, only occasionally attacking the leaves and never the stems or root.

The spots appear as a reddish-brown discoloration, becoming straw-coloured with reddish-brown margins and coalescing to form irregular discoloured areas. The spots usually occur just above the water line and often just below the ligule. Control measures have not been studied.

ARKANSAS FOOT ROT or BROWN SHEATH ROT. *Ophiobolus oryzinus* Sacc.

Arkansas Foot Rot occurs in the United States. The disease infects the leaf-sheath just before harvest, the sheaths so infected showing a brown discoloration from the crown to considerably above the water line. At maturity the straw is dull brown in colour. The disease is at present relatively unimportant. Control measures have not been studied. It is known, however, that certain paddy varieties, including red rice, are susceptible to it.

SEEDLING BLIGHTS AND FOOT ROT

SEEDLING BLIGHT. *Corticium rolfsii* Curzi = *Sclerotium rolfsii* Sacc

Seedling Blight, which attacks paddy seedlings from a very early stage of growth, is widely distributed throughout most paddy-growing countries.

Tisdale,[658] describing the disease, states that the base of the stems and the roots of diseased plants are dark in colour and often have a frosty appearance due to the presence of wefts of mycelium. Infected plants first show a stunted appearance, accompanied by yellowing and withering of leaves; often, also, the leaves have white stripes or may be almost entirely white. Affected plants die slowly, or the plants may recover when the land is irrigated. The symptoms are readily seen on badly affected seedlings, but plants may be attacked and killed before emergence.

The fungus appears to decrease in prevalence or vigour with a depletion of organic matter in the soil. It can, however, remain in the soil as sclerotia for long periods. The sclerotia float, so that the fungus can be disseminated in irrigation water. The disease is stated to be most common during warm moist weather and is most severe where there is a lack of water on the seed bed. Irrigation of the seed bed completely checks further development. Control of irrigation on the seed bed appears to offer the best means of controlling the disease.

SEED ROT AND DAMPING OFF.   Saprolegniaceous and Pythiaceous fungi.

This seedling rot, found in Japan and Formosa, caused by one or a number of fungi, may result in severe damage to seedlings. The first evidence of the disease is an outgrowth of the whitish hyphae of the parasites on the surface of glumes, or on the collar of the plumule. The hyphae may grow from the slit of the seed-coat opened or broken off by germination or the threshing operation, or by insects. When severely attacked, the seed fails to germinate and if the seedlings are affected when the plumules have already commenced growth, damping off takes place. Progress of the symptoms is influenced by the weather and vigour of the seedlings.

Control should aim at provision of conditions favourable to the development of vigorous seedlings and selection of seed free from mechanical injury.

BAKANAE DISEASE AND FOOT ROT.   *Gibberella fujikuroi* (Saw.) Wr.

This disease is well known in Japan under the name "Bakanae," in the Philippines as "Palay Lalake," while the so-called "Man Rice" in British Guiana is probably the same disease. It also occurs in other paddy-growing countries and is frequently responsible for severe damage.

Seedlings attacked in the nursery are pale and thin, and may die out. In the field, the most characteristic symptom (but not always present) is the appearance of occasional lanky tillers which come into shot-blade earlier than the rest of the crop, bearing pale green flags, which are conspicuous above the general level of the crop. This "bakanae" symptom, however, may be suppressed and the plants may even be severely stunted. Japanese workers have carried out considerable research on this interesting "bakanae" symptom. Yabuta and Hayasi[706] isolated two substances from cultures of *G. fujikuroi*; one they named fusaric acid has a formula $C_{10}N_{13}NO_2$ retards the growth of seedlings; the other, named gibberellin, which they thought to be an organic acid, stimulated the elongation of shoots of a variety of plants, including paddy. Several writers have noted that in fields where the temperature during the growing period is low, practically no "bakanae" plants can be found.

Thomas[652] observes that plants with the "bakanae" symptom invariably show fungus attack at the collar region and die within a period of two to six days. He adds that as a rule the leaves of infected plants dry up one after another from below, their margins first turning brown, while a long strip along both sides of the mid-rib still remains green. Eventually the green area also turns brown, when the leaf curls and droops. Another symptom described by the same writer is the development of adventitious roots from the first, second and sometimes the third node above ground level. The first node exhibits well-developed roots, while the node above it may show a few developed roots or early signs of such development. The account continues:

> On splitting open the culm of the infected tiller, there is a distinct crown discoloration of the spongy tissue of the nodular region confined in early cases of attack to the lowest root-bearing nodes but visible in advanced stages at the upper one or two nodes as well. In the latter case, long before the death of the tiller the fungus growth is found to spread through the hollow of the lowest internode. Though the root-bearing nodes are discoloured within, the underground root system remains intact, showing the healthy white colour.
>
> Some plants which develop the symptoms described above show externally a white or pink bloom of fungus growth at the lowest one or two nodes. This bloom is often conspicuous on the dead sheaths. When the plants are dead, the bloom extends upwards along the sheath up to a distance of four inches above the collar. If the dead plants are left in the field sufficiently long, the fungus growth on the sheath develops into a pink incrustation which consists of a thick matting of mycelium bearing myriads of conidia (spores). When irrigation water stands at a high level, the portion of the sheath under water does not show the white bloom, but when the field gets drained, the bloom is evident down to ground level. Dead plants when pulled out snap at the collar, leaving the root behind.

An additional symptom that may be found is a fasciculation of the root due to the abnormal branching of the main roots.

The disease may be carried in the seed, or be soil-borne, soil moisture and soil temperature playing an important part in its development. Nitrogen applied to the soil stimulates the disease, an effect that is not modified by the addition of potash or phosphates.

Certain varieties of paddy are more resistant to the disease than are others. It is probable that further research regarding resistant varieties may lead to favourable results. The treatment of seed with formalin and mercurial dusts is effective.

DISEASES OF THE GRAIN AND INFLORESCENCE

BLACK SMUT OR BUNT. *Neovossia horrida* (Tak.) Padwick & Azmatullah Khan.

Black Smut has been recorded from many countries, but is not considered to be a serious disease, as usually only a few ears are attacked, and these often only partially. In this disease the grain is wholly or partly filled with black spores, which burst through the glumes at the time of ripening.

The disease is said to be more prevalent when paddy is irrigated during dry weather than when planted during the normal growing season. Severity of attack may be associated with quantity and timing of nitrogen application.

It is doubtful whether seed treatment with one of the recognized disinfectants is effective in controlling the disease. Certain varieties of paddy are said to be resistant to the disease.

FALSE SMUT OR GREEN SMUT. *Ustilaginoidea virens* (Cke.) Tak.

Although this disease is widely distributed it rarely causes much damage. The infected grains are transformed into large, velvety, green masses which may be twice the diameter of the normal grain. The green colour is superficial, the inner part of the swollen mass being orange-yellow near the surface and white in the centre.

Satisfactory control measures are not known. When paddy is milled by hand, the diseased grains are easily recognized and can be removed by hand.

MINUTE LEAF AND GRAIN SPOT. *Nigrospora* spp.

This condition of the ears and grains of rice occurs usually on plants already weakened by other causes, such as malnutrition, insect pests and diseases, and the symptoms are usually those caused by the primary agent. The fungi associated with this condition of rice are three species of the genus *Nigrospora* (Moniliales). The disease appears to be of minor importance and there is no information on methods of control.

"UDBATTA" DISEASE. *Ephelis oryzae* Syd.

"Udbatta" disease attacks paddy in India and Sierre Leone, and has also been reported to attack certain other grasses. The symptom is characteristic: the ear, on emergence, is reduced to a straight spike and covered with mycelium, which becomes hard and dotted with black. No grain is formed.

SCAB. *Gibberella zeae* (Schw.) Petch.

Scab has been reported from many rice-producing regions, and is identical with scab disease of wheat. Infected grains may show a reddish appearance and discoloration appears as brown spots covering the entire seed. The infected grain is light, shrunken and brittle, but the seeds do not necessarily show signs of infection. Diseased grain gives rise to diseased seedlings. The nodes may also be attacked; they become blackened and disintegrate, the stems wilt, break down and fall.

Treatment of seed with mercurial dressing may offer some degree of control.

BLACK ROT OF RICE GRAINS. *Pseudomonas itoana* Tochinai.

Iwadare[295] states that this disease is characterized by partial blackening or black spotting on hulled grain, especially at the apical part, sometimes at the middle and rarely at the base. The centre of the black spot usually lies on the apex or on the groove of the grain. It is stated that the morbid change is limited mostly to the aleurone layer and the upper parts of the endosperm. The affected tissues die off and turn black.

The causal organism attacks the rice grain at its milky-white stage through wounds. The disease occurs most severely in years when the temperature is high in July and August. Control measures have not been stated.

LEAF BREAK

This disease, caused by a species of *Neottiospora*, has been described by Deighton[166] from Sierra Leone where it has caused damage in limited areas. The fungus attacks the leaf at the juncture with the sheath causing the leaf blade to wither and fall off prematurely. The damage causes reduced yields, but little is known about the disease.

DISEASES CAUSED BY NEMATODES

"UFRA" OR "DAK PORA." *Ditylenchus angustus* (Butler) Filipjev.

"Ufra" is a serious disease in the restricted area of eastern Bengal and has also been reported from Malaya and Burma. The disease was the subject of close study by Butler.[101, 103] The attack may commence at an early stage in the development of the plant and, given favourable conditions from the time of infection until maturity, the plants produce little or no grain. The most severe attacks affect floating varieties of paddy broadcast in the low swamp areas which remain submerged for most of the year and are either damp or actually under water at harvest time.

Although seedlings may be attacked by the disease at an early stage, the death of seedlings due to ufra is probably rare. The disease is first evident when the plants are about two months old, but it may not be apparent until the ears begin to form in the bud. The upper leaves are chlorotic as a whole or in streaks, and are thin and weak, and the plant is somewhat stunted. The plants have, in fact, been infected for a considerable time before these symptoms are seen. Later, a few scattered brown stains appear on the leaves and sheaths. The inner layers of the sheaths may be faintly stained brown, and there is a tendency towards wrinkling of the layers. Later the stains become darker and the stems in portions of the upper internodes become quite dark brown. There are two distinct types of symptoms seen at heading-out time, viz. "thor" or swollen ufra, and "pucca" or ripe ufra. In the former, the ear remains entirely enclosed within the leaf-sheath, the whole structure being enlarged into a spindle-shaped swelling. The sheath may be stained over a considerable area

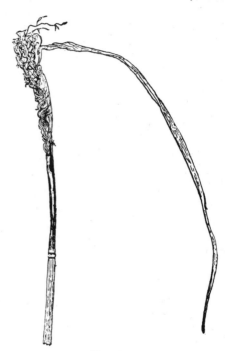

FIG. 31

Ufra disease, *Ditylenchus angustus*.
A severe attack showing the spirally twisted inflorescence. × ½

or confined to small oval or elliptical spots. The spiral twisting of the ear, coupled with the dark-brown colour, and the absence in most cases of insect attack, are characteristic of the disease. There may also be a tendency towards branching of the stem in the infected portions, and even the formation of two or three distorted ears surrounded by one sheath. In "pucca" ufra the ear emerges from the sheath and usually produces some normal grains, especially near the tip. The peduncle turns brown or black, and flowers in the lower part of the ear remain unfertilized and have the typical brown colour, or may contain partly formed grains.

AA

A microscopic examination of affected material at harvest reveals the presence of nematodes. They are mainly found at the base of

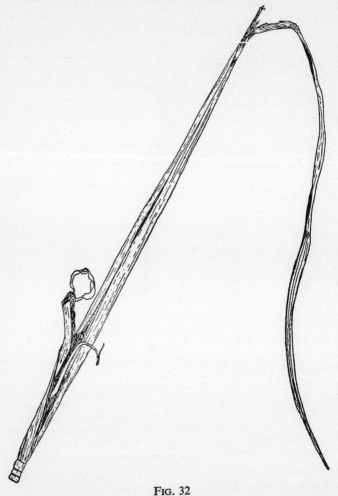

FIG. 32

Ufra disease, *Ditylenchus angustus*. A very severe attack ('thor ufra'), the inflorescence being almost unrecognizable. × ½

the peduncle, the stem just above the next node lower down and in the glumes. These are the areas which have the typical discoloration.

Infection takes place, if humidity is sufficient, even when seedlings are four days old. They climb up the stems and attack the growing tissues. They enter the bud and can find their way into the inner portions by working their way between the folds. They do not penetrate bodily through the tissues, but protrude their stylets, which are inserted into the epidermal cells and suck the plant sap. The nematode is believed to be incapable of feeding on decomposing vegetable matter, or on any plant other than paddy.

Unless land can be drained or adequately cultivated, the only effective method of controlling the disease is by the complete removal of all infected straw. So long as affected fields are used for cattle-grazing without removal of the straw, or so long as a crop such as gram is broadcast amongst the ripening and partly diseased crop, there is no hope of destroying the dormant nematodes by physical means.

"White Tip" caused by the nematode *Aphelenchoides besseyi* Yokoo (= *A. oryzae*) is serious in parts of America and Japan. The parasite causes characteristic sterile conditions of the upper part of the panicle which emerges white and papery. Fukano and Yokoyama report the effects of seed disinfection by hot water treatment and in America seed disinfection with 1 oz. per forty bushels of 3-*p*-chlorophenyl-5-methyl rhodamine is said to be effective.

Other nematodes recorded attacking paddy include *Radopholus oryzae* (Breda de Haan) and *Anguillulina oryzae* (Breda de Haan) Goodey,[214] which attacks the roots.

Brown[720] has pointed out that the intensely cultivated irrigation tropical and sub-tropical areas are particularly liable to plant nematode attack, the problem being aggravated in these regions by the transport of nematodes in the irrigation water. In Texas[716] surveys were made to determine what parasitic nematodes were present in paddy fields. Eleven parasitic forms and seven suspected parasitic forms were found. Populations varied from field to field, probably affected by rotational systems.

DISEASES CAUSED BY UNFAVOURABLE SOIL CONDITIONS

STRAIGHTHEAD

Straighthead is a symptom of a physiological condition that may be due to one of several causes. Under various names it occurs in many countries, and in the United States, where it is common, it sometimes causes extensive damage.

The leaves of diseased plants turn a deeper green and are stiffer than usual. The heads emerge slowly, or the plants may even fail to head. The entire flower may be absent, or only one glume is absent and the other distorted and curved. Sterile flowers may be present and most of the flowers never open, while others open but fail to produce kernels. The plant produces numerous tillers from the lower nodes and crown. These develop into secondary growth after harvest. The root system is enlarged by long coarse roots, showing only a few ramifications and root-hairs.

Straighthead occurs only after the most unfavourable conditions of soil aeration when certain other conditions are satisfied. It is most severe when paddy follows a series of non-irrigated crops, or on virgin land. The nature of a superabundance of organic matter is thought to be a contributory cause.

Control measures recommended in the United States include thorough preparation of the land before sowing, followed by irrigation to a depth of about four inches about ten days after the plants emerge, or when they are about six to eight inches tall. Where attack is anticipated, the soil should be drained five to six weeks after the application of water; it should be allowed to dry until the surface cracks, the water then being again applied to a depth of four to five inches and retained thus for the remainder of the growing period.

Straighthead symptoms may be due to climatic causes. Dickson[174] instances the disease occurring in Italy known as "bianchetta" or "gentilomo" with similar symptoms, except that the stalk bearing the panicle is said to rot. The cause is thought to be a sudden decrease in temperature in the later stages of growth, or to hail storms. In the disease in Italy called "colatura," where the panicle stands upright, part of the inflorescence fails, and the organs of the blossoms are turned into a "tuft of white threads," the probable causes are thought to be decrease in temperature, hail storms at the time of formation of the panicle, lack of nutrients, or to high nitrogen content.

FIG. 33
Inflorescence of a rice plant suffering from 'straighthead.'
× ⅓

Dry Leaf Disease or Pan-Sukh occurring in India has symptoms very similar to those of Straighthead. Only a few green leaves are seen amongst a mass of brown dry leaves. The flowers are sterile but the glumes are normal in shape and colour and there is no distortion. The root symptoms are identical with those of Straighthead. The disease appears to be mainly due to poor soil aeration, accentuated by, or possibly resulting in, lack of available nitrogen. Resistant varieties of paddy are known.

Straighthead is a serious disease in Portugal.[151] In that country investigations showed that application of minerals—especially of trace elements— either reduced considerably or eliminated the disease. Of mineral elements applied alone only copper prevented, or reduced markedly, the incidence of the disease. Results of chemical analyses and field trials support the assumption that straighthead arises from a reduction of mineral elements in the soil subject to continuous irrigation.

FIG. 34

Straighthead. On the left a grain from a healthy plant, the remainder from a diseased plant. Note the sickle shape, the absence of one glume, and the hollow shrunken appearance. × 2

STERILITY

Sterility in paddy may be caused by certain of the diseases mentioned or by other causes (see Chapter VII). Tisdale and Jenkins[659] suggest the following additional types of sterility:

Alkali injury resulting in stunted and rusty appearance of the plants and failure to produce seed; drought injury resulting in death; nitre spots, the symptoms being retention of green colour up to harvest time, the plants remaining sterile and erect though otherwise lacking the straighthead symptoms. Dry hot winds give a blasted appearance of the heads as if scorched by fire. Poor grassy land results in sterility, commonly accompanied by staining of the glumes due to invading fungi.

Other diseases caused by unfavourable soil conditions include a disease reported from Japan[441] caused by lack of oxygen in the soil, brought about by the sulphate-reducing bacteria, *Microspira desulphuricans* (Beijerinck) van Delden and *Pseudomonas* sp. The symptoms are curving and checking of elongation of the first leaf, which eventually dies and rots, and checking of development of the root, which withers and is blackened. In the disease known as "Senthal" in Ceylon,[467] the central shoot becomes pinkish and tubular and fails to develop further, but tillering is stimulated under favourable conditions. It occurs chiefly on sandy soils which have had a heavy application of bulky green manure which has not decayed completely.

DEFICIENCY DISEASES*

Nitrogen. A nitrogen-deficiency disease, known as rice *Cadang-cadang*, is described in the Philippines. The affected plants manifest a yellowing of the leaves, the older becoming light orange or yellow. The roots are almost brown. Applications of nitrogenous fertilizers appear effective in controlling the disease.

The disease *penyakit merah* in Malaya is now considered to be caused by a deficiency of nitrogen for metabolism, particularly during the stage of highest nitrogen requirement. This may be due either to insufficient uptake of nitrogen from the soil or to its physiological non-availability within the plant.[365]

Phosphorus. In central Burma phosphate deficiency caused the crop to remain green at the normal time of maturity. The symptoms of phosphorus deficiency were found to include stunting, reduced tillering, bunching of leaves, and a dark or blue tinge.

Potash. The disease known as "Mentek" in Java has probably been applied to a number of diseases with somewhat similar symptoms. From time to time, considerable damage is caused by this disease in Java and Sumatra. The term "Mentek" there refers to a combination of shortening of leaf-blades and sheaths from an early stage, accompanied by yellowing and partial failure of emergence of the ears and reduction in length of the culms. Nitrogen, potash and phosphate deficiency are considered possible causes of the disease.

Iron. Chlorosis of paddy occurring on calcareous soils is considered to be due to the iron being rendered unavailable.

The disease known as Bronzing or Browning is reported in Ceylon[496] to be associated with excess iron. Yamada, however, contends[707] that bronzing covers a diversity of symptoms. Plants with severe bronzing show little development of roots and this results in imbalance of nutrients and to potassium and phosphorus deficiencies. There also appears to be an inverse relationship between bronzing and silification. In other cases an excess of H_2S seems to exert toxic effects.

Calcium and Magnesium. The "White Tip" disease in the United States appears as white areas on the tips of one or more of the new leaves during the mid-season or late flowering period. If the flag-leaf is affected, the panicle remains tightly enrolled within its sheath, the head often emerging through the side, giving rise to only a few sterile flowers, or at best, distorted grains. While there appears to be some evidence that the trouble may be caused by calcium and magnesium deficiency, there is also contradictory evidence.

* See also Trace Elements on page 229.

Boron, Copper and Manganese. Boron deficiency is stated[272] to result in chlorotic spotting of leaves at the tip; manganese deficiency to chlorosis of the mid-vein, with a resultant striped appearance of the foliage; and copper deficiency in reduced weight of plants.

Sulphur. A disease said to be due to sulphur deficiency is reported from Burma. The plants turn yellow and remain stunted; later they regain their green colour and increase in height, but give a reduced yield. It is found that the plants regain their green colour when fertilized with chemicals containing sulphate.

VIRUS DISEASES

DWARF OR STUNT DISEASE

Until the cause of this disease was discovered, resulting in steps being taken to control its cause, widespread damage was experienced in Japan.

The disease manifests itself as yellowish-white specks along the veins of newly unfolded leaves. These specks elongate and spread out along the leaf parallel to the mid-rib, forming fine interrupted streaks. Growth is stunted, the internodes shortened and numerous diminutive tillers develop, producing a rosette appearance. Affected plants tend to develop dark green foliage. The roots are much arrested in growth, are small and extend horizontally.

The infectiousness of the disease, the invisibility of the causal agent under the microscope, and the mode of transmission, all point to the fact that it is caused by a virus. Though much is known about the transmission there is little information about its physical and chemical properties. It was early discovered by the Japanese that the causal virus is transmitted by certain leaf hoppers, viz. *Nephotettix apicalis* Motsch var. *cincticeps* Uhl. and by *Deltocephalus dorsalis* Motsch. There is no known method of control of the disease other than by control of the vector.

STRIPE DISEASE

This disease, unknown outside Japan, first appears about ten days after transplanting and becomes more destructive as the plants grow. The young leaves show the symptoms; twisting, abnormal elongation and final drooping. The leaves of the affected plants appear slender and pale and one or more yellowish-green or yellowish-white stripes develop parallel to the mid-rib. The plants usually produce no ears, or at best, unfilled ears. The disease is caused by a virus transmitted by *Delphacodes striatella* Fall. No control measures are known.

Mosaic Disease

Mosaic was observed in a newly-introduced Japanese paddy variety in the Philippines.[378] It is of virus origin and appears to be similar to the mosaic diseases reported on other gramineous plants in Puerto Rico, Tunisia and South America. Plants are stunted and have foliar mottling. Infected leaves gradually turn brown and wither.

Hoja Blanca

This virus disease has for long been known in Cuba and various countries in South America, but it was not until 1956 that it appeared in the United States when it was discovered in Florida. In the following year or so it was found in many regions of the United States and the Caribbean.

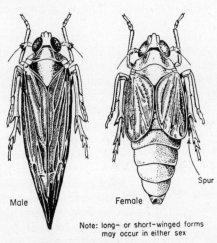

Male

Female

Spur

Note: long- or short-winged forms may occur in either sex

Fig. 35

Sogata orizicola

It is stated that heavy infection may cause a loss of 75 per cent of the crop. Fields in Cuba have been observed with 90 per cent infection and total loss of crop. In 1956 the disease caused such widespread loss of crop in Venezuela[92] that it was probably the most significant single factor in the decline of paddy production in that country.

The disease is spread by the plant hopper *Sogata orizicola* Muir, the adult of which is dark-coloured with a lighter stripe on the back and is 3 to 4 mm. long. The insect has five nymphal states and requires about 25 days to complete its development from egg to adult. It thrives best in high humidity and moderately high temperature.[387] Destruction of the insect vector is the only method of control of the disease,[625] apart from the use of resistant varieties.

Mcguire and Mcmillian[387] gave a full account in 1960 of the disease and its insect vector, with an exhaustive bibliography. The symptoms of the disease they describe as follows:

The leaf on which the inoculation occurs may show a few chlorotic spots or be completely unaffected. An infected plant observed throughout its growing period develops the following symptoms: (*a*) Depending on its stage of development at the time of inoculation, the next leaf to emerge shows symptoms which vary from a few chlorotic spots at the base of the leaf to an extensive mottled or yellow-striped area which does not extend to the tip of the leaf. (*b*) The second leaf to emerge may exhibit a general yellowing, mottling, or yellow stripes which will run the whole length of the blade. (*c*) The third leaf to emerge usually is completely chlorotic and often dies before the other leaves; necrosis begins at the tip and upper edges and progresses downward and inward.

Plants affected when young show the complete progression of the disease, whereas older plants do not show the more advanced symptoms. If infection occurs before or during the boot stage, the panicle may not completely emerge and all or some of the spikelets may fail to set seed. However, if the infection occurs after the emergence of the panicle, only a small reduction in seed production may occur. . . . Extreme height reduction of plants may occur since the younger leaves will die sooner than those preceding them and the emerging leaves will be stunted.

It was found that all the major varieties of rice were susceptible to the disease, but disease-resistant varieties and strains were discovered and have been developed. A new variety Gulfrose, resistant to Hoja Blanca and with good field properties, has been released for cultivation. It is reported that five States hold stocks of resistant varieties for distribution in the event of a serious outbreak of the disease in any of the main rice-producing areas.[148, 361]

SEED DISINFECTION

Chemical seed treatment is increasingly used against a number of diseases. It is successful against foot rot and seedling blight, but as "blast" is less amenable to control by this means, fungicidal dusts and sprays are employed to a limited extent against this disease. Since the cost of chemical seed treatment is slight compared with the value and importance of the crop, such treatment is generally adopted as a type of crop insurance.

In countries where paddy is sown direct in the field, e.g. the United

States of America, the benefits resulting from chemical seed treatment are immediately apparent and both drilled and broadcast crops have shown notable increases in stand and yield. Ryker[577] reported emergence and stand increases varying from 4 to 30 per cent; so also have several other writers. In France, Juillet and Turquois[317] obtained earlier germination and improved emergence by using treated seed. Yield increases in early American experiments have varied from 6 to 12 per cent.

Seed treatment has also proved successful with transplanted paddy. Records of height of plants, length of ears, number of tillers, percentage of leaf area infection and yield of grain and straw have resulted from seed treatment. It was estimated that during the season 1949–50, 70,000 acres of paddy were sown with "Agrosan" GN treated seed in Bengal, and the additional yield of clean rice amounted to nearly 11,000 tons. In trials in India, although significant differences in seedling mortality have not always been observed as a result of treating seed infected with *Helminthosporium*, a 15 to 25 per cent increase in yield has been reported.

In Japan,[255, 256, 379] seed is carefully disinfected to control seed-borne diseases such as (*a*) blast (*Piricularia oryzae*), (*b*) Bakanae disease (*Gibberella fujikuroi*), (*c*) brown rot, *Helminthosporium* leaf spot or Sesame leaf spot (*Ophiobolus miyabeanus*), (*d*) seed and seedling rot (*Pythium oryzae*), *Achlya* spp. and *Pythiomorpha* sp. and (*e*) white tip (*Aphelenchoides oryzae*). The methods of disinfection and the diseases thereby controlled are as follows:

Method of Disinfection	Diseases most effectively controlled
Formalin	b, a, c
Mercury	a, b, c, d
Copper sulphate	d
Cold and hot water treatment	c, e

Formalin Disinfection. Seed soaked in water for one or two days, then slightly dried. Formalin (40 per cent) is diluted with water (50 to 1) and seed soaked in it for three hours, and then in water till ready to sow.

Mercurial Disinfection. Usplun (the major component is phenyl mercury chloride containing 2·5 per cent mercury) is used, or Mercuron may be employed. Seed is soaked in water, but not germinated. It is then steeped in a 1/1,000 Usplun solution for six hours at about 18° C. and subsequently sown without removal of the disinfectant by washing. (Metal vessels should not be used.)

Copper Sulphate. About 19 grams copper sulphate are dissolved in 18 litres of water in a wooden receptacle, in which the seed is soaked for twenty-four hours and then in water.

Cold and Hot Water Treatment. The seed is placed in a bag, soaked for twenty-four hours and then dipped in and out of warm water (45° C.) several times, after which it is steeped in hot water (52° C.) for ten minutes. The seed is then steeped in cold water for a further twenty-four hours.

CHEMICAL CONTROL OF SPECIFIC DISEASES

Helminthosporium oryzae. As early as 1922, Nisikado and Miyake[436, 437] demonstrated the effectiveness of mercuric chloride, copper sulphate and formaldehyde against this disease. Later, Nisikado and Nakayama[438] claimed good control in immersing the seed for forty-eight hours in a solution of Usplun (see above). Cralley and Tullis,[723] in America, showed that a high degree of control of seed-borne infection could be obtained with ethyl mercury phosphate and ethyl mercury chloride dusts. In later experiments organo-mercurials, yellow cuprocide, thiram and quinones gave appreciable increases in stand and yield, and for the last ten years recommendations for all these fungicides have been made. Organo-mercurials capable of effective control are now available for use as powder, slurry and liquid treatments. Seed treatment has become general in the southern United States, Arkansas, Louisiana and Texas.[58] One of several fungicides are used, supplied in slurry form at a rate of ½ to 1 oz. per bushel.[5, 145, 146, 147]

Some investigators have pointed out that if seed treatment is carried out only in isolated nurseries, attack of *Helminthosporium* in the early stages of growth will be inhibited, but later leaf spotting caused by secondary airborne spore infection from untreated surrounding areas cannot be prevented. If all seed over a large area is treated, this secondary infection could be considerably reduced.

Gibberella fujikuroi. As *Gibberella* is largely seed borne, the use of seed treatment has resulted in a considerable measure of control. In Japan, where the disease was at one time of economic importance, it is now almost non-existent due to extensive use of seed treatment.

Early work by Thomas[653] in 1933, showed that seed treatment with organo-mercurial dusts and by steeping in copper sulphate gave a large measure of control. This was confirmed by Sundararaman[638] in 1937, while more recently Abeygunewardena[1] has shown that organo-mercurial formulations are the only satisfactory ones, and that differences between the various proprietary products are not statistically significant. He found that copper compounds were less effective. Mercurials are usually used for drilled seed, but because of the relative solubility of mercury and copper, yellow Cuprocide may be more effective where the seed is sown in water.

Piricularia oryzae. This disease is largely airborne and seed treatment cannot be expected to give complete control. Reports from Brazil and Formosa state that a measure of control can be obtained with mercurial seed dressings, but Japanese consider that the degree of control afforded by this means is negligible. The main advantage of seed treatment with organo-mercurials for "blast" is probably the improved germination resulting from the removal of superficial contamination on the seed. Control of "blast" has been achieved by the use of fungicidal dusts or sprays on the growing crop. Padmanabhan *et al.*[456] reported significant reduction in neck infection and increases in yield with four applications of either Bordeaux mixture, Perenox or Dithane Z-78. In Japan, powder organo-mercurial preparations diluted with lime have been found more effective and are extensively used for "blast" control. For this purpose a 2·5 per cent mercurial product is diluted 1:9 with lime and applied at about 30 lb. per acre. Unless the infection is especially severe, one or two applications only are made, more than three being uneconomic.

PART III

RICE:
THE PRODUCT

What am I to buy for our sheep-shearing feast? Three pounds of sugar; five pounds of currants; rice—What will this sister of mine do with rice? But my father hath made her mistress of the feast, and she lays it on.

—W. Shakespeare, *Winter's Tale*, IV, scene 2.

Chapter XVI

STORAGE OF PADDY AND RICE

SMALLHOLDERS' METHODS OF STORAGE

METHODS of storing paddy by the Eastern peasant are of the simplest. Provided that the crop is reasonably dry, unhusked rice (paddy) apparently remains in good condition for a considerable period. The writer has examined paddy stored by peasants for four or five years and found it to be in reasonably good condition. Much of the damage to paddy in store, however, is not very apparent until husking, when it may be found that there are a large number of empty glumes. The cultivator invariably stores the crop as paddy, which he husks in small quantities at a time, sufficient to supply current domestic needs. Paddy in excess of his estimated requirements is usually sold soon after harvest to middlemen who in turn sell without delay to millers.

The paddy store is generally situated at one side or adjacent to the owner's dwelling in a wooden or plaited bamboo shed provided with a plank or round timber floor and a leaf or corrugated iron roof. Sometimes the walls are omitted. The store is raised on piles a few feet from the ground, or on a platform of earth to protect it from damp. Bins in such a shed are usually circular and constructed of plaited split bamboo or, in Malaya, often from a single piece of bark of the *kepong* tree (*Shorea sericea* Dyer). The bins are covered with a piece of the same bark or with planks. Apparently rats find some difficulty in gnawing through split bamboo or *kepong* bark. In Burma,[525] where plaited bamboo is also mainly used for constructing bins for storing seed paddy, the plaited bamboo is daubed with a mixture of clay and cow dung to prevent the grain from escaping and to exclude rain and rats. The paddy store usually seen in Burma is a rectangular building of plaited bamboo, with corner posts of wood and a roof of leaves or grass. It is usually built on piles, has a floor of bamboo matting or plank, and sometimes of both, the space between the upper floor of bamboo matting and the lower one of plank being filled with paddy husk to support the weight and to keep out damp. Paddy is stored in bulk and is thrown through a doorway which, as the grain rises, is closed from the bottom upwards by dropping planks into vertical slots in the door posts. Mill godowns

351

(stores) and those of the larger stockholders are usually of corrugated iron, but plaited bamboo is often used in them to divide compartments or for flooring.

A very similar store is used in the northern state of Kedah, in Malaya,[582] where in a good season the cultivator has paddy for sale after making provision for his own needs.

In Thailand, the paddy store is near the house, but not attached to it; the floor should be a foot or two higher than that of the house, for respect should be paid to the paddy.

In Ceylon[474] stocks of between 50 and 300 bushels are stored in a *bissa* made from tough jungle creepers plastered with clay and lime, and placed on wooden or stone pillars. In Lower Burma a large part of the paddy crop is not placed in storage until it reaches the mill. The threshed grain is taken to collecting points, usually adjoining waterways or rail, where it remains in large unprotected heaps in the open during the first three months of the year. Rain damage is extremely unlikely during this period of the year.

Village grain stores in Pakistan are often large earthenware jars, some 12 feet in height, which when filled, are closed with clay. They are rat-proof, and if dry grain is stored they keep it in good condition.

The paddy cultivator is usually in need of money and therefore disposes of his crop at the earliest opportunity. Stocks held by cultivators are therefore usually small so that no question of more ambitious methods of storage is presented.

STORAGE AT MILLS

On arrival at mills in the East, paddy is stored in large godowns where it remains for a short time before milling. The miller, therefore, considers it unnecessary to erect elevator storage such as is usual in America where, however, the quantity of grain produced by individual farmers is considerable. In Burma, while it is appreciated that adoption of elevator storage would facilitate pest control in the grain, it is considered that the cost and other disadvantages of the system outweigh any possible advantages. The aim of the miller is to dispose of stocks before monsoon rains begin. The paddy, therefore, is in a dry condition which gives improved milling and obviates heating and sweating and thereby lessens attack by rice weevils which thrive under conditions of warmth and damp. The State Agricultural Marketing Board of Burma has built a substantial amount of flat storage but many stores would not meet minimum sanitary standards in the U.S.A. and both paddy and milled rice deteriorate fairly rapidly.[548]

The elevator system of storage as practised in many countries for grain storage has the advantage that, in addition to effecting economies in handling, it facilitates manipulation of the stock to control insect pests by providing good, dry storage conditions. The absence of up-to-date storage godowns, however, does not mean that rice or paddy cannot be kept in equally good condition. The cardinal factor of storage is that the crop must be well dried before storage. The Asian cultivator is usually well aware of the necessity for storing in a dry condition, for he appreciates the fact that apart from rats, practically all other destructive agents arise from excess of moisture. While paddy[298] stored in a reasonably dry condition remains edible for a considerable period under ordinary storage conditions, rice is scarcely edible after eight months' storage, but under rat-proofed and well-ventilated conditions it may be stored for two years.

CAUSES OF LOSS IN STORAGE

The causes of loss in grain during storage have been summarized by Oxley[453] as follows:

(1) Metabolism of grain tissues.

(2) Metabolism of micro-organisms.

(3) Metabolism of insects and mites.

(4) Metabolism by rodents and birds, causing fouling and loss of material.

EFFECT OF MOISTURE CONTENT OF STORED GRAIN

Moisture content has a profound effect on the first three of the above-stated sources of loss, causing "spontaneous heating," loss of viability, loss of material, and chemical changes. Oxley further points out that the storage life of a bulk of grain is determined by its dampest point, for spontaneous heating can begin with a damp pocket and may initiate heating throughout the bulk. It is thus clear that control of moisture content to reduce losses of grain must include not only control of the mean moisture content, but also control of the distribution of moisture in the bulk. The exchange of water vapour by diffusion is held to be insufficient to ensure even distribution of water, for a wet pocket may take months or years to equilibrate with other parts of the bulk. The damage of wet pockets is especially to be guarded against in freshly harvested grain. It follows, therefore, that if the homogeneity of water content could be assured, grain might be safe for storage at higher levels of water content than have hitherto been expected.

Oxley[453] states that in most Californian mills, paddy with a moisture content about 14 to 15 per cent produces the best result, while rice for export cannot obtain a government certificate of grade if it contains more than 14·5 per cent moisture. Uncured rice may be expected to sweat in the warehouse, however dry when it goes in, but it comes through the sweat without damage if sufficiently dry. Hukill[280] points out that moisture content limits are variable for different species of mould and types of insects and also depend upon storage temperature. With lower temperatures, a higher moisture content may be tolerated. It follows that moisture content must be less when storing in the tropics than in temperate climates.

A portable rapid moisture tester, devised by the Pest Infestation Laboratory of the Agricultural Research Council, gives an almost instantaneous reading, correct within 1 per cent and with a range of 12 to 25 per cent moisture. The instrument works on the principle of measuring the electrical resistance between electrodes plunged into the grain. It consists of nine steel spears, each eight inches long, arranged parallel to each other on an insulating base and cross connected. With this instrument it is possible to decide quickly and without opening the sacks, whether a consignment of grain is evenly dry, so that damp sacks may be isolated for drying, thus effecting a considerable saving of time and expense in drying.[455]

Normally, in the East, there is no difficulty in drying paddy sufficiently by spreading it for a few hours in the sun (at the risk of sun-cracking the grain—see page 147), but it is evident that in storing paddy, and particularly rice, in bulk, greater precautions are necessary to obviate the danger of development of fungal micro-flora.

The fungus flora[308] of stored grain is essentially the same the world over, consisting chiefly of species of *Penicillium*, *Aspergillus*, *Alterraria*, *Fusarium*, *Cladosporium* and *Rhizopus*. Excessive heating of grain is caused by respiration of the fungi. At moisture content above 14 per cent, the fungus spores germinate and grow, although some species of fungi are able to do so at lower humidities. Clean, high-quality grain is less subject to attack by fungi than if broken or injured, for not only is the food material in the latter more readily available for fungi, but it absorbs moisture more readily and encourages the ravages of insects, some of which, in fact, cannot attack perfect grain.

CONTROL OF MOISTURE IN STORAGE

Prevention of high moisture content is the best means of protecting grain against fungus or insect damage, while the efficient ventilation of grain may also be possible if the air available is drier than the air in intimate contact with the grain. Bulk drying in a stream of untreated air ("Bin Ventilation"), or in a stream of dried air, is suggested by Oxley. The former appears to have limitations, and depends more on the "cooking effect" than the drying effects. For bulk drying in a stream of dried air, the temperature of the air should be raised by about 10° C. When this method is adopted, precautions must be taken to obviate an excessively long air path which would result in a bad moisture distribution in the bulk. The efficacy of the Edholm drier[188] depends on the fact that when grain is dried in a series of short periods with relatively long intervals of rest between, the amount of water removed in each drying period is greater than with continuous drying, because once the outer skin of the grain is dry, time is needed to enable moisture from the grain to diffuse to the skin. The Edholm drier therefore consists of a storage bin traversed at several levels by layers of air ducts. In each layer, air is blown into alternate ducts and sucked out by others. Dry grain is continually removed from the bottom of the bin and damp grain added at the top, the divisions being so arranged that the grain spends about three minutes between ducts in a stream of air and an hour resting between the layers.

STORAGE TEMPERATURE

Oxley[454] points out that most grain pest insects are of tropical and sub-tropical origin, their optimum temperatures lying between 28° and 35° C., and their maxima (above which they die or at least cannot reproduce) usually between 33° and 40° C. If possible, therefore, grain in store should be kept as far below the optima as possible, or alternatively, at temperatures above the maxima. The latter is considered impracticable, as it would lead to other troubles.

HERMETIC STORAGE

Perhaps the most interesting development in the technique of storage is provided by hermetic storage, by which grain is absolutely protected from any exchange of gases or liquids with the outside environment. It is claimed that such a store will protect grain from both insects and rodents. It has been found that when carbon dioxide reaches 18 or 19 per cent of the total volume, adult insects, their larvae, and even their eggs are killed. Carbon dioxide is emitted by the live grain in direct relation to the amount of moisture contained in the grain, and also by the respiration of insects in the grain.

A second point of importance in hermetically sealed storage is that the grain cannot become overheated. Vayssière[684] discusses the type of hermetic store which is most suitable. As regards the site the choice between under and above ground depends on convenience and economy which may vary with locality. Doyère favours the underground site, which he describes as a container made of thin sheet metal, shaped like a bottle, the imperviousness of which has been ascertained. Its opening is closed by a pressure lid. The sheet metal is preserved against oxidation either by zincing or application of a thick coating of tarry varnish. The container is placed in a pit under a concrete form and covered with masonry to support the lateral thrust and the top weight of the ground. The sheet metal only serves as a covering which, while thin, is nevertheless perfectly waterproof, holds up, cannot crack or disintegrate and can be fitted with one or more hermetic closing devices. Hall and Hyde,[242] in an excellent description of modern hermetic storage, assert that concrete pits with vapour-proofed walls will preserve grain, if moisture content is less than 13 per cent, in good condition for several years, while grain of a considerably higher moisture content than 13 per cent has been kept in good condition in welded metal silos. It is thought that, although underground concrete pits may successfully store grain with moisture content up to about 15 per cent, they might be unsuitable for wetter grain than this because they are not as airtight as welded metal silos.

Welded metal silos cost more than underground concrete pits but are more airtight. A less expensive design is the ctesiphon store, in which 2 or 3 inches of mortar are applied to hessian scrim supported on a framework of timber or tubular metal. The weight of the mortar causes the scrim to sag, so that a ribbed arch is formed, which is considerably stronger than a plain arch of similar thickness. Once the mortar has hardened the framework may be removed and used again. The construction is, however, liable to crack at the top of the ribs. Modification may overcome this difficulty.[40]

Vayssière sums up the advantages of hermetic storage as follows:

(1) Disinfects stored foodstuffs by destroying insects, irrespective of their stage of development, as well as other pests at the time of storage.

(2) Positively forestalls the admission of insects and other pests.

(3) Forestalls mould and overheating when the product contains a relatively high degree of moisture, without preventing the development of acidity caused by anaerobic fermentation when the humidity is excessive.

(4) All products that are dry at time of storage remain dry.

(5) Saves time and money by dispensing with handling and shifting.

The ideal method of storage is held to be drying, followed by hermetic storage. Widespread adoption of this storage method would undoubtedly result in a tremendous saving of rice and improved standard of quality, especially if such precautions against deterioration were made not only in mills and granaries but also—and this is most important—in ships that carry the grain. Hermetic storage is stated to be unsuitable for grain destined for seed purposes as it adversely affects germination. Iso, however, proved[293] that thoroughly air-dried seed stored in air-tight zinc bins of about five bushel capacity gave a rapid germination of 98 per cent after thirty-two months.

Airtight storage, states Oxley,[454] deserves thorough trial in hot countries provided that the grain can be harvested dry, or where drying facilities exist. He considers that the underground type of store found in the tropics is, in fact, almost airtight and the success of such stores may be a testimony to the efficacy of this system.

TRANSPORT

Internal transport—from field to buyers and from buyers to millers is usually by rather primitive means, though water-transport is usual in larger centres of production. From mills to export markets, rice is usually shipped in sacks. Recently, however, bulk shipment has been tried from California to Puerto Rico. If successful, this method may be extended to other destinations.[131]

INSECT PESTS OF STORED PADDY AND RICE

Many species of insect attack stored rice and paddy, only a few of which cause serious injury to the crop. Nevertheless, the damage occasioned by them may be very great, damage which is usually preventable or might be reduced by the observance of the simple rules for good storage.

By far the most destructive pest is the rice weevil, *Sitophilus oryzae* L., closely related to the granary weevil, *Sitophilus granarius* L. Other insect pests associated with stored paddy and rice include *Rhizopertha dominica* F., *Sitotroga cerealella* Oliv., *Oryzaephilus surinamensis* L., and *Cadra (Ephestia) kuehniella* Zell. Other insects of less importance may attack damaged grain, decaying grain, or may discolour the product, thus reducing its market value.

RICE WEEVILS

Both the rice weevil and the granary weevil are small, reddish-brown to dark brown in colour, about one-eighth inch long, with mouth parts prolonged into a snout. The rice weevil is marked on the back with four light-reddish or yellow spots and has functional wings, whereas the granary weevil is without the spots and is unable to fly. The snout is used to bore into the grain to reach the endosperm as well as to excavate a small cavity in the grain in which to place an egg, which is then sealed with a gelatinous cap to protect it from damage.

In a few days the egg hatches and a small, fleshy, white grub emerges which feeds on the endosperm of the grain until it is fully grown, when it emerges. By passing the development period within the grain the defenceless immature stages of the weevil are protected from predaceous enemies and sudden destructive changes in temperature. Under favourable conditions the period from egg to adult weevil is about four weeks.

The size of the weevil depends largely on the size of kernel of grain; a small grain will be almost completely devoured by one weevil, whereas a kernel of maize will provide food for several weevils, which ultimately will be larger than weevils bred in a grain such as rice.

The rice weevil is of greater importance than the granary weevil because it can fly to the fields and attack grain before it is harvested.[138]

In the colder countries of Europe the rice weevil usually dies. These two weevils multiply mostly in badly kept mills where grain residues are left in machinery, and in corners that have been inadequately cleaned.[384]

THE LESSER GRAIN BORER (*Rhizopertha dominica* F.)

Under favourable conditions this pest may cause great damage to grain. During the Second World War it was the principal insect pest in Australian bulk depots, while *Calandra oryzae* (small strain) was the most troublesome in bagged wheat.[192]

The habits of this borer are somewhat similar to those of the rice weevil, except that the grubs can feed outside the kernel as well as inside. The grubs and beetles may completely hollow out kernels so that only the bran coat is left.

Turning and cleaning infected grain is of no value in the control of the pest; in fact, it merely disperses the insects throughout the grain, so that higher dosages of fumigant are necessary to control the attack.

It breeds freely in warm climates, and will also breed and hibernate in mills in the temperate climates of Europe. Mayné states that it is prevalent in Belgian mills, and could easily become in a short time one of the greatest enemies of stored grain.[384]

THE SAWTOOTHED GRAIN BEETLE (*Oryzaephilus surinamensis* L.)

This is a slender brown beetle with six peculiar toothlike projections on each side of the thorax. It sometimes occurs in great numbers in bins of farm-stored grain, but does little real damage since it feeds chiefly on cracked and broken grain. It rarely flies, but walks rapidly. On account of its small size it is able to enter tightly packed food packages.

THE ANGOUMOIS GRAIN MOTH (*Sitotroga cerealella* Oliv.)

This moth is second in importance only to the rice and granary weevils as a pest of stored grain. The moth flies to the fields as the kernels are beginning to form and lays its eggs on the developing grain. The young caterpillars that hatch, burrow into the kernels and complete their development hidden from view. Before transforming to the pupal stage, the caterpillar makes an escape tunnel to the outside of the seed, leaving only a thin layer of seed coat intact for the moth to push through as it leaves the grain.

The insect is troublesome only when harvesting and binning grain is delayed. The soft-bodied moths are unable to force their way below the surface of binned grain, so that much of the damage can be prevented by early harvesting.[138]

MEDITERRANEAN FLOUR MOTH (*Cadra kuehniella* Zell.)

This is a pale-grey moth, the larva of which spins threads wherever it goes, thereby webbing the flour together. It is easily controlled by fumigation.

RUST-RED FLOUR BEETLE (*Tribolium castaneum* Hbst.)

The rust-red beetle lays eggs in flour and grain, the grubs subsequently feeding on the grain. It is frequently a serious pest of flour mills, but is usually easily controlled by maintaining clean conditions in the mill.

PEST CONTROL BY INSECTICIDES

Fumigants are used for rapid destruction of insect and other pests throughout a bulk of foodstuff. The aim is to obtain an even distribution of fumigant in the shortest possible time. The choice of fumigant and method of fumigation will depend on local circumstances. While the best treatment is in chambers especially designed for the purpose, fumigation may be effectively carried out in the warehouse, and for economy of fumigant by covering the sacks or bulk to be treated with a gas-proofed sheet of rubberized, plastic-coated material or polyethylene tarpaulin and introducing the fumigant below the covering.

The method of treating grain will depend on storage conditions. For large bulks, spraying the fumigant above the surface may be effective; for grain stored in silos, liquid or granular fumigants can be mixed continuously or intermittently with the grain stream as the bin is filled, or liquid fumigant can be sprinkled over the surface at intervals during the filling of the bin. A most effective method is to fit the bins with means for circulating the intergranular air so that the fumigant vaporized into the stream of air is rapidly distributed throughout the bin.

The effectiveness of a fumigant also depends on the extent to which it is absorbed by the grain; where absorption is high a larger proportion of fumigant will be rendered ineffective and the greater the attention that must be given to the eventual "airing" to rid grain of contamination by the fumigant which otherwise may cause a taint, or even render the grain poisonous.

There are many fumigants, varying considerably in their toxicity to insects. The choice may be largely decided by considerations of availability and cost.

Hydrogen cyanide, one of the first fumigants to be widely used to control pests in stored foodstuffs, is highly toxic to man and should therefore be handled only by trained operators. It is still commonly used, particularly in the treatment of empty warehouses, mills and the holds of ships.

Carbon disulphide is now little used because of the considerable explosive risk which attends its use. It is, however, still employed in some countries, particularly in the treatment of grain by hand sprinkling, or by spraying through pipes and nozzles.

Chloropicrin, less used than formerly, is used in the "spot" treatment of mill machinery and to control surface infestations in silo bins.

Ethylene oxide is a very effective fumigant, but can seriously affect seed germination. Owing to its inflammability in air, for use it is usual to mix it with carbon dioxide in the proportion by volume of one part of the fumigant to nine parts of carbon dioxide. Burns Brown[99] states:

In Great Britain since 1940 considerable use has been made of a method of fumigation in which crushed solid carbon dioxide is first distributed above the commodities to be treated and the usual ethylene oxide fumigant is applied after an interval of a half to one hour. The carbon dioxide is usually applied at a rate of 20 lb. per 1,000 cu. ft. of air space, the aim being the production of a concentration by volume of 10 per cent or more. At such concentrations of CO_2 the susceptibility of most insects to ethylene oxide is appreciably increased and the dose of this fumigant can be reduced to a point at which the maximum concentration reached throughout the space as a whole remains below inflammability limit. This procedure greatly reduces, even if it does not entirely eliminate, the explosion hazard. The risk is minimized when it is possible to stir the air in the fumigated space or when the solid carbon dioxide and liquid ethylene oxide are mixed and vaporized into the space using a simple form of heated vaporizer.

Methyl bromide is now one of the most widely used fumigants. Its toxicity to insects is high and its absorption low. Methyl bromide is, however, highly toxic to man and it should be handled with proper precautions. Chloropicrin is commonly added to the extent of about 2 per cent, as the lachrymatory property of this substance draws attention to leaks in fumigating apparatus or in the compartment being treated.

Methyl bromide is normally introduced from cylinders through a system of copper or plastic tubing with spray nozzles attached. Advantage can be taken of the high density of the vapour to aid downward penetration into loose bulks of material, and in Great Britain it has been employed for the treatment in barges of bulks of grain.[99]

Aliphatic chlorohydrocarbons are less toxic to insects than the above fumigants, but safer and therefore recommended to those who are not familiar with the application of fumigants. They are, therefore, suitable for fumigating small quantities, empty bags, and for treating grain in farm bins, being applied from a sprinkling can, or by means of a stirrup pump. The most popular fumigant of this class is a mixture of three parts by volume of ethylene dichloride (1,2-dichloroethane) and one part of carbon tetrachloride, used at the rate of 5 gallons per 1,000 bushels of grain. For a large silo it has been added with the grain at the rate of $2\frac{1}{2}$ gallons per 1,000 bushels. Carbon tetrachloride readily penetrates downward through bulks of grain. Frequently it has been used as a carrier for a more toxic compound, such as methyl bromide 10 per cent, ethylene dibromide 5 per cent, chloropicrin 15 per cent, 1,1-dichloro-1-nitroethane 15 per cent. These additions, however, make the fumigant more dangerous to use, consequently they should only be operated by specialists.[99]

Cotton and Gray[138] review grain preservation in some detail and give extensive references. They state: "Rough rice stored in concrete elevators may be fumigated successfully at the following dosages per 1,000 bushels: carbon tetrachloride with ethylene dichloride (1:3 mixture), 3 gallons. In wooden-crib bins the dosage should be doubled. For best results these fumigants should be applied in proportionate dosages to every 1,500 bushels as the bins are filled. Paddy may also be treated in concrete elevator bins with calcium cyanide at a dosage of 15 lb. per 1,000 bushels. Milled rice in bin storage can be treated with surface applications of the fumigants at dosages recommended for treating paddy in concrete elevators."

Where fumigation is impossible, contact insecticides are widely used. The most important are the naturally occurring pyrethrins (either as ground pyrethrum flowers or in the form of extracts), and the two synthetic products, DDT and gamma BHC (Lindane). Contact insecticides do not penetrate like fumigant gases, so for grain treatment admixture is necessary. This rules out DDT[268] as the dosage required is considerably greater than the permitted limit of 7 parts per million (Medical Research Council). Gamma BHC gives very good results at application rates as low as 1 p.p.m.[357] while the maximum residue acceptable to the Medical Research Council is 2·5 p.p.m. With pyrethrum flowers the application rate of ½ lb. per 200 lb. bag[75] is considerably more expensive.

In Asia, the rhyzomes of Sweet Flag (*Acorus calamus*) have for long been known as a drug, but it is only recently that its insecticidal properties have been appreciated. The rhyzomes contain 1·5 to 3·5 per cent aromatic oil from which has been isolated asaryl aldehyde and an amorphous bitter glucoside acorin. Experiments at the Central Rice Institute, Cuttack, show that the powder is better than the chemicals usually used for killing stored grain pests. It has been successfully used at the rate of 2 lb. of the dried ground rhyzome in 100 lb. paddy. It leaves no taint or odour, even after prolonged storage.

The chief uses of contact insecticides, however, lie in the treatment of godowns and stacks of bagged foodstuffs. For warehouse treatment residual spray deposits of DDT or gamma BHC are becoming increasingly popular because of their high persistence and the realization that infestation of cereals largely occurs during storage. Water dispersible powders are most commonly used for this purpose. The persistence of DDT deposits is greatest on non-absorbent surfaces, while gamma BHC has advantages on porous surfaces because its volatility enables it to come to the surface slowly over a long period.[239]

Short persistence militates against pyrethrin as a residual deposit, but in the form of mists for quick knockdown of flying insects it is outstanding. Pyrethrin dusts and sprays are also used on bagged foodstuffs because they are more quickly effective than DDT or gamma BHC, especially against moth larvae. In India, Malaya and Africa, 0·5 per cent gamma BHC dusts are widely used for the prolonged protection of bagged cereals, the application rate being up to 1 oz. per square yard of surface. Roberts,[566] however, points out that when rice is stored in contact with BHC germination is not affected but the seed accumulates gamma BHC. He found that after two months' storage, deformities appeared on germination and after nine months' storage these deformities reached a level of severity which was equivalent to growing undressed seed in solutions containing 29·1 to 291 p.p.m. gamma BHC.

For warehouse treatment, smoke generators are of particular value for, whereas there is no residual effect when gases are used for fumigation, the solid particles from smoke generators persist for a considerable time.[123]

Ghosh[209] stresses the value of gamma BHC used as a smoke in warehouses before introducing grain. He obtained 100 per cent elimination in six days, but found reinfestation a month later, the residual effect at this dosage being negligible. Smoke generators based on DDT or gamma BHC are attractive because of simplicity and cheapness, no applicator being required. The DDT smoke cloud contains the insecticide in fine droplets which crystallize after deposition, while the BHC smoke cloud is largely vapour from which the gamma BHC crystallizes directly. The convection currents set up by the combustion distribute the insecticide cloud throughout the store and deposits are obtained in stacks of grain which cannot be dusted or sprayed adequately. The persistence obtained is much less than when godown walls are sprayed with dispersible powders because the deposit is much lower; repeat treatments at monthly intervals are therefore generally advised. This insecticidal smoke treatment is especially useful in mills where aqueous sprays are not desirable and kerosene sprays may give rise to taint.

Rice is sometimes oiled to prevent deterioration and infestation during storage. Oiling is effected in the rice-milling process by adding a very small quantity of refined white mineral oil to the rice when it passes through a slowly rotating drum set at a slight angle to the horizontal, thus assuring even distribution over the surface of each grain. The oil is tasteless and cannot be detected when the rice is eaten. Normally, only highly milled qualities of rice are oiled. In Italy, nut oil, castor oil or vaseline is used, castor oil being the most usual. The rice is sometimes tinted red by the addition of an aniline dye to meet the demand in some Italian districts for a coloured rice.

Chapter XVII

MILLING AND MILLING PRODUCTS

PRIMITIVE MILLING METHODS

THE rice grain is enclosed in glumes which remain in close contact with the grain and from which it has to be separated; this process is known as hulling. A variety of native implements have been devised for the purpose of hulling, the most commonly seen throughout the East being the mortar and pestle, made of wood and worked by hand, foot or water power.

In the type worked by hand, the pestles are about six feet long and heavy. Usually two or three pestles are worked by a like number of people on paddy contained in one mortar. When worked by foot the pestle is on a fulcrum. The pestle is then about a foot in length and is fixed on the underside of a beam of wood. Rather more than halfway from the pestle, along the beam, is the fulcrum. A large stone may be tied on the beam above the pestle to give added weight to the pounding. The worker presses the beam down with the foot, thus raising the pestle; on releasing the foot the pestle falls on the paddy in the mortar. This operation is continued for some time, after which the paddy is winnowed. The portion remaining consists of rice and paddy. The operation of hulling is repeated several times until practically all the husk is removed and rice remains. Paddy that has escaped husking is removed by hand. Mortars are of various sizes, holding from 10 to 50 lb. paddy and about 50 lb. paddy can be hulled in a hour. Water power is sometimes harnessed to work a pestle, or more frequently, a battery of pestles.

Another type of huller consists of two portions of the trunk of a tree, superimposed vertically. The lower portion is solid, the top part being carved to the shape of an inverted cone. The upper contains a receptacle for paddy through the bottom of which is a hole leading to the juncture of the upper and lower portions. The underside of the top portion is smooth and conical, being made to fit into the serrated cone. The top portion also has affixed to it handles about a foot in length. Paddy is placed in the receptacle at the top. The worker stands facing the implement with a hand on each handle. The handles are then pushed and pulled alternately, causing paddy to run through the hole to be rubbed between the upper and lower portions on the serrated cone. The husk is thus separated from the grain; the husk and grain mixture is then hand-winnowed and again hulled, until freed from all husk.

There are several variations and improvements on this means of hulling. In one improved type the huller, described by Jack,[297] and worked on the same principle, the lower portion is composed of un-baked clay or "white ant earth" tightly bound by plaited bamboo or rotan. Under the lower grinding block dried coconut fibre is tightly packed into the basket-work which is firmly pegged to the ground in a wooden frame. The object of packing is to reduce the tendency for the clay to crack under the vibration of rotation. The basket-work of the upper mill block is continued upward to form a receptacle for paddy to be milled. Each mill block has a grinding surface of about twenty-two inches composed of chips of hard wood, "bakau" (*Rhizophora* spp.) from one and a half to three inches wide and one-eighth to one-quarter of an inch in thickness, sunk to a depth of four or five inches into the hardened clay. They are spaced about a quarter of an inch apart and arranged in rows running from the centre of the circumference of both grinding surfaces. The upper block is provided with a central aperture and is free to rotate on a pivot and can be adjusted to regulate the space separating it from the lower block. The pivot of the lower block is placed through the central portion of the upper block, thus keeping the upper portion in position. On the pivot rests a wooden beam embedded in the clay of the upper block and protruding through the basket-work about one foot on each side. A strong wooden rod about four feet long is provided with a strong iron peg fitting loosely into a socket in the protruding end of the beam. The other end of the rod is fastened rigidly to the centre of the wooden hand-grip which is suspended about six feet above the mill.

Paddy enters the mill through the central aperture in the upper grinding surface and through the same aperture the pivot of the lower grinding block projects. The operator holds the grip with both hands and pushes it forward, causing the upper block to rotate on the stationary lower block. The rice, together with some paddy and chaff after passing between the grinding surfaces, is retained in a trough formed round the mill by the continuation of the basket-work encircling the lower grinding surface. The mixture of paddy and rice is winnowed and remilled until the rice is freed from all paddy and chaff. (See Plate 57.)

The primitive methods described above are devised mainly to hull paddy, that is, to free it from the glumes. The more it is pounded in the mortar, or ground between surfaces, the more germ and epidermis of the grain is removed. This is a milling and polishing process which, with such primitive methods, is never completely effective, so that the rice still contains some of the outer coats of the grain and so, incidentally, most of the nutriment and flavour. But modern taste in rice, as in wheat, demands first and foremost appearance, so that flavour and health are sacrificed for the white appearance which can only be obtained by machines that remove these outer layers and the germ, and "polish" the rice.

SMALL-SCALE HULLERS AND POLISHERS

There are a number of hullers and polishers on the market suitable for small-scale production of rice. They are claimed to produce a clean marketable rice of fair quality and are suitable for smallholders, or groups of smallholders, who wish to husk and polish rice for home consumption and thus replace the ancient, slower and less effective methods of pounding paddy. Whereas, however, the older methods resulted in an imperfectly polished rice and much of the vitamins and other nutrients were therefore retained, the amount of polishing that can be effected in the modern small-scale mill is considerable, the finished product approximating to the rice of commerce. Medical authorities have therefore urged the discouragement of these machines because the highly-polished rice produced in these mills further increases the incidence of beri-beri and other deficiency diseases in areas and amongst a class of people at present relatively free from such ailments. The smallholder, however, will not remain content with antiquated and slow methods of milling. This fact must be recognized and other ways found to protect him against the ill-effects of modern milling. Desikachar *et al.*[171] comment that before the advent of mechanical mills, hand-pounding was the traditional method employed in India and is still used in the villages. This method is being replaced by mechanical mills. The mechanical mill has made inroads so fast that it has become necessary for the Government to encourage hand-pounding in view of the employment potentialities this offers to the rural population.

Machines are available for hulling paddy only, or for performing the two operations of hulling and milling with the aid of a small-powered engine. Hand-operated machines are also on the market for hulling paddy only. The operation of hulling and milling in these machines follows closely the principles of large-scale milling. Most manufacturers of rice-milling machinery produce mills for small-scale rice production. The following are examples of such machines, but it should be understood that the writer does not thereby deny the merits of other manufacturers' mills.

As an example of a machine designed only to hull paddy may be cited Grant's Special No. 4 rice huller, which is driven by a 4 h.p. engine and has an output of 80 to 100 lb. rice per hour. Somewhat similar hullers are manufactured by the same firm requiring 12 to 14 b.h.p. and having an hourly output of 300 to 650 lb. rice per hour. Combined rice hullers and polishers are made in many sizes by a number of manufacturers.

An example of a combined huller and polisher is the McKinnon No. 7 "Bon-Accord" rice huller and polisher with suction fan. It requires an engine of 9 to 12 b.h.p. to drive the belt which produces 750 to 900 revolutions per minute. It is claimed that this machine will give an output of 300 to 480 lb. cleaned rice per hour and to be suitable for milling either raw or parboiled paddy which is free from refuse. A similar machine with a higher output and requiring greater power-driving is also produced by the same maker. These and similar small-scale hullers and polishers are quite simple to operate and should be inexpensive to run. Spare parts are carried by makers.

Hand-operated machines for hulling paddy are suitable for use by smallholders and do not carry with them the objection of removing nutriments from the grain. Machines manufactured in the United Kingdom are usually based on the design originated by the Engelberg Huller Company of the U.S.A., as are many of the smaller engine-powered hullers and polishers. Under the name of the original designers they are well known in the East. The small hand-powered machine in the accompanying illustration is but one example; it is inexpensive and simple in construction. One man can work the machine which, it is claimed, will treat about 40 lb. of paddy per hour. Hand-hullers are, however, apt to be unpopular on account of their small capacity coupled with the price and the not inconsiderable effort required to work them.

MILLING QUALITY OF PADDY

The milling quality of paddy depends on the size and shape of grain, i.e. on the variety, conditions under which it was grown, the degree of ripeness and amount of exposure to the sun. Over-ripeness and excessive exposure results in the development of cracks in the grain, leading to excessive breakage in milling. Age of grain, moisture content and conditions under which it has been dried and stored also materially affect the milling quality (see page 353).

In the United States, for many years grades of paddy were determined by the Smith Shelling device which was officially recognized by the Department of Agriculture. This has now become obsolete and is replaced by four devices which determine the milling quality and are standard for official purposes. The Carter Dockage tester,[612] consisting of a series of screens and air blast, is used for separating weed seeds and other foreign material from grain. After paddy has passed through this machine it is subjected to the McGill Sheller,[613] a small machine which removes only the hulls, leaving the seed with its bran and germ intact. This device can also be used to examine seed rice and to ascertain the grade of brown rice that can be produced from a sample of paddy. For the third stage in determining the quality of paddy the McGill Miller[614] is employed. This device removes the bran and germ and breaks the weaker kernels in much the same way as in the huller of a commercial mill. The operating time is accurately controlled. The final step in the examination is determination of head rice and total yield of rice by means of the Sizing Device.[615] The sizing plates used in this device are constructed so that the indents into which the different sizes of brown kernels fall are of a size and shape which makes a sharp and uniform size separation. With this machine it is possible to determine the percentage of brewer's rice, screenings, second head and head rice in a sample.

A rice-sampling mill which accurately reproduces the conditions of a normal cone mill is designed to produce a sample of white rice from paddy in a few minutes. Such a machine is most useful in a rice mill to provide a quick check on the setting of cones and has also been found invaluable in paddy-breeding work. The Minghetti Rice Testing Mill, made in Italy, is an example of such a machine. Grant's Rice Sampling Cone (Plate 61) is a similar machine made in the United Kingdom. To prepare the sample, the paddy is fed into the hopper, the cone rotated for two to four minutes according to the degree of milling required, and the sample collected from the discharge spout free from husk and bran. The machine is small and compact and requires a $\frac{1}{2}$ b.h.p. producing a speed of 1,750 r.p.m.

To test the amount of breakage in milled rice from sheller, cone or polisher, a hand trieur may be used (Plate 62). The Grant Sampling Hand Trieur performs this operation in two to three minutes. A measured sample of milled rice is fed into the open end of the trieur on which a cylinder with suitable indentations has been previously fixed. The trieur is then revolved steadily by hand for a minute or two, when the brokens are discharged on a tray and the whole grains may be removed separately from the machine.

LARGE-SCALE MILLING

Rice mills are of various types and sizes; the larger mills may have a capacity of 200 to 500, or even 1,000 tons of paddy a day, while a small mill may be able to deal with 10 to 75 tons a day. The former are usually situated at or near ports or in the centre of large paddy-producing areas and are used for production of rice for the export trade; the latter are usually spread around producing areas and mill paddy for local consumption.

The process in both large and small mills is essentially the same, although rice production for the export trade necessarily calls for greater care in grading the paddy and in variations in milling—particularly the degree of milling and the proportion of broken grain in the finished rice—to conform with the requirements of importing countries—than does rice production for local consumption. Thus, low-grade rice is the product from the same milling process as for the higher grades, except that the degree of milling and polishing is limited in the former. For high-grade rice production the paddy passes through five processes in the mill, viz. cleaning, hulling (also known as shelling), pearling, polishing and grading.

CLEANING

Despite care in winnowing in the field or on the threshing floor, paddy as received at the mill is still in an unsuitable condition for milling, for it may contain 5 per cent or more of extraneous matter, such as small lumps of soil, stones, stalk, dust, twine and nails. It must therefore be put through a cleaning process. The machine that performs this operation may be a simple sieve riddle, a travelling flexible endless screen or a perforated cylinder with sections of differing perforations. Usually an aspirator is fitted to the cleaning machine which removes all dust before the grain falls on the sieve. In the OZm Paddy Intake Separator, for instance, all extraneous matter larger than the paddy grain, such as straw and string, is carried away by the screen and discharged at the tail of the machine. The sound paddy passes through the screen on to a screen which removes sand, dust and small impurities and then flows in a thin stream into an aspirating leg, where it is subjected to a current of air which carries away dead grain and any remaining dust or light impurities. Other makes of machine work on much the same principles, the basis of which is a preliminary aspiration followed by a flow over two or more screens of varying mesh, and then final aspiration.

The paddy may then be carried over a magnetic separator, which is attached to any chute or spout and is designed to remove metal impurities in the paddy, such as nails and wire, which would injure the sheller discs of the hulling machine.

By the use of meshes of different perforations in the cleaning

CC

machine, or by passing paddy from the cleaning machine to a grader, the paddy may be graded as a preliminary to hulling. In this operation, the cleaned paddy passes through a revolving meshed cylinder, the thinnest grains falling through the first mesh, larger grains through succeeding meshes, the perforations of which are progressively larger.

If the moisture content of paddy exceeds 15 per cent it is necessary to dry it before milling. Normally, paddy as received at the mill in the main centres of production in Asia is sufficiently dry, but in America the use of combine harvesters results in paddy with excessive moisture content which necessitates artificial drying before milling (see page 381).

(see page 381).

HULLING

There are four systems of milling paddy, viz. the Engelberg type cylinder, which consists of a fluted cylinder running in a horizontal casing; the disc sheller, a cone mill in which an emery-surfaced truncated cone revolves within a casing of steel wire mesh; the rubber band husker in which grain passes between an endless belt of rubber and an iron-grooved roll; and the rubber roller husker in which paddy passes between two horizontal rubber rollers, revolving in opposite directions and at different speeds.*

The essential principle of the Engelberg huller is that of a roller revolving inside a casing. Round the face of the roller are ribs, those at one end of the machine being spiral and those at the other end longitudinal. Paddy is fed into the end of the machine above the spiral ribs and as the cylinder revolves it acts as a screw, propelling the paddy along the cylinder between the straight ribs. An adjustable blade is held in position which prevents the rice swirling round with the cylinder. In consequence of this action, pressure is exerted, causing the grains to rub against each other. The paddy husk, being of an abrasive nature, causes the paddy to become shelled and ultimately whitened and is then discharged with the bran at the end of the machine. The function of the machine exerting slight pressure on the grain results in a less efficient shelling than is obtained with the cone rice mill. In spite of its higher breakage with most rices, this system is widely employed in most modern American factories for milling or whitening after shelling and separation, in preference to the cone-type whitener, although the shelling or hulling may be done with disc hullers as is more usual in Asia (Fig. 39). In addition to the high rate of broken rice, the Engelberg type husker suffers from the drawback that the power required is very high: a 4 h.p. motor gives an

* In 1957 FAO published in English, French and Spanish, a useful *Illustrated Glossary of Rice Processing Machines.*

output of about 80 lb. per hour, whereas the same power applied to a disc sheller would produce about 3,000 lb. per hour.

The disc huller or sheller consists of a rigid pan or saucer, an adjustable feed hopper, a stationary horizontal upper disc and a lower rotating disc or runner. The adjacent faces of both discs are covered with an artificial stone dressing and special emery composition, which must be kept flat and rough. The composition is made up of emery or carborundum, a special cement and a solution of special salts. The emery to be used depends on the particular grain, and experience of the grain to be milled is the only sure guide as to which grade of emery should be used. Paddy is fed into the hopper at the centre of the stationary disc and is carried outwards by centrifugal force. The space between the discs is adjusted to allow the paddy to pass and in so doing the husk is removed with the minimum of damage to the rice (Fig. 39).

The product from the huller consists of hulled grains, small paddy which has escaped hulling, husk and broken rice. To separate these various portions the product is subjected to winnowing fans which draw off the husk and passed over shifts which remove the broken rice, known as points, and separate the bran, points and bran being discharged separately at bagging points.

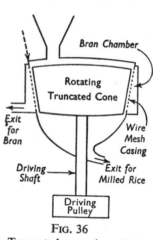

FIG. 36
Truncated-cone rice mill

The next process is to separate the paddy which has escaped the hulling process from the rice. This is done by passing the product through a special sieve and/or through a compartment separator. The principle upon which this machine works is by throwing the grains so that they impinge against a series of sharp corners, whereby grains of greater specific gravity are impelled in one direction, while lighter grains are driven apart in the opposite direction, the body of the machine, sliding on rockers, being driven to and fro by means of an eccentric.

The mixture of grain to be separated is fed at the top of the machine; thence it passes through numerous zigzag compartments, built at right angles to the direction in which the machine is reciprocating and sloping downwards. The paddy gradually moves up the machine to the top of the compartment and is returned to the hullers, while the rice drops to the bottom of the compartment ready for pearling. Each feed aperture can be regulated independently and separation can be adjusted during operation by a hand-wheel which causes the body of the machine to tilt its underframe. The shelled rice from the huller, termed *Loonzain* in Burma, is a rough rice from which the germ and most of the pericarp have not been removed. It is also known as Cargo rice.

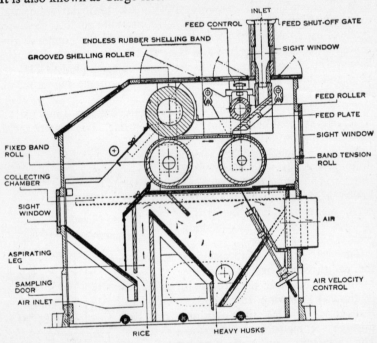

FIG. 37

Sectional drawing showing construction of the "Wemanco" rice huller
(Thomas Robinson & Son, Ltd.)

An example of the rubber band husker is the "Wemanco" Ideal Huller. In this machine the shelling surfaces consist of a wide endless belt of special motor-tyre-quality rubber, precision ground to uniform thickness throughout its length and width, and a diamond-hard chilled iron-grooved roll. The rubber belt or band runs over two parallel cylindrical rolls, one of which is fitted with special tensioned gear having an automatic compensating gear to prevent side wander, while the front or "cushion" roll over which the grain is shelled rotates in a fixed position. The fast grooved roll is mounted adjustably above the cushioned roll, with its vertical centre line slightly in advance of the latter, so that when grain passes through the nip between the two surfaces, the band is free to deflect until it reaches solid support from the roll. Both the horizontal offset and vertical clearance between shelling and cushioning rolls are independently adjustable by handwheels giving control of the pressure to which the grains are subjected so that no grain need be broken if correctly adjusted.

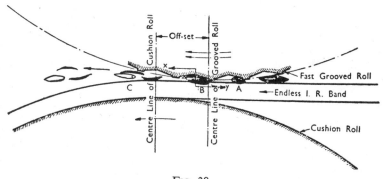

FIG. 38

Section at shelling point of the "Wemanco" rice huller
(Thomas Robinson & Son, Ltd.)

The grains travel into the shelling point on the surface of the rubber band in a continuous single-layer stream across its full length. Each grain, as it reaches the position A (Fig. 38) is entrained in a groove of the fast roll and firmly gripped by the tooth behind, against the leading edge of which it gets firmly wedged and begins to travel at grooved-roll speed, while the lower hull surface is gently pressed into partial embedment in the resilient rubber. The band deflects easily under the grain during its travel through the ingoing side of the nip so that the pressure is light and grain slips easily over the rubber. As the grain approaches position B, the band resistance to deflection increases very rapidly and the grain becomes deeply embedded until the lower hull is momentarily held from slipping and the leading edge of the hard grain of rice is forced through the brittle hull by the force couple x-y acting in opposite directions on either side. On reaching position C the shelled grain and hulls are then thrown off the band into the hopper. The makers claim that every mature grain is shelled whatever its size or shape and that the ends do not get chipped, no endosperm is lost and even the germ is preserved intact. Somewhat similar claims are, however, made for the disc sheller, but it is believed that the "Wemanco" has an advantage over the disc sheller in retaining a greater percentage of the endosperm and germ.

The mixed shelled rice and husk pass into the lower end of the vertical rising leg of the internal aspirator, up which is drawn a powerful current of air. This carries off the husk particles and the rice falls out of the lower leg. Husk carried off in the airstream passes out of the top of the leg into a settling chamber. The output of this machine is about 2,200 lb. per hour using 5 h.p. In the United States these rubber band huskers are used for husking the unhusked rejects from the primary processing.

The rubber roller husker is composed of two horizontal tangential rubber rollers, revolving in opposite directions and at different speeds. Paddy runs between the rollers in a thin even sheet. The difference in speeds causes the husks to be crushed and removed from the kernels. A regulating wheel makes it possible to control the pressure on the paddy between the rolls. Paddy feed is regulated by an admission shutter concealing a small distributor cylinder. This type of machine, which appears to have originated in Japan, is becoming increasingly popular. Its advantages are that husking is very gentle, the yield of husked rice is high, breakage rate is low and practically no meal or bran is obtained. On the other hand, rolls wear unevenly and should therefore be inverted after about 400 tons and changed after 800 tons. Changing rolls is simple and they can be retreaded.[20]

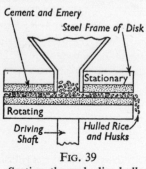

Fig. 39
Section through disc huller

Mortar mills were used in Italy originally, but were replaced in 1880 by a purely Italian development, the *Elichi* or *Helice*, a screw mortar, developed from the ancient mortar and pestle. In place of the mortar action, a worm or Archimedian screw is substituted. The shelled rice is thus agitated and by the grains rubbing together, against the screws and the walls of the bowl, the grains are polished.[648]

MILLING, PEARLING OR WHITENING

Rice grain has a series of thin coats which are removed, or partly removed, as bran in the process of pearling. The rice grain has, in fact, five very thin layers which together constitute the coat or cuticle, viz. the epicarp, the mesocarp, cross-layer, testa and aleurone layer.

The removal of most of these layers is effected in the process of pearling or whitening.

The Rice Pearling Cone (Fig. 36) is the standard machine for milling rice. In this machine the cuticle of the rice is removed by means of cones, usually made of cast iron and mounted on a vertical spindle taking the form of an inverted cone with the outer surface covered with an artificial dressing of emery. This cone revolves inside a casing lined with special steel wirecloth, leaving a narrow annular space surrounding the cone. The cone rotates at a high speed and rice is fed in at the top, passing down the annular space between the abrasive face and the casing. In this way the rice is "milled," that is, the waxy cuticle is scoured off. The resultant meal or bran is propelled through the meshes of wirecloth and is automatically collected and delivered in bags. For milling white rice, the casing is fitted with a number of adjustable rubber brakes which have the effect of increasing the milling action. For white rice, the cones are worked two or three in series, or in some cases even more, according to the standard of milling required. The milling space between cone and casing is adjustable, so that the standard of performance can be varied by raising or lowering the cone. The closer the space between cone and casing the higher the degree of milling and the greater the quantity of broken rice and bran produced in relation to white rice.

Bran discharged through the wirecloth is mixed with a small quantity of broken rice, known as "brokens". These are separated in bran or meal machines. The bulk of the broken rice, however, is discharged with the rice and conveyed to the polisher. At some mills in Burma, broken rice is separated from whole rice before being passed to the polisher and a proportion of the broken rice is afterwards fed back to the rice according to the percentage of brokens allowed in the particular grade.

A photometer has been devised[633] and tested which measures the difference in optical density of rice. The reading is directly proportional to the percentage of surface lipids. The photometer, therefore, offers an excellent means of quickly checking the rice so that the degree of milling can be controlled during the milling operation.

POLISHING

If a very fine appearance is desired, rice from the pearlers is passed through one, two or more polishers. A polisher is similar to a pearling cone except that instead of a stone- or emery-dressed cone it contains a drum covered with strips of sheep skin or buffalo hide. The rice is brushed between the skin and casing and thus polished. The spindles can be adjusted vertically, as with the pearling cones, thus varying the space between drum and casing. A small quantity of broken rice is produced in the process which is later separated. Where a very fine appearance is aimed at, two or more polishers are used and a small quantity of dry colouring matter to impart an appearance of increased whiteness may be fed with the rice in the last machine of the series.

For certain markets, notably European and American, a rice with a fine glossy and transparent appearance is desired. This is obtained by passing the rice through glazing drums, the glazing materials—usually talc with a small quantity of very dilute glucose solution—being added with the rice to the first drum of the series of polishers.

GRADING

Rice from the polishers consists of rice and broken rice, which has now to be separated, retaining, however, a proportion of broken rice in the finished product which may vary according to the standard on which it will be sold. This separation and grading may be carried out in a series of sieves or perforated cylinders equipped with different sizes of perforations which, stage by stage, permit the smaller sizes and grades of broken rice to pass, until finally rice containing the correct percentage of broken grain is discharged. A Carter Disc separator may be used for the purpose.

Another method of removing and grading broken grain is by passing the product through a series of cellular cylinders or Trieurs. The internal surface of each cylinder revolves slowly, the broken or smaller grains are caught and lifted up in these pockets and delivered by the internal mechanism to the end of the cylinder.

The "Kapak" separator is not universally used in rice mills but is sometimes employed for special grading. It is designed to perform the same operation as the above described separators, but it does it more rapidly. It classifies grain according to length and can thus be used to separate broken from whole grain and to grade short paddy from long. On account of the internal arrangement of the machine, all the grains are kept in close contact with the cylinder and thus the smaller grains are able to enter the cells more freely than in the Trieur.

ELECTRIC SORTING

Sorting machines are now on the market which make use of the photo-electric cell to remove all grain that is not white. Adjustment is possible to vary the degree of selection by colour. The capacity of such machines is at present small. They work well with "round" seed such as peas, but not with long seed as with paddy. They may be used for cleaning rice and there are a number in use for this purpose in America. A single machine has an output of almost 60 lb. per hour.[30] A photo-electric apparatus has, it is stated,[543] been devised for expressing in micro-ampères and lux-values the values of whiteness and transparency and therefore the degree of milling in processed rice in comparison with a fixed standard of whiteness to transparency.

SUMMARY OF MILLING OPERATIONS

Paddy is poured into a hopper at the receiving end of the mill. From there it passes either direct or by means of an elevator, according to the type of mill, to the paddy-cleaning riddle. The cleaned paddy passes in front of the magnet to extract any metal and is then lifted by an elevator and delivered to the sheller. The product from the sheller, consisting of shelled rice, husk, a little paddy and some rough bran and small points, passes up an elevator to a sieve over the husk-winnowing aspirator. This sieve recovers the bran and points and discharges them to a bagging point.

Shelled rice passes up an elevator and is delivered to the pearling cone or cones. The resultant bran is automatically collected and delivered to bags and the milled rice elevated to the polisher or polishers. Finally, the rice is elevated to the classifier. The whole rice and brokens then pass through the finishing aspirator and thence to bagging points.

It will be realized that a large mill may regroup machines to allow for full working of all machines with the greatest possible continuity, minimizing handling and movement of grain from one point of the process to another. For instance, paddy graders are of various capacities up to over sixty tons per hour, the Wemanco rice huller will deal with about one ton of paddy per hour, a large pearling machine may be expected to treat about three tons of paddy an hour and a polisher about four tons in the same period. It follows, therefore, that in a large mill there will be batteries of each machine, the number of units in each battery depending on the desired maximum output of the mill.

PARBOILING

There is a considerable demand in the East, the West Indies and parts of South America for parboiled rice. Nearly 57 per cent of the rice produced in India is parboiled. In that country,[171] increased production of high-yielding soft varieties of paddy has stimulated the parboiling industry, because soft varieties have to be hardened by parboiling before they can be milled. In Burma, parboiled rice accounts for 22 per cent of the total rice produced and 12 to 15 per cent of rice exports are parboiled.

Parboiling is a process of steeping paddy in heated water and afterwards subjecting it to steam at low pressure before drying and milling it in the ordinary way. The result of parboiling is to make it easier to remove the husk and for this reason less broken rice is obtained and the amount of milling necessary is less than for the preparation of white rice. The process as usually carried out in Asia gives the grain a yellowish colour and a distinctive flavour which render it unacceptable in many markets both in Asia and the Western Hemisphere.

The off-flavours of parboiled rice are caused by the multiplication of yeasts and bacteria on the grain during the soaking stage. Desikachar et al. found[170] that increasing the temperature of the soaking water to 65–70° C. prevents development of off-flavour and reduces the time required for soaking from two or three days to three or four hours. Development of micro-organisms may also be prevented by adding 0·0024 per cent sodium hypochlorate to the soaking water.

The advantages of parboiling have been summarized as follows: "Parboiling makes it possible to produce from a given amount of paddy more rice with less breakage in milling; to use a lower grade of paddy; to obtain a rice with superior keeping qualities; and to retain more of the nutrients of the grain during milling, washing, and cooking. As a consequence, the adoption of parboiling would result in a large saving of rice and, even more important, of valuable vitamins and minerals."[537] The additional recovery of rice is considerable; from normal-grade paddy 70 per cent as against 66 per cent by milling white rice; from low-grade paddy 70 per cent as against 50 per cent by ordinary milling. In addition, parboiled rice has better keeping qualities than white rice and greater resistance to insect and fungus infestation.

In the traditional method of parboiling, paddy is steeped in large brick tanks for a period of one to three days, the longer period being necessary for the bolder types of paddy, which are also subjected to higher initial temperature of water. The initial temperature of water may therefore vary from 140° to 180° F. The period of steeping also varies with the season. Instead of steeping for one to three days, paddy may be boiled for twenty minutes. It is then transferred to steel containers where it is subjected to low-pressure steam (15 lb.) for ten to twenty minutes, the bolder types of grain demanding the longer period. By this time the grain will have become completely gelatinized. In the more modern plants paddy is steeped and boiled in the same steel or concrete container and by using higher average steeping-water temperatures, the whole process is reduced to a period varying from eight to sixteen hours.

The paddy is then removed to drying floors, being either sun-dried or placed on steam-heated floors. Sun-dried grain is considered in Asia to be superior; artificial drying, it is claimed, tends to give the grain a sour smell which, however, disappears when the rice is cooked for eating. It is said also to give the grain a yellow colour. More modern plants dry the grain in special drying towers, employing hot air for the purpose, and in this way eliminate the excessive labour force required by other methods. The paddy is then milled.

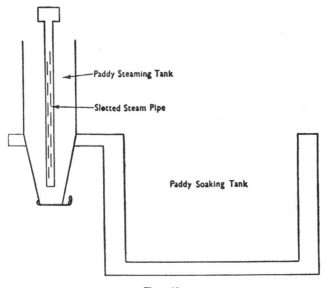

FIG. 40

Diagram of layout for parboiling paddy

In India,[616] home-made parboiled rice is prepared as follows. Paddy is placed in a brass vessel, earthernware pot or tin canister and covered with water. The container is heated to boiling point until the grains are slightly swollen and soft and some of them burst. The water is then drained off and the paddy spread to dry on the floor under shade. This reduces the incidence of sun check and consequent breakage in husking. Grains thus parboiled are not completely gelatinized for they have an opaque core of raw rice and they are not as hard as fully parboiled rice. Parboiled by this method, the paddy is intended for hand-husking and not machine-milling. It is stated that home-made parboiled rice is less smelly and coloured and is more attractive than that produced commercially.

The method of parboiling known as *sela* is commonly employed in Uttar Pradesh, India. In this method, paddy is steeped in fresh water and heated for a period of 24 to 48 hours over a smouldering fire. It is then removed from the fire, mixed with sand and roasted for about five minutes over a hot fire, the mixture being continuously stirred. It is then sun-dried for two days. The *sela* method is reported to impart a pleasing fragrance to rice which is not obtained in other methods of parboiling, and breakage of grain in hulling is reported to be less.[616]

The desirability of replacing white by parboiled rice to effect a saving in supplies and to retain a greater proportion of the vitamins and other nutrients, has led to research into modifications in the technique of parboiling to overcome consumers' objections to parboiled rice. The following technique has been suggested[537] to achieve this object: cleaning paddy by blowing and washing, soaking at 25° to 30° C. for one day, changing the water several times during soaking; steaming in autoclave at 120° C. for fifteen minutes and drying by a counter-current of air. The same authority claims that improvement in the parboiling technique is both desirable and possible by simple modifications of the present methods and suggests: in cleaning, the water must be changed several times; the temperature should be sufficiently high to shorten the soaking time to about twelve hours, parboiling by live steam for thirty minutes. Drying at too high a temperature should be avoided to prevent the grain becoming discoloured.

Improvements were made in the method of parboiling in British Guiana[539] by speeding up the operation as a result of steeping the paddy in water kept in constant circulation at a temperature of about 160° F., thereby reducing soaking by about four hours. Thereafter, the paddy is steamed for about ten minutes only. By this method it is claimed that there is no fermentation with resultant odour and a greatly improved product is obtained. The Crystal Rice Plant, manufactured by Gariboldi in Italy, embodies modern principles for production of a high-quality parboiled rice.

According to Subrahmanyan and his co-workers,[636] parboiled rice can be almost as white and palatable as polished rice—colour and flavour depending largely on the technique of parboiling. They state that colour depends to some extent on the colour of the husk and also on the methods used in parboiling. Charlton[122] also showed that much of the objectionable flavour and odour is caused by incorrect methods of preliminary soaking which encourage development of fermentation due to anaerobic bacteria.

Parboiled rice when cooked for eating has better keeping qualities than ordinary white rice and does not so readily turn sour. Simpson assumes[604] that the keeping qualities of parboiled rice are considerably superior to those of undermilled rice, even if they are not so good as polished rice, because the process of parboiling removes the greater part of the oil in the grain. Furthermore, the steaming process, he states, is likely to sterilize the grain and thus destroy enzymes and moulds which might subsequently damage the grain. He adds that "provided the final drying of the grain is sufficient, there appears to be no reason why parboiled rice should not be capable of storage for considerable periods without undue deterioration."

DRYING PADDY AND RICE

To obtain the best milling results the moisture content of paddy should not exceed 14 per cent. Little difficulty is usually experienced by millers in the East to ensure that paddy is sufficiently dry. The grain is usually spread on a concrete floor in the open, where a few hours' exposure to the sun is sufficient to ensure dryness. Rice after parboiling is usually dried in the same way, although artificial drying is now largely replacing sun-drying of parboiled rice. Some millers in Brazil stack paddy and leave it unturned to produce stack-burn and consequent discoloration. The milled product is a yellow rice for which there is a ready sale in some areas.[190]

The paddy drier is a tower

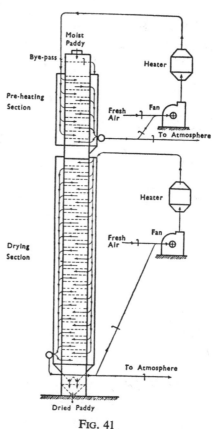

Fig. 41

Diagrammatic arrangement of paddy drier
(Thomas Robinson & Son, Ltd.)

provided with a series of louvres. The top portion pre-heats the paddy before subjecting it to the drying medium. Air is drawn in by a fan and heated before being introduced to the tower. The air temperature and therefore the temperature to which the paddy is heated, is controlled thermostatically.

Damp paddy is fed by means of a hopper at the top of the drier, from whence it flows by gravity over the louvres to the exit at the bottom of the tower. The passage of paddy down the tower is automatically regulated to the amount of feed.

Parboiled paddy leaves the boiling pans at a high temperature so that no pre-heating before drying is necessary. The preheater section of the column is therefore dispensed with and the whole column employed for drying, for which one heater and one fan are sufficient to supply the hot air. Steam is the usual medium for the hot air, air being drawn in by a fan and heated by radiator-type heaters. Paddy husk is usually employed as fuel for the furnace. In British Guiana it was found[539] essential before drying that paddy should be thoroughly cleaned to enable the grain to travel smoothly through the drier and it was necessary to remove shelled grain, otherwise, after parboiling, such grain became shapeless and sticky and gummed up the elevators, conveyors and driers. To effect this cleaning, a Scalperator, a Monitor and a Carter Disc Separator were installed ahead of the soaking tanks. Furthermore, it was found necessary to dry parboiled paddy to at least 13 per cent moisture, otherwise the paddy gummed up the hullers and the brush. Drying problems were eventually solved by drying to 18 per cent moisture content in a Robinson drier and then passing the paddy on to a Hess drier for extraction of the remaining moisture. Sluyters found[608] that at low moisture content the percentage of broken grains, expressed as a percentage of the out-turn, rose rapidly within three hours after drying. A rest period of at least three hours was found necessary for reliable milling tests. The lowest percentage of brokens occurred at 16 to 17 per cent moisture content.

MILLING PRODUCTS

The weight of husk is about 21 per cent of the weight of the paddy. In addition, there may be about 5 per cent of dirt, dead grain and other extraneous matter in paddy, so that the miller may expect to obtain about 74 per cent of the paddy in rice and its by-products. In milling and polishing rice, the following percentage products are therefore obtained: whole rice, 50 points and broken rice 17; bran 10, meal 3, husk 20. These figures will vary according to the variety of paddy, its age and moisture content and on the degree of milling and polishing.

In many countries of production, steps have been taken by governments to control the milling rate in order to increase rice supplies. Many of the existing mills in Asia are, however, said to be either worn out or outmoded and are therefore incapable of being adjusted for undermilling to any appreciable extent. These, however, were problems of the immediate post-war years. With a return to more normal conditions, mills are turning out the class of rice demanded by the consumer. On an average, the rates of conversion of paddy to rice approximate 70 per cent in Asia and 65 per cent in non-Asian countries.

TABLE 21

MILLING YIELD FROM PADDY

	Average U.S.A.†	Southern Brazil†			Burma* Parboiled
		Variety Japanese	Variety Blue Rose	Variety Agulha long-grain	
Head rice ..	57·0	52·0	46·0	38	71·61
First heads ..	3·5	10·0	16·0	10	0·5
Second heads ..	6·0	4·0	4·0	10	
Brewers' rice ..	2·0	3·0	2·0	2	
Total ..	68·5	69·0	68·0	60	72·11
Rice polish ..	2·0	8·0			
Rice bran ..	8·5				2·45
Hulls	20·0	23·0			25·44
Waste (trash, etc.)	1·0				

* Source: State Agricultural Marketing Board, Rangoon.
† J. N. Efferson.[190]

Burma has for long been the most important exporter of rice. In that country there are over 600 mills, most of which are small, for the few large mills in Lower Burma take most of the crop. Consequent on its world trade, very numerous grades of milled rice are exported to satisfy the particular requirements of each market. These grades depend on several factors, in particular, the variety of type or paddy from which it is milled, the degree of milling and percentage of broken grain. Similarly, but to a less degree, grades are recognized for rice obtained from other centres of production.

BROKEN GRAIN

The amount of broken grain resulting from milling rice depends mainly on the variety of paddy, its condition—especially its handling after harvest—and the amount of milling to which it is subjected.

Several grades of broken rice are recognized in the trade, grade depending largely on the grades of milled rice from which it was obtained. In Italy,[648] brokens are made into rice flour, sometimes mixed with wheat flour to make "bread of real luxury with a most agreeable taste."

RICE MEAL AND RICE BRAN

Two kinds of bran are obtained from the milling process. Cow-bran is produced in hulling paddy. It is a coarse meal of low food value. The bran or meal produced in the pearling process comprises the pericarp, the aleurone layer, the embryo and some of the endosperm, and contains most of the vitamins and proteins of the grain. It has, therefore, a high food value and commands a ready market—mostly as a stock food. Burma recognizes two main grades, No. 1 Bran or White Meal, produced from white rice milling and No. 2 Brown Bran, produced from milling parboiled rice.

The composition of rice bran varies widely according to the quality of paddy and method of milling. Analyses of Italian meals gave the following figures:[661]

Albumenoids	..	11·25 to 13·37 per cent
Fats ..	..	10·63 to 14·8 ,, ,,
Carbohydrates	..	39·82 to 43·01 ,, ,,

The digestibility was over 75 per cent and the meal is considered in Italy a perfect and agreeable food for the milch cattle. Fine white polishings have been used in bread-making in the proportion of one-third polishings to two-thirds wheat flour, resulting in a bread with an excellent flavour.

EXTRACTION OF OIL AND WAX FROM RICE BRAN

Rice bran contains a percentage of lipids which are about 14 to 17 per cent oil,[375] of which 3 to 9 per cent is wax. On the bran basis this is equivalent to 0·4 to 1·5 per cent crude wax. The yield of available lipids and the oil-wax relationship, however, depend on the solvent temperature conditions, source and history of the bran and on other factors.[520] Bran also contains about 12 per cent protein, 45 to 50 per cent soluble carbohydrates and 5 to 8 per cent fibre.

Mechanical and solvent methods of oil extraction from rice bran have been practised for many years, especially in Japan and Italy, but the greenish oil usually obtained contained a great deal of free fatty acids which rendered much of it unsuitable for edible purposes.

THE FILTRATION-EXTRACTION PROCESS

The rice-bran oil Group of the United States Department of Agriculture Southern and Western Regional Research Laboratories, New Orleans, and the Rice Growers' Association of California have pioneered adoption of the filtration-extraction method, originally developed for cottonseed,[241] to extract oil from rice bran.[222] The former body commenced the study of oil extraction from bran in 1947, while the Rice Growers' Association operated a plant at an even earlier date. The success of these ventures has encouraged commercial production of bran oil at other centres. A plant with a capacity of about 5,000 tons of oil a year is in full production in Texas and a factory in Chile is processing about 5,000 tons of bran annually. The Indian Council of Scientific and Industrial Research, in conjunction with the Indian Ministry of Commerce and Industry, is developing bran-oil production in India,[465] and there are said to be several extraction plants working in Japan and one in Formosa.

Oil-extraction installations for processing 80, 160 and 240 tons of cottonseed daily are suitable for processing 60, 115 and 170 tons of rice bran, respectively. Some preparation equipment used for cottonseed processing, such as 5-high rolls, is unnecessary for rice-bran filtration-extraction.

Filtration-extraction,[206] a continuous process for direct solvent-extraction of oil-bearing materials, derives its name from the fact that it is designed around the unit operation of filtration and has as its major equipment unit a continuous horizontal rotary vacuum filter. It differs from conventional solvent-extraction systems in that the prepared oil-bearing material is contacted with solvent in a mixing vessel for a sufficient time to dissolve the oil, after which a standard rotary horizontal vacuum filter is employed to separate the concentrated miscella from the residual meal. The Southern Regional Research Laboratories have devised a method for evaluating the processing characteristics of oil seeds for filtration-extraction, using simple laboratory apparatus and a few pounds of the oil-bearing material.[223] Investment costs, operating expenses and profitability of filtration-extraction mills, and costs for converting hydraulic and screw pressing to filtration-extraction are presented by Discossas *et al.*[163] They show that investment costs for filtration-extraction mills are less than those for comparable mills of direct- and process-solvent types.

RANCIDITY OF BRAN

Rice bran rapidly becomes rancid, due mainly to the activity of a lipolytic enzyme in the bran.[313] Measures taken to stabilize bran

DD

against enzymatic activity, which increases the free fatty acid content of the oil, have not been entirely successful. Bran from "converted" and parboiled rice is relatively stable, but even with this type of material, the free fatty acid content of the extracted oil is frequently 2 to 3 per cent. Bran from milling white rice yields oil of higher free fatty acid content unless extraction follows immediately after milling. If the crop becomes wet during or after harvest, acidity of the oil increases rapidly to figures between 30 and 40 per cent. Increase of free fatty acids can be stopped if the bran is put through a heating and drying process at 200° F. for one hour and the moisture reduced to about 3 per cent. Bran thus treated may be stored for about 25 days. Burns and Cassidy suggest[100] treatment of the material with live steam at 210° F. followed by further heating externally at 212° F. for 4 to 5 minutes. The most satisfactory method of checking acidity is immediate extraction of the oil. With this object in view, one factory has organized a truck system to transport bran rapidly from mill to the extraction plant.

PROBLEM OF "FINES"

At the Regional Research Laboratories, rice bran was subjected to a cooking process to eliminate "fines" and thus render the bran more suitable for treatment, the material being heated to a temperature of about 210° F., water or live steam added to bring the moisture content to approximately 19 per cent, after which the bran was dried to about 9·5 per cent. This cooked bran was solvent-extracted with commercial hexane in a counter-column and the oil and meal products recovered by conventional methods.[223] In the California mill,[396] a "batch" technique was adopted instead of a continuous solvent-extraction because it eliminated the problem of "fines" and therefore obviated the need for specialized preparation equipment; it was also found to be more flexible with regard to tonnage processed, while the simplicity of equipment enabled the plant to be operated by less skilled personnel.

Morris *et al.* state[419] that the tendency of "fines" to become suspended in the miscella is dependent on the moisture content of the bran; fewer fines passing into the miscella when bran of 15 to 16 per cent moisture is extracted with hexane, while moisture up to 16 per cent has no adverse effect on yield of oil recovered from solvent-extraction.

CHOICE OF SOLVENT

An objection to the use of hexane as a solvent is its inflammability; for this reason a number of substitute solvents have been suggested. Haynes *et al.*[241] state that attempts by small operators to use trichloroethylene resulted in production of rice bran that was toxic to live-stock. The Indian Council of Scientific and Industrial Research claim to have developed an alternative process using alcohol as the solvent.[465] It is most desirable that a non-inflammable and non-toxic solvent be found for this purpose.

EXTRACTION OPERATION

Mickus describes[396] the operation of the batch-type solvent extraction which the Rice Growers' Association have perfected. Commercial hexane percolates through the bran in the extractor. The resultant miscella flows to a collection header and thence to a settling chamber consisting of a tank within a tank. The miscella enters the top of the inner tank, passes out at the bottom and moves up between the inner and outer tank walls to flow to storage tanks. Fine bran particles are deposited on the extractor screen and in miscella storage vessels and are returned to extractors for recovery.

The miscella is passed to a preheater and then flows to an evaporator where it is heated to 180° F. which vaporizes about 90 per cent of the solvent. The remaining hexane and moisture are removed in the reboiler with the additional aid of steam injected into the oil stream. The oil is then cooled in storage tanks and passed through a filter press, which removes gums, waxes, phosphatides and residual bran particles.

The extracted bran passes to steam-jacketed driers where it is heated to 70° F. to vaporize the solvent. The vapours are drawn to a scrubber, where fine particles entrapped in the stream are removed by direct water spray to prevent fouling of condenser tubes, and then drawn to the condenser and thence to decanters where hexane-water separation is effected.[396]

QUALITY OF BRAN OIL

Refined rice-bran oil is a clear, light-coloured, odourless oil of low free fatty acids, which is exceptionally stable after hydrogenation. It is acknowledged to be a superior cooking oil and has also been used as a carrier for insecticides and for other industrial purposes. Possibly its greatest value will be as an anti-corrosion and rust-resistant oil. It is also anticipated that the oil will find several applications in the cosmetics and pharmaceutical industries.[207]

VALUE OF EXTRACTED BRAN

Removal of oil from rice bran raises the nutritive value of the residual bran by increasing proportionately the content of protein and carbohydrates. For this reason, and because of its better keeping qualities, extracted bran usually commands a higher price than untreated bran. Mickus describes[396] extracted bran as free-flowing, very light in colour and weight, difficult to handle with conventional equipment and inclined to dust, which increases losses in handling. Addition of about 3 per cent feed-grade molasses reduces these disadvantages. Equipment is being installed at one factory to convert the extracted bran into pellets which can be crumbled to whatever degree of fineness is required in making mixed feed formulations.

RICE BRAN WAX

The Rice Growers' Association of California are not, at present, separating wax from bran oil, although it is recognized that quality of oil is increased when waxes and gums are removed. In the filtration-extraction plant in Chile, extraction of oil is effected at temperatures of 80 to 90° F. and the oil refined by the conventional method, the wax together with a small quantity of solid glycerides being separated in a "wintering" process at 5° C. before disodouring. At the Southern Regional Research Laboratory, New Orleans, hard waxes of high melting points have been obtained from bran while simultaneously producing oil. The wax is reported[26] to be largely melissyl ceritate and has a melting point between 80 and 85° C. These investigations have been summarized by Pominski *et al.* as follows:[494]

> These waxes were produced by the following two methods:
> 1. Selective cold hexane-extraction of cooked rice bran to remove the oil, hot hexane-extraction to remove the wax, chilling of the hot miscella and separation of the precipitated wax by centrifugation.
> 2. Single hot hexane-extraction of raw or cooked rice bran, hot water washing and chilling of miscella, separation of the wax precipitate by settling and centrifugation, and multiple cold hexane-washings of the wax. Wax can also be processed from rice oil settlings by the latter method after a miscella has been prepared. The cold extraction-hot extraction method should be preferable as a process when conducted on a single continuous filtration-extraction unit without reslurrying. Indications are that oil refining losses may be decreased by this method. Yields of rice wax varied from 0·22 to 1·82 per cent of the extracted oil.

Recently it has been stated[313] that such losses can be reduced by the addition of amino- or hydroxyl-containing compounds at the beginning of the refining process.

The rice-bran oil Group in New Orleans has shown that, when refined and bleached, the wax is very similar to carnauba wax.[313] The additional investment and operating costs to produce rice wax are considered reasonable.

INDUSTRIAL USES OF RICE PRODUCTS

Rice is mainly used as a food, being boiled or steamed and eaten with meats, fish and vegetables. It has also many other uses in food and commerce. In 1930 it was estimated, for instance, that 86·5 per cent of Japanese production was used as food, 5·2 per cent for making wines, 4·9 per cent for cakes, 1·2 per cent for seed, 1·1 per cent for sugar and smaller amounts for salted bean paste, soya sauce and vinegar, and for starch. The following notes indicate some of these uses of rice.

STARCH

Rice with the minimum of proteins is required for starch manufacture. Highly polished rice—whether it is much broken does not matter—is therefore largely used. Over-boiled rice is used in Asia for starching clothes. Rice is employed as a material in the European starch industry and also to some extent in Asia. Rice powder is used in Asia as a cosmetic.

BEVERAGES

Various alcoholic beverages are manufactured from rice, *Saki* in Japan and *Wang-tsiu* in China being the best known of these. *Saki* has a higher alcohol content than *Wang-tsiu*. To manufacture alcohol from starch the Asian employs cultures of fungi which convert starch into dextrose and these, being associated with yeast, lead to the production of alcohol. An established trade in these cultures is familiar throughout the East. They are made up in the form of small, generally flat cakes in India, China, Japan, Indo-China and Java to inoculate fermentable liquids and for beers, wines and other alcoholic drinks. Very old, dry and finely ground rice is used as a base, to which are mixed various strong-smelling substances, mostly spices, the main function of which is probably to assist the acids which the fungi produce in suppressing bacteria, supply a little food to the fungi and yeasts, and encourage changes which alter the flavour. The wet mixture is infected with the fungus and the yeasts from old stock, lightly covered or shaded and kept in a cool place. In a few days the fungus sends its hyphae through the cakes; the cakes are then dried, the fungus and yeasts in them having passed into a resting stage. The fungi present depend on the origin of the preparation, the Japanese form contains *Aspergillus oryzae*, elsewhere species of *Mucor* are present and seem to be the most important. A common genus is *Rhizopus* and there are others. The fungus turns the starch of the grain into glucose; the yeasts then convert the glucose into alcohol—the first is an aerobic process, the second anaerobic.

Pure cultures of the Chinese *Mucor* (*Chlamydomucor*) and the yeasts can be purchased for obtaining alcohol from rice for the manufacture of pale beers.

Among the hundreds of varieties of rice grown in Japan only a few are considered suitable for preparing *Saki*. Specific differences in the oryzenias are said to account for the distinctions.[397] White-cored rice grains have for long been appreciated by brewers in Japan. These grains are larger and heavier than normal grains. Nitrogen dressings increase and shade decreases the percentage of white-cored grains on a panicle at time of heading. The cause of the phenomenon is thought to be starch deficiency in the centre of the grain.[426]

Wang-tsiu is produced from glutinous rice which is placed in water with yeast and allowed to stand for many weeks during winter. The liquid filtered off is boiled for a specified time, the exact time being treated as a wine-maker's trade secret. Wine produced in this manner contains 10 to 15 per cent alcohol and is yellow in colour. Its quality depends on its age. It is stored in heavy, well-stoppered jugs.[464]

For making rice beer, the rice is boiled, spread out and inoculated with one of the above-mentioned "cakes", which is sprinkled over it. It is then wrapped in fresh leaves and kept moist, when a slightly alcoholic, sweet fluid with a sweet-sour taste exudes, which must be consumed within a few days as it will not keep. It is frequently used for yeast in cake-making, while the slightly fermented rice is used in food.

Rice wine is made from glutinous rice, which is boiled and inoculated with fungi and yeast "cake" and left for a prolonged period in open tubs, then decanted into closed vessels which are then buried for several months.

In the manufacture of rice-spirit, or arak, the Chinese boil partly milled rice until it is soft, when with the addition of water it is inoculated. The brew is allowed to stand for twenty-seven days and is then distilled. The process in a Chinese distillery in Indo-China is said to consist in boiling and inoculating rice and allowing the mash to ferment one day in open vessels and then for a week in closed vessels, by which time the process is complete.

Rice is also used in the manufacture of beer in the United States of America. The advantages of malted rice in brewing are quick liquefaction at low temperatures, owing to disintegration of the kernel as the result of modification of the starch and proteins by the enzyme during malting, high extract yields, good flavour and aroma, and lengthened shelf life. Breweries in the U.S.A. use about 25 per cent of all rice consumed in that country. Californian short-kernel rice is preferred for brewing purposes and is purchased on a rigid specification. In preparing rice for addition to the brewing mash, it is boiled for about 20 minutes in a "cereal-mash" consisting of water, rice and about 10 per cent of the malt. When the rice has been gelatinized and the cereal-mash is cooked, it is mixed with the main mash consisting of the balance of the malt and water. With this mixing, enzymes in the barley malt convert the starches into maltose sugar.[24] For a more detailed account of the use of malted rice the article by Zimmerman[714] should be consulted.

RICE IN MEDICINES AND MAGIC

As is to be expected, the use of rice in various forms as a medicine is general throughout Asia; likewise its employment in magic and religious ceremonies is but natural when one remembers how closely this cereal has entered into everyday life of Asians through countless centuries. These subjects are, however, beyond the scope of the present book.

HULLS (HUSKS)

The hulls are valueless as food, not only because of their low nutritive value, but because their high silicon content renders them harmful to the digestive and respiratory organs of animals. Analysis of hulls is as follows (percentage): moisture 9·02, crude proteins 3·27, fats 1·18, carbohydrates (by difference) 33·71, crude fibre 35·68, ash 17·14.

The chief use of hulls is as a fuel to supply power for the mill, their fuel value being 5,000 to 6,000 B.t.u./lb. Because of their high ash content they are rather difficult to burn. In the southern United States they are fed to the furnace by screw conveyor. Lathrop[349] describing the technique, explains that upon falling into the furnace the hulls meet a jet of steam and are blown towards a small target. Under these conditions they burn in the air and the ash and carbonized hulls fall to the furnace floor from which they are removed by a stream of water which continuously washes them into a sump.

Mills produce sufficient hulls to supply all fuel requirements in the mill and still have a surplus of about 20 per cent hulls. The disposal of this surplus is frequently an embarrassment to mill owners since no outstanding large-scale industrial use for them has been developed. They have, however, been used for a number of purposes and some possibilities merit consideration.

Hulls are used in building materials. Light-weight concrete briquettes have been made[85] from partly burnt hulls. The blocks weigh about 40 lb. per cubic foot and can be sawed and nailed. Insulating bricks have been made with cement and hull ash which resist very high temperatures and are suitable for use in furnaces. Treated hulls, to render them flame-proof, have been prepared as an insulating material. An Italian firm has patented a process for treating hulls to render them inert and suitable as aggregate. Pressed insulating board, a high quality cement tile and a cement breeze block can be made from this material. The breeze block weighs about 55 lb./cu. ft. and has a crushing strength of 300 to 500 lb./sq. in. The recommended mix is 1 cement: 3 aggregate. The breeze block is said to have good heat and sound insulation, is rat proof and not damaged by water nor subject to shrinkage or warping. Two analyses of rice-hull ash are given by Borasio[86] as follows:

TABLE 22

ANALYSIS OF RICE-HULL ASH

	Sample 1	Sample 2
Silica (SiO_2)	94·50	93·95
Calcium oxide (CaO) ..	0·25	2·28
MgO	0·23	—
Sodium oxide (Na_2O) ..	0·78	—
K_2O	1·10	3·15
Ferric oxide (Fe_2O_3) ..	trace	1·01
P_2O_5	0·53	—
Al and Manganese oxide	trace	trace

Belladen and Galliano[78] refer to the value of rice-hull ash for refractory insulators. They state that it melts at Seger cone 30, d. 2·20. Bricks formed of this ash are good heat insulators; they can be used up to 1,450° C., or even higher under certain conditions.

Some success has attended the employment of hulls for making paper and hardboard. Rice, however, has nothing to do with the rice-paper of commerce, which is manufactured from a shrub, 3 to 6 feet or more tall, *Tetrapanex papyriferum* (Hook) Koch. It is a native of Formosa and China, but is found as an ornamental plant in most countries of the tropics and sub-tropics.[486] Hulls are also used in the East, especially in Japan, as a packing material for fragile china. In rolling mills, rice hulls spread on the red-hot steel plates burn instantly to a dense ash, insulating the surface so that the metal cools more evenly. It is stated that charred hulls have been used in New Orleans as a substitute for bone-black in refining sugar, while in the Philippines a distillate from the incomplete combustion of hulls is known as a home medicine. By reason of its high silica content, the ash from hulls may find application in the glass industry.

Hulls are sometimes used as stable litter, as a fertilizer, as a supporting medium for growing vegetables hydroponically, and as a soil conditioner.

By applying the modern systems of cellulose saccharification the alcohol yield of rice hulls is not inferior to that of wood, i.e. around 19 to 21 per cent. This utilization may be important if there are wood alcohol and cellulose works near rice-growing centres.[631]

Much has been written [349, 631] regarding the use of rice hulls for the manufacture of furfural. Furfural is used for a number of purposes; it is employed in the manufacture of synthetic resins and solvents, absorbent detergents, weedkillers, wood preservatives and as a raw material for the manufacture of a chemical constituent of nylon.[107] Furfural may be obtained from rice hulls by distillation in the presence of sulphuric acid under steam pressure. Operating costs have been presented by Hitchcock and Duffey.[276]

The outstanding properties of rice hulls, viz. their abrasive character and high ash content (around 18 per cent containing 94·5 per cent of finely divided silica), offer the best opportunities of developing industries which will use large quantities of hulls.

In the Second World War it was found that a mixture of 60 parts corncob and 40 parts of rice hulls particles under an air blast of 90 lb. pressure cleaned carbon and dirt from aeroplane pistons and cylinders both safely and economically.[350] Soft-grit blasting has since extended widely in industry.[128] A very large field exists for cleaning and polishing agents. Rice hulls included with other agents has proved most successful in the "tumbling barrel" method of cleaning and polishing. It is considered[631] that the field for burnishing and polishing by use of rice hulls is relatively simple.

For shop use, hand soaps usually contain a mild abrasive. Rice hulls, ground to pass a 20-mesh and be retained on a 100-mesh screen are being used for this purpose. The amount of abrasive in such soaps varies from about 30 to 60 per cent.

RICE STRAW

Rice straw is used for the manufacture of strawboards, and in Korea for making building board. In Japan it is used for braiding and imported rice straw is employed in the Philippines for hatmaking. It is also used for mat-making and in China for mushroom culture. In Formosa it is used for mulching pineapples. Lye from burned straw ash with other substances is used in Java for washing the hair and, taken internally, is regarded as an abortifacient. In Japan, rice-straw ash, applied as a top-dressing 15 days before transplanting paddy seedlings is said to promote root growth. This beneficial effect is attributed to an increase in the sucrose content of the seedlings.[712] "Soil-ash" bricks made from soil and rice-straw ash, using emulsified asphalt as a soil stabilizer, give a high degree of insulation, are light and can absorb atomic radiation.[23]

The average food content of dry straw, according to Tognato,[661] is—albuminoids 3·7 per cent, fats 1·42 per cent, carbohydrates 32·33 per cent. He discusses the use of rice straw in feeding cattle. The digestibility of the straw is inferior to that of other cereal straws, but this authority states that experience has shown that, mixed with potatoes, beet or beet juice, or other concentrates, it can be fed to milch cows and bullocks in quantities up to half the total daily food. Ensilage of rice straw is also possible. Straw is stacked in the open and covered with stones or earth to create a pressure of about 100 lb. per square foot for several months. The straw assumes a brown colour and pleasant odour and is readily consumed by cattle. The percentage analysis is: albumenoids 4·8, fats 2·2, non-nitrogenous extracts 25·6.

Chapter XVIII

NUTRITIONAL VALUE OF RICE

QUALITY, QUANTITY AND BALANCE

THE majority of Asians subsist almost entirely on rice, millions of them on an insufficient quantity and many on the verge of starvation, while there are others—not necessarily the poorest—who suffer in health as a result of an unbalanced diet consisting mainly of rice. Recent statements by a Socialist leader in New Delhi that 100 million people in India are living on twopence a day and 270 million on threepence a day appear to have passed unchallenged. The problem therefore confronting the dietician is to supply a sufficient quantity of diet of the highest possible food value; it is a simple question of quality and quantity.

The need for balance of nutrients in dietary is stressed by nutritionists. Vitamin deficiency may be produced in protein malnutrition when the vitamin is low relative to the amount of protein, except when other factors, such as a relatively high level of carbohydrates in the diet, increases the requirement for a particular vitamin. Conversely, protein deficiency must be balanced by a supply of other nutrients. It is probable that zymotic diseases, such as malaria, may increase the body's requirements for proteins and it is unlikely that this will occur without affecting the utilization of many of the B vitamins.

Among rice-eating people the general level of health is low in comparison with Western standards, resulting in high mortality rates, short expectation of life, the prevalence of disease and poor physical development and working capacity. One effect of the poor nutritive value of the diet is the incidence of the disease beri-beri and a number of deficiency diseases less spectacular but none the less insidious in undermining the health of vast populations.

Evans[191] states that lightly-milled rice has a vitamin B_1 content of 0·7 milligram per 1,000 non-fat calories compared with only 0·18 milligram per 1,000 in the highly-milled product. In a typical 2,500 calorie diet with rice as the staple food, he continues, 2,000 or more calories are provided by the rice while the remaining 500 calories, drawn from other foods, are unlikely to carry with them more than 0·4 milligram of vitamin B_1. Highly milled rice will not provide the additional 0·5 milligram which is necessary if the danger of beri-beri is to be avoided.

When higher calorie requirements have to be met, for example, those of labourers utilizing 3,500 or 4,000 calories daily, it is usual to meet these additional needs by increasing the consumption of rice. The consumption of other foods is rarely increased in proportion. As a result, dependence on rice for the provision of the requisite amount of vitamin B_1 becomes even more marked and, if it is highly milled, the deficit becomes more pronounced. Only rice providing 0·5 milligram or more per 1,000 non-fat calories could act as an adequate safeguard against the occurrence of beri-beri under these conditions. Such level is only found when rice is lightly milled, parboiled or "fortified".[191]

Pecora and Hundley[481] have shown that a diet containing 90 per cent milled rice is markedly improved by the addition of lysine and threonine, while Sure[639] recently found an additional supplementary value of methionine to the protein in milled rice in the presence of

TABLE 23

AMINO-ACID CONTENT OF WHOLE RICE AND OF PERCH (M. C. KIK)

Amino-acid	Whole rice[1]		Perch[2]	
	In dry matter per cent	In protein per cent	In dry matter per cent	In protein per cent
Arginine[3]	0·64	9·02	5·7	0·25
Aspartic acid	0·34	4·85	5·0	6·35
Cystine	0·12	1·71	1·1	1·39
Glutamic acid	0·82	11·69	11·5	14·60
Glycine	0·45	6·41	5·1	6·47
Histidine[3]	0·22	3·13	1·7	2·15
Isoleucine[3]	0·34	4·84	4·0	5·08
Leucine[3]	0·56	7·98	5·6	7·11
Lysine[3]	0·26	3·74	6·4	8·12
Methionine[3]	0·23	3·27	3·8	4·81
Phenylalanine[3]	0·31	4·43	3·6	4·57
Proline	0·30	5·27	2·4	3·04
Serine	0·30	4·56	5·0	6·35
Threonine[3]	0·27	3·85	3·8	4·82
Tryptophan[3]	0·09	1·28	1·0	1·27
Tyrosine	0·29	4·13	3·0	3·81
Valine[3]	0·50	7·13	4·9	6·22

[1] Protein content, 7·01 per cent.
[2] Protein content, 78·8 per cent.
[3] Nutritionally essential.

lysine and threonine. The practical application of these findings is demonstrated by Kik[333] who has shown that by replacing part of the protein in milled rice by an equivalent amount of fish (perch), the body weight of animals is markedly increased, indicating that perch has better nutritive value than milled rice at the level of protein intake. The value of fish in the diet of rice eaters is therefore evident. In this connection the results of amino-acid determinations made by Kik,[333] expressed as percentage of dry matter and also as the percentage in the crude protein (Nx 5·95), are of great value.

Good cooking rice, according to Okazaki and Oki,[449] contains considerable amino acids, especially glutamic acid, aspartic acid and arginine; little or no proline is found. In polished rice, glutamic and aspartic acids and alpha-alanine form about 60 per cent of the amino acids. Mickus states[397] that the main protein of rice is glutelin soluble in dilute alkali; there are lesser amounts of globulin. Studies to date have failed to discover alcohol-soluble proteins in the grain.

The FAO has pointed out that the intake of calories in the East is insufficient for health and efficiency and advocates as the most practicable way of increasing it a larger consumption of rice provided due regard is paid to the nutritional balance.[542] But as shown above, rice is not a complete food so that a nutritional balance cannot be obtained by eating it in larger quantities. Only by improving the standard of diet by the consumption of greater quantities of other desirable foods may any material improvement in the health of Asian rice-eaters be assured. An improvement in the quality of rice would go far towards eliminating some of the worse and widespread of the deficiency diseases and would therefore raise the general health standard amongst the people, while fish production on paddy lands, mainly for consumption locally, is both feasible and profitable and would greatly assist in providing a balanced diet.

NUTRIENTS IN RICE

The composition of rice differs with the variety. It is also said to vary according to the soil in which it is grown and with manuring. Information on these points is incomplete; while analyses of a number of varieties show variation, little work has been done towards correlating nutrient content with improved varieties, although investigations with this end in view are stated to be in progress in France and the United States, consideration being given not only to the quantity of protein in the grain but to its quality. Information on the effect of cultivation and manuring on nutrient content of the grain is still inconclusive, but it has been established that correct timing of nitrogen fertilizer to the growing crop increases the precentage of protein and each amino acid in the rice grain. Liming the soil also influences the protein content of the grain (see page 227). Increasing the percentage of protein is considered important if the rice is to be used in formulating cereal milks for infant feeding. It is possible, however, that the use of rice for this purpose is limited by the fact that infants with a positive family history of allergy show a high susceptibility to rice intolerance.[309] Kik and Easterling have shown[334] that proteins of milled white rice and whole brown rice may be improved by adding small amounts of casein but that further supplementation with amino acids is not beneficial.

TABLE 24*

COMPOSITION OF RICE—HUSKED AND POLISHED

(Percentage, on moisture-free basis)

	Husked			Milled			Losses on milling and polishing		
	Platt	Kik and Williams	Rose-dale	Platt	Kik and Williams	Rose-dale	Platt	Kik and Williams	Rose-dale
Fat	2·45	2·0	2·23	0·37	0·3	0·4	84·9	84·6	86·5
Crude fibre ..	0·88	1·0	0·6	0·16	0·2	0·4	81·8	79·1	33·3
Ash	1·22	1·9	1·19	0·36	0·4	0·9	70·5	78·5	24·1
Protein ..	8·67	8·9	9·54	8·15	7·6	6·7	6·0	11·4	29·4
Carbohydrates	86·67	77·0	86·34	90·79	79·0	91·4	4·7	6·5	5·5

The fat content of rice is low and much of the fat is lost in the process of milling. The protein content of mill rice is low in comparison with other cereals, although the whole grain contains about the same quantity as is found in wheat. It compares favourably with other cereals in amino-acid content and digestibility of the proteins is high, being 96·5 for the whole grain and 98 per cent for milled rice. The low content of lysine is the most serious amino-acid deficiency. Rosedale[572] gives the following amino-acid analysis of the protein of rice: (in percentages) Ammonia 6·5, Humin nitrogen 5·2, Total bases nitrogen 27·3, Arginine N. 13·7, Histidine N. 0·9, Lysine N. 8·9, Mono-amino N. 43·7, Cystine N. 1·1, Tryptophan N. 0·9.

MINERALS

Comparison of the mineral composition of husked and polished rice is given in the following table.

* References in Bibliography.

TABLE 25

MINERAL CONTENT OF HUSKED AND POLISHED RICE
(percentage)

	Husked	Polished
Chlorine (Cl) ..	0·2863	0·048
Phosphorus (P_2O_5)	0·393	0·380
Calcium (CaO) ..	0·0927	0·014
Magnesium (MgO)	0·0778	0·036
Sodium (Na) ..	·0·0542	0·022
Potash (K_2O) ..	0·1421	0·074
Sulphur (SO_4) ..	0·0024	0·0038
Iron (Fe)	0·003177	0·00102
Copper (Cu) ..	2·3γ in 100 gm.	1·3γ in 100 gm.
Manganese (Mn)	15·7γ ,, ,, ,,	13·8γ ,, ,, ,,
Iodine (I)	3·88γ ,, ,, ,,	2·67γ ,, ,, ,,

The human nutritional requirement of iron is estimated to be about 10 to 15 micrograms daily—husked rice will supply about 19 micrograms and polished rice not more than 6 micrograms. The calcium/

TABLE 26

TRACE ELEMENT CONTENT OF PADDY AND STRAW
Average of four samples from Malaya
(in parts per million)

Element	Grain	Straw
Manganese	56*	120†
Cobalt..	<0·03	<0·08
Chromium	<0·005	<0·12
Molybdenum ..	0·27	0·32
Nickel	1·12*	0·70†
Vanadium	<0·02	<0·04
Lead	>0·03	3·1
Tin	0·15	0·5
Strontium	1·7	40
Barium	12*	175†
Rubidium	50	400
Lithium	3·3*	27†
Boron	9	—
Copper	3	—

From figures kindly supplied by Dr Muir, Pedology Department, Rothamsted, obtained from spectrographic analysis.

* Ranges:
    Mn 26–80; Ni 0·27–4·00; Ba 2–20; Li 0·2–10·0.

† Ranges:
    Mn 70–150; Ni 0·33–0·97; Ba 50–300 (2 samples); Li 15–40 (2 samples); Cr. 0·03–0·22.

phosphorus ratio is unfavourable, being about 1:10 instead of 1:2 which is regarded as the optimum ratio.

The amounts of trace elements contained in grain and straw is shown in Table 26.

With the possible exception of nickel, straw had a considerably higher content of trace elements than grain in these samples.

VITAMINS

The amount of fat-soluble vitamins A and D in rice is negligible, but the vitamin E content of whole rice is considerable. Husked rice has a high content of vitamin B, at least one-tenth that of dried yeast. The riboflavin content is low and vitamin C practically absent. The average amounts of vitamins of the B complex, particularly thiamine (B_1), riboflavin and niacin are of the order 4 micrograms* of thiamine, 0·6 micrograms riboflavin, and 50 micrograms of niacin per gram. Kik[332] has shown that the content of thiamine and riboflavin is influenced by geographical location: for instance, the variety Nira showed 4·63μ.g./gm. of thiamine in Arkansas, 4·74 in Louisiana, 3·3 in Texas, and 5·05 in California. Niacin, however, appears to be little affected by locality. Further, Kik found that thiamine, riboflavin, and niacin content differs between varieties. Rice is a

TABLE 27

VITAMIN B_1 CONTENT OF FRACTIONS OF THE RICE GRAIN

Part of grain	Proportion of grain (%)	Vitamin B_1 content (i.u./g.)	Equivalent vitamin B_1 in whole grain (i.u./100 g.)	Proportion of the total vitamin B_1 of the grain (%)
Pericarp aleurone ..	5·95	10·5	62·5	} 35·2
Covering to germ ..	0·20	4·0	0·8	
Epiblast	0·27	26·0	7·02	3·9
Coleorhiza	0·2	31·5	6·3	3·5
Plumule	0·31	15·5	4·8	2·7
Radicle	0·17	21·5	3·65	2·0
Scutellum	1·25	63·0	78·8	43·9
Outer endosperm ..	18·8	0·45	8·46	} 8·8
Inner endosperm ..	73·1	0·1	7·31	
Total			179·64	
Vitamin B_1 actually found in whole ..			186·0	

* Approximately 3 micrograms per gram equals 1 International unit.

good source of pantothenic acid and pyridoxine, two other vitamins of the B complex.

Early workers, realizing that high milling of rice resulted in the incidence of beri-beri, assumed that thiamine content of the rice is mainly present in the aleurone layer and the embryo of the rice grain. However, Altson and Simpson[16] in 1941, by dissecting the grain, showed that about 50 per cent of the thiamine content is concentrated in the embryo. It followed, therefore, that to preserve the thiamine the retention of the pericarp was of secondary importance to the embryo. Continuation of their research work was interrupted by the war in Malaya, and it was Hinton[273] who, in England, investigated the distribution of vitamin B_1 in wheat and other cereals and in 1948 extended his investigations to both red and white rice. His results for white rice, dehusked by hand, are given in Table 27.

The results show that, as with other grains, there is a high concentration of vitamin B_1 in the scutellum (44 per cent), while the aleurone layer contains 35 per cent, the embryo 12·3 per cent, and the endosperm 8·8 per cent. There appears to be a normal tendency, states Hinton, for vitamin B_1 to be concentrated in young leaves still in the process of differentiation, and as explaining the high concentration of B_1 in the scutellum and aleurone layer, it is pointed out that the former is regarded as a modified leaf and becomes, as it were, fixed in a stage of partial differentiation and may therefore partake of this tendency to concentrate vitamin B_1.

The distribution of vitamin B_1 in red rice was found to be: scutellum 50 per cent, aleurone layer 33 per cent, embryo 9·7 per cent, and endosperm 6·3 per cent of the total vitamin B_1.

In view of these conclusions, it follows that milling should be designed to remove the pericarp, but to retain the scutellum and as much of the aleurone layer as possible.

EFFECT OF MILLING ON NUTRITIVE VALUE

Loss of nutrients resulting from milling and polishing rice is very considerable. The degree of milling and polishing determines the amount of nutrients removed. Proteins, fats, vitamins and minerals are present in greater quantities in the germ and outer layers than in the starchy endosperm. The removal of the protecting pericarp also facilitates the extraction of soluble substances from the aleurone layers during washing immediately before cooking the grain. The pericarp, however, is fibrous and also contains much phytin, which forms insoluble compounds with calcium and iron and may, therefore, immobilize these elements from absorption during digestion. Rosedale shows that losses on polishing are

EE

29 per cent of the protein, 79 per cent of the fat, 84 per cent of the lime, and 67 per cent of the iron. He continues: "The difference in protein content between the two rices which is about 2 grams per 100 grams may not at first sight appear to be large, but a calculation shows that it may be very important. A man who eats 21·4 oz. (2,200 calories) of husked rice would get 53 grams of protein, whereas by eating a similar quantity of polished rice he would get only 38 grams of protein. This really constitutes the difference between a minimum protein requirement and a sub-minimal amount or shortage of protein if he eats polished rice. The League of Nations Technical Commission recommended 1 gm. of protein per kg. of body weight as satisfying requirements. Oliveiro[450] showed that normally nourished people weighed 58·1 kg. Thus, 53 gms. of protein goes far in securing the protein requirement."

Loss of nutrients due to milling and polishing are stated in Table 24. Variations shown in the figures of different authorities doubtless reflect conditions of environment under which the rice was grown, different varieties and varying degrees of milling.

Kik and Williams[331] state that the average thiamine, riboflavin and niacin content of thirteen varieties of husked rice is 3·55, 0·6 and 53·08 micrograms/grams, while the corresponding figures for milled rice were 0·8, 0·26 and 19·62 micrograms/grams. In addition, therefore, to loss of protein, fat and valuable minerals, milling and polishing results in losses of 76 per cent of the thiamine, 56 per cent of the riboflavin and 63 per cent of the niacin.

LOSSES IN WASHING, COOKING AND STORAGE

It is customary to wash rice before cooking, often with several changes of water, to remove dust, insects, husks and other impurities. The amount of washing considered necessary depends on the condition of the rice, badly stored grain containing a large amount of broken rice and dirty rice demanding more attention than does a fine sample of highly milled and well-stored rice.

The effect of washing is to dissolve some of the nutrients from the grain, the amount removed depending on the degree of milling and the amount of washing.

Methods of cooking vary in different countries. The four main methods are:[45]

(1) Large amounts of water are used and the excess drained away, carrying with it much starch which has been rendered soluble.

(2) Rinsed raw rice is immersed in water just sufficient to swell the grains properly and cooked in a double boiler or over a slow fire to avoid charring at the bottom, until the water is fully absorbed.

(3) Rinsing the cooked rice. This is often done to ensure the complete removal of the films of soluble starch on the surface of the grains.

(4) Rice is sometimes half-cooked by boiling, after which the water is drained off and the rice steamed to a state of tenderness in a pan or basket in an enclosed space over freely boiling water.

Habitual rice-eaters affirm that there is no one way to cook rice; some varieties of rice and rice grown in certain localities require different treatment in cooking.*

To enable comparisons in cooking quality to be made, the following standardized method[3] of cooking has been adopted in the United States. Twenty-five gram samples of each rice are placed in small "teaballs" and cooked in a covered saucepan. The rice is cooked in water for 12 to 20 minutes and then steamed over the water for 5 to 15 minutes. The samples are then tested for such characteristics as texture, colour, flavour, odour, expansion and water absorption.

The use of excess water causes the most depletion of vitamins. Excess washing of uncooked rice and discarding the cooking water result in a very serious loss of nutrients and calories. The losses resulting from the washing and cooking methods commonly used in India were calories 15 per cent, proteins 10 per cent, iron 75 per cent, calcium and phosphorus 50 per cent.[517] Washing milled rice may result in the loss of 40 per cent of the thiamine, 25 per cent of the riboflavin and 23 per cent of the niacin.

Cooking rice in a double boiler results in a small loss of vitamins and other nutrients, but large losses are inseparable from cooking in open vessels. As will be seen below, better retention of vitamins results from cooking, by whatever method, rice enriched by recently introduced methods.

Loss of nutrients as a result of faulty storage is self-evident. Spoilage of grain by insects and moulds may be reduced to a minimum by ensuring that rice is sufficiently dry before storage. Husked and undermilled rice which is thoroughly dry and kept in properly constructed and ventilated stores will remain undamaged for a considerable period, although it is more liable to attack than are highly milled rice and paddy. The admixture of lime to milled rice improves the keeping quality provided the mixture is stored in a thoroughly dry condition.

Prolonged storage of rice under bad conditions affects cooking quality, probably as a result of changes in the starch fraction. Loss of vitamins appears to be inseparable with storage under normal conditions. Kik[332] shows that whereas cold storage for two and a half

* See also Howe, R. (1959). *Rice Cooking*. Published by André Deutsch.

years did not cause any significant loss of vitamins, the average percentage losses in the whole kernels kept at room temperature for the same period were 24·9 thiamine, 5·3 riboflavin and 3·9 niacin.

EFFECT OF PARBOILING

The method of parboiling rice is described in Chapter XVII. In this process paddy is soaked in water for three or four days, after which it is steamed for a short period. This parboiled paddy is then dried, hulled and pearled.

Parboiling toughens the grain and reduces the amount of breakage in milling. The milled product is less liable to insect attack and has better keeping qualities than milled raw rice. In parboiling, some of the vitamins are driven into the endosperm and by gelatinizing the starch of the outer layers seals the aleurone layer and the scutellum, so that they are not readily removed in milling. Milled parboiled rice contains two to four times as much thiamine and niacin as milled raw rice and rather more riboflavin (Table 28).

TABLE 28
VITAMIN CONTENT OF HUSKED AND PARBOILED RICE
(percentage)

Variety	Thiamine		Riboflavin		Niacin	
	Milled parboiled	*Milled raw*	*Milled parboiled*	*Milled raw*	*Milled parboiled*	*Milled raw*
Nira ..	1·35	0·59	0·47	0·30	49·0	20·6
Caloro	1·61	0·84	0·33	0·26	45·2	18·5

Washing affects the water-soluble vitamin content of parboiled rice much less than it does that of raw rice. Swaminathan[642] has shown that whereas raw milled rice loses about 77 per cent of its thiamine in washing and cooking, the loss from parboiled rice similarly treated is only about 36 per cent. After washing, parboiled rice may contain four times as much thiamine and niacin as washed raw rice. The explanation appears to be that the penetration of the water-soluble vitamins into the endosperm during steaming makes them less "accessible" to water used in washing.

Hinton[274] demonstrates that parboiling or conversion treatment (which is in fact a parboiling process) leads to the redistribution of vitamin B_1 in the grain, with the result that the endosperm is considerably enriched. He suggests that the redistribution is mainly due to the entry into the grain, as the starch gelatinizes, of a small amount of water condensed on its surface. He found that a proportion, varying according to the conditions of treatment, was not redistributed but lost. This was mainly an effect of the steaming treatment to which the scutellum appeared to be more sensitive than the embryo.

Hinton confirms that there is a marked retention of the scutellum in milled parboiled rice as compared with milled raw rice. "How far the retention of the germ is responsible for the higher vitamin B_1 content of the rice milled after parboiling is not clear, but the fact that the germ is not so readily dislodged from parboiled grain does indicate the need for experiment on how far the type or severity of the milling process and the detailed conditions of pre-treatment influence the quality of the final product." Done[180] found that the loss of aneurin in parboiled rice depended upon the temperature and length of time of parboiling. While parboiling inevitably results in some loss of aneurin, soaking the paddy for 2 hours at 80° C. gave the most satisfactory results, causing a redistribution of aneurin and nicotinic acid in the grain so that a high proportion of the substances was conserved in the milled product.

DEFICIENCIES OF RICE DIETS

It has been shown above that rice is subjected to a series of conditions and treatments from the time it is harvested to the time it is consumed which seriously depletes it of nutrients—protein, fats and carbohydrates; minerals and vitamins. The rice-eater, whose health largely depends on the quantity and quality of the rice he eats, consumes a product of satisfactory appearance from which most of the nutrients have been removed. Some of the losses of nutrients are inevitable; milling is essential, but faulty milling, caused frequently by mills in need of repair and replacement, results in a high percentage of breakage and consequent loss of vitamins. Washing and cooking are essential, but rice relatively free of impurities would necessitate less vigorous and extensive washing and a consequent saving of calories and nutrients; cooking is essential, and here well-directed propaganda is desirable to ensure that rice is cooked in the minimum quantity of water in order to conserve the nutrients. Veen[685] has observed that drastic washing of rice and discarding the cooking water will nullify any improvements in the nutritive value of rice previous to household preparation.

The most important deficiencies of typical rice diets are in the B group of vitamins, vitamin A and calcium. It is suggested[535] that the thiamine content of milled rice should be 1·8 micrograms per gram to ensure that the rice as consumed will not be dangerously poor in this important vitamin. Further, it is considered that a greater intake is desirable of protein derived from food other than rice. The amount of fat eaten in rice-consuming countries is low and in view of the fact that fat facilitates the absorption of certain vitamins and "spares" thiamine, an increase in consumption of fat is desirable.

DEFICIENCY DISEASES

Deficiency diseases may be caused by an insufficient intake of food, by deficiencies in the quality of the food eaten, or by an ill-balanced diet.

Beri-beri is the best known of the deficiency diseases caused by rice. Rare before the introduction of the truncated-cone type of rice mill, it has since become widespread throughout rice-eating regions of Asia. While the cause of the disease has for long been known and its prevention and cure is well understood, the beri-beri problem remains unsolved. It is stated, for instance, that in the Philippines, of a total population of 14 million in 1946, the deaths by beri-beri were 18,582 infants and 4,567 adults. The problem remains unsolved because prejudice and inertia dictate that it shall be so. Lord Dunsany recounts[184] how, speaking at King's College, London, he referred to the folly of polishing rice till all the nutriment was extracted from it, and quoted from *The Times* an account of a journey in tropical Asia when the porters died one by one, not from the rigours of nature, but from beri-beri. "One student, an Indian," he adds, "asked me, when I had finished, if I knew that unpolished rice was brown and dirty. I asked him if he knew what beri-beri was, and received the astonishing answer: 'Certainly I do. Many members of my family suffered from it.'"

The irony of the situation is that the beri-beri patients are cured by giving them the very vitamins they had discarded from their rice.

Over sixty years ago Admiral Takaki eliminated beri-beri from the Japanese navy by partially replacing milled rice in the diet by barley and wheat. In 1910 undermilled rice was given to the Philippine Scouts instead of polished rice, when the incidence of beri-beri fell from 10 to 1 per cent within a year; and beri-beri disappeared from Javanese prisons when husked rice was introduced.

Dr Charles Hose, Bishop of Singapore, Labuan and Sarawak in 1890, suspected a dietary origin of beri-beri in Sarawak. He noticed that the disease developed amongst employees on plantations who were away from home for months at a time and fed on imported rice, while their womenfolk at home, using freshly-husked rice, were not affected.

Eykman and Gryns in Java from 1890 to 1900 established the fact that beri-beri is a food deficiency associated with the consumption of milled rice and stated that it could be prevented by replacing milled rice by husked rice or undermilled rice. It was further observed that beri-beri was rare in areas where home-pounded rice was eaten. This last observation, however, may be partly explained, as is pointed out by Simpson,[604] by the fact that the diet of those who pound their own rice is supplemented to a considerable extent by green vegetables and other sources of vitamin B_1. The present writer has observed that green vegetables as consumed by villagers who pound their own rice are usually very lightly cooked, so that the retention of vitamins is considerable. Dr. Braddon, working among Indians who eat parboiled rice and Chinese labourers who eat polished rice, observed the important fact that eaters of parboiled rice rarely contract beri-beri.[89] The antineuritic value of parboiled rice has since been demonstrated by many authorities.

Research has clearly demonstrated the anti-beri-beri properties of undermilled rice. The consumption of rice not deprived of its outer layers will prevent the disease, while a diet including the "polishings" obtained in the process of removing the outer layers of rice will effect a cure of the disease provided it is not in a too advanced stage. "The disease in its acute form often leads to the sudden death of breast-fed infants during the second to the fourth month of life. If recognized it can be effectively treated by the timely injection of thiamine and the recovery of an infant within twelve to twenty-four hours after the injection of a few milligrams of thiamine can be very dramatic."[45]

But beri-beri is not, unfortunately, the only deficiency disease associated with polished rice. Keratomalacia, stomatitis, glossitis, cheilosis, "burning feet," and hepatic cirrhosis occur most frequently amongst rice-eaters, states *Rice and Rice Diets*,[45] while, the same authority adds, experience in prison camps in the East during the war proved that neurological manifestations were associated with deficiency of factors in the B complex of vitamins. "Burning feet," retrobulbar neuritis, spinal ataxia, spastic ataxia, and simple spastic paraplegia were among the conditions observed. The authority for the above statement concludes that "further research on this subject —which is greatly needed—is likely to provide more evidence of the ill-effects of malnutrition on the human organism and to show that deficiency states which are still relatively unfamiliar are exceptionally prevalent among rice-eating populations."

Prejudice and inertia are difficult to overcome—and are by no means confined to Asia (cf. the prejudice in the Western Hemisphere against bread that is not white). But whereas the varied diet in the West compensates for deficiencies of any particular food, the great dependence in the East on rice as the mainstay of the diet emphasizes the necessity of ensuring that the quality of this cereal as consumed should be of a high order. While international and intergovernmental action is designed to insist on the degree of milling in conformity with a high nutritional quality in the milled product, it is unlikely that such action alone will go far enough to overcome the present dangers associated with overmilled rice.

Hitherto, governmental action has been directed to undermilling rice in order to prevent undue loss of vitamins and other nutrients. The two main objections to this policy are: first, the prejudice of rice-eaters against undermilled rice and secondly, the fact that undermilled rice has poorer keeping qualities than highly polished rice. Recent developments designed to ensure the high quality of rice have been directed to the improvement of present milling processes; alternatively, to enriching by artificial means highly polished rice to the level of the original unpolished or husked rice.

The methods of improving the nutritional value of rice which are available for commercial application include two developments of the parboiling process, viz.: the H.R. Conversion Process and the Malek Process; and two methods of artificially enriching rice, viz.: the Hoffman-La Roche Method and the Fieger Method.

PARBOILING PROCESSES

THE H.R. CONVERSION PROCESS

In this process paddy is cleaned in the usual way, followed by the removal of light grains, hulls and other light matter through flotation. This is effected by placing the paddy in a trough of turbulent water, the light matter rising to the surface and being floated off, while the heavier grain is removed from the bottom of the trough by an enclosed screw conveyor.

The wet paddy is then placed in a large vessel which is evacuated (to twenty-five inches or more) for at least ten minutes. Hot water (75 to 85° C.) is then introduced under a pressure of 80 to 100 lb. per square inch and the paddy steeped under these conditions, with recirculation of the water for a given time, varying from 120 to 165 minutes, depending on the variety of paddy, moisture content, the length of time it has been in storage and on the colour desired in the final product. The steeping water is then drawn off and the paddy introduced into a cylindrical, rotating, steam-jacketed vessel, which is then partially evacuated. At this point steam is introduced and the paddy heated for a short time. The steam is then blown off and a vacuum of twenty-eight to twenty-nine inches applied. The product is thus dried under vacuum in the rotating steam-jacketed vessel until the moisture content is rather less than 15 per cent. It is possible to air-dry the product without damage to the milling quality provided that the grain temperature never exceeds 145° C.

Hot, dry, "converted" paddy is then placed in bins and cooled by passing air through it; it is allowed to remain for at least eight hours in the bins before milling; this "tempering" period is considered necessary to ensure a state of moisture equilibrium throughout the mass. The paddy is then milled in the usual way. A smaller amount of bran is obtained than is usual in milling unconverted paddy, and a very small amount of polish is obtained—suggesting undermilling.

The finished product is said to have a yellow colour, but comparison with white rice in the cooked state shows only a barely discernible yellow colour. The grain is said to be more resistant to insect attack than untreated rice. This process is being operated commercially in the United States.

The average retention of vitamins in converted rice is stated to be 92·25 per cent of the thiamine, 70·82 per cent of the riboflavin, and 77·62 per cent of the niacin in the original rice.

Gariboldi's patented "Crystal Rice" parboiling process has many similar features to the H.R. Conversion Process. In Gariboldi's plant the paddy is floated in cold water to remove impurities, steeped in warm or hot water at controlled temperature for a specified period and then steamed at controlled pressure in a special autoclave. The paddy is then dried under vacuum in the same autoclave and afterwards removed to a "tempering" bin, preparatory to milling. It is claimed that breakage in milling is practically nil, the rice does not develop an unpleasant smell during cooking, it may be overcooked without becoming mush and it retains a high nutritive value.

Kondo *et al.*[339] have devised a method which they claim retains the thiamine in rice. They soak unpolished rice in 1 per cent acetic acid for 24 hours at 39° C. After drying, the rice is polished. The thiamine content of this polished rice is three times that of polished rice obtained from unprocessed natural rice and 1·5 times as much as that contained in ordinary polished rice.

MALEKIZED RICE

Malekized rice is the product of another patented process of parboiling paddy. Paddy is soaked in water at 100° F. for four to six hours, then steamed for about fifteen minutes at 15 lb. pressure, dried, and milled in the usual manner.

The finished product is either packed in bulk or is boiled and canned in vacuum-sealed tins, being sold as canned-Malek cooked rice. The cooked rice in the cans is absolutely sterile. Kik[332] gives the following figures for vitamins in bulked Malekized rice, in micrograms per gram: thiamine 2·0, riboflavin 0·4, niacin 44·0. The canned product showed 0·6, 0·3, and 30·0 micrograms per gram respectively.

ARTIFICIALLY ENRICHED RICE

Two methods of artifically enriching rice that have been developed are based on the restoration of nutrients to the level found in husked, unpolished rice. In both the enrichment is carried out in two steps: (a) producing a fortified premix, and (b) mixing or diluting the premix with ordinary white rice during the usual polishing process.

THE FIEGER METHOD

In this method the polished rice is impregnated with a water solution of thiamine, niacin and a highly soluble salt—sodium phosphate. The treated rice contains a high concentration of vitamins and is intimately mixed with untreated rice at the ratio of 1:100. After drying, the impregnated rice is coated with a thin collodion membrane so that while the vitamins are protected from loss when the rice is washed, they are available in the cooked rice, since the film is removed by hot water.

Lease *et al.*[352] describe a method for making a premix containing riboflavin. Niacin, thiamine and iron are placed under a coat of zein and confectioner's shellac on the rice. The riboflavin, as riboflavin-5'-phosphate sodium, is applied in a solution containing polyethylene glycols or methyl cellulose, which promotes rapid dispersion of the yellow vitamin. Ferric pyrophosphate is used as a marking agent to cover the yellow colour of the riboflavin in the raw rice premix grain. The premix furnishes rinse-resistance for the niacin, thiamine and iron but not for the riboflavin. It blends well and does not cause spotting in the cooked rice.

By this method of enriching rice, loss of thiamine in washing was reduced to 13·5 per cent, and the loss during cooking in a double boiler 6·4 per cent; when cooked in an open vessel it was 49·1 per cent. In washing, 14·1 per cent of the niacin was also lost.

THE HOFFMAN-LA ROCHE METHOD

In this method developed by Hoffman-La Roche Inc. of New Jersey, white rice is impregnated with a concentrated solution of the vitamins, followed by coating the fortified rice with film-forming edible substances, designed to protect the vitamins against deterioration and to prevent any substantial loss of vitamins during washing before cooking.

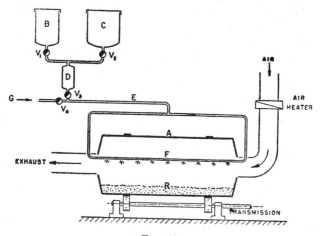

Fig. 42

Diagram of Roche pilot plant for production of rice premix

The operation of this process has been described as follows:[147] White rice is introduced through a hopper into a motor-driven trumble A—a rotary device used for coating or mixing rice after polishing. The trumble is rotated at a fixed rate while the vitamin solution from a kettle B is allowed to flow through the measuring cylinder D and into the trumble via a distributor pipe E, which slowly sprays the solution over the rotating rice grains through the perforated section F. After the final portion of the vitamin solution is blown out of the sprinkler pipe with compressed air from G, the blower is started to draw preheated air through the rotating trumble until the rice is thoroughly dry. Half the coating solution in kettle C is measured into the system through D and sprayed over the rotating rice through F. After thorough coating has been achieved and the major part of the solvent evaporated, an iron pyrophosphate mixture is added by a scoop which slides in F. A second coating of protective solution is then applied and dried as before. The finished premix is removed from the trumble through discharge slots and screened to remove "agglomerates" which form to the extent of about 1 per cent of the rice during processing. Enriched rice is prepared by mixing premix and white rice in the ratio of 1:200, either in the trumble or in any other suitable mixer. On a commercial scale the mixing can be carried out conveniently during the coating of the white rice.

Blending premix with white rice during the polishing process in the rice mill results in a product in which—if thiamine and niacin are used—neither the premix nor the enriched rice differs in appearance from ordinary polished white rice; the addition of riboflavin, however, changes the colour of the premix sufficiently to make it visible in the blend.

Fortification of premix with 1 mg. thiamine and 13 mg. niacin per one gram of premix and a ratio of 1:200 premix to white rice restores approximately the vitamin content to the standard of brown quality rice. Enriched rice prepared on this basis contains 5 mg. thiamine and 65 mg. niacin per kg. (2·27 mg. thiamine and 29·5 mg. niacin per lb.). The cost of the two vitamins, the cooking ingredients, the manufacture of the premix, and the blending is estimated not to exceed 0·114 cents (gold) per lb. of the enriched rice, or $0·25 per person per annum.

The premix is homogeneously distributed throughout the finished enriched rice, and the usual washing of rice before cooking will not remove more than 1 or 2 per cent of the added vitamins. It is claimed that the flavour and cooking quality are not affected by this fortification process. Furthermore, it is stated that storage for a year at room temperature does not affect the thiamine or niacin incorporated. When stored for three weeks at a temperature of 45° C. a loss of 3 per cent of thiamine resulted, but there was no loss of niacin. Loss of vitamins by washing the rice before cooking was 7·9 per cent of the thiamine, 3·45 per cent of the riboflavin, and 9·09 per cent of the niacin. When cooked in an open vessel, 14·33 per cent of the thiamine and 11·15 per cent of the riboflavin were lost; using the double boiler 3·12 per cent of the thiamine and 2·68 per cent of the riboflavin were lost.

In the United States the Federal Food and Drug Administration has recently laid down the following standards for enriched rice. Each pound of milled rice that is labelled "enriched" must contain 2·0 to 4·0 milligrams of thiamine, 1·2 to 2·4 milligrams of riboflavin, 16 to 32 milligrams of niacin and 13 to 26 milligrams of iron. Vitamin D, calcium, or both may be added, in which case the product must contain 250 to 1,000 U.S.P. units of vitamin D or 500 to 1,000 milligrams of calcium. Unless the label bears the statement, "To retain vitamins do not rinse before or drain after cooking", the washed rice must contain not less than 85 per cent of the minimum quantities of the specified substance or substances used.

South Carolina, U.S.A., was the first State to pass a law, effective

1 July 1956, making it compulsory that milled rice be enriched before it may be sold. Similar laws have been passed in the Philippines, Puerto Rico and Cuba. Rice enrichment is also promoted in Japan and Formosa.[333]

PARBOILING OR FORTIFICATION?

It is evident from the above that the only alternative methods of obtaining rice of high nutritional value are by parboiling or fortification. As to the choice that should be made between these two methods it is pertinent to quote medical opinion:

> There is a large measure of agreement between nutritional scientists states Professor Platt,[489] that it is desirable to meet nutritional needs as far as practicable from natural foods and in Britain indiscriminate fortification, with vitamins or other nutrients, is considered unnecessary and unsound apart from a few instances. It is not unreasonable to apply our present-day knowledge to restoring the nutritive values to food stuffs that have been highly purified. . . . It is another matter to refine wheat flour to such a degree that the diets of some—especially the poorest members of the community who eat large amounts of bread—have barely enough of some of the vitamins contained in the original wheat berry, and it is not justifiable to argue that the addition, as synthetic substances, of some of the nutrients removed necessarily restores the value of the food. If it is argued that refined white flour has good nutritive value, then there is no case for enrichment; if there is alleged to be a case for enrichment, then it is better to mill the grain to yield a good flour and retain as much as possible of the natural complex of nutrients as is consistent with good baking qualities and acceptability to the consumer.

The reader will have no difficulty in appreciating the force of this argument applied to rice.

DEVELOPMENT AND APPLICATION OF NEW PROCESSES

The methods of preparing rice detailed above variously aim at preventing loss in bulk in milling, retaining or improving the quality of nutrients, particularly vitamins, in the finished product, and protecting these nutrients against loss in storage, preparation for cooking and cooking. Considerable strides towards the achievement of these objects are evident, while the palatability of the treated produce has not been impaired to any great extent.

The adoption of improvements on a large scale, however, presents difficulties. Rice which is different in appearance from ordinary rice will meet with disfavour. The aversion of rice-eaters to rice having a different flavour is, unfortunately, very real but might be overcome by suitable propaganda. The difficulty in overcoming this prejudice is not insuperable provided that the difference in flavour is not too pronounced; meanwhile, it would appear advisable to avoid as far as possible, giving the consumer ground for complaint. Another difficulty in putting into effect a large-scale programme of enriched rice is the provision of capital and operational costs. The problem is surely a national one and its solution must rest with governments concerned with malnutrition. The present loss through disease, lowered vitality and premature death, as well as the widespread misery caused by malnutrition throughout Asia, is so immense and the cost of maintaining medical and other services so great, that one is prompted to conclude that no price is likely to be too high to overcome these conditions. Purely on a basis of economics it must surely pay to develop an ambitious scheme that would ensure the advantages of high quality rice to the peoples of Asia—and one cannot believe that the cost would be so prohibitive as not to be borne, at least in part, by the consumers.

The choice of method to be adopted to ensure that the population is supplied with a rice diet rich in vitamins will depends upon local circumstances, such as the present preferences of the population, size of population and available capital for the project. For instance, for a population accustomed to eating parboiled rice, an improved parboiling process is indicated, whereas a population demanding a highly polished rice of high quality would take more kindly to enriched rice. Further, a combination of undermilling with enrichment might be considered in certain cases.

It is understood that in consequence of a decrease in beri-beri of 72 per cent amongst the population in the Bataan area of the Philippines fed on vitamin-enriched rice, the government has extended the use of enriched rice to further regions in that country. It is recorded that consumers have not objected to enriched rice; on the contrary they prefer it to the normal. The preliminary investigations which led the Philippine Government to undertake this project are of great interest and the outcome of this ambitious scheme will undoubtedly exert an influence and serve to stimulate action in other countries where the problem of malnutrition is no less evident than in the Philippines.

SUMMARY

Possibly over 600 million people in Asia derive 50 per cent or more of their food calories from rice and the majority exist at a low level of consumption of calories per capita. There is abundant evidence that this undernourishment has seriously affected their health, pointing to the urgent necessity for a close examination of the subject with the object of devising methods to improve diets. It is desirable that the nutritional value of rice should be as high as possible and that the diet should be more varied than at present. In this connection fish rearing in paddy lands should be encouraged. There would appear to be great scope for development in this direction. More fish in the diet would greatly improve the protein/carbohydrate ratio while fish culture would also serve as a valuable additional source of revenue for the cultivator.

A Nutrition Committee was convened in accordance with the re-commendations of the Rice Study Group of the Food and Agri-cultural Organization of the United Nations in 1947 to consider nutrition problems in the East, with special reference to rice.[535] The Committee stated that effective regional nutrition programmes "should be concerned with the elimination of waste at all stages between production and consumption; the improvement of the nutri-tion content of rice by better milling practices; the extended use of parboiled rice and the introduction of enriched rice; and the improve-ment of rice diets by suitable supplements and substitutes for rice."

The need for action is urgent and the lines upon which such action should be taken are defined. Research will doubtless suggest further means for improvements. It is therefore to be hoped that well co-ordinated action at national and international levels will continue to improve the diets and the health of the numerous rice-eating nations in Asia.

ACKNOWLEDGEMENT

Details of most of the new processes described above are freely drawn from Bulletin No. 458 of the University of Arkansas, by M. C. Kik, and many of the vitamin analyses quoted are from the same source. Articles on the Nutritional Improvement of Rice by A Sreenivasan[626] and Rice and its Nutritional Aspects, by L. Nicholls[433, 434] have also been consulted in the preparation of this chapter. Other sources of information are indicated by biblio-graphical references in the text.

Chapter XIX

PRODUCTION, YIELDS AND CONSUMPTION

IMPORTANCE OF RICE IN ASIA

THE great rice areas of the Far East, such as the deltas of the Irrawaddy, Bhramaputra, Mekong and the greater part of the Gangetic plain and the Krishna areas are the results of erosion. Without erosion there would be far less land suitable for paddy. It is probable that paddy is grown because there is no other cereal which can grow under such high monsoon rainfall. Rice has enabled the populations of Asia to survive and indeed increase, because paddy checks—but does not entirely prevent—erosion. Had the people of Asia attempted to live by any other cereal they could not possibly have maintained their high density population for thousands of years. To prove the truth of this assertion one has only to compare the population density in countries of large rice production with those of other tropical countries where rice is not produced as the staple crop. Growing paddy necessitates water conservation and this in turn ensures soil conservation. Some of the terraced fields in Indonesia, the Philippines and south China are over two thousand years old and are typically conservation projects. This more than any other factor accounts for the predominance of rice as the staple food in south-east Asia, in countries of high rainfall.

Rice remains the most important food of countless millions of people in Asia and among the poor it is practically their only food. The very poor, especially if they live outside a rice-producing region, may not be able to afford rice and will subsist on other—and often inferior—grains or pulses; ragi (*Eleusine coracana*), for instance, is the main diet in certain parts of India, but once a ragi eater becomes accustomed to rice it is with the greatest reluctance that he will return to eating ragi. The FAO has stated[542] in this connection:

> Rice is the traditional crop and the traditional staple food. It is almost inconceivable in most districts, that growers would change over to producing and consuming some other cereal instead of rice. It was noted above that in Korea, for example, some growers used to sell their rice and buy cheaper cereals for their own consumption. But over most of the rice-growing world this does not happen, not only because the people have a strong preference for rice but also because other

416

cereals are not grown anywhere near, to any extent, and transport facilities are too poor for them to be imported into the district at competitive prices.

Pakistan made an effort to change the eating habits of her people from rice to wheat, because wheat is said to cost less than rice. But the preference for rice in Pakistan remains strong and it is extremely doubtful whether the government can convert the population from rice to wheat within this generation.[548]

More or less compulsory changes of diet brought about by the war may have had a more permanent effect. Wheat, in particular, has competed with rice in some areas. The FAO has concluded however, that if real incomes in the Far East were much higher than at present, the amount of rice consumed would be at about twice the present level.

The fact that rice is the staple food of the great majority of the people of Asia makes it of vital importance to the economy of the countries concerned. In the extensive rice-producing areas practically the entire population is either directly or indirectly dependent on the success of the crop, a dependence that extends beyond the growers to the commercial community, for ability to buy depends on the proceeds of the rice harvest. Outside rice-producing areas, the influence of rice on the economic life of the communities and the countries may be more subtle but is just as important as in them. Inability to buy rice freely through interruption of normal imports causes disruption of labour conditions which may affect countries outside the region directly concerned. Wages are largely ruled by the price at which the workers can purchase rice; if supplies are short, causing a rise in price and invariably the creation of a black market, increases in wages are demanded and are difficult to resist, resulting in an all-round increase not only in the cost of living, but in the production cost of export goods upon which the country may be dependent.

The importance of rice in the agriculture of many countries in Asia is succinctly stated by Wickizer and Bennett[699] in the following table showing the rice acreage as a percentage of the total crop-producing area:

Indo-China	..	..	86	Java	..	..	..	45
Burma	..	..	65	Korea	..	..	..	30
Philippines	..	..	64	India	..	..	..	23
Formosa	..	..	54	China	..	..	..	21
Japan	..	..	45					

AREAS OF PRODUCTION

About one-half the world's arable land is under cereals and about one-fifth of the total cereal area produces rice. Excluding the U.S.S.R. from which no information is available, the total area under paddy in the season before the outbreak of the war in 1939 was between 200 and 212 million acres. Post-war efforts to step up production to meet increased demands have led to an increase in area of approximately 85 million acres. It is possible that this figure rather exaggerates the difference because of more accurate estimates in later years. Shortage of supplies during the war provided an incentive to production in Africa and the Western Hemisphere, but despite this, 90 per cent of the area under this crop is still to be found in Asia. In south-east Asia—the traditional home of the crop—and in eastern Asia, vast areas of low land have for centuries produced an annual crop of rice, while smaller areas follow the course of rivers far inland; in some regions the crop extends up the steep sides of hills that, with infinite care and skill, past generations of paddy-planters have terraced and irrigated to provide conditions suitable for their staple food crop.

The most important regions of rice production are China, India, Pakistan, Indonesia and Thailand, which account for over 66 per cent of the world total area under the crop.

In Asia, in the thirty years before the Second World War, the area planted remained static in the countries of greatest importance, with the possible exception of Indonesia, where the area increased from about $5\frac{1}{2}$ million acres in 1912 to over 9 million acres in 1939, an increase due entirely to the vigorous policy of the Dutch Government, which was determined to make the territory self-sufficient in the crop upon which the well-being of the population depended. The Indian acreage also showed an apparent increase during this period; this may in some measure by due to improved statistics, but in any case it was nullified by the very considerable increase in the local population. The total increase in area in the eleven most important Asian countries of production between the years 1920 and 1939 was in the region of $15\frac{1}{2}$ million acres, representing an annual increase of 0·6 per cent. The planted area in these countries has increased a further $2\frac{1}{2}$ million acres in the last decade.

In Japan[356] there has been a gradual increase in area, production and yield during the past sixty years. This is attributed mainly to the increased use of fertilizers and improved varieties.

In many parts of Asia there was necessarily a set-back to planting during the war from 1939 to 1946. Recovery, due largely to the

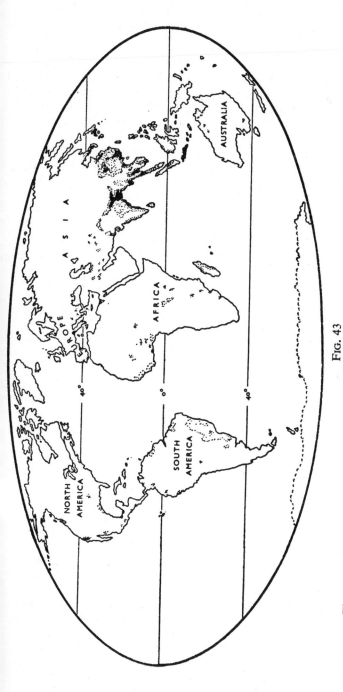

Fig. 43

The pre-eminence of Asia in rice production. The total world area under paddy is nearly 300 million acres; about 230 million acres or 90 per cent of this is within the heavily shaded regions. The climatic range of paddy production is approximately within 45° north and 40° south of the Equator, although these are not the extreme limits of paddy cultivation.

dire necessity of the planters, has been rapid in some countries, but slow in others where political unrest militates against full recovery.

Outside Asia the cultivation of paddy has in recent years assumed growing importance and there is reason to believe that if favourable prices are maintained, the area may be further increased. The area has been well maintained in Europe, but no very large expansion may be expected in that region. A report on rice production in Africa[347] indicates that paddy-growing may eventually be developed extensively. The possibilities here are, in fact, enormous; there may be millions of acres of swamp jungle suited to the crop provided that irrigation and drainage are feasible. In Sierra Leone, the available area is probably a million acres, and taking into account production in Nigeria, Ghana and Gambia, the potentialities in Commonwealth countries alone are almost incredible. In addition, vast areas of potential paddy-land exist in other countries in equatorial Africa. The main difficulties are lack of population and capital; development, therefore, involves the outlay of considerable capital on water control and drainage. Yields are low and there is ample scope for scientific work in African regions directed towards the improvement of yields.

In North and Central America, the United States is the only important centre of cultivation. There was a very considerable increase in the planted area during the war. Brazil is the largest producer of rice outside Asia. There is probably a vast area of additional land suitable for paddy cultivation in the Amazon valley, but in view of the sparse population, much capital would be necessary for mechanized development on a large scale. Work on an ambitious project to reclaim up to 500,000 acres of fertile swampland in Surinam (Dutch Guiana) has been initiated by a non-profit-making institution called into existence by the Netherlands and Surinam Governments. Using modern mechanized rice-farming methods, this organization has converted 15,000 acres of uninhabited tropical swampland into a highly productive rice-producing area.[703]

DEVELOPMENTS IN AUSTRALIA AND THE SOUTH PACIFIC

A survey showed that extensive areas could probably be developed for large-scale rice production without artificial irrigation in the Kimberley district of Western Australia and the Darwin-Katherine area of the Northern Territory of Australia.[490] Experimental paddy fields at Liveringa on the Fitzroy River about 70 miles from Derby, Western Australia are a prelude to development of some 20,000 acres.

The reclamation for paddy, legumes and linseed of an area of about 750,000 acres in the Northern Territory of Australia has not materialized, due, it would appear, to inadequate preliminary investigations and to the uncertain water supply.

Developments are also possible in the Territory of Papua—New Guinea.[491] The Koembe project in Netherlands New Guinea, which aimed at large-scale paddy cultivation near Merauke, was commenced in 1952. The pilot scheme of about 600 acres, proposed for mechanization, was planned in the light of experience gained in Surinam under comparable conditions. It was hoped to extend the development to an area of 30,000 acres in combination with cattle-raising. A report on rice production in the South Pacific region[693] states that prospects for expanding rice production are not bright in New Caledonia and New Hebrides because of low and irregular rainfall, shortage of labour and interest in other crops. Climatic and other conditions are, however, suitable for rice in the Solomons, Papua and New Guinea. In these areas production through mechanization could be expanded to satisfy local requirements and possibly to provide an excess for export.

To sum up the position regarding world areas under paddy: the area under the crop in Asia has regained its pre-war position but may be unable to extend to a degree to keep pace with growing demand. This conclusion is based on the past trend of increase in area, on the growing competition of other crops that have a greater appeal to Asians and to the fact that the areas suitable for rice without additional expensive irrigation systems are limited. Most of the really extensive areas in Asia suitable for paddy cultivation are already planted with the crop. Some extension of the planted area may be anticipated in consequence of the awareness of the majority of governments of the dangers of the present position. There are indications that under the influence of international organizations and with the prospect of provision of more adequate resources and funds for development, considerable efforts will be made to extend paddy cultivation and to ensure that the most efficient use is made of land suitable for this crop. It is becoming widely appreciated that the aim should be self-sufficiency in rice production so far as it can be attained and that to rely on imports to satisfy increasing demands for rice may be to court shortages caused by disruption of normal trade relations or failure of the crop in areas of large production. The tendency to rely on wheat imports to replace ample rice requirements is seen in some Eastern countries and is to be deprecated. The substitution of wheat from far-distant countries is not a· satisfactory alternative to local rice production supplemented, if needs be, by imports of rice from nearby Asian countries.

TABLE 29
WORLD AREA AND PRODUCTION OF PADDY

Country	Area (thousand acres)		Production (thousand metric tons)				Paddy Production 1962–63 provisional
			Paddy		Estimated Rice equivalent		
	1948–52 Average	1961–62	1948–52 average	1961–62 prov.	1948–52 average	1961–62	
ASIA:							
Afghanistan	510B	519A	333	319D	216	207	
Brunei	7	7	6	6	4	4	
Burma	9,282	10,048	5,481	6,851	3,605	4,652	7,176
Cambodia	2,677	2,695	1,266	1,250	810	800	1,700
Ceylon	921	1,194	570G	897	342	538	1,003
China, Taiwan ..	1,881	1,932	1,682	2,508	1,177	1,756	2,628
Federation of Malaya	847	961	635	926	400	583	900
Hong Kong	40	20	37	30	24	20	
India	74,384	83,632	34,011	51,223	20,407	30,734	50,000
Indonesia	14,514C	16,836	9,441A	12,528	5,665	7,517	14,274
Iran	543D	800D	424D	576D	276	374	
Iraq	430	157	203	68	132	44	
Japan	7,400E	8,153	11,991	15,523	8,837	11,433	16,261
Korea, North.. ..	973E	973D	1,558E	1,558D	1,137	1,137	
Korea, Republic of ..	2,628D	2,786	2,879D	3,706	2,092	2,705	
Laos	2,038F	1,531	540	540	346	346	
Lebanon	—	1	—	—	—	—	
Nepal	3,199	3,448	1,134KD	1,315D	737	855	
North Borneo ..	82	96	42	82	27	53	
Pakistan	22,237	23,954	12,399	16,118	7,439	9,671	14,948
Philippines	5,805	7,852	2,767	3,910	1,771	2,502	4,011
Port. India (former) ..	—	—	39C	39D	25	25D	
Port. Timor	—	—	6L	6D	4	4D	
Ryukyu Islands ..	35B	27	26J	32	17	21	
Sarawak	489	279	98F	115	64	75	
Saudi Arabia	5	5D	2	2D	1	1D	
Syria	10	2D	13	13D	8	5D	
Thailand	12,871	13,965	6,846	7,845	4,450	5,099	8,926
Turkey	77	145	109	233	71	151	
Viet-Nam, North ..	5,614D	5,726	5,193D	4,660D	3,324	2,982	
Viet-Nam, Republic of	4,481	5,813	2,469C	4,609	1,580	2,950	5,026
Total Asia ..	170,973	184,093	97,070	137,430	63,096	89,329	
Add CHINA, MAINLAND	66,243	77,804A	58,188F	85,000D	37,822	55,250	
EUROPE:							
Albania	5C	7C	4	5	3	3	
Bulgaria	30	25	37	36	24	24	
France..	32	82	46	134	30	88	137
Greece..	30	54	39	85	26	56	
Hungary	44	54	48	38	32	25	
Italy	368	306	723	674	477	445	652
Portugal	67	99	115	177	76	117	
Romania	39	27	35J	31	23	20	
Spain	143	153	272	394	180	261	390
Yugoslavia	5	15	5	20	3	13	
Total Europe ..	766	815	1,320H	1,590	871	1,049	
U.S.S.R.	336C	247	202	240	133	158	
AFRICA:							
Algeria	5B	5	8	10	5	6	
Cameroon	15	20B	5	8D	4	5	
Congo (Leopoldville)	373	378B	152	164A	99	107	
Former Fr. Eq. Africa	40	40N	12	12D	8	8	
Congo (Brazzaville) ..	12B	12A	3D	4A	2	3	
Former Fr. W. Africa							
Guinea	837	837N	208	323A	135	210	
Ivory Coast	499	494A	104	160A	68	104	
Mali	450	405A	148	143A	96	93	
Niger	10	22	3	10	2	6	
Senegal	141	170A	52	83	34	54	
Upper Volta.. ..	30	94A	11	31	7	20	
Gambia	27	59	20	29	13	19	
Ghana	49	69D	23C	34D	15	22	
Kenya ▌	25M	25D	6M	15	4	10	

TABLE 29 (contd.)
WORLD AREA AND PRODUCTION OF PADDY

Country	Area (thousand acres)		Production (thousand metric tons)				Paddy Production 1962–63 provisional
			Paddy		Estimated Rice equivalent		
	1948–52 Average	1961–62	1948–52 average	1961–62 prov.	1948–52 average	1961–62	
Liberia	642F	642D	150F	150D	97	97	
Madagascar ..	1,519	1,897	829	1,221	539	794	1,250
Mauritius	—	—	1F	1D	1	1	
Morocco	5	5	8C	13	5	7	
Mozambique	1	1D	1M	1	1	1	
Nigeria	422	398	250H	203	162	132	
Rhodesia-Nyasaland Southern Rhodesia	—	—	1F	1	1	1	
Nyasaland	10E	10D	2	9D	1	6	
Ruanda-Urundi (form.)	2D	2D	1	3	1	2	
Sierra Leone	783J	699	274J	264	217J	172	
Swaziland	2L	5D	1L	4D	1L	3D	
Tanganyika	125J	125D	62J	23	40J	15	
Togo	27	37D	7	11D	5	7	
Uganda	20	7	5H	3D	3	2	
United Arab Republic	632	558	971	1,142	631	742	1,250
Zanzibar and Pemba	20	15	11	7	7	5	
Total Africa	6,743	6,842	3,360	4,130	2,194	2,684	
OCEANIA:							
Australia	35	49	68	134	44	29	142
Fiji Islands ..	37	32	23	22	15	14	
Total Oceania ..	72	81	90	160	59	43	
NORTH AND CENTRAL AMERICA:							
British Honduras ..	2	2	2J	2D	1	1	
Costa Rica	61	145D	33	57A	21	37	
Cuba	198GD	482D	106	370D	69	240	370
Dominican Republic	108	108D	65	126	42	82	
El Salvador ..	37D	27A	27D	21	17	14	
Guatemala	20J	22	9J	13	6	9	
Haiti	69F	69D	29C	29D	19C	19D	
Honduras	27	32	18	23	12	15	
Jamaica	7	5	6	5	4	3	
Mexico	237	412	173	429	112	279	
Nicaragua	44	59	23	39	15	25	
Panama	153D	247	84D	109	55	71	
Puerto Rico ..	10	10B	3	2D	2	1	
Trinidad and Tobago	20F	20D	18	18D	12	12	
United States ..	1,857	1,588	1,925	2,458	1,251	1,598	2,923
Total North and Central America	2,816	3,359	2,520	3,720	1,703	2,418	
SOUTH AMERICA:							
Argentina	123	131	152	182	99	118	
Bolivia	30C	40B	18C	23B	12	15	
Brazil	4,760	7,496D	3,025	5,300D	1,966	3,445	5,300
British Guiana ..	111	227	101	210	66	136	242
Chili	64	72	76	83	49	54	
Colombia	361	585D	249	407D	162	265	
Ecuador	175	277	141	187	92	122	
Paraguay	22	17	17	17	11	11	
Peru	131	198D	205	349D	133	227	
Surinam	44	64	53	72	34	47	
Uruguay	35	44	44	62D	29	40	
Venezuela	86	143	41	85	27	55	
Total South America	5,953	9,287	4,120	6,980	2,678	4,537	
WORLD TOTAL ..	253,175	297,918	164,600	242,200	106,990	157,430	

A 1960–61   B 1959–60   C Average of 3 years   D Unofficial or preliminary figures.
E 1949–50   F Average of 2 years.   G 1952–53—1954–55.   H 1950–51   J Average of 4 years,
K 1945–46—1949–50.   L 1952–53.   M 1948–49.   N 1948–49—1957–58,

WORLD PRODUCTION OF RICE

Table 29 above gives details concerning total crops and acreages under paddy for early post-war years and for the year 1958. Before 1939 the total world crop of paddy was about $147\frac{1}{4}$ million tons, giving, after deduction for seed purposes, approximately $94\frac{1}{2}$ million tons (metric) of milled rice. During the war, production diminished greatly in Asia and expanded in the Western Hemisphere, the net reduction being about 10 per cent. Present production is at least 50 per cent greater than in the first post-war year. At the end of the war, world rice production was about 16 million tons less than pre-war. From 1946 onward, production gradually recovered until in 1949 it exceeded the pre-war figure, although Asian production did not fully recover until 1952, by which time Asia had 100 million more people to feed than in 1938.

Both rice production and the rice-eating population increase by about 2 per cent annually. But, as pointed out by FAO, rice consumption per head is increasing as living standards improve. World import demand thus remained strong in 1962, since available supplies *per caput* were smaller.

No data are given for rice production in Russia, about which little is known in recent years. Before the war, Turkistan and Transcaucasia provided about 75,000 tons of rice, while the total Russian consumption at that time was some 175,000 tons. Extensive developments were planned in the Far Eastern Region, Semirechensk, Transcaucasia, the Caucasus and the Lower Volga, and it was expected that once necessary irrigation works had been completed the area would supply Soviet needs and provide an exportable surplus. Test sowings in 1929 near the rivers Ili and Karataisk showed that conditions for paddy cultivation were excellent and in 1930 a State farm was started to cultivate some 30,000 acres, using the waters of the two rivers.

YIELDS

The yield of rice per unit of land varies considerably in different countries, ranging from over 3,500 lb. rice per acre in Spain to about 550 lb. in some tropical countries. While therefore, yields vary considerably between countries, they are comparatively stable in each country (see Table 30), so that fluctuations in world production are largely due to the area sown. The great difference in yield between the highest producing countries and the lowest points to the conclusion that the level of production could be materially raised in the countries of low yield. The possibilities of improving yields are necessarily limited in countries where production per unit of land is already high. In Japan, for instance, it is stated that under present practices, the increase in yield per unit is considered to have already reached the limit, notwithstanding the fact that experimental results have not been disseminated widely amongst paddy growers.

TABLE 30

YIELD OF RICE IN CERTAIN COUNTRIES

Cwt. per Acre

Country	Average 1948–49 to 1952–53	1956	1957	1958	1959–60	1960–61	1961–62
Spain	25·2	31·6	31·5	31·9	31·9	33·4	34·5
Australia	26·3	26·6	30·2	33·0	35·0	33·4	33·2
Italy	26·2	26·0	27·4	28·9	29·9	26·2	29·6
Japan	23·0	22·2	25·5	26·5	27·2	27·8	26·9
Portugal	23·6	23·4	24·6	25·1	25·3	23·1	26·4
Un. Arab Rep.	19·6	28·1	28·8	25·7	26·0	25·8	26·2
United States	13·3	18·1	18·6	18·2	19·6	19·9	19·8
Korea, Rep. of	15·3	12·9	16·5	16·5	16·4	15·6	18·5
Brazil	8·5	8·8	8·5	8·4	8·8	9·2	9·5
Indonesia	8·1	8·5	8·3	8·5	8·7	9·0	9·3
Burma	7·9	8·9	7·3	8·9	9·2	8·7	9·1
Pakistan	7·3	8·1	7·4	7·0	7·9	8·5	8·8
India	6·0	7·2	6·3	7·3	7·4	8·2	8·1
Africa	6·4	7·4	7·8	7·1	7·8	8·2	7·7
Thailand	6·9	7·6	6·8	7·1	7·0	7·2	7·3
Philippines	6·1	6·2	5·6	6·5	5·8	6·0	6·4
Cambodia	6·5	6·7	6·2	4·8	5·0	6·4	5·9

A number of reasons may be advanced to account for low yields, but the most obvious, easily appreciated by those conversant with conditions in Asia, is the hazard of unsuitable weather, especially in the absence of adequate control over drainage and irrigation. The sown acreage in Thailand,[512] for instance, often exceeds by 15 per cent the acreage harvested, either because of drought or excessive rains and floods. At least so far as Asia in concerned, the improvement of irrigation and drainage is the most important factor in raising the general level of production.

The second most promising is the improvement of seed supplies by selection and breeding. In many countries selection has already given satisfactory results and increases of yield from 25 to 30 per cent are by no means unusual. The facility with which this method can be applied has tended to overshadow the possibility of evolving new and better varieties by breeding and it is probable that by this method greater increases in yield may be obtained ultimately although progress is bound to be slower.

Many authorities stress the importance of increased use of fertilizers if yields are to be raised and the Food and Agriculture Organization of the United Nations is insistent upon this point. This insistence, however, shows a rather unrealistic attitude. It is uncertain how far fertilizers are economic under tropical conditions, and as one writer[354] states, "it hardly appears sensible to pour in fertilizer each year, only to have it go out to sea with the next rain", or, one might add, to be rapidly "fixed" in the soil and so be unavailable to the crop.

TABLE 31

YIELD OF CLEANED RICE* IN POUNDS PER ACRE IN DIFFERING DEGREES OF
LATITUDE, NORTH AND SOUTH OF THE EQUATOR

Latitude 0 to 10°		*Latitude 11 to 20°*		*Latitude 21 to 30°*		*Latitude over 30°*	
ASIA:							
Malaya ...	1,337	Burma ...	986	India ...	900	Iraq ...	650
Ceylon ...	1,147	Cambodia	661	Pakistan	986	Korea ...	2,072
Indonesia	1,042	Thailand	818			Iran ...	1,112
		Philippines	717			Turkey ...	2,300
		Formosa	1,947			Japan ...	3,012
EUROPE:							
						Italy ...	3,313
						Spain ...	3,864
						France ...	2,462
						Greece ...	2,225
						Portugal	2,957
AFRICA & OCEANIA:							
Nigeria ...	730	Guinea ...	870			Australia	3,718
Liberia	389	Madagascar	940				
Ivory Coast	464	Fiji ...	980				
NORTH & CENTRAL AMERICA:							
Costa Rica	550	Dominican		Cuba ...	1,100	United	
Panama...	626	Republic	858	Mexico ...	1,530	States	2,218
		El Salvador	1,066				
SOUTH AMERICA:							
Colombia	1,010	Peru ...	2,606			Chili ...	1,650
British		Brazil ...	1,064			Uruguay	2,150
Guiana	1,225					Argentina	1,900
Surinam	1,572						

Improved methods of cultivation are also often suggested as a means of improving yields. The traditional methods used in some Asian countries may be wasteful of labour but are usually sound in principle, and while modern implements and machinery may lead to more profitable crops through economies of labour, they are unlikely to result in greatly increased yields. In some countries, however, both implements and methods of cultivation are lamentably poor.

* Conversion rates of paddy to rice are stated in Appendix IV.

For instance, crop yields in India and parts of Pakistan could be doubled by the use of improved seed and better tillage methods. A similar assertion has been made in regard to China and Thailand, though possibly with less justification. One is informed that the introduction into India of the so-called Japanese system of cultivation has resulted in greatly increased yields.

The Asian system of cropping paddy-land is also held to explain the lower yields compared with those obtained in new lands in South America under roughly similar climatic conditions. This may be correct, but the fact remains that some of the best rice-lands in the East have been planted to paddy for many years without manure and still continue to give high yields. As an example may be quoted an area in Malaya some 50,000 acres in extent, provided with a good irrigation system, which has been continuously cultivated in paddy for sixty years at least without manuring, and which continues to give annual yields little inferior to those recorded in Italy and Japan. The existence of such areas is one justification for hopes of greatly raising yields in Asia once the underlying factors responsible have been discovered. Yields per acre on the Murrumbidgee Irrigation Area of New South Wales are approximately the highest in the world. It is therefore pertinent to examine the possible reasons for this satisfactory result. Successful cultivation in Australia is stated to be dependent upon:

(1) Sufficiently high temperatures during the growing period.
(2) Freedom from extreme hot to cold changes.
(3) A dependable water supply during the growing period.
(4) Soils that are comparatively flat or level and overlying an impervious subsoil.
(5) Satisfactory surface drainage.
(6) Freedom from water weeds.
(7) The application of nitrogenous fertilizers. It is however, now unusual to apply fertilizers in this area.

While these conditions no doubt contribute to this satisfactory result they do not offer a full explanation for high yields, while they also apply in equal measure to conditions obtaining in some other countries where yields are considerably lower. One must therefore conclude that climate, type of paddy cultivated (*japonica*), and the rotational crop system are largely responsible for high yields. In almost every country where paddy yields are exceptionally high, this crop is rotated with grass carrying stock and/or other crops. The introduction of any such system in Asia where it may be possible, would entail a revolutionary reorientation of agriculture which, however, might ultimately be justified.

EFFECT OF CLIMATE ON YIELDS

Yields obtained when the crop is grown in sub-tropical and warm temperate climates are almost invariably higher than when it is grown under fully tropical conditions. It seems likely that this is attributable to the longer day length during the growing period, the varieties grown, coupled possibly with the occurrence of cold winters which may favourably influence soil conditions. Moreover, in most of the sub-tropical and warm temperate countries where rice is produced, paddy forms part of a regular crop rotation, a feature which is most certainly conducive to high yields.

Nevertheless, while admitting that yields may be affected by local secular facts, it seems inescapable that paddy is better suited to the sub-tropical and warm temperate zones than to the full tropics, notwithstanding that it is most widely grown in the latter region. Copeland[135] in 1924 pointed out that the highest yields are obtained in countries with temperate climates, but attributed this to the use of fertilizers, although he added, "the difference is still sufficiently great and constant to suggest that climate may be a factor". Knowledge of the effect of climate on growth of paddy has advanced greatly since Copeland wrote. More recently Paul[474] stated that "countries with a temperate climate give much higher yields than those in the tropics". The effect of cool nights on respiration rate may be important, as explained in Chapter XIII. The extremely high yields on the Mwea-Tabere irrigation scheme in Kenya, almost on the equator, amounting to over 6,000 lb. paddy per acre, are probably due to a combination of high light intensity with cool nights and cool irrigation water from Mount Kenya. On the other hand, Wickizer and Bennett,[699] discussing rice yields in Asia, appear to disregard the effect of climate and attribute the difference to such factors as the absence of flood and drought hazards, the use of manures, better seed and better cultivation.

Table 31 shows the approximate annual yields of rice in most of the countries in which the crop is grown, classified according to the latitudes in which they are located, and brings out the point in question. From this data the following average figures are obtained.

Comparing these figures with those of six years previously, it is of interest to note that the present yield per acre in latitude 0° to 10° is 6·5 per cent less, whereas present yields in latitudes over 30° increased 25·6 per cent. It is permissible to conclude that the normal average yield of rice when the crop is grown in the tropics

TABLE 32

RICE YIELDS IN DIFFERENT LATITUDES

Latitude (degrees)	Average yield in lb. per acre	Approx. percentage to total world area in each category
0 to 10	918	11
11 to 20	1,128	25
21 to 30	1,135	57
Over 30	2,374	7

within 20° North and South of the Equator is in the region of approximately 900 lb. per acre, while when it is grown between 21° and 45° North or South it becomes progressively greater, rising steeply at latitudes above 30°. There are, of course, some anomalies. The soils of British Guiana and Surinam are rich in organic matter, a point that also applies to the very high-yielding area in Malaya referred to on page 427, and the result may at least in part be attributed to this. In some of these areas, two crops of paddy are harvested annually. Among Asian countries within latitude 11° and 20° Formosa is remarkable for its high yields; but here much of the land yields two crops annually, cultivation standards are very high and heavy manuring is extensively practised. Particular importance attaches to Peru, where in a latitude of less than 20°, yields have doubled in the past twenty-five years and now stand at around 2,630 lb. rice, thus placing this country on a par as regards yields with the warm-temperate countries. Efferson[190] attributes this increased yield to the fact that rice in Peru has changed from a food to a major cash crop of some importance. Transplanting has replaced broadcasting, water is used more efficiently by constructing bunds on the contour instead of in small rectangular plots, greater efficiency has resulted from using tractors in cultivation, while there is increased use of fertilizers and better harvesting methods.

Of the countries lying between 20° and 30° North and South, the majority conform to the criteria, with the exception of India, Cuba and Brazil. So far as concerns India it appears highly probable that with better cultivation, better seed and improved water control yields could be materially increased. Indeed, where the so-called Japanese method of cultivation has been tried, the increases have been quite startling. If Indian and Pakistan yields could be raised to the level assumed to be characteristic of these latitudes it should go far to lessen apprehension of a world rice shortage for some years to come.

THE POSSIBILITY OF RAISING YIELDS

If it is admitted that the environmental factor is dominant in determining the magnitude of production, it becomes possible to assess the limitations to potential yield increases for any particular area and conversely to determine where, by the application of accepted methods, increased yields may be anticipated. Thus, while it must always be admitted that local influences require to be taken into account, it should be possible to raise yields in latitudes between 0° and 20° to 1,000 lb. per acre, and in latitudes between 20° and 40° to perhaps 1,800 lb. per acre or more. These figures are, of course, generalized and do not rule out the possibility of an all-round increase above these limits as a result of cultural, manurial or varietal improvements.

But if only this potential were attained it would materially affect the production of rice in the world. About 36 per cent of the world area under paddy is grown between 0° and 20°, nearly 60 per cent between 20° and 30°, and the remainder in latitudes over 30°. Consequently, it appears at least possible that improved methods might lead in the aggregate to the production from existing paddy areas of a total world crop of 200 million metric tons of rice, or roughly double the present output.

To exemplify some of the possibilities; Burma and Thailand are the main rice-exporting countries of Asia. They both lie between latitudes 11° and 20° North and their average production of rice per acre is respectively 818 and 730 lb. If this could be raised to 1,000 lb. per acre it would add about 3 million tons of rice to available supplies.

It is unnecessary here to discuss in any detail the various means available for improving production, since they have been dealt with in previous pages. It may, however, be appropriate to stress that of all the methods available the simplest and cheapest is the improvement of seed supplies.

In vast areas in Asia the varieties cultivated are so mixed that marked improvements in yield can be obtained in one or two seasons by field selection based upon a single character. From a practical point of view the aim should be the cultivation of a single strain in any one field, thereby eliminating the competition which is bound to arise when a number of different forms are grown together, e.g. tall forms and short forms. Mass selection has been recommended as a sound first step; pure-line selection has been undertaken in many countries and although the results have not been uniformly satisfactory, it has usually led to marked improvements in yield. In

Thailand, for instance, the increases which have resulted from its employment are stated to amount to 15 per cent, and in Malaya to 25 per cent.

The production of new varieties by hybridization may be expected in the long run to give the best results since not only can it provide higher yielding types, but it can also eliminate or reduce losses from lodging and improve resistance to pests and diseases. The production of hybrids is long-term work of a very laborious character; it demands a high degree of skill and much more precise knowledge of the characters of existing strains than is at present usually available. The characters should be classified and catalogued so that the performance of each type under different environmental conditions can be better understood. Hybridization has produced spectacular results in the case of wheat and there appears to be no obvious reason why equally striking results should not follow its application to rice.

Under field conditions selected strains do not remain pure indefinitely; they tend to become mixed with seed from other sources. Moreover, experience with other cereals shows that varieties may evince a certain mutability under continuous cultivation. Disease-resistant varieties may exhibit diminution in their powers of resistance owing at times to changes in the diseases themselves. For all these reasons it is necessary periodically to supply growers with fresh seed supplies and this necessitates continuous effort to enable these to be produced and distributed to growers.

Under Asian conditions, the limiting factor to yield improvement through better seed is probably the low educational standard and apathy of cultivators. The peasantry are not antagonistic to improvements, but slow to absorb new ideas and to appreciate the possibilities of improvement. Chandraratna, for instance, has remarked[115] that Javanese peasants have shown a decided preference for their own non-descript seed, and that in Java, as in Ceylon, the gap between precept and practice is deplorably wide, for in both countries, with an assured water supply, it should be possible to double present yields.

Some ten years ago concern was expressed over the apparent decline of yields. As a direct result of the war, both yields and area planted were adversely affected. The unsettled political condition in the East militated against an early recovery of the industry and was mainly responsible for the decline in yield. With an improvement in the political sphere, the planted area returned to normal and crop yields showed an improvement. The lower yields of a decade or so ago were not due, as was suggested, to exhaustion of the land as a result of continuous paddy cropping. The tendency should now be towards an increase in yield throughout Asia, mainly as a result of better drainage and irrigation and more adequate control of insect pests. Statistics of food production in Asia are not always very accurate. Many of the technical workers in India, for instance, are emphatic in their belief that past crop reports have underestimated total production. They stated[189] "that average yields of food crops, especially rice, are at least stable compared with pre-war and, if moving in either direction, are increasing gradually with improved varieties, cultural methods, and fertilizer use". What is expressed in regard to India applies equally to a great many countries.

To sum up: one of the main factors governing the yield per unit of land is climate, it being held that the paddy plant is only capable of yielding its maximum crop under sub-tropical or warm temperate climatic conditions. While, therefore, paddy grown under tropical conditions may possibly not be capable of giving the high returns possible in more temperate climates, the yield in most countries still falls short of the amount that should be expected under their particular environmental conditions. It is probable that they can be raised to a higher level in most countries of Asia and South America by planting improved seed, better cultural methods and at least in some regions by the extended use of natural manures supplemented by artificial fertilizers. It has been estimated in some quarters that yields could be raised by at least 25 per cent by planting improved seed. Further very material gain could be expected from improved drainage and irrigation and also by preventing excessive loss through the depredations of pests in the field and store. Taking all these factors into consideration, together with others of less importance, the aggregate increase in crop might easily be of such an order as to justify the present writer's contention, arrived at on theoretical grounds, that the potential crop from the existing world area under paddy might be double that at present obtained.

CONSUMPTION

Asians are not only the largest producers but also the largest consumers of rice, since about half the rice produced in the Far East is consumed by the growers and most of the rice from surplus-producing countries is sold in Asia. The system of cultivation practised in the East necessitates a very great expenditure of labour and accordingly, paddy cultivation is most general in regions of dense population. Hand labour and lack of capital limit the amount of land that any one owner can cultivate; the area cultivated as a unit is therefore very small, usually from one to six acres. The cultivator in most regions grows paddy primarily to supply his domestic needs. Part of the excess crop, if any, he may store for future need should the next crop be insufficient, and for seed for the coming season. The remainder is sold for local consumption and, after this market is satisfied, the rest is available for export outside the country of origin. For example, in 1954 the net exports of rice as percentage of production in the more important exporting countries were as follows: Burma 34, Thailand 31, United States 51.

TABLE 33

PRE-WAR AND POST-WAR SOURCES OF RICE EXPORTS
(thousand metric tons)

Country	1937–39 Average annual net exports	Percentage of total	1961 Net exports	Percentage of total
Burma	2,966	38·3	1,591·4	26·5
Thailand	1,386	18·0	1,566·0	26·3
Indo-China (Laos, Viet-Nam, Cambodia) ..	1,225	15·8	374·7	6·3
Formosa	638	8·2	70	1·2
Pakistan	279	3·6	—	—
United States	122	1·6	829·6	13·9
Italy	136	1·8	220·3	3·7
Egypt (U.A.R.) ..	101	1·3	228·6	3·8
Iran	54	0·7	—	—
British Guiana ..	15	0·2	91·7	1·5
Australia	13	0·2	58·6	1·0
Ecuador	10	0·1	21·2	0·4
Madagascar	8	0·1	25·1	0·5
Spain	—	—	92·8	1·6
Brazil	54*	0·7	150·8	2·6
Surinam	6*	0·1	19·3	0·3
Uruguay	2*	—	19·9	0·3
China	9	0·1	—	—
Other countries ..	690	9·7	600	10·1
Total	7,734		5,960	

* 1934–38.

It is probable that the producer's family consists on an average of six persons, who together will consume about 1,800 lb. of rice a year, that is, the produce from about two and a half acres of land. Add to this the consumption of rice by non-producers in the area and one realizes why the exports of rice form a relatively small proportion of the total production, even from the extensive areas such as exist in Burma.

Taking Burma as an example of a region of great production and export, the facts are as follows. Before the Second World War Burma cultivated almost 12½ million acres of paddy, and after deduction of seed required to plant in the succeeding season, about 4,587,000 tons of cleaned rice were obtained. But of this total she was able to export

TABLE 34

NET IMPORTS OF RICE IN PRINCIPAL CONSUMING COUNTRIES
(in thousand metric tons)

Country	Average annually		1961
	1934–38	1948–52	
India	1,883	788	404·3
Japan	1,732	686	125·8
China	610	—	47·4
Malaya Federation of	541	468	557·3
Ceylon	530	416	469·0
Hong Kong	176	179	344·7
Indonesia	261	472	1,065·1
Cuba	201	257	136·1
Pakistan	—	—	110·9
United States.. ..	122	61	103·0

only a little over 3 million tons, or 67 per cent of production. In 1956, with a lower production, Burma was able to export only 54 per cent of her production, and the figure has now dropped to 34 per cent.

Practically all countries in Asia are producers of rice, but only three are in a position to export rice in appreciable quantities; the

TABLE 35

EXPORTS AND IMPORTS BY REGIONS
(thousand metric tons)

Region	Exports		Imports		Net Exports		Net Imports	
	1948–49	1961	1948–52	1961	1948–52	1961	1948–52	1961
Western Europe ...	233	366	388	539	—	—	155	273
Eastern Europe ...	13	11	*	289	—	—	*	278
U.S.S.R. ...	—	—	*	20	*	20	—	—
North America ...	540	836	37	36	503	800	—	—
Latin America ...	251	339	363	305	—	—	54	34
Near East ...	271	247	*	373	—	—	*	126
Far East	*	4,235	*	3,922	*	313	—	—
Africa	25	45	172	487	—	—	147	442
Oceania	29	59	—	—	—	—	—	—

— Nil. * No information.

remainder are usually under the necessity of importing rice to supplement local production. The three exporting Asian countries are Burma, Thailand and Indo-China (Viet-Nam, Laos and Cambodia). Increasingly large amounts are exported from certain European countries, the United States and certain of the South American States. The pre-war and post-war sources are shown in Table 33.

About 75 per cent of total world exports of rice are consumed in Asia. In normal years the more important exporters send rice to other Asian countries and failure to do so spells undernourishment in the importing countries.

THE POST-WAR POSITION

The area planted in Asia in the first post-war year (1946–47) was 188½ million acres, being nearly 4¼ million acres less than before the war. Increased planting in other parts of the world covered this deficiency, but the total production showed a decline of 3¼ million metric tons of milled rice, due entirely to a drop in Asian production. Shipments of rice from exporting countries were 1·9 million tons in 1946 and 2·2 million tons in 1947 as compared with 8·3 million tons per annum before the war. In 1961 shipments were 6 million tons of rice.

Whereas before the war 70 per cent of rice exports came from three countries—Burma, Thailand and Indo-China, the Japanese occupation of these countries denied the world these sources of supply.

TABLE 36

WORLD AREAS AND PRODUCTION OF PADDY

By Regions

| Region | Area | | Production | | Percentage of World Total | | | |
| | thousand acres | | thousand metric tons | | Area | | Production | |
	1948–49 to 1952–53	1961–62	1948–49 to 1952–53	1961–62	1948–49 to 1952–53	1961–62	1948–49 to 1952–53	1961–62
⸱rope	770	820	1,320	1,590	0·4	0·4	1·2	1·0
⸱rth America	1,850	1,580	1,920	2,460	1·0	0·7	1·8	1·6
⸱tin America	6,920	11,070	4,720	8,240	3·7	5·1	4·3	5·4
⸱ar East ...	2,150	2,170	2,060	2,340	1·1	1·0	1·9	1·5
⸱r East ...	169,470	192,590	95,980	136,230	90·4	89·8	88·5	88·5
⸱rica	6,100	6,270	2,390	2,990	3·3	2·9	2·2	1·9
⸱eania... ...	70	70	90	160	0·1	0·1	0·1	0·1

During the war years production assumed greater importance in the Western Hemisphere and in the immediate post-war years the world relied to a large extent on maintenance of supplies from this region, for in the first post-war year Burma was able to export but 12 per cent and Thailand 33 per cent of pre-war averages. Before the war the United States exported about 205,000 tons, including shipments to its own territories. In 1952, however, it exported 791,000 tons, most of which went to China, Cuba, Korea and the Philippines. In 1951 more than 28 per cent of the 4·9 millions that moved in international trade came from the United States, Ecuador, Mexico and other non-Asian countries. In 1952 this percentage increased to 31·8 per cent. Subsequent developments have been described by the Food and Agricultural Organization as follows:

A radical change in the rice situation occurred towards the end of 1952. High prices had stimulated production and restricted demand. In 1952–53, larger crops were reaped in every continent and this increase was continued even more sharply in 1953. As the Asian crop expansion had taken place mainly in the importing countries, the reaction on international trade in the following years was very marked. From 1952 to 1953 India's imports fell by about three-quarters and Indonesia's well over one-half. Rice shipments were determined by the decisions of importers rather than by the quantities made available for export. In making these decisions, importers were greatly influenced by the fall in the price of other cereals which had gained more widespread acceptance among consumers during the period of acute rice shortage. Most of the monopolies concerned with the export of rice were slow to adjust their prices to the changed conditions, with the consequence that the volume of sales was greatly reduced. The consequent decline in exports led to an abnormal accumulation of stocks in South-east Asia.

For the past three years, exporting countries have been unable to find buyers for as much rice as they would have liked to supply. Nevertheless, some corrective measures have begun to operate. Restrictions on rice consumption have been gradually removed; rationing has been abolished almost everywhere with the notable exception of Japan. Foreign trade has been liberalized and imports—except in a few countries—restored to the hands of private merchants whose interest lies in expanding their markets. Countries in Asia have made greater efforts to meet the wishes of buyers: more attention is being paid to quality in processing, and old stocks which had deteriorated are being sold off at cut prices for animal feeding. The fall in prices has reduced the export pressure from other regions: rice shipments from the U.S.A. and Italy have declined sharply from the peaks reached in 1953, and the burden of stock-holding has been partly shifted from South-east Asia to North America and to countries on the Mediterranean.

In contrast, FAO stated in 1963:

> The world rice situation in 1961–62 was characterized by scarcities and high prices, following a fall in production due to unfavourable weather. Stocks were depleted and the volume of exports decreased to 5·7 million tons in calendar 1962, 7 per cent below the 1957–59 average. . . . In 1962–63 the paddy harvests were generally bigger, but still lagged behind the targets set in the national plans of several major producers. Though export supplies were more ample, therefore, this increase was more than matched by the strength of import demand . . . the short-run prospects are for a modest recovery in the volume, and a substantial increase in the value, of rice exports in 1963.

The FAO has suggested[542] the establishment of an intergovernmental group on the economic aspects of rice whose functions would be to review from time to time the world rice situation and other economic aspects of the industry. Further to stabilize the market they suggest that exporting countries should hold national stocks in addition to those held against their normal requirements and should endeavour to follow a co-ordinated national stock policy; the aggregate stocks held by them being equivalent to at least six months' exports, i.e. about 2 to 3 million tons of rice or 2 to 3 per cent of world output. It was also suggested that the intergovernmental group might discuss whether a stabilization scheme such as a multilateral contract scheme, an export quota scheme or an international buffer stock should be started.

While some international agreement, possibly on the lines indicated above, appears to be desirable to ensure a steady supply of rice at a reasonable price in countries whose inhabitants subsist mainly on this staple, the problem still remains of devising methods of raising production to a higher level than ever before to ensure adequate supplies to keep pace with the ever-growing population of rice-eaters in the East. In this connection it is still imperative to eliminate waste of paddy and rice as far as possible. Figures placed before the International Rice Meeting at Baguio[536] in 1948 indicated that "more than 10 million tons of rice are lost annually, principally through the following causes: (*a*) insect and rodent infestation; (*b*) faulty methods of storage at all stages; (*c*) wasteful milling and (*d*) current methods of household preparation." It is, of course, quite impossible to give an accurate figure for the amount of rice lost annually from the causes stated and one must regard such an estimate as an informed surmise. But it emphasizes the undoubted fact that the losses from the causes mentioned are widespread and very serious; they are losses that cannot be tolerated so long as there are hungry people in the world. One might add to them, losses occurring in the field, chiefly by insect pests, such as stem borers and paddy bugs, rats and birds, as well as losses due to faulty handling of the crop at harvest.

The problem of increasing supplies is more difficult than the more immediate problem of distribution. According to the FAO, the rate of increase of the basically rice-eating population of the world approximates to 10 million each year. In order to feed these additional people, world production of rice must be increased annually by at least 1·3 million metric tons (milled or cleaned basis). The rate of increase in population in the densely populated areas of Asia depends on available food supplies; when undernourishment, if not actual starvation, prevails, the rate of increase slows down, whereas in times of plenty it increases more rapidly. Further, demand for rice depends on the living standard of the people. There is no doubt that consumption varies according to the purchasing power of the people.

The demand for greater rice production can be met in two ways; either by increasing the yield per unit of area and/or the total area under paddy. As has already been stated, there are great possibilities of raising the yield per unit of area, both in Asia and elsewhere and it would appear that development in this direction might lead to earlier results than would the increase in area under the crop. It is obvious, however, that rice production cannot increase indefinitely at the rate of over a million tons a year; the ultimate solution seems therefore to be limitation of population either by natural causes or birth control.

There appears to be a fear in some quarters, mostly amongst exporters but obviously also felt by the FAO, that production is outstripping demand for rice. Statistics of production post-war as compared with those pre-war do not support that contention. It is obvious that, despite the attraction of other cereals in some countries, the demand for rice is as great as ever and will increase. Poverty and the low standard of living amongst the rice-eating populations of the East remains acute: this, and probably this fact alone, is responsible for the present position. The "surplus" producers are anxious to find a market; a vast population, living on a sub-standard diet, want more rice but cannot afford to buy it. Countries that encourage their population to substitute wheat or other grains for rice will confer no benefit on their people. The answer is now what it was before the war —the policy of self-sufficiency in rice production. Has everybody forgotten the rice shortage of 1919–21?

PRICES

The price of rice is quoted in terms of cleaned or brown rice and not as paddy, and at first sight rice appears to be the most expensive of the cereals, though tariffs and other methods of control may change the price relationship. It is consistently higher in price than the inferior cereals such as oats and rye, while for many years it has tended to become cheaper in relation to wheat. Rice prices are less variable than wheat prices because, apart from loss of crop on account of climatic conditions, the area planted is approximately the same each year and there are no alternative crops suitable for cultivation in many of the paddy-growing areas. The paddy-grower, therefore, has no alternative to the production of his annual crop of paddy.

The miller is guided in the price he pays for paddy by the type of rice and the expected milling results. Naturally he is anxious to obtain the greatest possible quantity of paddy of any one type. A grade of rice is not necessarily obtained from a single variety of paddy, though to obtain uniform grade, varieties of paddy of similar nature are necessary. Frequently the price of paddy shows seasonal fluctuations, depending upon the quality of paddy held by growers and the competition for supplies by the miller.

Thailand rice on the Eastern market commands the highest price, Burma rice takes second place, while that from Cambodia and Viet Nam is at a further discount. The popularity of rice, however, varies somewhat in different countries; in Japan, for instance, domestic rice obtains premium prices, rice from California being at a discount and Cambodia and Viet Nam rice at a further discount.

The price of rice of different grades from the same country of origin reflects largely the content of broken grain. This broken-grain content is no chance characteristic but is carefully controlled at the mills. Other factors in judging quality from a commercial standpoint are colour and uniformity of grains, foreign matter, amount of chalky grain, unevenness of type and general appearance.

Asians have very strong likes and dislikes regarding rice, tastes differing considerably on a national basis. Wickizer and Bennett[699] state:

> The basis for such highly developed preferences is not wholly clear. Why the Japanese prefer one flavour and the natives of Thailand another appears to be based partly upon tastes that have been developed over generations. Rice varieties adapted to the soil and climatic conditions of one region probably possess flavour characteristics differing from those adapted to other regions. When conservatism is so strong in matters of taste and when the population tends to be immobile, the local consumer might well be inclined to regard rice grown in more distant regions and possessing different flavours as in some vague sense inferior. Furthermore, the extent to which rice is consumed in the Orient tends perhaps to develop discriminations beyond the comprehension of the typical Western consumer.

The purchasing power of rice has a profound effect on the well-being of the Asian. During the third decade of the present century this purchasing power declined in comparison with the second decade; while this was to the advantage of the non-cultivator consumer, it caused distress among the growers. Prices continue to favour cultivators; this supplies an excellent opportunity for government, through co-operative societies, to assist the cultivators to place themselves in a sounder economic position to face future fluctuations in the fortunes of paddy cultivation.

GOVERNMENT INTERVENTION IN THE RICE INDUSTRY

Government intervention in the rice industry may aim at stimulating production with the object of improving the lot of the cultivator, or at attempting to make the country self-sufficient so far as rice supplies are concerned. In some countries government determines the price of rice or the area to be cultivated, with the object of maintaining prices. Most government interventions have, however, proved costly and have not produced results commensurate with the cost. Manipulation of the market price of the product, either in favour of the producer or consumer—or both!—is of no lasting benefit to either producer or consumer. In a crisis, however, stocks and prices are justifiably controlled, but in normal circumstances a healthy industry is one that can stand on its own feet. Lack of organization amongst producers, together with lack of capital, often places them at the mercy of a chain of organized buyers and of their government. The paramount necessity of maintaining and increasing rice production may provide justification for governmental intervention, distasteful as this is from many points of view. One prefers to look upon this as an interim means of alleviating the condition of producers and protecting the consumers, pending a sounder solution of the problem that can only come to pass when the producer is educated in the principles of co-operation, whereby he may build up capital for production and exercise some control in the sale of his produce. In the meantime, governmental intervention (if possible of a paternal nature) must be accepted as a palliative, but should not be considered as an alternative to the independence of the cultivator, for the best cultivator is the one most conscious of his independence.

Note: The subject of this chapter has been exhaustively treated in *The Rice Economy of Monsoon Asia* by V. D. Wickizer and M. K. Bennett.[699] For this reason it has been treated but briefly in this chapter. The author has freely used facts and figures from the above-mentioned publication and from publications of the FAO.

Statistics of areas and crops should be treated with reserve.

Chapter XX

ECONOMIC CONDITIONS

As over 90 per cent of the world supply of rice comes from Asia, the economic position of the Asian cultivator must profoundly affect world supplies of this cereal. The most important factor affecting the area cultivated and yield per acre is the unsatisfactory economic position of the cultivator. The development in south-east Asia of large-scale cultivation of export crops such as rubber, which attracted the small-scale producer, resulted in neglect of paddy in favour of these new and attractive crops, while the pre-war price of rice was so low that cultivation was uneconomic except in the more favoured areas. The competition of other crops with rice was most pronounced in regions where paddy was not the sole or indeed the major crop. It was less felt where vast areas of land were planted with paddy under conditions unsuited to alternative crops; therefore, despite the attraction of other crops and the unsatisfactory price of rice, paddy cultivation persisted and in many regions extended. Post-war conditions brought higher prices for rice and thus proved an incentive to planters, but in some cases the government of the country rather than the cultivator received the main benefit from these improved prices.

LAND TENURE

Two major factors are responsible for the unsatisfactory condition of paddy cultivation: viz. the condition under which the cultivator holds the land and his financial instability. An examination of systems of land tenure and finance is, therefore, necessary if one is to understand the difficulties facing the cultivator. During the past twenty years or so there has been a steadily increasing appreciation of the fact that the future of agriculture is largely dependent on agrarian reform, a term which embraces land tenure, consolidation of fragmented holdings and breaking up of large estates. In most countries, therefore, and especially in the under-developed countries of Asia and South America, legislation has been directed to improving the conditions under which the cultivator holds the land he farms. In Latin America reforms are directed to obtaining for the smallholder the benefits of large-scale production, whereas in Asia the primary object appears to be the improvement in status of tenant

441

cultivators and their greater security of tenure as owners. Systems of land tenure vary considerably throughout the tropical world and in many cases are complicated by customary laws of inheritance of property. These complications cannot be lightly swept away for they are the basis of society as understood amongst the people.

BURMA

The extensive paddy-fields of Lower Burma have been brought into cultivation since the year 1870. To develop this sparsely populated area the government encouraged immigration from Upper Burma and India by giving leasehold rights on land after continuous payment of land revenue for a period of twelve years. Agricultural policy is directed to the abolition of absentee landownership and strengthening the position of peasant cultivators, mainly through extension of credit facilities and improvements in conditions of tenancy.

CEYLON

It is the rule rather than the exception for paddy-land to be owned in Ceylon by non-cultivating landlords; in fact, about 75 per cent of the land is so held. Except in the areas served by the major irrigation schemes, where the unit owned may be 50 to 100 acres, ownership is generally in areas of about five acres, while the average area under individual ownership is about half an acre only. In many cases[474] ownership is complicated by the fact of "infinitesimal" shares, due to the custom of equal inheritance of property, with the result that the fields are cultivated on the system of alternate cultivation by the co-owners, in which each owner cultivates the land for one season and takes his turn again when the full round of co-owners have each had their turn. A further complication is that owners are usually non-resident, or have a number of fields in scattered places, the cultivation being carried out by tenants.

A holding is about half to three-quarters of an acre. There are three main systems of tenancy, viz. the share system, the system of fixed rent, and the hire system of cultivation. Under the share system the fields are leased out for one or more seasons, generally on a half-share basis of the crop, which is divided at threshing time after deduction for such items as seed paddy and hire of buffaloes, which are usually provided by the owner. In the system of fixed rent, the rent is paid in kind or in cash. The amount varies with the district and in some cases with the season. Under the hire system of cultivation the owner engages labour for all operations and pays for the work with a part of the crop, or the produce from a definite area under cultivation.

MALAYA[230]

In Malaya, all land which is not alienated, or reserved for a public purpose, reserved forest, held under a government licence for temporary occupation, or under an approved application, is State Land. State Land is divided into five categories, one of which is "Country land not exceeding 10 acres in extent," and it is under this category that most of the paddy-land falls. The title to such land is either Grant or Lease, for which the lessee pays to government a fixed annual rent. As an inducement to cultivate foodstuffs, an annual rebate is allowed on land planted with paddy or other approved crops. To protect the paddy-planting industry, the government now makes a condition that only paddy shall be planted in specified areas which are considered suited to this form of cultivation. Further, to ensure that the needs of the indigenous population are adequately guarded, the Malay Reservation Enactment gives power to the government to declare an area to be a Malay Reservation, in which the land cannot be sold to a non-Malay. Much of the paddy-land is situated within such Reservations and as practically the entire paddy area is cultivated by Malays, the cultivator is safeguarded against loss of ownership. A somewhat similar system obtains in Indonesia, where the government owns the land and leases it to the native cultivator, who may not transfer ownership except to another native cultivator.

THAILAND

As in Malaya so in Thailand, all land is vested in the state and may be alienated to individuals for the payment of a premium, survey fees, and an annual rent. Usually for paddy-land these fees are under about five shillings an acre.

The tenure from government is freehold. Landlordism exists, more so in the Central Plain than elsewhere in the country, and even in the Central Plain the amount of land rented is not considerable except near Bangkok where most is rented. Here the landlord takes but little interest in his property or in his tenants, while the latter are usually under a one-year tenancy and take all they can from the land with little or no respect for the condition of the land at the termination of their tenancy. Disputes and frequent changes of tenants are common and altogether the position is considered most unsatisfactory. Terms of tenancy vary and rent may be paid in cash or in paddy. A typical rate is 50 per cent of the crop to the landlord, who pays the land tax due to the government. The usual cash rate is three *bahts* per *rai* (about fourteen shillings an acre), the tenant paying government dues. Alternatively, the landlord may charge a fixed rent in paddy for which an agreed area is rented, the landlord may or may not pay government dues according to the terms of the tenancy.

The land tax payable to government is usually at the rate of about eightpence per acre and may be as low as about sixpence for the poorer land. Land values vary according to local circumstances, but typical figures are about £5 to £10 per acre, the higher figure being the more common, but in the "floating rice" regions where yields are heavy, the land may change ownership at rates corresponding to £35 to £70 per acre. There would appear to be no particular difficulty in finding tenants or in colonizing new areas, but no special inducements are offered or considered necessary to attract settlers.

The average size of holding in the Central Plain is about 12 acres; a holding of 8 acres would be considered small and holdings up to 20 acres are farmed, while there are holdings of over 40 acres managed by family units. Over most of the country the holdings are smaller, the owners being concerned merely to grow sufficient rice to satisfy home needs. Holdings of over four acres are the exception, although in the north they tend to be larger.

In the Central Plain the land is excellent for paddy cultivation, but practically useless for other crops. The government imposes no conditions on the cultivator as to the crops he should or should not grow, but the cultivator, traditionally a paddy planter, would be unlikely to consider the cultivation of other crops.

INDO-CHINA (CAMBODIA, LAOS, VIET NAM)

The nature of the tenancy and the size of the holding vary considerably in Indo-China. In Tonkin, peasant ownership is general; about 61 per cent of the holdings are one acre or less in size, 30 per cent are between one and five acres, and only 9 per cent exceed five acres. In Annam, the holdings are rather larger. In Cambodia, although small holdings are still in the majority, the average size is again somewhat larger. Only 36 per cent are $2\frac{1}{2}$ acres or less in size, 52 per cent are between $2\frac{1}{2}$ and $12\frac{1}{2}$ acres, and 12 per cent exceed $12\frac{1}{2}$ acres. In these territories, with the exception of Cambodia, there is a dense population, consequently numerous small-sized holdings are the rule. In Cochin China, rice-growing is of more recent development and large estates are common.

The peasant is normally the owner, but in Cochin China 65 per cent of the 25,000 holdings are worked on a tenancy basis. The rent is usually upwards of one-half of the crop reaped from land of average fertility. If buffaloes are hired from the landlord, a rent in cash or kind is also charged.

The scale of land taxes appears to vary in each of the five territories. In Cochin China, for example, the gradation is dependent on the quality of the land and varies from 10 cents (Indo-China) per hectare in the case of newly cleared unimproved land to 2 piastres per hectare for first-class paddy-land. In Cambodia there are seven grades of taxes ranging from 20 cents (Indo-China) to 3 piastres per hectare.

INDIA

Indian land tenancy has developed from a feudal system, the land-lords being full owners of the land and the cultivators in the position of tenants-at-will. In some parts of the country, however, the system known as *ryatwari* has long been established, under which cultivators have the rights of full owners, subject to payment of land revenue, and can sell, mortgage, bequeath or otherwise dispose of their holdings. Much of the land is cultivated on share tenancy, known as *batai*, under which the landlord claims a share of the produce at harvest. Contracts are usually yearly, so that the cultivator is reluctant to carry out improvements from which he will not benefit.[364] Recent legislation provides for the abolition of land-lordism (*zamindari*) in order to establish peasant proprietorship on a wide scale.

Legislation has been enacted in most States to regulate land rent, security of tenure, ownership for tenants and size of holdings. However, rents have yet to be reduced to the recommended levels, and effective supervision of "voluntary" surrender of lands has not materialized. The Third Plan (1961–66) places much emphasis on work programmes to utilize manpower resources in rural areas and the formation of labour co-operatives.[36]

FORMOSA

Under recent land reform laws, nearly 80 per cent of the cultivators now own the land they farm. Government regulations control transfer of property and all paddy land in excess of 7 acres not worked by the landlord or immediate members of his family have been sold to other cultivators who pay for the property out of crop earnings. In this way, some 300,000 families have bought their land during the past few years.

PHILIPPINES

The widespread system of tenancy is ownership of most of the land by large wealthy family groups who, in most cases, have little interest in improving production and provide little incentive for tenants to do so. There is, however, a strong feeling in the country towards reform, which is likely to bear fruit in the near future.

PAKISTAN

Pakistan has formulated land reform policies which provide for the abolition of the *zamindar* (landlord) giving ownership to the cultivator. In West Pakistan, despite legislation, the landlord seems to have relinquished little of his power. While peasant ownership has increased greatly in the Punjab, in Sind there is little evidence of increasing land ownership amongst the peasant population. It is certain that land reform has proved to be a blunt weapon with which to strike at the roots of the country's economic and social life.

JAPAN

Before the war more than half the area of paddy land in Japan was farmed by tenants and owned by small landlords. Rents were usually paid in kind—generally as high as 42 per cent of the crop. With a view to improving tenancy, the Government attempted unsuccessfully to implement various policies to improve the position of the small cultivator, but it was not until 1946 that land reform law became operative. This legislation provided that cultivated lands owned by absentee landowners were restricted in area. Compulsory purchases of excess land were sold to small landowners and tenant farmers who then became owner-farmers.

Tenancy conditions have been improved; tenants are protected from unreasonable rent and eviction, and written contracts on tenancy must be prepared between the two parties and approved by an Agricultural Commission. Provision is also made to prevent fragmentation of land and also to prevent land reverting to non-cultivators.[21]

INDONESIA

All land in Indonesia is owned by the government. Land suitable for paddy cultivation is leased by government to Indonesians, who may not transfer their ownership rights to any but Indonesians. In the sugar-producing areas, government provisions of tenure compel a rotation in which sugar is grown on the land for one year in three or four, paddy three times in two years. If ample irrigation is provided, other crops in the rotation may be maize, cassava, sugar, sweet potatoes and groundnuts.[366]

The above notes on land tenure in parts of Asia are typical of the complexities evident throughout the continent, and illustrate some of the very grave difficulties encountered by the cultivator. Reflection will make evident the improvements that would inevitably follow if some of the more one-sided agreements between landlord and tenant could be removed. The poverty of the cultivator is mainly responsible for making him dependent on the goodwill of the land-lord, a goodwill that is maintained on account of the large share of the profits enjoyed by the latter. The following conclusion of the F.A.O. Mission to Thailand in 1948[534] may be held to apply generally to landlordism in Asia: "A high degree of tenancy is associated with unstable social conditions. Notable features are little respect for the law, lack of education, and poor farming practices. Neither the landlord nor the tenant gives much thought to the productive factor—the land. The tenant is unwilling to improve the land, for none of the value created by his efforts will accrue to him. The landlord is unwilling to improve the land, for he cannot trust the tenant. Thus, land improvement, with a corresponding increase in productive efficiency, does not and cannot take place in this un-healthy situation."

CHINA

The Chinese Agrarian Reform Law abolished the land ownership system, but land and other property used by landlords directly for the operation of industrial and commercial enterprises is not con-fiscated. The law provided that "After agrarian reform is completed the People's Government shall issue title deeds and shall recognize the right of all landowners to manage, buy, sell or rent out land freely." How far this has been implemented one cannot say. One point is certain: the Chinese have not recognized the dictum of equal distribution of land at the expense of agricultural efficiency and output. It is claimed that land reform has done away with bureau-cratic capitalism, limited the incidence of rent where tenancy is allowed, kept the Land Tax within reasonable proportions and has cut the roots of squeeze and usury.

Tenants pay the owner 25–30 per cent of the gross produce of the main crop, but the net revenue of the non-cultivator owner cannot exceed 8–10 per cent of the gross produce of the main crop. The Land Tax in China is realized in kind—the Public Grain therefore stands for rural taxes in general. In 1952, 30 per cent of national income was Public Grain.[204]

AFRICA

With the coming of independence to the many countries of Africa, agrarian reform is necessarily somewhat uncertain, but the general picture of the situation can have altered but little in the past decade. In 1956, a United Nations publication stated:[42]

Many problems in these areas are different from those in other parts of the world. From the point of view of the indigenous agricultural systems, the main problem is the transition from tribal forms of tenure to more individualized forms, which are better adapted to economic development. Disintegration of the institutional framework as the result of population growth, accompanied by the increasing impact of the market economy, has led the administrating authorities to adopt measures to protect the indigenous population against exploitation and loss of land and to foster a more rational utilization of agricultural resources through individual farming.

LATIN AMERICA

Writing in 1954, the United Nations Department of Economic Affairs reported that the governments of Mexico, Bolivia and Puerto Rico had introduced measures of land reform. In the first two countries, the principle of restitution of land to village communities is followed; in Mexico, distribution of land from large to small owners. In Puerto Rico three reform programmes have been introduced, for private ownership of large profit-sharing farms, of family-farm settlement and for settlement of squatters in homestead communities.

CUBA

Under the Cuban Land Reform Act of 1959, holdings of estates exceeding 1,000 acres are prohibited. An exception is made in the case of land for sugar and rice which provides, in the case of rice, that the rice plantation area normally yields not less than 5 per cent above that which in the judgement of the National Land Reform Institute is the average national production for the variety concerned.

On land reform in Latin America, Sir Joseph Hutchinson has summed up the position as follows:[283]

> Land reform is a subject you hear discussed in all Latin countries. Too often it is taken to mean splitting up the properties of those who have large acreages and giving out smallholdings to those who have not. It seemed to me evident that the pattern of land holding—small "fincas" of 10 to 20 ha. in the mountainous coffee areas and large "haciendas" ten times that size or more on the valley floors and the low country— was well suited to their agricultural circumstances. . . . So land reform should be considered in the context of the farming system to be adopted, and on its capital and labour requirements. . . .

FRAGMENTATION

Fragmentation of land, i.e. ownership by individuals of scattered small pieces of land, is found in many countries. This uneconomic division of land arises as a result of laws of inheritance which necessitate division of property and results in successive generations inheriting smaller and smaller pieces of land. This leads to wastage of land, loss of time, limits the use of machinery and makes crop production and animal husbandry difficult. In India, where fragmentation is widespread, efforts are being directed towards consolidation of such holdings. Before the present regime in China, fragmentation was found throughout the country; it is believed that compulsory consolidation has been effected in recent years. Liversage[364] has pointed out that consolidation is not an easy task.

Much persuasion is necessary to obtain the agreement of the majority There are difficulties of valuation, of distribution of wells, realignment of roads and irrigation channels. Even when consolidation has been carried out, no final achievement has been accomplished. The root cause persists. No doubt there is a certain tendency for co-heirs who have observed the benefits of consolidation to endeavour to reach agreement among themselves to minimize fragmentation, but some degree is almost inevitable. In the Punjab the aim is to follow consolidation with the establishment of Better Farming and Better Living co-operative societies, the members of which are pledged to give continuity to the work.

But land reform, as Jacoby has so aptly said,[300] is not only a reform of the way land is held, but just as much reform of the man who tills the land.

INDEBTEDNESS

"Rural debt" states Liversage[364] "has been described as 'the unseen plague of peasant Europe', and its effects are no less serious in the new lands overseas which have been colonized by Europeans. In the East the village moneylender is the indispensable basis of rural life." The writer goes on to remark that in practically every part of the world a large proportion of the occupying owners are struggling under a heavy burden of debt.

In many cases the conditions under which land is held by the cultivator are directly concerned with financing cultivation, but the landlord is not alone in taking advantage of the financial instability of the cultivator. Reports from almost every country in Asia, Africa and South America provide evidence of the poverty of the cultivator and his consequent heavy burden of debt, usually contracted at high rates of interest.

The Burma cultivator has fallen more and more into the hands of the moneylender to whom, in many cases, ownership of the land has passed, so that now 44 per cent of the paddy-land is owned by non-cultivators, while of the 56 per cent who are owners, but few possess areas exceeding 100 acres. Landlords are not necessarily of the professional moneylending class—the Chettiars—but as they own little else than the land, they rely on Chettiars for cash advances as much as do the cultivators. The cultivator has to find money for current expenses, implements, seed and for advances, shelter and food for his labourers who possess nothing until the paddy is harvested. For all these expenses he looks to his landlord, who borrows from the moneylender, but if the cultivator is also the owner, he looks direct to the moneylender. Thus, most of the money lent by the landlord is borrowed from the Chettiar at $1\frac{1}{4}$ to $1\frac{3}{4}$ per cent per month, who lends this money to the cultivator at $1\frac{1}{2}$ to $2\frac{3}{4}$ per cent per month. Loans are repayable to Chettiars in cash, but landlords usually expect repayment from cultivators in paddy.

If the cultivator is unable to obtain loans from the Chettiar or the landlord, he is financed by traders and village shopkeepers who, because the risk is greater, charge higher rates and insist on repayment in paddy, on which they make a further profit.

It is easy to imagine how wide is the interest in the crop at harvest time, everyone looking for the return of money lent, either in cash or paddy. The cultivator, too, usually pays his labourers for work during the season in an agreed quantity of paddy.

The Burma Rice Marketing Section Survey Report[525] sums up the position in the following terms: "The main stumbling-block in the way of marketing progress is the cultivator's chronic state of financial embarrassment. If, in the improved-strain areas, relief from this could be given it should not be impossible to get the paddy unmixed to the primary assembly points. Here it could be graded, and could be sold under standardized and supervised conditions of weighing and measuring. The mutual distrust which finds present expression in adulteration on the one hand and chicanery in measuring and weighing on the other, might then be expected to give place gradually to a mutual interest in maintaining grade standards."

In India, Malaya, and the Philippines the plight of the cultivator is very similar; heavy indebtedness to moneylenders and shopkeepers and a complete absence of financial stability compel him to borrow at high rates of interest and to mortgage his land; this leaves him with very little of the fruits of his endeavours.

Indebtedness, however, appears to be less serious in Thailand. In the non-commercial paddy-growing regions indebtedness is not usually heavy and interests not unduly high. The legal limit of rate of interest is 15 per cent per annum and this is not, in fact, exceeded to any considerable extent. The rate of interest is also restricted by law in Malaya, but is evaded by the moneylender who may compel the borrower to sign for a greater sum of money than is actually borrowed. There are the usual arrangements of loans and repayments in Thailand, usually to the disadvantage of the borrower, but despite this, it is unusual for arrears of interest to be accumulated with the principal, nor are foreclosures for debt very frequent. Land and jewellery are the main securities throughout Asia, but in Thailand many loans are arranged without security.

In Indo-China the moneylenders are Annamites and Chinese, who are usually also local shopkeepers and/or dealers in paddy. Rates of interest charged by them are stated to be frequently very high—they may be anything up to 100 per cent per annum. Before the economic crisis in 1931–2, the majority of the paddy farms were mortgaged, but the position has since improved as a result of government regulations regarding interest rates, coupled with improvement in the market price of rice.

Before the present government assumed power in China, the cultivators in that country suffered from very much the same financial and economic difficulties that beset his counterparts in other Asian paddy-growing regions. It is claimed that at the present time private moneylenders have almost disappeared in China and have been replaced by various measures of co-operative finance.

One may, as Liversage suggests, give insufficient credit to the force of custom when considering the financial arrangements made by the smallholder and the exorbitant rates of interest charged by the moneylenders. But, he suggests that something should be said for the moneylender:

> The village moneylender may use consummate art in getting the cultivators into his toils and keeping him there. He may falsify accounts and add exhorbitant interest to the principal. He may take the cultivators' produce at less than market value. On the other hand, he is often a settled member of the local community, living in the same way and on much the same standard as the rest. His assets are merely book balances, much of them completely frozen. He may seldom actually oust a cultivator from his holding and may always be ready to provide him with the wherewithal to buy food and seed, to carry on through a period of extraordinary expenditure or misfortune. In such case he acts merely as an agency for the computation of paper balances, while the real life of the community goes on undisturbed, even stabilized by his activities. Nevertheless, all observers agree as to the ill effects of indebtedness and it is easy to see that with the gradual diminution of custom and communism in village life the redistribution of claims to wealth will have very serious repercussions on the system of incentives which result in the production of that wealth.

There is one important point of similarity regarding the indebtedness of the paddy planter in almost all regions in Asia—it is that the difficulty is caused less by the needs of the land for capital than by the thriftless nature of the planter. Given the capital, given the loan to tide him over till harvest, in many cases the money will be diverted from the purpose for which it was borrowed. The poverty of the paddy planter is not usually caused by the uneconomic conditions of cultivation or marketing, though they may contribute to his position; his poverty is caused almost invariably by his own improvidence. This must be appreciated if any fruitful endeavour is to be made to better his position. So long as the growers' attitude is as at present, any improvements resulting from new methods of cultivation, better planting material, or more efficient marketing organization, will only add to the prosperity of the moneylender and the landlord. This fact has been too frequently overlooked in the past in connection with various schemes devised by governments to better the lot of the cultivator. There is no short cut to this betterment; the solution of indebtedness still depends on the personal efforts of the cultivators themselves—the will to become independent.

COST OF PRODUCTION

It is difficult to estimate with any accuracy the cost of production of rice in Asia since it is usually cultivated with family labour working at uncertain times. A number of authorities have, however, examined this subject in some detail; their conclusions form a basis upon which one may construct a price-standard that could ensure the well-being of the cultivator and consequently the maintenance of the area under the crop in Asia. It is certain that if the financial returns from the cultivation of paddy are insufficient to ensure an adequate standard of living for the producer, the development of industry in other directions will result in widespread abandonment of paddy cultivation, which once started will be difficult to stem.

Leonard[356] gives interesting data (Table 37) on the labour required to produce an acre of paddy in (*A*) the Saitama Prefecture, and (*B*) of an acre of dry-land paddy in the Iberagi Prefecture of Japan.

(*A*) produces 49·6 bushels of brown rice or 86·4 bushels of paddy; (*B*) produces 21·2 to 25·5 bushels of brown rice or 36·9 to 44·4 bushels of paddy.

It is difficult, however, to reconcile some of these figures; why, for instance, does it require 6·1 man days to thresh 86·4 bushels of paddy from the wet-rice area and 12·1 man days to thresh half that quantity from the dry-land area? It is to be noted also that no allowance is made for work in connection with irrigation.

TABLE 37

LABOUR IN JAPAN PER ACRE

(A) Wet rice			(B) Dry rice		
	Man days	Horse days		Man days	Horse days
Growing seedlings	12·1	1·2	Harrowing ..	2·0	—
Ploughing ..	4·5	4·5	Fertilizing and		
Levelling	4·9	4·0	sowing.. ..	8·1	—
Transplanting ..	8·9	—	Cultivation ..	6·1	—
Cultivation ..	13·0	—	Weeding	16·2	—
Weeding	2·0	—	Harvesting ..	12·1	1·2
Harvesting ..	5·7	—	Drying	2·8	—
Drying	1·2	—	Threshing ..	12·1	—
Transportation ..	0·8	—	Hulling	4·0	—
Threshing ..	6·1	—	Preparation ..	5·3	—
Drying seed and ..			Packing	2·0	—
preparation ..	18·2	—			
Packing for market	2·4	—			
Total ..	79·8	9·7	Total ..	70·7	1·2

Contrast the above estimate with that made in the Report of the Philippine Farmers' Committee on a Visit to the U.S.A. in 1946; that in the latter country two men can farm from 300 to 400 acres of paddy-land with the aid of two 35 h.p. tractors and thirteen other machines, including ploughs, harrows, levellers, drills and harvesters.

Efferson[190] gives the following man hours per acre on Louisiana rice farms: preparation and planting 6·98, growing 17·02, harvesting 18·20—a total of 42·2 man hours per acre on a mechanized farm.

Burgess,[97] writing of conditions in Thailand in 1940, states that the cultivator probably does not consider whether paddy-planting pays. From experience he knows that even in a bad season his food supply is secure, clothing and shelter cause him no anxiety, while if the crop is good and the market price favourable, he enjoys a cash income. This attitude probably applies in all cases where paddy is grown commercially in Asia. In Thailand, as elsewhere, the attitude is different where the land suitable for paddy is limited and where other and more remunerative sources of income exist.

The number of days required to cultivate an acre of paddy in the State of Negri Sembilan, Malaya,[229] is shown in Table 38.

Cultural methods in Java necessitate much hand labour; the actual labour required depends on the nature of the soil, the irrigation conditions, and on the yield of grain. In one neighbourhood the figure is put at 100 days per acre.[210]

TABLE 38

LABOUR IN MALAYA PER ACRE

	Days' work		
	Men	Women	Buffaloes
Part cost of erection of dam or water-wheel ..	5	—	—
Waterways ..	1	—	—
Ploughing—first with buffaloes ..	10	—	10
Digging—by women ..	—	20	—
Fencing and preparation of nursery ..	4	—	—
Transplanting ..	—	12	—
Lifting seedlings from nursery and transport ..	1	—	—
Weeding and after-cultivation	10	—	—
Upkeep of waterways, dams, etc. ..	4	—	—
Harvesting ..	—	20	—
Totals ..	35	52	10

Chandraratna[115] states that in Java the number of hours work on each cultural operation is as follows: ploughing 30–47, second ploughing 27–34, first harrowing 12–27, second harrowing 26–29, uprooting seedlings 35–46, transplanting 151–246, weeding 169–270, harvesting 221–587.

In British Guiana, using a pair of oxen and plough, about 37 man days are required. In this colony, however, the crop is little weeded, if at all, and harvesting is performed with a sickle or by combine.

At the present time, when the price of rice is unusually high, it is fruitless to attempt to estimate the profit obtained by growing rice. Before the war, however, when prices were more stable, it was estimated that the gross income of the cultivator on the Central Plain of Thailand was about £12 per acre. The net income is difficult to arrive at as the work is usually performed by family labour.

The economic position of the cultivator depends less upon the actual price which he obtains for his paddy or rice than upon its purchasing power. Wickizer and Bennett[699] have shown that this purchasing power in some countries, and probably all countries of monsoon Asia, was substantially lower in the 1930's than in the 20's, and distress among the cultivators was certainly evident in the later decade.

THE POLICY OF SELF-SUFFICIENCY

In Asia, for some years past, there has been a growing realization that reliance on outside sources for rice constitutes a weakness in the social system; many efforts have been made to rectify this by various methods of increasing local production, aiming at making paddy cultivation more attractive. Government intervention in the paddy-growing industry was inevitable, but in reviewing the results of various expedients adopted to achieve this object, one is forced to the conclusion that, considering the great effort and expense involved, in the majority of cases the results have been below expectation. Apart from projects designed to improve the lot of the producer by such means as better water control, distribution of improved seed, creation of marketing organizations and the like, which may be considered justified in principle, the most usual method of intervention has been the far more doubtful one of manipulating the price of the product, either in the producers' favour or in that of the consumer—or both. The Japanese, for instance, for years attempted to control the price of rice. Wickizer and Bennett[699], who review these manipulations in considerable detail, conclude that "after two decades of experience, the problem of satisfactorily reconciling the conflicting interests of Japanese farmers, producers in the colonies, distributors and dealers, and rice consumers generally does not appear to have been solved." They point to the great expense of the schemes devised by the Japanese Government in this connection, and conclude that "paying the producer the maximum price and selling to the consumer at the minimum, which amounts to direct subsidy to both, always results in a loss which the government must absorb."

The same writers also examine efforts in the Philippines to control rice and conclude that this "experiment in rice control has apparently not as yet been seriously confronted with the irreconcilable facts that higher prices for the rice grower mean more expensive rice for the consumer."

One is drawn to the conclusion that, necessary as price control may be during a crisis, as a normal means of improving the lot of the producer, of protecting the lot of the consumer, or of attempting to increase production it is unsound, both morally and economically. Wickizer and Bennett remark that the steps to ameliorate the unfavourable economic position of the rice grower in monsoon Asia "that have been taken by governments seem hardly to have touched the fundamental circumstances of rural poverty. Perhaps," they conclude, "the problem is beyond the reach of governmental agencies, or perhaps most of the countries of monsoon Asia can ill afford a drain on national treasuries or a burden on consumers of a magnitude sufficient to raise appreciably the incomes of domestic rice producers." These writers are apparently attracted by some of the more grandiose schemes for rice control which have been proposed, but it is not clear that they are fully aware of some of the more unobtrusive work which has slowly developed, aimed at improving the lot of the cultivator with the minimum of governmental interference. It is true that complete self-sufficiency has never been attained in any of the rice-importing countries of Asia, but a very close approximation to it was attained under the Dutch regime in Indonesia and it seems not unreasonable to hope that its solution may be possible in some other Asian countries.

There is increasing tendency amongst rice-exporting countries to control production within their borders in order to maintain prices at a fair level for growers. Thus, United States farmers voted strongly in favour of marketing quotas and thus take advantage of their Government's scheme under which price support is conditional on compliance with acreage allotments. Italy and Spain have reduced planting to prevent undue accumulation of stocks; Egypt effectively exercises control of the area planted by varying annually the allocation of water for cultivation. In New South Wales, the area to be planted is subject to control by decisions of a Board consisting of representatives of interests concerned.

FINANCING THE CULTIVATOR

CO-OPERATION IN THE EAST

There can be no question that measures for improving supplies of irrigation water and control of water in paddy-fields, improving paddy varieties, introducing better cultural practises including manuring, and research leading to greater knowledge of the requirements of the crop, are essential for increasing production. Apart from these considerations, the greatest obstacle to increased production, especially among the peasant rice growers in the East, is the inadequate financial resources of the cultivator. Consequently, some brief discussion of this aspect is necessary and it is useful to contrast the position as it exists in the East with that in the rice-growing areas of the United States of America, where a high degree of organization in this regard has been built up.

It has become accepted that the remedy for the evils and difficulties which beset the small grower, not only of rice but also other crops, is the introduction of the co-operative principle, and many efforts have been made to introduce co-operative methods among communities of small cultivators not only in the East but also in other parts of the world, based on the success which has attended similar efforts among smallholders in some European countries.

These efforts were, in the first instance, directed mainly to providing financial assistance, but latterly they have been extended to the marketing of produce, the purchase of supplies, and more recently still it has been proposed to apply co-operative methods to the collectivization and cultivation of smallholdings. The beginnings of co-operative finance in the East were in India and took form with the passing of the Co-operative Credit Societies Act of 1904, subsequently amended by another Act in 1912. Later it was extended to a number of other countries, including Ceylon, Burma, Thailand, Malaya, Indo-China, Indonesia and China.

It cannot, however, be said that, except in a few places, it has made any really effective contribution towards solving the difficulties of the small cultivator.

In India progress was rapid in the earlier stages; by 1927 65,000 agricultural credit societies had been registered with a total membership of 2,175,000; their activities covered all forms of peasant agriculture, including rice growing. It will be seen, however, that bearing in mind the size of the population of India, which at that time was approaching 300 million, they affected only a small fraction of the total. Moreover, even at that time, many difficulties and shortcomings had become apparent. The societies were for the most part of the unlimited liability type, following the principle of Raiffeisen, which is based upon pledging the credit of all members to the limit of their resources as a security for money borrowed. For success, it demands the utmost punctiliousness on the part of members in repayment of loans and honouring their obligations, combined with strict adherence to and understanding of co-operative principles, which are by no means simple.

In India the movement has been the subject of repeated committees and commissions of inquiry. As long ago as 1925 the Oakden Commission reporting on the movement in the United Provinces found that "the village society was mostly a sham, the principles of co-operation were not understood and the staffs were unfit for the work they were supposed to do."

Commenting on the position in 1928 the Royal Commission on Agriculture in India remarked: "for these disquieting conditions lack of training in and understanding of co-operative principles was the most important cause. The democratic principle is not so potent a force in checking abuses as is sometimes supposed. Members take insufficient interest in the working of their society; they exercise little restraint over their president and committee, and hesitate to evict from office an incompetent or dishonest neighbour. Office holders on their side dislike incurring the unpopularity attendant on stringent action against recalcitrants and the recovery of overdue debts by legal processes."

The Commission concluded: "the only remedy which appears to offer any sure prospect of success is the patient education of the members of primary societies in the principles and meaning of co-operation by teachers competent to perform the task under adequate supervision."

Since then, experience in many other countries has emphasized and confirmed this dictum. The success which has attended individual efforts among backward communities where these principles have been rigidly applied shows beyond any doubt that co-operation has inherently the power greatly to improve the lot of small cultivators in primitive conditions, but the circumstances and mental outlook of the people themselves make the task one of considerable difficulty.

Among efforts to improve the economic position of small paddy planters, mention may be made of the establishment by the Dutch in Indonesia in 1900 of what were termed "dess lumbungs" or village granaries. They accepted for storage surplus paddy, and lent paddy to be repaid in kind at harvest time. A parallel development was the "dessa" banks or village banks which made small money advances. Both types were under the direction of village headmen, and were supervised by the Algemeine Volkscrediet bank, organized in 1934, which also made somewhat larger loans to cultivators. Attempts were made to introduce co-operative principles into the working of the "dessa" banks but without much success. There was also provision for Native Co-operative Societies, and Government Regulations were enacted for their registration and conduct. In 1935 some 300 societies were in existence, mostly credit societies, but with an increasing number of producers and marketing societies.

In an effort to obtain increased production, the Burmese Government is providing credit for producers. Most producers, however, must still rely on local sources and pay exorbitant interest rates.[548]

In Pakistan, facilities for procuring credit are very closely connected with the work of the extension services. Co-operative societies may acquire capital at 5 per cent from the Agricultural Development Bank of Pakistan or from Regional Co-operative banks. Aid to cultivators is administered through co-operative societies at Union Council level, where credit facilities are available to all cultivators at 7 to 9 per cent interest.

In Thailand, a Co-operative Department, established about forty years ago, organizes Rural Credit Societies. Money is obtained by the societies at 6 per cent and loaned to members at 12 per cent, the loans being utilized mainly for the purchase of land, stock and equipment, though the society may also settle a member's debts on the security of his land. Loyalty of the members to the societies and the regularity of repayment of debt are said to be very satisfactory. A society is usually ready to accept paddy in payment of debt, and societies have now entered into the paddy-buying business.

In Indo-China the co-operative movement had been working for but a few years before the outbreak of war in 1941, and progress was recorded. Through such societies growers have contracted to grow improved strains of paddy supplied by the Bureau du Riz and to entrust the selling of the crop to the societies. Each member receives a cash payment on surrendering his paddy to the society and final settlement is made when all stocks held by the society have been sold. The scheme ensures that large stocks of one approved variety are marketed, and this uniformity enables the society to obtain a satisfactory price. Rural Credit Banks have been formed and serve a useful function in advancing loans to cultivators and in supporting the campaign to increase the use of fertilizers by furnishing credit for their purchase.

In Malaya various efforts have been made to relieve the cultivator of his financial burden. Government rice mills are in operation in competition with the Chinese-owned mills, with the object of stabilizing prices paid for paddy at the mill, and a minimum price for paddy is guaranteed by government. The Co-operative Department has laboured steadily for some years to inculcate the idea of thrift amongst the cultivators. Short-term or seasonal credit is the great need of the cultivator. Usually he obtains such credit from shopkeepers, but this accommodation proves expensive, for the security demanded is usually the crop, which has to be sold to the creditor at an agreed price below the market value. Efforts have been made to organize the smallholders into co-operative credit societies with a view to providing seasonal credit more beneficial to the producer. In many cases such societies have been most successful—so long as they restrict their operations to the supply of seasonal credit—but many get into difficulties by using funds designed to supply short-term credit for long-term purposes, such as the redemption of mortgages.

In China, finance for the farmer, according to Ganguli,[204] is provided either by co-operative finance assisted by State finance or, in the absence of the former, by State finance alone. Large numbers of agricultural co-operative banks have been started under the leadership of the Peoples' Bank, China's Central Bank. Co-operative banks are, however, virtually run by the Peoples' Bank through local branches of the Savings Department. This Department has branches even in remote villages and mobilizes credit for rural economy and agriculture. Every village has its Commissioner of Finance through whom credit is channelled. The Government makes large annual appropriations in the budget for low-interest advances against future delivery of agricultural products. Government also provides fertilizers, seed, draught animals and improved farm implements.

Increased output is encouraged by exempting from tax that portion of the crop exceeding the average for a given area.

In the Philippines, the Farmers Co-operative Marketing Associations make loans to farmers for crop production and farm improvements. It also purchases fertilizers and pesticides for its members. In 1957 there were 455 of these associations. They possess storage facilities with a total capacity of 8 million bushels of rice, and they handle 150 million bushels of rice per annum. This development has been made possible by United States aid through the International Co-operation Administration.[548]

To sum up, it can be agreed that, subject to the limitations already indicated, co-operative methods offer the greatest promise of providing a solution to the economic problems of the small grower.

CO-OPERATION IN THE UNITED STATES

Efficient and well-managed growers' co-operatives have operated in all paddy-growing areas of the United States[63] for many years, and have co-operated closely with various governmental programmes relating to the crop. Before enactment of crop-control legislation in the early 30's, the co-operatives were already exercising some control over members' production by limiting credit to growers. Through close contact with producers, co-operatives have been able to exert an important influence on members in other ways. They advise growers regarding the probable supply and demand, supply them with seed paddy, fertilizers and machinery, furnish irrigation facilities and credit, set up mills, sell the produce and provide storage pending sale of the rice.

No one co-operative performs all these services, for growers' preferences in this respect are not the same in all paddy-growing areas. In each area, therefore, the growers determine which services incident to the production and marketing of the crop shall be undertaken co-operatively. The annual volume of rice handled co-operatively in the United States is stated to be between 25 and 30 per cent of the total production.

Early paddy-growers' organizations have been succeeded by the present American Rice Growers' Co-operative Association, which functions through fourteen member-locals, and operates eleven co-operatively owned warehouses for storing paddy, a credit association, an irrigation company, a land-leasing corporation and a farm supply-buying organization. Two paddy-grading laboratories are also maintained to enable a thorough check on the quality and condition of rice which its members offer for sale. The policy of informing growers regarding all aspects of the marketing situation is said to have contributed much to the excellent relations between members and the Association.

The "locals" operate as separate entities, select their own officers and retain possession of revenues derived from membership fees or other assets acquired by them. Individual growers in areas served by incorporated locals sign marketing agreements with their respective locals, which in turn have a contract with the central association.

In Texas the grower is financed by the Association through the Gulf Coast Credit Corporation, the primary purpose of which is to provide working capital to produce the crop. It also makes loans for harvesting, storage and marketing, and is prepared to make advances to growers on their rice pending sale. The Houston Division of the Association owns and operates an irrigation system which supplies water to some 45,000 acres.

An outstanding development in co-operation in recent years has been the ownership and operation of modern mills for the processing of their members' rice in California and Arkansas. The Arkansas Rice Growers' Co-operative Association now owns three mills, and also owns and operates warehouses with a total storage capacity of about two million bushels of rice. The Association markets only rice grown in Arkansas by the members. The grower may receive up to 75 per cent of the value of the paddy on delivery to the Association and when it is milled an additional advance is made to him.

The Rice Growers' Association of California owns and operates a large rice mill, thoroughly modern in every respect. In addition to its rice-milling and marketing functions, the Association aids its members in financing their paddy crop.

It is a feature of all rice association activities in the United States that members retain control over affairs by election of the directors and by regional representation on the controlling boards. A second feature is that close touch is maintained between associations and members, and every effort is made to keep the latter fully informed of the progress of the affairs of the association and of fluctuating marketing conditions. Thus, while government requirements are largely implemented by the associations, the members give ready co-operation by reason of the smooth working of the machinery of control.

Results of co-operation in the United States are so striking that they need no comment; obviously if parallel developments could be brought about in the paddy-growing regions of Asia they would go far in solving many of the problems. Admittedly, the units cultivated in the United States are much larger, the growers are far better educated, have a wider and more informed outlook and a far higher standard of living. Nevertheless, if the Eastern cultivator could be brought to practice co-operative principles and methods they could not fail to produce striking results.

BETTERMENT OF ECONOMIC CONDITIONS

In most countries in Asia there is appreciation of the fact that the well-being of the country depends in no small measure on maintaining and even increasing the production of rice. On the one hand, paddy cultivation must be sufficiently attractive to the producer; the price to the consumer must be as low as possible, for in the East the cost of living and therefore labour rates of pay depend largely on the price of rice. The solution of this problem of greater profits for the producer and cheaper rice for the consumer can be solved—not by government control of prices as has been attempted in Japan—but by increasing the yield per acre and decreasing the cost of production. Efforts to increase yields have already achieved some success and further advances in this direction may be expected. Further, mechanization of some, at least, of the operations of cultivation, especially transplanting, will lower the cost of production. There remain, however, other problems: unsatisfactory conditions of tenancy, antiquated laws of inheritance (especially those that result in fragmentation of lands), and financing the cultivator. Fragmentation can only be solved by somewhat ruthless alterations in the law and by adjustments in individual holdings. As regards finance, it must be admitted that most of the trouble is due less to the lack of money to finance the cultivation of the crop than to the thriftlessness, improvidence and individualism of the cultivator. While this continues, co-operative societies will have but a limited success. The cultivator must learn thrift, and the initial effort of co-operative departments, aided, let it be hoped, by improved education, must be to teach the necessity for thrift. The problem may be stated in another way; while government aid in improved irrigation and drainage, provision of good seed, better marketing facilities and the like, may encourage the cultivator, the policy of "something-for-nothing" does not pay; people in the Orient, as also in the Occident, appreciate the things they have to pay for more than those that are free. The salvation of the paddy cultivator depends on himself, on his own efforts to free himself from financial embarrassment; this he may achieve through education and co-operation. This has been stated by one authority in the following words:

> It is the fundamental principle of all co-operative activity that material progress is of little avail without a corresponding educational advance in self-reliance, responsibility, and citizenship. But once the stage of governmental assistance in guidance and education has been passed, the co-operative movement in any Colony should proceed on its own momentum as a dynamic people's movement. It will then produce its own leaders and educationists from the ranks of its own members, and gain confidence, experience, and ability with each step forward.[529]

Appendix I

TESTING SEED PADDY FOR PURITY BY THE SEQUENTIAL ANALYSIS METHOD*

A QUICK and statistically valid method of estimating the purity of paddy seed is provided by the method of Sequential Analysis. The main points upon which this method is based are:

(*a*) It is possible to say how many samples of a given size having a given mean content of off-types will be found to contain 0, 1, 2, 3 ... *n* off-types.

(*b*) The number of samples which should be drawn to ensure acceptance or rejection of a bulk lot according to its estimated degree of mixing is reduced to a minimum.

(*c*) The statistical risks involved can be fixed beforehand.

It is desired to know whether a bulk sample is mixed to an extent greater than 1 per cent, and the acceptable risk both as regard to the possible rejection of a lot better than the standard (say, of 1 per cent) and also worse than this standard. The two risks need not necessarily be the same; for instance, the risk of rejection of a "good" sample may be lower than that for acceptance of a "bad" sample. One can also set the highest limit of contamination that is acceptable. The procedure is then as follows:

(1) Fix the size of samples. This will be $\frac{1}{4}$ oz. each. A $\frac{1}{4}$ oz. sample will contain about 2·6 off-types on average if 1 per cent mixture is present.

(2) Fix the acceptable risks of rejecting a good sample or accepting a bad one. These are to be P=0·01 and P=0·05 respectively.

(3) Draw up a sampling table showing acceptance and rejection numbers for a series of samples.

Sampling Table for $\frac{1}{4}$ oz. paddy samples when the maximum mixture is 1 per cent and P=0·01 and 0·05 respectively for rejecting a good sample or accepting a bad one.

---

* Abridged from a simple explanation of the system contained in *Notes on the Improvement of the Yields of Paddy in Ceylon* by D. Rhind.[553]

465

II

No. of samples examined	Acceptance Number	No. of off-types found in each sample	Running total of off-types	Rejection Number
1	*2*	*3*	*4*	*5*
1	—	—	—	17
2	—	—	—	20
3	0	—	—	23
4	3	—	—	26
5	5	—	—	29
6	8	—	—	32
7	11	—	—	35
8	14	—	—	38
9	17	—	—	41
10	20	—	—	44

(4) Proceed to draw the first $\frac{1}{4}$ oz. sample. Examine grain by grain and count those which appear to be off-type. Enter the number in column 3 and the running total in column 4. Continue to draw samples and treat as above until either:

(*a*) The total number of off-types equals or is less than one of the figures in the acceptance column. (*N.B.* If samples 1 or 2 or both show zero off-types a third sample is necessary); or

(*b*) equals or exceeds one of the numbers in the rejection column.

Example 1. A series of $\frac{1}{4}$ oz. samples are drawn, examined and the following figures for off-types obtained:

Sample No.	Column 3	Column 4	
1	2	2	At the 8th sample the work stops.
2	1	3	The total rogues found in the 8
3	3	6	samples equals the acceptance
4	0	6	number (14) and the bulk is passed
5	1	7	as up to (or above) standard, with
6	2	9	a probability of 1 in 20.
7	4	13	
8	1	14	

N.B. It is not correct to say that with 14 rogues in 8 samples the average rogue content is 14/8 or 1·75 per sample. This figure is negatively biased and the true average is higher. The reverse holds for rejection samples.

Example 2:

Sample No.	Column 3	Column 4	
1	3	3	The 5th sample brings the total rogues to 30 which exceeds the rejection figure of 29 for 5th samples. The bulk is rejected with a risk of only 1 in 100 of a mistake being made.
2	7	10	
3	4	14	
4	11	25	
5	5	30	

Rule:

(*a*) When the total in column 4 equals the rejection number (or exceeds it), the bulk is totally rejected and sampling stops.

(*b*) When the total in column 4 equals the acceptance number (or is below it), the bulk is passed and sampling stops.

(*c*) When the total in column 4 lies between the acceptance and rejection numbers a further sample or samples must be drawn until either (*a*) or (*b*) happens.

The assumption has been made that the number of grains per sample does not vary widely. For some small-grained types this is not true but the only effect in practice is to make the test rather more severe.

Example 3. For $\frac{3}{4}$ oz. paddy samples when the maximum mixture is 2·5 per cent and $P=0·01$ and 0·05 respectively for rejecting a good sample or accepting a bad sample.

Sample No. 1	Acceptance Number 2	No. of off-types in each sample 3	Running total of off-types 4	Rejection Number 5
1	—	—	—	40
2	—	—	—	48
3	—	—	—	55
4	7	—	—	62
5	14	—	—	69
6	21	—	—	76
7	28	—	—	83
8	36	—	—	91
9	43	—	—	98
10	*	—	—	105

* Accept if not rejected at the 10th sample.

THE SCOPE AND WORK OF THE INTERNATIONAL RICE COMMISSION

THE Food and Agriculture Organization of the United Nations early recognized that the world's most insistent problem is that of expanding rice production, for not only is rice the staple food of about half the human race, but the daily diet of almost all the peoples of south-east Asia is based on this cereal. By 1950 total rice production had regained pre-war level, but the *per capita* rice consumption levels in the East remained seriously low, because the total population of the areas had increased about 10 per cent since 1937. It was evident that early action should be taken to increase the total production of rice. This urgency for increased production was appreciated by Asian governments, and individually they were pursuing investigations towards this end. It was considered, however, that much greater progress would be made if these governments pooled their knowledge and planned overall rice programmes. Consequently, in May 1947 a group of rice experts from ten countries met under F.A.O. auspices at Trivandrum, India, to study these problems. Their recommendations, which covered a wide field, were summarized in the *Report of the Rice Study Group, Trivandrum, India,* 1947, a F.A.O. publication.

The F.A.O. Conference at its third session, August 1947, noted the recommendations of the Study Group and authorized an international meeting at governmental level to consider putting them into effect. Accordingly, a Rice Meeting was convened at Baguio, Philippines, in March 1948. The nineteen government representatives present made concrete recommendations to governments concerning rice improvements as previously outlined by the Study Group. In order to maintain a continuing rice improvement programme internationally, the Baguio meeting recommended the creation of an International Rice Commission. The establishment of such a body within the framwork of F.A.O. was approved at the 1948 session of the F.A.O. Conference. The International Rice Commission was established in 1949 with a membership of seventeen nations and held its first meeting in Bangkok, Thailand, in March 1949. The fifth session was held in November 1956. The Commission is the first international body having the express function of studying the problems of production and consumption of rice.

The Rice Commission recognized the improvement of rice varieties as the most essential and direct method available to many countries as a means of increasing yields. Consequently, at its first meeting the Commission set up a Rice Breeders' Working Party to co-ordinate the activities of scientists working on this problem. This Working Party held its first meeting in Rangoon, Burma, in 1950; several meetings have been held since.

Following the Rangoon Meeting, a co-operative project, carried out by the Central Rice Research Institute at Cuttack, India, had as its object the hybridization of *Indica* and *Japonica* types of rice, the seed being contributed by co-operating countries for experimental crossings. As a result, the Institute sent out seed of hybrid lines to rice-breeding stations participating in the project. It is hoped that successive generations will be grown in these countries and selections made therefrom in order to secure varieties better adapted to local conditions of soil, climate, disease and pest hazards.

One of the advantages of a hybridization programme such as this is that through crossing and selection a variety can be produced which meets the particular needs of a certain region. Thus in crossing for new varieties of rice, parents have been chosen to fit the specific requirements of each participating country, be it resistance to disease or pest, the need for a strong straw, a variety that does not shatter, or any other character.

The primary aim of rice breeding in Asia is to increase yield, but the value of improved varieties can only be realized to the extent to which they are used by cultivators. It has been estimated that yields in most rice-producing countries could be increased by 10 per cent if seed of the best varieties now available were generally adopted. A well-organized pure-seed production and distribution programme is therefore a prerequisite to the extensive use of improved seed by cultivators. Many countries lack an effective method of raising the general level of seed supplies. The question of how best to secure a wider use of good seed is one of the problems engaging the attention of the Working Party on Rice Breeding.

Realizing the great possibilities in the use of manures and fertilizers for increasing rice production, the International Rice Commission established at its 1950 meeting a Working Party on Fertilizers, which held its first meeting in Indonesia in 1951 and has met once annually since that year. By bringing together the technicians carrying on the work in different countries, the Working Party on Fertilizers expects to obtain a clearer picture of work already done and to show how the experiments can benefit the rice economy, especially in countries where little experimental work has been conducted. The Working Party will also determine the main gaps in knowledge in rice areas for the most effective use of fertilizers and manures and will outline the problems which need to be solved. A number of interesting papers have been published which enables scientists in different countries to compare methods used in their experiments. Consideration has also been given to the problem of training local technicians and International Training Centres have been successfully established.

Working Groups have been set up to study specific aspects of rice production, including mechanization of rice production, storage and processing of rice, and problems of soil-water-plant relationship in the production of rice.

The policy of the International Rice Commission is to concentrate its efforts on a limited number of projects at a time and to branch out into other fields of activity when conditions warrant.[544] This flexibility, wisely guided, should be of very great value to scientists and to the future development in the rice industry.

STANDARDIZATION OF RICE TERMINOLOGY

REPRESENTATIVES of nineteen governments and eight organizations meeting at Baguio in the Philippines in 1948[536] formulated a list of standard terms which appeared desirable in view of the great variety of terms and definitions applied to rice in different countries. The following terms were suggested as being descriptive of the products, would obviate confusion in the trade and assist collection and classification of rice statistics.

Rough Rice or Paddy, defined as rice in the husk after threshing. At present the term *paddy* is used in Burma, India, Ceylon, Thailand and Indo-China; *padi* in Malaya; *palay* in the Philippines, *rough rice* in Japan, Korea and most of the Western Hemisphere; *gabah* in Indonesia and *kwo* in China.

Stalk Paddy. This is defined as unthreshed rice in the husk, harvested with part of the stalk. This applies to some of the paddy, usually cut with the small harvesting knife, with about eight inches of stalk and sold in this condition in bundles. Paddy of this description is sometimes marketed in Malaya, Surinam and Indonesia.

Husked Rice. Rice from which the husk only has been removed; it still retains the bran layers and most of the germs. Such rice is sometimes referred to as *brown rice* even though there are varieties having red or white bran coats. In some regions in Latin America, it is known as *hulled rice*, *cargo rice* in Thailand, *loozein* in Burma, *petjahkoelit* in Indonesia and *pinawa* in the Philippines.

Milled Rice, defined as rice from which the husk, germs and bran layers have been substantially removed by power machinery. This is known as *polished rice* in the Western Hemisphere. Rice is milled to various degrees; if milled to a high degree it is generally called *white rice*.

Undermilled Rice. Rice from which the husk, germs and bran layers have been partially removed by power machinery. This has been known as *unpolished rice* in the United States.

Hand-pounded Rice is rice from which the husk, germs and bran layers have been partially removed without the use of power machinery. This is frequently known as *home-produced rice*, *hand-milled rice*, or in Malaya as *kampong rice*.

471

Coated Rice, defined as rice milled to a high degree and then coated with a foreign substance such as glucose or talcum. This has been called *polished rice* in Europe, whereas in the United States polished rice has referred to rice which has been milled to a high degree. In Japan the same term is usually used for highly milled rice treated with polishing powders. The term "polished" therefore causes much confusion and is now replaced by the word "coated".

Whole-grain Rice should refer to husked, milled, or home-pounded rice which does not contain any broken grains smaller than three-quarters of the whole grain. Previously, the term "whole rice" has been used for husked rice, but also for whole-grain rice, thereby causing confusion.

Broken Rice. Husked, milled, or hand-pounded rice, consisting of broken grains smaller than threequarters of the whole kernel. Various classifications of broken rice are used by the trade, depending on size of grains and amount of foreign material.

Brewers Rice. Very small broken rice, generally used for industrial purposes.

Husks, also called *hulls* or *chaff*, is now defined as the by-product from the milling of rice, consisting of the outer-most covering of rice kernels.

Bran. A by-product from the milling of rice, consisting of the outer bran layers of the kernel with part of the germ. Efferson[190] adds in explanation that it is the product of the first run in the milling process and is equivalent to the term *cargo bran* as used in Thailand and *cow bran* in Burma. The bran obtained from milling parboiled rice in Burma is termed *brown bran*.

Rice Polishings. Now defined as the by-product from milling rice, consisting of the inner bran layers of the kernel with part of the germ and a small percentage of the starchy interior. It has been known as *rice polish* in the United States and variously as *rice meal* and *rice flour* elsewhere.

Glutinous Rice. A type of rice which, after cooking, has a peculiar stickiness regardless of how it is cooked. It can be milled to various degrees or home-pounded in the same way as ordinary rice and will then be called *glutinous milled*, *glutinous home-pounded* rice etc.

Parboiled Paddy. Paddy which has been specially processed by steaming, or soaking in water, heating (usually by steam), and drying. Parboiled paddy can be milled to various degrees or home-pounded in the same way as ordinary paddy and will then be called *parboiled milled*, *parboiled home-pounded* rice. In India, the term raw-rice is sometimes used to indicate that rice has not been given any heating treatment, such as parboiling.

Appendix IV

USEFUL DATA

DATA ON IRRIGATION

One inch of water	= 22,622 Imperial gallons per acre
	= 101·28 tons per acre
	= 3,630 cubic feet per acre
One ton of water	= 35·953 cubic feet
One cubic foot of water	= 6·25 Imperial gallons
	= 7·48 U.S. gallons
	= 62·5 lb. (at 62° F.)
One acre-foot	= 43,560 cubic feet
	= approx. 1 cusec. per 12 hours
One cusec (cubic foot per sec.) for 24 hours	= 86,400 cubic feet or 2 acre-feet (approx.)

CONVERSION RATE, PADDY TO RICE IN VARIOUS COUNTRIES (PERCENTAGE)

Japan, 72; Korea, Rep. of, Mozambique, Portugal, 71; Cambodia, U.S.A., 70; Ceylon, 69·5; U.A.R. (Egypt), 68·8; Formosa, 68·5; Burma, Hong Kong, Brazil, France, Italy, 68; Mainland China, India, Madagascar, Peru, 67; Pakistan, 66·7; Thailand, 66; Philippines, Viet-Nam Rep., 65; Indonesia, Malaya, Surinam, 64; Panama, 62; British Guiana, Australia,* 60.

Note: Official figures revised by FAO Consultative Sub-Committee on the Economic Aspects of Rice. Many estimates are conventional figures subject to a wide margin of error.

CONVERSION: WEIGHTS AND MEASURES

One barrel rice (U.S.A.)	= 162 lb. paddy (rough rice)
One bushel rice	= 45 lb. paddy (rough rice)
One gantang	= 1 Imperial gallon
	= 5·6 lb. paddy (approx.)
One pikul	= 133⅓ lb.
One catty	= 1⅓ lb.
One kilogram	= 2·2046 lb. (avoir.)
One kilogram per hectare (Kg./ha.)	= 0·89 lb. per acre

* 71·5 per cent for paddy exports.

One pound per acre (lb./ac.)	= 1·121 kilograms per hectare
One metric quintal	= 100 kilograms
	= 220·45 lb.
One metric ton	= 1,000 kilogram
	= 0·9842 long ton
	= 1·1023 short tons
One acre	= 4,840 sq. yards
One are	= 100 sq. metres
	= 119·6 sq. yards
One hundredweight (cwt.)	= 112 lb.

SPECIMEN FIELD AND LABORATORY RECORD CARDS FOR RICE SELECTION WORK

19...... MAIN RECORD CARD No..........

VARIETY................ SPECIES.................

CULTURE No.	Pure Line ..	P				
	Mixture ..					
	Selection ..					
	Hybrid ..	X				

No..........................in (19......Record) (Cross Diary)

Objective ....

....

ORIGIN AND LATITUDE..

NORMAL SEASON AT ORIGIN..

WATER AT ORIGIN..INCHES

FIELD PLOT No............................ FIELD RECORD CARD No..........

PLOT SIZE............ × ....ft. = ...acre   SPACING............ × ....INCHES

WATER DEPTH..INCHES

FERTILIZERS ....

YIELD FRESH PADDY..........................lb/plot = ...lb/acre

YIELD DRY PADDY ....lb/plot = ...lb/acre

STRAW WEIGHT..........................lb/acre   PADDY/STRAW..........................

TILLERS: No..........................Height..........................cm.   Angle (*a*) (*b*) (*c*)

LEAF WIDTH..........................mm.   Lodging..........................

PANICLES: Length..........................cm.   Exertion..........................cm.   Weight..........................g.m

LIFE PERIOD..........................days

PADDY: Length..........................mm.   Breadth..........................mm.   Thickness..........................mm.

RICE: Length..........................mm.   Breadth..........................mm.   Thickness..........................mm.

PADDY: Length/Breadth..........................   RICE: Length/Breadth..........................

BEALE'S CLASS..........................   ENDOSPERM: opaque; translucent; abdominal white.

PADDY (dry) 1,000 grain weight..........................gm.

RICE (dry) 1,000-grain weight..........................gm.   BUSHEL WEIGHT..........................lb.

HULLING%..........................   WHOLE RICE %..........................

SHATTERING..........................   AFTER HARVEST RIPENING PERIOD..........................weeks.

475

Pigmentation	Remarks
Caryopsis	
Apiculus	
Husk	
Awn	
Sterile gls	
Stigma	
Leaf sheath	
Auricle	
Ligule	
Node	
Intermode	

ORDERS FOR NEXT CROP............................lb.

SEED AVAILABLE IN STATION............................lb.

19............... FIELD RECORD CARD NO.............................. .

VARIETY.. SPECIES...............................

CULTURE NO.	Pure Line ..	P					
	Mixture ..						
	Selection ..						
	Hybrid ..	X					

No...in (19.........Record) (Cross Diary)
Objective ....
....

Field Plot No......................   Plot Size...................×....................ft. =.................Acre
Sown.....................   Cultural Method..
Spacing..................×.................in.   Water Depth.............................in.
Fertilizers ....
Field Establishment ....
Vegetative Development ....
Flowering.......................................   Panicle Exertion.............................
Harvest Appearance..............................   Lodging...
Other Notes ....
....

Yield Fresh Paddy........................lb/plot =........................lb/acre
Available Seed.........................lb.   Stored...
Orders for next season...

GRAIN SIZE FREQUENCY DISTRIBUTION

LENGTH		BREADTH		THICKNESS	
Class interval 0·1mm.	No.	Class interval 0·05 mm.	No.	Class interval 0·05 mm.	No.
Total		Total		Total	
Mean		Mean		Mean	
S.E.		S.E.		S.E.	

Length/Breadth: Paddy.................   Rice.................   Beale's Class.................
1,000-Grain Weight: Paddy.........gm. Rice.........gm.   Bushel Weight.........lb.

Germination %	Milling Test				
	Paddy Sample Weight	Total Rice Weight	Brokens Weight	Hulling %	Brokens %
At Harvest					
1 Month					
2 Months					
At Sowing					

Colour	Leaf Width (mean of 20 flag leaves)
Caryopsis	1......... 6......... 11......... 16.........
Apiculus	2......... 7......... 12......... 17.........
Husk	3......... 8......... 13......... 18.........
Awn	4......... 9......... 14......... 19.........
Sterile gls.	5......... 10......... 15......... 20.........
Stigma	
Leaf sheath	Total
Auricle	
Ligule	Mean
Node	
Internode	Tiller Angle: Erect; Recumbent; Decumbent

Plant No.	Flowering Date	Tiller No.	Height	Panicle Length	Panicle Weight	Plant No.	Flowering Date	Tiller No.	Height	Panicle Length	Panicle Weight	Plant No.	Flowering Date	Tiller No.	Height	Panicle Length	Panicle Weight
1						35						69					
2						36						70					
3						37						71					
4						38						72					
5						39						73					
6						40						74					
7						41						75					
8						42						76					
9						43						77					
10						44						78					
11						45						79					
12						46						80					
13						47						81					
14						48						82					
15						49						83					
16						50						84					
17						51						85					
18						52						86					
19						53						87					
20						54						88					
21						55						89					
22						56						90					
23						57						91					
24						58						92					
25						59						93					
26						60						94					
27						61						95					
28						62						96					
29						63						97					
30						64						98					
31						65						99					
32						66						100					
33						67						B.F.					
34						68						B.F.					
Total ..						Total ..						Total ..					
Mean ..						Mean ..						Mean ..					

Flowering Date	No.	Tiller Nos.	No.	Height	No.	Panicle Length	No.	Panicle Weight	No.
		Total.........		Total.............		Total.............		Total.............	
		Mean.........		Mean.............		Mean.............		Mean.............	

Mode ....days   Remarks:

Range ....days

Life Period ....days

Red Card used for recording data at Rokupr, Sierra Leone, designed by Dr. E. Roberts

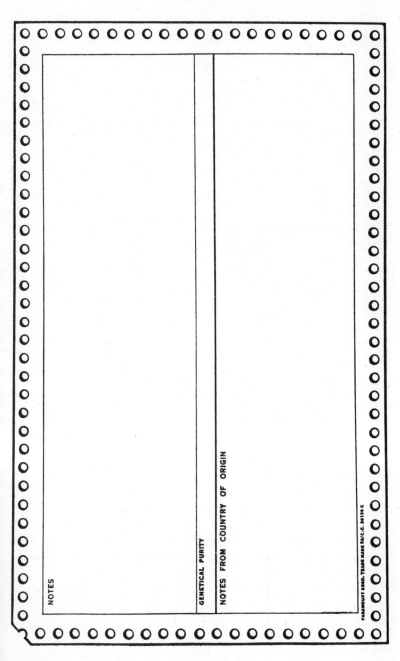

NOTES

GENETICAL PURITY

NOTES FROM COUNTRY OF ORIGIN

PARAMOUNT BDGS. TRADE MARK 56/C.C. 36136 C

KK

Appendix VI

SPECIES OF RICE

A COMMITTEE appointed at a Symposium on Rice Genetics and Cyto-genetics held at the International Rice Research Institute at Los Banos in the Philippines in 1963 drew up a standard classification and nomenclature of the genus *Oryza*. This classification they based on the previous classifications of Roschevicz, Chevalier, Chatterjee and others which made use of the conventional morphological characters of taxonomy.

The committee agreed that in the light of available evidence, the following forms should be recognized as distinct, valid species.

O. sativa L

O. glaberrima Steud.

O. breviligulata A. Chev. et Roehr.

O. australiensis Domin

O. schlechteri Pilger

O. coarctata Roxb.

O. officinalis Wall. ex Watt.

O. minuta J. S. Presl. ex C. B. Presl.

O. eichingeri A. Peter

O. punctata Kotschy ex Streud.

O. latifolia Desv.

O. ridleyi Hook. f.

O. alta Swallen

O. brachyantha A. Chev. et Roehr.

O. angustifolia C. E. Hubb.

O. perrieri A. Camus

O. tisseranti A. Chev.

O. longiglumis Jansen

O. meyeriana (Zoll. et Mor. ex Steud.) Baill

The committee stated that the form usually designated *O. subulata* Nees should be excluded from *Oryza* and recognized as *Rhynchoryza subulata* (Nees) Baill.

NEW PADDY TRANSPLANTER

A PADDY transplanter, made of wood and costing under £10, is being developed by the Overseas Liaison Unit of the National Institute of Agricultural Engineering at Silsoe, Bedfordshire, United Kingdom.

The transplanter is intended to be an improvement on types being used in China and to be cheaper to make. Its construction should be within the ability of local carpenters. The unit is expected to be capable of planting an acre a day. Only one man is required to pull and operate it, but three working as a team will be required to operate at optimum efficiency. The plants will be in rows to facilitate cultivation.

Seedlings are held in a box. With the handlebar raised a grip control is squeezed to operate by means of a cable two "fingers", which grip each of the seedlings in turn. As the handlebar is lowered the seedling is pressed into the soil and the grip released. The bar is raised and the transplanter, which is mounted on a sledge, is dragged forward and the operation repeated. A lever moves the box from side to side to bring seedlings into line with the gripper fingers.

BIBLIOGRAPHY*

[1] ABEYGUNEWARDENA, D. V. W., SURIYADASA, B. and PEIRIS, J. W. L. (1956). Control of seedling blight of rice caused by *Fusarium moniliforne* Sheld (*Gibberella fujikuroi* (Saw)W.). *Trop. Agriculturist*, **112**, 109.

[2] ABRAHAM, E. V. (1959). Control of crabs (*Paratelphusa hydrodromus* H.) in rice fields. *Madras Agric. J.* **46** (2), 56–57.

[3] ADAIR, C. R. (1955). Breeding rice for improved milling and cooking qualities. *Int. Rice Comm. News Letter*, No. 13.

[4] ADAIR, C. R., BEACHELL, H. M. and JODON, N. E. *et al.* (1942). Comparative yields of transplanted and direct sown rice. *J. Amer. Soc. Agron.* **34**, 129–37.

[5] ADAIR, C. R. and CRALLEY, E. M. (1950). Rice yield and disease control tests. *Bull. Ark. Agric. Exp. Sta.* Rep. Ser. No. 15.

[6] AGARWALA, S. D. (1955). On the control of paddy hispa (*Hispa armigera* Oliv.) at Pusa (Bihar, India). *Ind. J. Entomol.* **17** (1), 11–16.

[7] AIYER, S. P. (1936). The agriculturally important soils of Burma. *Emp. J. Exp. Agric.* **4** (15).

[8] AIYER, S. P. (1945). Chlorosis of paddy due to sulphur deficiency. *Curr. Sci.* **14**, 10.

[9] AIYER, S. P. (1945). The significance of sulphur in the manuring of rice. *Ind. J. Agric. Sci.* **15**, 283–97.

[10] ALIM, A. and SEN, J. L. (1955). Floating paddy in East Pakistan. *Int. Rice Comm. News Letter*, No. 14.

[11] ALLEN, E. F. and BEWLEY, E. W. (1949). Investigations into the mechanical cultivation of padi at Chenderong Balai, 1948–1949. *Malay Agric. J.* **32**, 208.

[12] ALLEN, E. F. and HAYNES, D. W. M. (1953). A review of investigations into the mechanical cultivation and harvesting of wet padi with special reference to the latter. *Malay Agric. J.* **36** (2), 61–80.

[13] ALLEN, E. F. and HAYNES, D. W. M. (1955). The mechanical cultivation of wet padi in Malaya. *Int. Rice Comm. News Letter*, No. 13.

[14] ALLEN, E. F. and MILBURN, J. R. (1956). Double cropping of wet padi in Province Wellesley. *Malay Agric. J.* **39**, 48–62.

[15] ALLEN, P. (1958). Plant nutrients: Foliar or soil application. *Span*, No. 2.

[16] ALTSON, R. A. and SIMPSON, I. A. (1941). A note on the distribution of vitamin B_1 (Thiamin) in the rice grain. *Malay Agric. J.* **29**, 127–28.

[17] ANDAYA, L. (1926). The effect of leaf cutting upon the production of rice. *Phil. Agriculturist*, **16** (4), 267.

[18] ANDERSON, M. S., JONES, J. W. and ARMIGAR, W. H. (1946). Relative efficiencies of various nitrogenous fertilizers for production of rice. *J. Amer. Soc. Agron.* **38**, 743–53.

* FOR additional list of references, see page 516.

[19] ANDRIRS, J. R. and MOHAMMED, A. F. (1958). *The Economy of Pakistan.* Oxford.

[20] ANGLADETTE, A. (1954). [Comparative study of various types of rice processing equipment.] (French.) *Industries et Travaux l'Outre-Mer.*

ANONYMOUS AND MISCELLANEOUS REFERENCES

[21] (1958). *Agriculture in Japan.* FAO Association, Tokyo.

[22] (1959). Applying nitrogen in irrigation water. *Rice J.* **62** (5), 26.

[23] (1955). [Bricks from rice hull ash.] *Ind. and Eng. Chem.* **47** (10), 11A–12A.

[24] (1956). The story of Brewers rice. *Rice J.* **59** (1), 34–35.

[25] (1917). *Bull. Imperial Inst.* **15**, 198–267.

[26] (1949). *Chem. and Eng. News.* **7**, Nov., 3279.

[27] (1951). *Investigations into Mechanical Cultivation of Padi in Malaya.* Spec. Bull. Mechanical Series No. 1. Dept. Agric., Malaya.

[28] (1960). Current Notes. *Malay Agric. J.* **43** (2), 121.

[29] (1959). [Damage caused by the total mutilation of the roots of rice plants at transplanting.] *Riso,* **8** (4), 15–17.

[30] (1958). Electronics in Agriculture. *World Crops,* **10**, 106.

[31] (1960). *Experiments at Rice Branch Experiment Station, Stuttgart, Arkansas.* Bull. 620. Agric. Exp. Sta. Univ. Ark.

[32] (1960). Faster work on broader acres. *Far Eastern Econ. Rev.* Sept., 562–64.

[33] (1954). *Fertilizers in Fishponds.* A Review and Bibliography. Colonial Office Fisheries Pub. No. 5. H.M.S.O.

[34] (1957). *Grain Crops.* A Review. Commonwealth Econ. Committee. H.M.S.O.

[35] (1959). *International Rice Yearbook,* 1959 ed. 16, 17, 23.

[36] (?). India: Land Reform from *World Agriculture* International Federation of Agric. Producers, Washington. Vol. IX, No. 4.

[37] (1957). The mechanization of rice cultivation. FAO account of findings of Working Group. *World Crops,* **9**, 233–36.

[38] (1954). Methods and equipment used in Japanese rice cultivation. *Min. of Agric. and For., Japanese Govt.*

[39] (1960). Korea fights for water. *International Rice Yearbook,* 1960 ed. 29.

[40] (1960). *The New Scientist,* **8**, 520.

[41] (1952). The potentialities of upland rice. *World Crops,* **4** (4), 135, 36.

[42] (1956). *Progress in Land Reform*—Second Report. United Nations Dept. Econ. and Social Affairs, N.Y.

[43] (1959). 1850–1959 Review of the growth of rice in Texas. *Texas Agric. Progress* of Texas Agric. Exp. Sta. and Texas Agric. Extension Service.

[44] (1956?). *Rice Hulls and Rice Straw, 1907–1955.* Library List No. 31, U.S. Dep. Agric., Washington.

[45] (1948). *Rice and Rice Diets.* FAO Nutritional Studies No. 1, Washington.

⁴⁶ (1957). Should you use a drying spray on rice when harvest is late? *Rice J.* **60** (12), 10.

⁴⁷ (1958). Time and methods of application of urea. Min. Agric. and For., Govt. of Japan. *Inter. Rice Comm. News Letter*, **7** (1), 14–15.

⁴⁸ (1949). Terraced rice cultivation in the Philippines. *World Crops*, **1**. ,

⁴⁹ (1962). Transplant seedlings upright. *Rice News Teller*, **10** (4), 74.

⁵⁰ (1955). Use of rice fields for fish culture in Thailand. *Int. Rice Comm. News Letter*, No. 13.

⁵¹ (1956). *Weed Control Handbook*. British Weed Control Council.

⁵² AOKI, M. (1939). [Nitrate reduction in paddy-field soil. 1.] *J. Sci. Soil, Japan*, **13**, 357–70.

⁵³ AOKI, M. (1941). [The behaviour of soil phosphoric acid under paddy-field conditions.] *J. Sci. Soil, Japan*, **15**, 182–202.

⁵⁴ ARAI, M. and KAWASKIMA, R. (1952). Weed tests by MCP in paddy rice growing. *Agric. and Hort.* **27**, 182.

⁵⁵ ARBER, A. (1934). *The Gramineae: A Study of Cereal, Bamboo and Grass*. Cambridge.

⁵⁶ ARUNACHALAM, S. (1960). Indirect application of phosphate to paddy through legumes. *Madras Agric. J.* **47** (3), 133–34.

⁵⁷ ASHBY, H. K. (1949). Dry paddy mechanical cultivation experiments, Kelantan, Season 1948–1949. *Malay Agric. J.* **32**, 170–84.

⁵⁸ ATKINS, J. G., CRALLEY, E. M. and CHILTON, S. J. P. (1957). Uniform rice seed treatment tests in Arkansas, Louisiana and Texas, 1955–56. *Plant Dis. Reptr.* **41** (2), 105.

⁵⁹ AZIZ, M. A., PIRZADA, A. R. *et al.* (1958). *Cultivation of Rice in West Pakistan*. Food and Agric. Council, Pakistan.

⁶⁰ AZIZ, MUHD. A. (1960). *Fifty Years of Agricultural Education and Research at Punjab Agricultural College and Research Institute, Lyallpur: Section 11, Rice (Oryza sativa L.)* Pub. Dept. Agric., West Pakistan.

⁶¹ BABA, I. and INADA, K. (1958). Physiological studies of the roots of crop plants. 1. Some characteristics of rice classified as to their age in relation to nutrient absorption. *Proc. Crop Sci. Soc., Japan*, **27** (2), 151–54.

⁶² BAIN, G. H. (1948). *Agriculture in the Sudan*. Ch. 16. Oxford.

⁶³ BAIN, H. M. (1943). *Co-operative Marketing of Rice and its Part in the War Emergency*. Circular No. C-129, U.S.A. Dept. Agric.

⁶⁴ BAL, D. V. and MISRA, R. N. (1932). Some aspects of the growth of rice in heavy black soils of the Central Provinces. *Agric. Livestock India*, **2**, 404–16.

⁶⁵ BAMJI, N. S. (1938). The ammoniacal nitrate and total nitrogen contents of rice soils. *India J. Agric. Sci.* **8**, 839–49.

⁶⁶ BARNETT, S. A. (1948). *International meeting on infestation of foodstuffs.* FAO, Washington.

⁶⁷ BARRERA, A. V. (1937). The effects of certain fertilizers and soil-amendment treatments upon total nitrogen of Nanhayer Clay, a local soil. *Philipp. Agriculturist*, **25**, 689–703.

[68] BARRITT, N. W. (1931). *Biochem. J.* **25**.

[69] BARTHOLOMEW, R. P. (1930). *Bull. Ark. Sta.* No. 257.

[70] BARTHOLOMEW, R. P. (1931). Changes in the availability of phosphorus in irrigated rice soils. *Soil Sci.* **31**, 209–18.

[71] BATES, W. N. (1957). *Mechanization of Tropical Soils.* Temple Press, London.

[72] BEACHELL, H. M. and BROWN, O. B. (1950). *Report on Mechanization and Organization of Rice Production in British Guiana.* Colonial Office, London.

[73] BEACHER, R. L. (1952). Improving fertilizer practices for rice. *Rice J. Annual.*

[74] BEALE, R. A. (1927). A scheme of classification of the varieties of rice found in Burma. *Bull. Agric. Res. Inst. Pusa.* No. 167.

[75] BECKLEY, V. A. (1948). *Pyrethrum Post,* **1** (2), 4.

[76] BELGRAVE, W. N. C. (1932). Padi experiments in Malaya. Part 2, 1930–31. *Malay Agric. J.* **19**, 587–92.

[77] BELGRAVE, W. N. C. (1935). Padi manurial experiments, 1933–34. *Malay Agric. J.* **22**, 583–99.

[78] BELLADEN, L. and GALLIANO, G. (1942). The ash of rice chaff as raw material for refractory insulators. *Chem. Zentr.* **1**, 2179.

[79] BERGER, L. G. DER. (1909). *Teysmannia,* **20**.

[80] BEST, R. (1959). Photoperiodism in rice. *Field Crop Abstr.* **12**, 85–93.

[81] BHALERAO, S. G. (1930). The grain shedding character and its importance. *Bull. Agric. Res. Inst. Pusa.* No. 205.

[82] BHIDE, R. K. and BHALERAO, S. G. (1927). The Kolamba rice of North Konkan and its improvement by selection. *Mem. Dep. Agric. India. Bot. Series,* **14**, 237–76.

[83] BHUIGAN, S. (1949). Transformation of nitrogen in rice soil. *Soil Sci.* **67**, 231–37.

[84] BLACKMORE, A. V., TALSMA, T. and HUTTON, J. T. (1956). *The Cumulative Effect of Rice Growing on two Soil Types on the Murrumbidgee Irrigation Area.* C.S.I.R.O. Division of Soils, Div. Report, Jan. 1/56.

[85] BODEMULLER, —. (1946). The use of treated rice hulls as a loose insulant. *Dept. Commerce and Industry, Louisiana, Barton Rouge.*

[86] BORASIO, G. (1928). [Analysis of rice-hull ash.] *Risicoltura,* **18**, 48–50, and (1930) *Chim. Ind. Application,* **12**, 24.

[87] BOWLING, C. (1957). Seed treatment for control of the rice water weevil. *J. Econ. Ent.* **50** (4).

[88] BOWLING, C. (1959). Control of rice water weevil. *J. Econ. Ent.* **52** (4), 767.

[89] BRADDON, W. L. (1907). *The Cause and Prevention of Beri-Beri.* Rabman, London.

[90] BROWN, F. B. (1957). Natural cross-pollination in rice in Malaya. *Malay. Agric. J.* **40**, 264–67.

[91] BROWN, F. B. (1958). Some effect of seedling age on transplanted rice. *Malay. Agric. J.* **41** (4), 221–65.

[92] BROWN, F. B. (1960). [The potentialities of the Delta Amacuro region for agriculture.] Informe, No. 1207, FAO, Rome.

[93] BRUCE, A. (1922). Bull. 57, Dept. Agric., Ceylon.

[94] BUCK, J. L. (1937). *Land Utilization in China*. Commercial Press, Shanghai.

[95] BULANADI, J. and ALDABA, P. B. (1958). Effects of water depth on the growth and yield of lowland rice. *Int. Rice Comm. News Letter*, 7 (1), 7–10.

[96] BULANADI, J., ALDABA, P. B. and RODRIQUEZ, V. C. (1959). Three years of rice irrigation research in the Malagaya Experiment Station. *J. Soil Sci. Philipp.* 11, 25–37.

[97] BURGESS, C. H. (1940). *A Report on a Visit to Thailand and French Indo-China to Study Padi Cultivation*. Dept. Agric. Malaya. (Not published.)

[98] BURKILL, I. H. (1935). *A Dictionary of the Economic Products of the Malay Peninsula*. 2 vols. Pub. for Malay Govt. by Crown Agents, London.

[99] BURNS BROWN, W. (1950). Fumigants for pest control in stored food-stuffs. *World Crops*, 2 (6), 241–44.

[100] BURNS, H. L. and CASSIDY, M. M. (1951). Method of treating rice bran and rice polish. *U.S.* 2,563,798. Aug.

[101] BUTLER, E. J. (1931). Diseases of rice. *Bull. Agric. Res. Inst. Pusa*, 34, 1–27.

[102] BUTLER, E. J. (1918). *Fungus and Diseases in Plants*. Thacker, Spink, London.

[103] BUTLER, E. J. (1919). The rice worm (*Tylenchus angustus*) and its control. *Mem. Dep. Agric. India, Bot. Ser. X* (1), 1, 37.

[104] CAMUS, J. S. (1921). Rice in the Philippines. *Philipp. Dep. Agric. Nat. Resources Bull.* 37.

[105] CARPENTER, A. J. and ROBERTS, E. H. (1962). Some useful techniques in speeding up rice-breeding programmes. *Emp. J. Exp. Agric.* 30 (118), 127–31.

[106] CASERONI, F. (1953). *Control of Grasses in Rice Fields*. Report from Solplant. (Not published.)

[107] CASS, O. W. (1947). Farm wastes to be used in the manufacture of nylon. *Chemurgic Digest*, 6 (6), 97–101.

[108] Ceylon Department of Agriculture (1955). *Major Pests of Paddy— Their Recognition and Control*. Circ. No. 29.

[109] CHAKRABORTY, S. P. and SEN GUPPA, S. P. (1959). Fixation of nitrogen by the rice plant. *Nature*, 184, No. 4704, 2033–34.

[110] CHAMBERS, J. E. (1956). Mechanization of rice production. *Trop. Agriculturist*, 33, 182–89.

[111] CHAN, T. P. (1955). Problems of *Tilapia* culture in rice fields in Taiwan. *Int. Rice Comm. News Letter*, No. 13.

[112] CHANDRARATNA, M. F. (1952). Photoperiod effects on the flowering of tropical rices. *Trop. Agriculturist*, 108, 4–10.

[113] CHANDRARATNA, M. F. (1954). Photoperiod response in rice (*Oryza*

sativa L). Effects on inflorescence initiation and emergence. *New Phytol.* **53**, 397.

[114] CHANDRARATNA, M. F. (1953). A gene for photoperiod sensitivity in rice linked with apiculus colour. *Nature*, **171**, 1162.

[115] CHANDRARATNA, M. F. (1951). Rice in Java. *Trop. Agriculturist*, **107**.

[116] CHANDRARATNA, M. F. (1955). The genetics of photoperiod sensitivity in rice. *J. Genetics*, **53**, 215.

[117] CHANDRARATNA, M. F., FERNANDO, L. H. and WATTERGEDERA, C. (1952), Seed dormancy in rice. *Trop. Agriculturist*, **108**, 261–63.

[118] CHANG, S. C., LIN, J. and PUH, Y. S. (1947). [The effect of continuous application of the same fertilizer on the yield of rice and the physical and chemical properties of the soil.] *Taiwan Agric. Res. Inst. Bull.* 3.

[119] CHANG, H. S. (1959). Production, certification and distribution of Ponlai rice seeds in Taiwan. *Int. Rice Comm. News Letter*, **8** (2), 8–16.

[120] CHAO, L. F. (1928). The disturbing effect of the glutinous gene in rice on Mendelian ratios. *Genetics*, **13**, 191.

[121] CHARI, K. V. (1957). Agricultural development in Madras State. *World Crops*, **9**, 33–37.

[122] CHARLTON, J. (1923). The prevention of nuisances caused by the parboiling of paddy. *Bull. Agric. Res. Inst. Pusa*, No. 146.

[123] CHATFIELD, H. W. (1950). " Smoke " generators for protecting stored crops. *World Crops*, **2** (2), 70–73.

[124] CHEVALIER, A. and VIGUIER, P. (1937). Sur l'origine Botanique des Riz Cultivés. *C.R. Acad. Sci. (Paris)*, **159** (2).

[125] CHI, C. T. (1936). Key to Economic Areas in Chinese History.

[126] CHURIKOV, I. (1938). [Green manuring for rice.] *Sovet Khlop.* **12**, 49–50.

[127] CLARK, T. F. (1950?). New abrasive for hard soap. *Soaps and Sanit. Chem.* **24** (8), 149–5).

[128] CLARK, T. F. and LATHROP, E. C. (1950). Soft grits provide low cost methods for blast-cleaning metals. *Materials and Methods*, **31** (5), 67–69.

[129] CLOUSTON, D. (1908). The transplanting of rice in Chatisgarh. *Agric. J. India*, **3**, 338–56.

[130] CODD, L. E. (1934). Increased yields of padi obtained by double transplanting. *Agric. J. Brit. Gui. na*, **5**, 274–76.

[131] CODDINGTON, J. W. (1960). Rice market highlights. *Rice J.* **63** (6), 26.

[132] COLEMAN, P. G., HAYNES, D. W. M. and HITCHCOCK, J. L. B. (1956). Observations on the control of weeds in padi fields by the use of herbicides. *Malay. Agric. J.* **38**, 191–99.

[133] COLLIER, G. A. (1947). *Rice Production and Marketing in the United States.* Farmers' Bull. 615. U.S.A. Dept. Agric., Washington.

[134] CONKLIN, H. C. (1957). *Hanunóo Agriculture.* FAO Forestry Development Paper No. 12, FAO, Rome.

[135] COPELAND, E. B. (1924). *Rice.* Macmillan, London.

[136] CORBETT, G. H. and MD. YUSOPE (1924). *Scotinophara coarctata* F. the Black Bug of padi. *Malay. Agric. J.* **12**, 91.

[137] CORBETT, G. H. and PAGDEN, H. T. (1933). Results of stem borer experi-

ments in Krian during the 1931–1932 padi season. *Malay. Agric. J.* **21**, 362–78.

[138] COTTON, R. T. and GRAY, H. E. (1948). Preservation of grains and cereals in storage from insect attack. *FAO Agric. Studies*, No. 2, Washington.

[139] COULTER, J. K. (1952). 'Gelam' soils. A study of their sulphur content. *Malay. Agric. J.* **35**, 22.

[140] COULTER, J. K. (1955). Soil survey of jungle swamps for padi cultivation. *Int. Rice. Comm. News Letter*, No. 15.

[141] COYAUD, J. (1949). [*Results of experiments with chemical fertilizers on fields in Tonkin.*] Arch. Off. Indochin. Riz. No. 36, 28.

[142] CRAIG, J. A. (1934). Agriculture in Kelantan. *Malay. Agric. J.* **22**, 178.

[143] CRAIG, J. A. (1933). Dry padi in Kelantan. *Malay. Agric. J.* **21**, 664–66.

[144] CRALLEY, E. M. (1939). Effects of fertilizer on stem rot of rice. *Bull. Ark. Agric. Exp. Sta.* 383, 17.

[145] CRALLEY, E. M. (1947). Rice seed treatment. *Ark. Agric. Exp. Sta. Rept. Series*, No. 5.

[146] CRALLEY, E. M. (1955). Rice seed treatment. *Ark. Fm. Res.*, Autumn, 1955, 5.

[147] CRALLEY, E. M. and FRENCH, R. G. (1951). Control of *Helminthosporium oryzae* seedling blight of rice by seed treatment with Ceresan M. *Phytopath.* **41**, 8.

[148] CRANE, L. E. (1959). New rice variety "Gulfrose" introduced. *Rice J.* **62** (12), 2.

[149] CRAUFORD, R. Q. (1962). Moisture changes in raw and parboiled paddy in West Africa and their influence upon milling quality. 1. Moisture changes in the ripening crop. *Emp. J. Exp. Agric.* **30**, 315–20.

[150] CRAUFORD, R. Q. (1962). 11. Changes during drying. *Emp. J. Exp. Agric.* **30**, 321–29.

[151] CUNHA, J. M. A. and BAPTISTA, J. E. (1958). Estudo da brança du arroz. 1. Combata da doenca. [A study of "Straighthead" of rice.] *Agron. Lusit. 1958.* **20** (1), 17–64. Esta Agron. Nac. Sacavém, Portugal.

[152] DASTUR, R. H. and MALKANI, T. J. (1933). The intake of nitrogen by the rice plant (*Oryza sativa* L). *Indian J. Agric. Sci.* **3**, 157–206.

[153] DASTUR, R. H. and KALYANI, V. V. (1934). Hydrogen ion concentration and the intake of nitrogen by rice plants. *Indian J. Agric. Sci.* **4**, 803–31.

[154] DASTUR, R. H. and PIRZADA, A. R. (1933). The relative growth rate, and carbohydrate contents and the yield of the rice plant (*Oryza sativa*) under different treatments. *Indian J. Agric. Sci.* **3**, 963–1012.

[155] DAVE, B. B. (1947). Manurial requirements of rice in the Central Provinces. *Indian J. Agric. Sci.* **17**, 245–60.

[156] DAVE, B. B. (1945). Wild rice problems of the Central Provinces. *Indian J. Agric. Sci.* **13** (pt. 1), 46–53.

[157] DAVIS, A. M. (1955). The effect of some post-emergence herbicides on rice. *Proc. 8th Southern Weed Control.*

[158] DAVIS, D. R. (1960). Induced mutations in crop plants. *J. Royal Soc. of Arts*, **108**, 596–607.

[159] DAVIS, W. C. (1955). Rice field weed control in Texas. *Southern Weed Control Conf.*, 182.

[160] DE, P. K. (1936). Fixation of nitrogen in the rice soils under waterlogged conditions. *Indian J. Agric. Sci.* **6**, 1237–45.

[161] DE, P. K. (1936). *Proc. India. Acad. Sci.* 33.

[162] DE, P. K. and MANDAL, L. N. (1956). Fixation of nitrogen by algae in rice soils. *Soil Sci.* **81**, 453–8.

[163] DECOSSAS, K. M., MANY, H. G. *et al.* (1957). Filtration-extraction process. Cost analysis application. *Indust. and Eng. Chem.* **49**, 930–35.

[164] DE COSTA, J.P. L. (1950). [The bird *Agelaius ruficapillus ruficapillus* as a plague of the rice fields in Santa Fe (Argentina).] *Publ. Inst. San Vegetal Ser. B.* **6**, 14.

[165] DEGUCHI, M. *et al.* (1958). Re-examination of the effect of liming on paddy rice. *Soil and Plant Food*, **4** (2), 53–56.

[166] DEIGHTON, —. Ann. Reports Dept. Agric. Sierra Leone, 1952 and 1954.

[167] DEL VALLE, C. G. AND BEBÉ, E. (1947). The tolerance of rice to sodium chloride in irrigation water. *Bol.* 66. *Esta Expt. Agron. Cuba.*

[168] DENNETT, J. H. (1932). A preliminary note on the reaction of padi soils. *Malay. Agric. J.* **20**, 518.

[169] DENNETT, J. H. (1936). The loss of phosphates and ammonia from padi soils kept in the laboratory under anaerobic conditions. *Malay. Agric. J.* **24**, 366–73.

[170] DESIKACHAR, H. S. R. MAJUMDAR, S. K., *et al.* (1955). *India. Bull. Cent. Food Tech. Res. Inst.*, *Mysore*, **5**, 50–53.

[171] DESIKACHAR, H. S. R. and SUBRAHMANYAN, V. (1960). Rice technology in India. *Int. Rice Yearbook*, 1960 ed. 26–28, 30.

[172] DHAR, N. R. and MUKERJIE, S. K. (1935). Further experiments on the fixation of atmospheric nitrogen in the soil and the utilization of molasses as a fertilizer. *Proc. Acad. Sci. U.P. India*, **5**, 61–70.

[173] DIAS, G. R. W. (1956). Rice mechanization in Ceylon. *World Crops*, **8**, 405–7.

[174] DICKSON, J. G. (1947). *Diseases of Field Crops.* McGraw-Hill Book Co.

[175] DIJK, J. W. VAN (1948). [Experiments on the use of ammonia in irrigation water applied to rice.] *Meded. Alg. Proefsta. Landbouw.* **70**, 8.

[176] DIRVEN, J. G. P. and POERINK, H. J. (1955). Weeds in rice and their control in Suriname. *Trop. Agric.* **32**, 115–23.

[177] *Diseases and Pests of Crops with recommendations for Control* (1955). Dept. Agric., Malaya.

[178] DOI, Y and YAMAGATA, M. (1958). Further studies on the roots of rice plants by means of transparent plastic pots. *Bull. Pac. Agric. Yamaguti.* No. 8, 713–22.

[179] DON, WAN MOHD. (1959). Some notes on the development of an improved animal-drawn plough. *Malay. Agric. J.* **42** (4), 211–16.

[180] DONE, J. (1949). The effects of various treatments of paddy rice on the

aneurin and nicotinic acid content of the milled grain. *Brit. J. Nutrition*, 3, 335–45.

[181] DORE, J. (1955). Dormancy and viability of padi seed. *Malay. Agric. J.* 38 (3) , 163–73.

[182] DOUGLAS, C. E. (1949). *Report on the Cultivation and Preparation of Rice in Egypt*. Govt. Egypt.

[183] DUDAL, R. (1958). Paddy soils. *Int. Rice Comm. News Letter*, 7 (2), 19–27.

[184] DUNSANY, LORD (1945). *The Sirens Walk*. Jarrolds, London.

[185] DZULAI, A. P. (1949). Selekuji i Semenovodstoo. (Breeding and seed growing), No. 3.

[186] DZULAI, A. (1946). [Extending the cultivation of rice in the central regions of U.S.S.R.]. *Soc. Seljie, Hoz.* No. 12, 46–50.

[187] EASTER, S. S. (ed.) (1948). *Preservation of Grains in Storage*. FAO Agric. Studies, No. 2, Washington.

[188] EDHOLM, H. (1932). *Tekniska Meddelanden fran Kungl. Vattenfalls-styrelsen*. Ser. E. No. 18. Uppsala, Sweden.

[189] EFFERSON, J. N. (1949). *The Market Outlook and Prospective Competition for United States Rice in Asia, the Near East and Europe*. Foreign Agric. Rep. No. 35, U.S.A. Dept. Agric.

[190] EFFERSON, J. N. (1952). The Production and Marketing of Rice. *Rice J.*

[191] EVANS, G. *Medical Treatment Principles and their Application*. Butterworth, London.

[192] EVANS, J. W. (1948). *Recent Developments in the Control of Insect Infestation of Stored Wheat in Australia*. Int. Meeting on Infestation of Foodstuffs, *FAO Agric. Studies*, No. 2.

[193] EVANS, L. J. C. (1957). Ratooning rice. *World Crops*, 9, 227–28.

[194] FAO Rice Report for 1963.

[195] FARMER, B. H. (1957). *Pioneer Peasant Colonization in Ceylon*. Oxford.

[196] FAULKNER, M. D. and MIEARS, R. J. (1961). Levelling land in water. *Rice J.* 64 (6), 10, 12–14.

[197] FAUTER, M. F., LAUTER, W. M. and RUBIN, S. H. (1946). Enrichment of rice with synthetic vitamins and iron. *Indust. and Eng. Chem.* 38, 486.

[198] FERNANDO, H. E. (1953). Admin. Rep. Dir. Agric. Ceylon, 1952. Part IV. Education, Science and Ant. (C). 47.

[199] FERNANDO, H. E., WEERAWARDENA, G. V. and MANICKAVASAGER, P. (1954). Paddy pest control in Ceylon. *Trop. Agriculturist*, 110 (3), 197–206.

[200] FINLOCK, D. C. (1963). Plastic levees in rice fields. *World Crops*, 15 (1), 17–18.

[201] FREEMAN, J. D. (1955). *Iban Agriculture. A Report on the Shifting Cultivation of Hill Rice by the Iban of Sarawak*. H.M.S.O., London.

[202] FRENCH, E. W. (1963). Weed control in rice fields. *World Crops*, 15 (5), 196–206.

[203] FUKE, Y. (1955). [On the genes controlling the heading time of leading rice varieties in Japan and their specific responses to day length and

temperature.] *Bul. Nat. Inst. Agric. Sci. (Japan) Ser. D. Pl. Physiol.* **5**, 1–7.

[204] GANGULI, B. N. (1950?). *Land Reform in North China*. Delhi School of Economics. Rangit.

[205] GARCIA DURAN, E. (1962). El cultivo de la "Soca" del Arroz. (Ratooning of rice.) *Arroz*, **11**, 124, 8.

[206] GASTROCK, E. A., D'AQUIN, E. L. and VIX, H. L. E. (1952). *Offic. Proc. Annual Convention Nat. Cottonseed Products Assoc.* **56**, 30–37.

[207] GASTOCK, E. A. *et al.* (1953). *Soyabean Digest*, **13** (8), 16–17.

[208] GEUS, J. G. DE (1954). *Means of Increasing Rice Production*. Centre d'Etude de l'Azote, Geneva.

[209] GHOSH, A. K. (1947). The use of Gammexane (666) for the control of insect pests of stored rice. *Ind. Farming*, **8**, 129–32.

[210] GIESSEN, C. VAN DER (1943). *Rice Culture in Java and Madura*. Contribution No. 11 of Chuo Noozi Sikenzyoo, Java.

[211] GIGLIOLI, E. G. (1957?). *Red Rice Investigations, 1951–56*. Brit. Guiana Rice Development Co. Ltd.

[212] GIGLIOLI, E. G. (1959). Mechanized Rice Production at the Mahaicony-Abary Scheme, British Guiana. *Trop. Agric.* (Trinidad), **36** (1), 11–12.

[213] GO, B. H. and SCHUYLENBORGH, J. VAN (1959). Leaf composition of lowland rice and sugar cane as an indicator of their performance. *Netherlands J. Sci.* **7** (2), 110–15.

[214] GOODEY, J. (1936). *Helminth.* **14**, 107.

[215] GOOR, G. A. W. VAN DE (1941). [Green manuring of lowland rice.] *Meded. Alg. Proefsta. Landbouw*, **50**, 28.

[216] GOPALACHARI, N. C. (1952). Phytohormones and nitrogen deficiency in paddy. *Madras Agric. J.* **36** (2).

[217] GORRIE, R. M. (1935). *The Use and Misuse of Land*. Oxford Forestry Memoirs No. 1. Oxford.

[218] GORRIE, R. M. (1954?). *Forestry Development and Soil Conservation in the Upper Damodar Valley*. Damodar Valley Corp. Alipore, Calcutta.

[219] GORRIE, R. M. (1954). Progress in tropical soil and water conservation. *Soils and Fertilizers*, **17**, 83–85.

[220] GORRIE, R. M. (1954). *Report on Kotmale Landslips and Adjoining River Catchments*. Sessional Paper XVII. Govt. Press, Ceylon.

[221] GOURLEY, D. W. (1931). *Rice Cultivation in China*. (Not published.)

[222] GRACI, JR. A. V. *et al.* (1953). Pilot-plant application of filtration-extraction of rice bran. *J. Amer. Oil Chem. Soc.* **30** (4), 139–43.

[223] GRACI, JR. A. V. *et al.* (1955). A bench-scale method for evaluating the processing characteristics of oilseeds for filtration-extraction. *J. Amer. Chem. Soc.* **32** (3), 129–31.

[224] GRAHAM, R. J. D. (1913). Preliminary note of the classification of rice in the Central Provinces. *Mem. Dep. Agric. Indian Bot.* **7**, No. 7.

[225] GRANT, J. W. and U THEIN AUNG (1941). Growth studies in rice. *Indian J. Agric. Sci.* **4**, 500.

[226] GRANT, J. W. (1939). *The Rice Crop in Burma.* Agric. Survey 17 of 1932. Reprint 1939.

[227] GRANTHAM, J. (1917). Some soils from the Kuala Pilah and Jelebu Districts. *Agric. Bul. F.M.S.* 4, 244.

[228] GRIGARICK, A. A. (1963). Rice insect control in California. *Rice J.* 66 (7), 46.

[229] GRIST, D. H. (1922). *Wet Padi Planting in Negri Sembilan.* Spec. Bul. No. 33, F.M.S. Dept. Agric.

[230] GRIST, D. H. (1936). *An Outline of Malayan Agriculture.* Dept. Agric., Malaya.

[231] GRIST, D. H. (1963). Fertilizing paddy. *Span,* 6 (1), 27–29.

[232] GRIST, D. H. and SYED ABDUL RAHMAN (1921). Cultivation of tengala padi. *Agric. Bul. F.M.S.* 9.

[233] GROSTIER, B. and ARTHAUD, J. (1957). *Ankor, Art and Civilization.* Thames and Hudson, London.

[234] GRUBER, F. (1958). [A new procedure for crossing rice.] *Novenyter-meles,* 7, 331–40.

[235] GUPTA, P. S. and MITRA, A. K. (1948). Possibilities of increasing the yield of rice by ratooning in the United Provinces. *Indian Farming,* 9, 13–15.

[236] GUSHCHIN, G. G. (1933). [The problem of increasing the production of rice.] *Bull. Al. Bot. Leningrad,* Ser. A, 5–6, 163–76.

[237] GUSHCHIN, G. G. (1934). De la classification botanique de sa culture. *Riz et Riziculture,* 18.

[238] GUSHCHIN, G. G. (1938). Le riz: origine et histoire de sa culture. *Riz et Rizie,* 12 (2).

[239] HADAWAY and BARLOW (1952). *Bull. Ent. Res.,* 281–311.

[240] HAIGH, J. C. (1943). The relation between grain and straw weight in the paddy crop. *Trop. Agric.* 95, 142–46.

[241] HAINES, JR., H. W., PERRY, G. C. and GASTROCK, E. A. (1957). Filtration-extraction of cottonseed oil. *Indust. and Eng. Chem.* 49 (6), 920–29.

[242] HALL, D. W. and HYDE, M. B. (1954). The modern method of hermetic storage. *Trop. Agric. (Trin.)* 31, 149–60.

[243] HALL, V. L. (1960). Water seeding of rice in Arkansas. *Rice J.* 63 (13), 13.

[244] HALL, W. J. (1954). *Plant Pests in British Colonial Dependencies in 1954.* FAO Plant Protection Bull. 3.

[245] HALPERIN, H. (1957). *Changing Patterns in Israel Agriculture.* Routledge and Kegan Paul, London.

[246] HANSON, A. P. (1933). Brief notes on the culture of upland rice. *Jamaica A.S.,* March, pp. 155–56.

[247] HARADA, T. (1954). Studies on the blue-green algae in Japan. *Int. Rice Comm. News Letter,* No. 10.

[248] HARADA, T. and EDO, Y. (1956). Influence of 2,4-D upon lodging. *Proc. Crop Sci. Soc. Japan,* 25 (2), 64–66.

[249] HARDCASTLE, J. E. Y. (1959). The development of rice production and research in the Federation of Nigeria. *Trop. Agric. (Trin.),* 36 (2).

[250] HARRIS, E. and KLINNER, W. E. (1955). Developments in motorized agricultural machinery. *World Crops*, **7** (10), 385–89.

[251] HARRISON, W. H. and AIYER, P. A. (1913, 1914, 1916). The gases of swamp soils: I. Their composition and relationship to the crop (Vol. III, No. 3, October 1913). II. Their utilization for the aeration of the roots of the crop (Vol. IV, No. 1, October 1914). III. A hydrogen-oxidizing bacterium from these soils (Vol. IV, No. 4, April 1916). *Mem. Dept. Agric. India* (Chem. Ser.).

[252] HART, M. G. R. and ROBERTS, E. H. (1961). Possibility of fixation of atmospheric nitrogen by the rice plant. *Nature*, **189**, 4764, 598–99.

[253] HARTLEY, C. W. S. (1949). Investigations into the mechanical cultivation of wet padi, 1948–49. A general review. *Malay. Agric. J.* **32**, 141–51.

[254] HARVEY, W. A. (1950). Weed control in rice with MCPA. *Down to Earth*, **8**, 1.

[255] HASHIOKA, Y. (1952). Application of new fungicides to rice cultivation. *Agric. and Hort., Tokyo*, **27**, 485–92.

[256] HASHIOKA, Y. (1952). Simplification of the rice seed disinfection and application of Arasan. *Plant Prot.*, Japan, **4**, 173–75.

[257] HAWKINS, J. C. (1958). Mechanization of rice growing. *Outlook on Agric.* **11** (2), 55–63.

[258] HAYNES, D. W. M. (1955). Rice mechanization in the Federation of Malaya. *Int. Rice Comm. News Letter*, No. 16.

[259] HAYNES, D. W. M. (1955). Further investigations into the use of self-propelled combine harvesters for the harvesting of wet padi in the North Kedah Plain. *Malay. Agric. J.* **38** (4), 237–56.

[260] HAYNES, W. D. M. (1955). Investigations into the mechanical collection and baling of padi straw during the 1953–54 harvest. *Malay. Agric. J.* **38** (1), 27–37.

[261] HAZIME, Y. (1941). The nature of rice blast disease. 3. Relation between rice-blast resistance and some physical and chemical properties of the different portions of the leaf blade of rice. *Bul. Soc. Fakultato Terkultura, Kyusyu Imp. Univ.* **9**, 297–306.

[262] HECTOR, G. P. (1922). Correlation of colour characters in rice. *Dep. Agric. Ind. Bot. Ser.* **11**, 153.

[263] HECTOR, G. P. (1927–28). Transpiration of rice. *Bengal Dept. Agric. Annual Report*.

[264] HECTOR, J. M. *Introduction to the Botany of Field Crops*. Vol. I, *Cereals*. South African Agric. Series, Vol. 16.

[265] HEDAYETULLAH, S., ROY, K. P. and SEN, S. (1947). A study on the effect of cultural factors in transplant paddy on the behaviour of some plant characters influencing the yield. *Indian Agric. Sci.* **17**, 69–80.

[266] HELY, P. C. (1957). *Insect Pests of the Rice Crop*. Dep. Agric. N.S.W., Australia.

[267] HENDRY, D. (1928). Manuring of paddy in Lower Burma. *Agric. J. India.* **23**, 327–68.

[268] HERFORD, G. V. B. (1952). *J. Sci. Food and Agric.* No. 1, p. 10.

[269] HERKLOTS, G. A. C. (1948). Rice cultivation in Hong Kong. *Food and Flowers*, No. 2, 1–20. Dept. Agric., Hong Kong.

[270] HESSE, P. R. (1961). Some differences between the soils of *Rhizophora* and *Avicennia* mangrove swamps in Sierra Leone. *Plant and Soil*, 14 (4), 335–46.

[271] HICKLING, C. F. (1947). Unpublished notes made in the course of a tour of the Far East in 1947. Colonial Office, London.

[272] HIGINBOTHAM, N. (1945). *Proc. Ind. Acad. Sci.*, IV, 37.

[273] HINTON, J. C. (1948). The distribution of vitamin B_1 in the rice grain. *Brit. J. Nutrition*, 2, 237–41.

[274] HINTON, J. C. (1948). Parboiling treatment of rice. *Nature*, 162, 913.

[275] HITCHCOCK, A. E., ZIMMERMAN, P. W. *et al.* (1949, 1950). Water hyacinth: its growth, reproduction and practical control by 2,4-D. *Contribs. Boyce Thomson Inst.* 15, 363 and 16, 91.

[276] HITCHCOCK, L. B. and DUFFEY, H. R. (1948). Commercial production of furfural in its twenty-fifth year. *Chem. Engr. Progress*, 44, 669–74.

[277] HOFFMAN, W. E. (1934). Preliminary notes on the freshwater fish industry in South China, especially Kwangtung Province. *Sci. Bull.* No. 5, Lingnan Univ., Canton.

[278] HOOD, C. R. (1961). Sod-seeding rice could cut costs. *Agric. Gaz. of N.S.W.* 72, Pt. II, 567–69.

[279] HUANG, H. S. (1946). The effect of water fallow practice in winter on the production of rice. *Soils Quart.* 5 (1), 25–29.

[280] HUKILL, W. V. (1948). Modern construction of storage places to reduce losses due to insects, rodents, and fungi. *FAO Agric. Studies*, No. 2.

[281] HUNGERFORD, D. (1950). The Australian rice harvest. *World Crops*, 2, 498–501.

[282] HUTCHINSON, J. B. and RAMIAH, K. (1938). Description of crop plant characters and their ranges of variation. 11. Variability of rice. *Indian J. Agric. Sci.* 8, 592.

[283] HUTCHINSON, J. (1961). Jonah and the airborne whale. *Emp. Cotton Growing Rev.* 38 (2).

[284] HWANG, S. T., FENG, C. L. *et al.* (1945). A five-year field experiment on the response of rice to different nitrogenous fertilizers. *J. Agric. Ass. China*, No. 179, 68–83, V–VII.

[285] ICHIKAWA, C. (1937). Effects of deficiency of three essential elements on the yield, ash constituents and nitrogen content of unhulled rice. *J. Agric. Chem. Soc. Japan*, 13, 639–48.

[286] IGNATIEFF, V. (1951). *Results of Experiments and Practical Experience in the Use of Fertilizers, Manures and Soil Amendments with Rice.* FAO, Washington.

[287] INGATIEFF, V. (ed.) (1954). *Report of the 4th Meeting of the Working Party on Fertilizers, Tokyo, Japan.* Int. Rice Commission, FAO.

[288] INGEBRETSEN, K. H., BASKETT, R. S. *et al.* (1957). Weeds in drained rice fields. *California Agric.* 11 (7), 5.

[289] INGRAM, J. W. (1950). Rice insects in Japan. *Rice J.* 53 (7), 30–32, 41.

[290] IRVINE, F. R. (1953). *A Text Book of West African Agriculture, Soils and Crops.* Oxford.

[291] ISELY, D. and SCHWARDT, H. H. (1934). The rice water weevil. *Ark. Agric. Exp. Sta. Bull.* 299.

[292] ISHIBASHI, H. (1939). The relationship between the effects of silica and nitrogen, and silica and phosphorus, in the nutrition of the rice plant. *J. Sci. Soil, Tokyo,* 13, 227–42.

[293] ISO, E. (1954). *Rice and Crops in its Rotation in Subtropical Zones.* Japan FAO Association, Tokyo.

[294] ITANO, A. (1928). The carbon-nitrogen ratio and microbiological investigations of the soil in rice fields. *Proc. First Int. Congress Soil Sci.* 3, 269–73.

[295] IWADARE, S. (1931). *J. Sapporo Soc. Agric. and For.* 22, 458–59.

[296] IYER, S. N. C. and MUDALIAR, C. R. (1950). Green manure plants for saline tracts. *Fact,* 4, 359–62.

[297] JACK, H. W. (1923). *Rice in Malaya.* Dep. Agric., Malaya Bull. 35.

[298] JACK, H. W. and JAGOE, R. B. (1930). Rice storage experiments. *Malay. Agric. J.* 18, 447–54.

[299] JACKS, G. V. and MILNE, M. K. (1954). *An Annotated Bibliography of Rice Soils and Fertilizers.* Commonwealth Bureau of Soil Sci., Harpenden.

[300] JACOBY, E. H. (1953). Inter-relationship between agrarian reform and agricultural development. *FAO Agric. Studies,* No. 26.

[301] JENKINS, J. M. and JONES, J. W. (1944). *Louisiana Expt. Sta. Bull.* 284.

[302] JEPSON, W. F. (1954). *A Critical Review of the World Literature on the Lepidopterous Stalk Borers of Tropical Graminaceous Crops.* Commonwealth Inst. Entomology.

[303] JIMENEZ-CUENDE, F. (1955). The increase of rice cultivation in Spain. *World Crops,* 7, 401–3.

[304] JOACHIM, A. W. R. (1940). Analysis of some manures, fodders and feeding stuffs. *Trop. Agriculturist,* 94.

[305] JOACHIM, A. W. R. and KANDIAH, S. (1929). Laboratory and field studies of green-manuring under paddy-land (anaerobic) conditions. *Trop. Agriculturist,* 72, 253–71.

[306] JODON, N. E. (1938). Experiments on artificial hybridization of rice. *J. Amer. Soc. Agron.* 30, 294.

[307] JODON, N. E. (1948). *Summary of Rice Linkage Data.* U.S. Dep. Bureau of Plant Industry, Beltsville. (Mimeographed.)

[308] JOHNSON, A. G. (1948). The role of fungi in the deterioration of grains in storage. *FAO Agric. Studies,* No. 2, Washington.

[309] JOHNSTONE, D. E. (1959). Rice tolerance in infants: Marked food allergy. *Ann. Allergy,* 17, 350, and 30, 87–88.

[310] JONES, J. W. (1934). *How to Grow Rice in the Sacramento Valley.* Farmers' Bull. 1240, U.S.A. Dept. Agric., Washington.

[311] JONES, J. W. and JENKINS, J. M. (1938). *Rice Culture in the Southern States.* Farmers' Bull. 1808, U.S.A. Dept. Agric., Washington.

[312] JONES, J. W. and LONGLEY, A. F. (1941). Sterility and aberrant chromo-

some numbers in Calero and other varieties of rice. *J. Agric. Res.* **62**, 381.

[313] JONES, MARIE A. (1959). Research on rice at the Southern Regional Laboratory. *Cereal Sci. Today*, **4** (10).

[314] JORDAN, H. D. (1957). Crabs as pests of rice on tidal swamps. *Emp. J. Exp. Agric.* **25**, 197–206.

[315] JORDAN, H. D. (1957). Hybridization of rice. *Trop. Agric.* **34**, 133–36.

[316] JORDAN, H. D. (1962). Traditional rice cultivation practices: Should there be a reappraisal? *Curr. Sci.* **31**, 269–70.

[317] JUILLET, A. and TURQUOIS, J. (1950). The role of anti-bunt products in the treatment of rice grain. *C.R. Acad. Agric. Fr.* **36** (1), 29–32.

[318] KADAM, B. S. (1935). A virescent white mutant of rice. *Curr. Sci.* **3**, 301.

[319] KADAM, B. S. and PATANKAR, V. K. (1938). Inheritance of aroma in rice. *Chron. Bot.* **4**, 496.

[320] KADAM, B. S. and RAMIAH, R. (1943). Symbolization of genes in rice. *Ind. J. Genet. and Pl. Breed.* **3**, 7.

[321] KADAM, B. S. and RAMIAH, R. (1943). Bibliography on genetics of rice. *Ind. J. Genet. and Pl. Breed.* **3**, 125.

[322] KAMOSHITA, Y. (1932). The cause of the unproductivity of a certain volcanic soil for paddy rice. *J. Imp. Exp. Sta. Tokyo* **2**, 39–47.

[323] KAPP, L. C. (1933). *Study of Rice Fertilization.* Bull. Ark. Agric. Exp. Sta. 281, 37.

[324] KARAI, M. (1936). Influence of N, P_2O_5 and K_2O upon the amount and quality of agricultural products. *J. Sci. Soil, Tokyo.*

[325] KARIM, A. and KHAN MAJLIS, M. A. (1958). A study of the formative effect of sulphur on the rice plant. *Pakistan J. Sci. Res.* **10** (2), 52–55.

[326] KARUNAKER, P. D. and DANIEL, F. L. (1960). Preliminary studies on pH fluctuations in rice soils during the growth of rice plants. *Indian J. Agric. Sci.* **20**, 173–84.

[327] KATAYAMA, Y. (1954). Studies on the haploidy in relation to plant breeding. 11. Offsprings from haploid individuals of rice. *Cytologia, Tokyo*, **19**, 152.

[328] KAUFMAN, P. B. (1953). Gross morphological responses of the rice plant to 2,4-D. *Weeds*, **2**, 223–53.

[329] KAUFMAN, P. B. and KRAFTS, A. S. (1956). Responses of the rice plant to different formulations and methods of application of 2,4-D, 2,4,5-T and MCPA. *Hilgardia*, **24** (15), 411–53.

[330] KELLY, W. P. (1911). *Hawaii Agric. Exp. Sta. Bull.* 24.

[331] KIK, M. C. and WILLIAMS, R. R. (1945). Nutritional improvement of white rice. *Nat. Res. Council Bull.* 112.

[332] KIK, M. C. (1945). Effect of milling, processing, washing, cooking, and storage on thiamine, riboflavin, and niacin in rice. *Univ. Ark. Bull.* 458.

[333] KIK, M. C. (1957). The Nutritive Value of Rice and its By-Products. *Bull.* 589, *Agric. Exp. Sta. Univ. Ark.*

[334] KIK, M. C. and EASTERLING, L. (1962). Rice protein supplementation. *Ark. Farm Res.* **9** (4).

[335] KIKKAWA, S. (1912). On the classification of cultivated rice. *J. Coll. Agric. Univ. Tokyo.* 3.

[336] KIRKPATRICK, H. (1958). Eradication and control of water hyacinth: Results of a campaign in the Belgian Congo in 1955–57. *World Crops,* 10, 286–88.

[337] KIYOSAWA, S. and AIML, R. (1959). The influence of temperature and shading on the development of the rice panicle. *Proc. Crop Sci. Soc. Japan,* 27 (4), 417–21.

[338] KOBER, E. A. M. (1957). [How to control *Solubea poecila* on rice.] *Lavoura Arrozeira,* 11 (124), 24–25.

[339] KONDO, K., MITSUDA, H. and IWAI, K. (1950). *Bull. Res. Inst. Food Sci. Kyoto Univ.* No. 3.

[340] KOSAKURO, ONO (1957). The relationship between rice diseases and potassium. Rev. of Potash Res. in Japan. *Int. Potash Inst. Berne.*

[341] KOYANAGI, T. (1939). Influence of potash on the amounts of carbohydrate in the leaves and stems of rice plants. *J. Agric. Chem. Soc. Japan,* 15, 757–67.

[342] KUILMAN, L. W. (1949). *Rice During and After the War. A Bibliography of the Literature on Rice during the Period 1940–1947.* Med. Alg. Proefst. Landb. No. 87.

[343] KURONUMA, K. (1954). *Carp Culture in Rice Fields as a sidework of Japanese Farmers.* Min. of Agric. and For. Japanese Govt.

[344] KUWADA, Y. (1910). A cytological study of *Oryza sativa* L. *Bot. Mag. (Tokyo),* 24, 267.

[345] LAAN, VAN DER (1951). *Landbouw.* 23, 295–356.

[346] LAMPEL, Z. (1958). *The Growing of Rice by Spray Method.* (In Hebrew.) Min. Agric. Israel.

[347] LACEY, G. and WATSON, R. (1949). The African Rice Mission Report. 19. H.M.S.O., London.

[348] LARTER, L. N. H. (1953). *Rice Variety Trials in Malaya, 1947–50.* Special Bull. Scientific Ser. 25. Dept. Agric., Malaya.

[349] LATHROP, E. C. (1952). The industrial utilization of rice hulls. *Rice Annual,* 1952.

[350] LATHROP, E. C. and ARONOVSKY, S. I. (1945). Soft-grit blasting of metals. *Compr. Air Mag.,* 50, 268–72.

[351] LAWHON, L. F. (1961). Water levelling of ricelands. *World Farming.* February 1962.

[352] LEASE, E. J., WHITE, H. and LEASE, J. G (1962) Enrichment of rice with riboflavin. *Food Technol.* 16, 146–48.

[353] LEE CHOW (1958). Rotational irrigation for rice.—A revolution in Taiwan. *Int. Rice Comm. News Letter,* 7 (1), 107.

[354] LEE, D. H. K (1957) *Climate and Economic Development in the Tropics,* Oxford.

[355] LE MARE, D. W. (1950). *Fisheries Dep. Annual Report 1949.* Fed. Malaya and Singapore.

[356] LEONARD, W. H. (1948). Rice as a crop in Japan. *J. Amer. Soc. Agron.* 40, 579–602.

500   Bibliography

357 LE PELLY and KOCKUM (1954). *Bull. Ent. Res.* **45**, 305.

358 LEVENSSON, E. (1937). Die Rieskultur in Bulgarien. [The cultivation of Rice in Bulgaria.] *Ernahr Pfl.* **33**, 177–79.

359 LEVER, R. J. A. W. (1963). Agriculture in the islands of the Western Pacific. *World Crops*, **15** (5), 210.

360 LEWIS, D. C. *et al.* (1962). Plastic rice levees shown economically feasible. *Calif. Agric.* **16** (3), 8–10.

361 LEWIS, R. D. (1959). New varieties open new horizons for U.S. rice. *Rice J.* **62** (9), 14.

362 LIBATIQUE, P. P. (1931). Comparative development of roots of rice plants grown in pots containing ammonium sulphate fertilizers of different amounts. *Philipp. Agriculturist*, **20**, 121–37.

363 LINGEN, —. VAN DER, PHIPPS, J. B. and TEMPLETON, H. A. (1960). Weed control in dams and irrigation channels. *Rhod. Agric. J.* **57** (5), 353–58.

364 LIVERSAGE, V. (1945). *Land Tenure in the Colonies.* Cambridge.

365 LOCKARD, R. G. (1959). *Mineral nutrition of the rice plant in Malaya.* Dept. Agric. Kuala Lumpur. Fed. Malaya.

366 LORD, L. (1929). Manurial experiments with rice I and II. *Trop. Agriculturist*, **73**, 67–73, 259–64.

367 LORD, L. (1932). *Annals Royal Bot. Gardens, Peredeniya*, **11**, Pt. 4.

368 LORD, L. (1935). The cultivation of rice in Ceylon. *J. Exp. Agric.* **3**, 119–28.

369 MA, F. C. (1958). Brief report on the agricultural mechanization in Taiwan. *Int. Rice Comm. News Letter*, **7** (4), 27–30.

370 MAACZ, G. J. (1960?). [Changes in form of the caryopsis of some rice varieties.] Lab. for Rice Breed. Res. Inst. for Irrigation and Rice Breed., Kopànca, Hungary.

371 MAGNE, C. (1960). The cultivation of upland rice in rotation with groundnuts in Senegal. *Int. Rice Comm. News Letter*, **9** (4), 30–33.

372 MANICKAVASAGAR, P. and MIYASHITA, K. (1959). The status of paddy stem borer, *Schoenobius incertulas* Walk. in South-east Asia. *Trop. Agriculturist*, **115** (2), 69–84.

373 MANN, H. H., JOSHI, N. V. and KANITKER, N. V. (1912). The "Rab" system of rice cultivation in Western India. *Mem. Dep. Agric. Ind.* Chem. Ser. 2, No. 3.

374 MANUEL, F. C. and PENA, DE LA R. S. (1960). Applying nutrients through rice leaves. *Philipp. Agriculturist*, **44** (6), 323–25.

375 MARKLEY, K. S. (1949). *Rice J.* **52** (10), 14, 30–35.

376 MARSDEN, R. H. (1959). A small rice thresher for peasant growers. *J. Agric. Eng. Res.* **4** (4).

377 MARTIN, E. L. (1958). Notes on some rice stem borers (*Lepidoptera, Pyralidae*) with the description of a new species of *Chilo Zinekan*. *Bull. Ent. Res.* **49**, 187–91.

378 MARTINEZ, A. L. *et al.* (1960). Mosaic of rice in the Philippines. *FAO Plant Prot. Bull.* **8** (7), 77–78.

379 MATSUO, T. (1955). *Rice Culture in Japan.* Yokendo, Japan.

³⁸⁰ MAYNE, J. E. (1950). The small farm and mechanization. *World Crops*, **2**, 466–8.

³⁸¹ MAYNE, J. E. (1954). Progress on the mechanization of farming in the Colonial Territories. *Trop. Agric.* **31**, 178–87.

³⁸² MAYNE, J. E. (1956). Progress in the mechanization of farming in the Colonial Territories. II. *Trop. Agric.* **32**

³⁸³ MAYNE, J. E. Progress in the mechanization of farming in the Colonial Territories. III. *Trop. Agric.* **33** (4).

³⁸⁴ MAYNÉ, R. (1948). Report on insects, mites, and other pests harmful to stored grains and flour in Belgium. *FAO Agric. Studies*, No. 2, Washington.

³⁸⁵ MCEWAN, J. M. (1935). *J. Jamaica Agric.* June.

³⁸⁶ MCKINLEY, K. S. (1957). Miscellaneous Report No. 188, Col. Pesticides Res. Unit, Arusha, Tanganyika.

³⁸⁷ MCGUIRE, J. U. and MCMILLIAN, W. W. (1960) Hoja Blanca disease of rice and its insect vector. *Rice J.* **63** (13), 15, 16, 20–24, 28.

³⁸⁸ MCNAUGHTON, E. J. (1939). *Rice in Formosa*. (Not published.)

³⁸⁹ MCNAUGHTON, E. J. (1946). *World Paddy Pests*. Prelim. Rep. Commonwealth Inst. Ent. Ref. C. 1846. Jan. 1946.

³⁹⁰ MENDIOLA, N. B. (1926). *A Manual of Plant Breeding for the Tropics*. Manila, p. 88.

³⁹¹ MENON, M. K. (1951). *On the Paddy Field Prawn Fishing of Travancore-Cochin and an Experiment in Prawn Culture*. Tech. Papers A– Inland Fisheries IPFC/C54/Tech 5.

³⁹² METZGER, W. H. (1929). *Effect of Nitrogenous Fertilizers on Physical Condition of Rice Soil*. Bull. Ark. Agric. Exp. Sta. No. 264, p. 30.

³⁹³ MEULEN, J. G. J. VAN DER (1939). Over de natuurlijke kruisbestuiving bij rijst en resultaten van een onderzoek daarover op Java. *Landbouw, XVII. Buitenzorg*.

³⁹⁴ MEULEN, J. G. J. VAN DER (1941). De rijstselectie in Nederlandsch Indie. *Landbouw, XVII, Buitenzorg*.

³⁹⁵ MEULEN, J. G. J. VAN DER (1950). *Economisch Weekblad voor Indonesie*, 14 Oct. 1950.

³⁹⁶ MICKUS, R. R. (1955). Advanced design spurs oil yield. *Food Eng.* March, 80–83, 191.

³⁹⁷ MICKUS, R. R. (1955). Rice (*Oryza sativa*). *Cereal Sci. Today*, **4** (5) 138–149.

³⁹⁸ MIDDLETON, A. D. (1948). *British Agric. Bull.* **1** (3).

³⁹⁹ MIKKELSEN, D. S. and FINFROCK, D. C. (1957). Fertilizer placement for rice. *Calif. Agric.* **11** (7), 7.

⁴⁰⁰ MIKKELSEN, D. S. (1963). Californian studies of rice physiology and nutrition. *Rice J.* **66** (7), 44.

⁴⁰¹ MILLER, N. C. E. and PAGDEN, H. T. (1931). Attempts to control padi stem borers. *Malay, Agric. J.* **18**, 334–40.

⁴⁰² MIRANDA, V. H. DE (1960). L'enfouissement de la paille dans la fertilisation organique du riz. *Rev. Agron. Lisboa.* **43** (3), 51–55.

502 *Bibliography*

[403] MIRCHANDANI, R. T. (1947). Role of cultural improvements in the increased production of paddy in Sind. *Indian Farmer*, **8**, 386–90.

[404] MISRA, G. and SAHU, G. (1957). After-effects of treatment of grains of early rice variety with plant growth substances. *Curr. Sci.* **26**, 258.

[405] MISRA, G. and SAHU, G. (1957). Control of flowering in rice by plant growth substances. *Nature*, London, **180**, 816.

[406] MISRA, R. N. (1932) *J. Ecol*, **26**, 441.

[407] MISU, H. and SHIMOHIRA, H. (1929). Availability of N of green manure for rice and the supplementary value of various fertilizers. *Ann. Agric. Exp. Sta. Chosen*, **4**, 65–94.

[408] MITRA, S. K. *et al.* (1928). Colour inheritance in rice. *Mem. Dep. Agr. Indian Bot. Ser.* 15, 85.

[409] MITRA, S. K. (1928). A note on glutinous rice. *Agric. J. India*, **23**, 484.

[410] MITRA, S. K. and GANGULI, P. M. (1937). Inheritance of inner glume colours in rice. *Indian J. Agric. Sci.* **7**, 126.

[411] MITSUI, S. (1954). *Inorganic Nutrition, Fertilization and Soil Amelioration for Island Rice*. Yokendo, Japan.

[412] MIYAKI, M. and HOSHI, S. (1960) [Comparison of rice culture systems in Hokkaido.] *Res. Bull. Hokkaido Nat. Agro. Expt. Sta.* 75, 53–59.

[413] MOKINE, N. (1933). [Manuring of rice.] *Riz et Riziculture*, **7**, 95–107.

[414] MOLEGODE, W. (1918). Green manuring of paddy fields in the Kandy District. *Trop. Agriculturist*, **51**, 349.

[415] *Monthly Bull. of Agric. Econ. and Statistics (FAO)*, **6** (6), 29.

[416] MORINAGA, S. (1935). Cytogenetical studies in *Oryza sativa*, 11. Autotriploid mutants. Spontaneous. *Jap. J. Bot.* **7**, 207.

[417] MORINAGA, S. and FUKUSHIMA, M. (1936). Cytogenetical studies in *Oryza sativa*, 111. Spontaneous, autotetraploid mutants in *Oryza sativa*. *Jap. J. Bot.* **9**, 71.

[418] MORIYA, M. and SATO, S. (1958). Effect of phosphate on the hardiness of rice seedlings transplanted under bad climatic conditions. *Proc. Crop Sci. Soc. Japan*, **27** (1), 40–42.

[419] MORRIS, N. J., SWIFT, C. E. and DOLLEAR, F. G. (1950). Rice bran oil. VII. The "fines" fraction of rice bran. *Rice J.* **53** (9), 6, 7, 10.

[420] MUDALIAR, B. S. (1944). Green manuring of paddy. *Indian Farmer*. **5**, 562–63.

[421] MUKUMOTO, T. (1956). Outline of farm management in Japan for rice production. Report of Meeting of Ad Hoc Working Group on Problems of Mechanization of Rice Production under Wet Paddy Conditions. FAO, Washington.

[422] MURRAY, A. R. (1947). Memorandum on Irrigation Practice, Malaya. (Not published.)

[423] MURTI, K. S. and RAO, G. V. (1957). A review of work on rice bran and rice bran oil. *Indian Oilseeds J.* **1**, 91.

[424] NAGAO, S. (1951). Genic analysis and linkage relationship of characters of rice. *Advances in Genetics*, **4**, 181.

[425] NAGAO, S. and TAKAHASHI, T. (1947), *Jap. J. Genet. Suppl.* **1**, 1–17.

[426] NAGATO, K. and EBATA, M. (1958). Studies on white core rice kernel.

1. On the occurrence of the white core. *Proc. Crop Sci. Soc. Japan,* **27** (1), 49–51.

[427] NAGATO, K. and KOBAYASHI, Y. (1957). Studies on the occurrence of notched-belly kernels in rice plants. *Proc. Crop Soc. Japan,* **26,** 13.

[428] NAIR, K. K. (1944). Calcutta sewage irrigation fisheries. *Proc. Nat. Inst. Sci. India,* **10,** 459–62.

[429] NARAYANAN, T. R. and VESUDEVAN, K. V. (1957). Foliar versus soil fertilizer application to crops. *Madras Agric. J.* **44** (12).

[430] NELSON, G. S. (1961). Application of rice seed and fertilizer with Venturi-type distributors. *Ark. Farm J.* **10** (4).

[431] NESTER, R. (1960). *Crops and Soils,* **12** (5), 24.

[432] NEVROS, K. (1936). Rice fertilizer experiments in Messenia (Greece) covering a period of 3 years. *Prakitka,* **9,** 136.

[433] NICHOLLS, L. (1949). The bearing of recent research on rice milling. *Brit. Sci. News,* **2,** 380–3.

[434] NICHOLLS, L. (1949). Rice and its nutritional aspects. *Research,* **2,** 401–7.

[435] NILES, J. J. (1951). Hybridization methods with paddy. *Trop. Agriculturist,* **107,** 25.

[436] NISIKADO, Y. and MIYAKE, C. (1922). [Studies on the *Helminthosporiose* of the rice plant.] *Ber. Ohara Inst. Landb. Forschungen,* **2,** 133–94.

[437] NISIKADO, Y. and MYIAKE, C. (1927). Studies on the Uspulan treatment of cereal seeds against *Helminthosporioses. Agric. Stud.* **11,** 36–64.

[438] NISIKADO, Y. and NAKAYAMA, T. (1943). [The disinfection of rice seeds affected by *Helminthosporium oryzae.*] *Ber. Ohara Inst. Landb. Forsch.* **9** (2), 214–29.

[439] NOGUCHI, Y. (1958). [Induction of mutation in rice by phosphorus starvation.] *Jap. J. Breeding,* **8,** 137–41.

[440] NORE, J. and THEVAN, P. V. (1959). Seed germination and seedling growth of rice. (*O. sativa*). *Trop. Agric.* (*Trin.*) **36,** 15–34.

[441] NOSE, H. (1940). *Ann. Phytopath. Soc. Japan,* **10,** 192–202.

[442] NOVELLO NOVELLI and ING. GIOVANNI SAMPIETRO. (1924) *La Risicultura en Italia.*

[443] O'CONNER, B. A. (1952). The rice leaf hopper, *Sogata furcifera* and "Rice Yellows". *Fiji Agric. J.* **23** (3–4), 97–104.

[444] OCHSE, J. J., SOULE, M. J. *et al.* (1961). *Tropical and Subtropical Agriculture.* Macmillan, New York, quoting Penders, J. M. A. (1941) De mogelijkheden van de meststoffen voorziening uit asnwezige bronen. *Lanbbouw,* **17,** (8,9, 10), 774–843.

[445] OGATA, T. and YOSHINOUCHI, K. (1957). On the properties of oxamide as gradually acting nitrogenous fertilizer. I. *J. Sci. Soil Manure, Japan,* **29** (2), 51–56. II. *Nippon Dojo-Hiryogaku Zasshi.* **29,** 383–88 (1958).

[446] OIKAWA, T. (1959). Studies on the ridge culture of rice plants. *J. Fac. Agric. Iwate.* **4** (2), 171–3.

[447] OKA, H. (1955). Studies of tetraploid rice. VI. Fertility variation and

segregation ratios for several characters in tetraploid hybrids of rice (*Oryza sativa L.*) *Cytologia, Tokyo,* **20,** 258.

[448] OKADA, T. (1932). Relationship of phosphorus fertilizer to the absorption of nitrogen. *Trans. Tottori Soc. Agric. Sci.* **4,** 67–70.

[449] OKAZAKI, S. and OKI, Y. (1961). [Studies on free amino acids contained in polished rice.] *Nippon Nogeikagaku Kaishi.* **35** (3), 194–99. Eng. abs. *Agric. and Biol. Chem.* **25** (4), A20.

[450] OLIVEIRO, —. (1937). *J. Malay. Branch B.M.A., Singapore.*

[451] OSSEWAARDE, J. G. (1927/28). *Landbouw.* **4,** 453–74.

[452] OU, S. H. and KANJANASOON, P. (1961). A note of the gall midge resistant variety in Thailand. *Int. Rice Comm. News Letter,* **10** (2), 9.

[453] OXLEY, T. A. (1948). The reduction of losses in grain by control of water content. *FAO Studies,* No. 2, Washington.

[454] OXLEY, T. A. (1948). *Brit. Agric. Bull.* **1** (1).

[455] OXLEY, T. A. (1955). A new moisture tester. *Agric. Merchant,* Sept. 1955.

[456] PADMANABHAN, S. Y., GANGULY, D. and CHANDWANI, G. G. (1956). Control of blast disease of rice with spray fungicides. *Ind. Phytopath.* **9** (1), 15.

[457] PADWICK, G. W. (1950) *Manual of Rice Diseases.* Commonwealth Mycol. Inst. London.

[458] PADWICK, G. W. (1956). *Losses caused by Plant Diseases in the Colonies.* Commonwealth Mycol. Inst. London, Phytopathological Paper No. 1.

[459] PADWICK, G. W. (1956). Disease and pests of rice in Japan. *Outlook on Agric.* **1** (1), 20–23.

[460] PAGDEN, H. T. (1932). Notes on padi stem borers *.Malay Agric. J.* **20,** 122.

[461] PALIS, G. T. and CALMA, V. C. (1948). Yields of broadcast and transplanted Seroup Kechil 36 rice. *Philipp. Agriculturist,* **31,** 226–30.

[462] PAN, C. L. (1952). Rice improvement in China. *Int. Rice Comm. News Letter,* No. 2, 10–12.

[463] PAN, C. L. (1962). Rice preparation in China, South Asia and the Far East. Originally pub. in *Getreide and Melh.* Sept. 1962. Eng. translation. *International Rice Yearbook,* 1963.

[464] PAN, C. L. (1963). On Chinese wine. *Int. Rice Yearbook.*

[465] PARPIA, H. A. B. and SUBRAHMANYAN, V. (1959). Some aspects of food research in India. *Food Sci.* **8** (5), 153.

[466] PARIJA, P. (1934). A note on the reappearance of water hyacinth seedlings in cleared tanks. *Indian J. Agric. Sci.* **4,** 1049.

[467] PARK, M. (1937). *Admin. Rep. Dir. Agric. Ceylon,* 1936, 28–35.

[468] PARK, M. and BERTUS, L. S. (1934). *Ceylon J. Sci.* Sect. A. Bot., XII, 11–3.

[469] PARKIN, E. A. (1949). The control of insects infesting stored foodstuffs. *World Crops,* **1,** 103–6.

[470] PARNELL, F. R. *et al.* (1922). The inheritance of characters in rice. II. *Mem. Dept. Agric. Indian Bot. Ser.* **9,** 75.

[471] PARR, C. H. (1946). Manurial experiments at Karnal with paddy followed by Berseem. *Sci. Reps. Imp. Agric. Res. Inst. 1944–5*, 26–27.

[472] PARTHASARATHY, N. (1938). Cytogenetical studies in *Oryza* and *Phalarideae*, II. Further studies in *Oryza. Cytologia.* **9**, 307.

[473] PATRICK, WM. H. JR. (1963). Rice fertilization in Louisiana. *Rice J.* **66** (9), 8–10.

[474] PAUL, W. R. C. (1945). *Paddy Cultivation.* Ceylon Govt. Press.

[475] PAUL, W. R. C. and JOACHIM, A. W. R. (1938). Paddy manurial and cultural experiments at Paranthan Paddy Station. *Trop. Agriculturist*, **91**, 135–42.

[476] PAULI, F. W. (1961). Humus and plant—the direct humus effect. *Soil Sci.* **49**, 427–37.

[477] PAWAR, M. S. (1963). Rice cultivation in the hills. *Indian Farming*, **13** (2), 24–29.

[478] PEARSALL, W. H. and BILLIMORIA, M. C. (1937). *J. Ecol.* **31**

[479] PEARSALL, W. H. and MORTIMER, C. H. (1939). Oxidation-reduction potentials in waterlogged soils, natural waters and muds. *J. Ecol.* **27**, 483–501.

[480] PEARSALL, W. H. (1950). The investigation of wet soils and its agricultural implications. *Emp. J. Exp. Agric.* **18**, 289–98.

[481] PECORA, L. J. and HUNDLEY, J. M. (1951). Nutritional improvement of white polished rice by the addition of lysine and threonine. *J. Nutr.* **44**, 101.

[482] PEIRIS, M. E. A. (1956). Broadling—A promising new technique in paddy cultivation. *Trop. Agriculturist*, **112**, 105–8.

[483] PENDLETON, R. L. (1943). Land use in North-eastern Thailand. *Geogr. Rev. Amer. Geograph. Soc.* **33**, 15–41.

[484] PENDLETON, R. L. (1947). The formation, development and utilization of the soils of the Bangkok Plain. *Nat. Hist. Bull.* **14** (2).

[485] PENDLETON, R. L. (1933). *Reconnaissance Soil Survey of a Portion of Kwangtung Province.* Nat. Geol. Survey of China. Soil Bull. No. 6.

[486] PERDUE, R. E. JR. and KORAEBEL, C. J. (1961). *Econ. Bot.* **15** (2), 164–79.

[487] PIACCO, R. (1959). The first varieties of rice cultivated in Italy. *Riso. Milano.* **8** (12), 12–14.

[488] PLATT, B. S. (1939). *Nutrition in the Colonial Empire.* 1st Report. Pt. 1.

[489] PLATT. B. S. (1956). Vitamins in nutrition: Orientation and perspective. *Brit. Med. Bull.* 12, 83.

[490] POGGENDORFF, W. (1950). *Rice Production Possibilities in the Kimberleys and Northern Territory.* Rice Equalisation Association, Sydney.

[491] POGGENDORFF, W. (1953). *Rice Production in Papua and New Guinea.* Dept. of Territories, Australia, Sydney.

[492] POGGENDORFF, W. (1956). Rice rotations in New South Wales. *Int. Rice Comm. News Letter*, No. 17

[493] POLGAR, S. (1960).[Experiences with rice fertilization.] *Magyar Mezogazdasag, Budapest*, **15** (12), 17–18.

[494] POMINSKI, J., EAVES, P. H. *et al.* (1954). Simultaneous recovery of wax and oil from rice. *J. Amer. Oil Chem. Soc.*, **61** (11), 451–55.

[495] PONNAMPERUMA, F. N. (1955). Some aspects of the chemistry of rice soils. *Trop. Agriculturist*, **111**, 92.

[496] PONNAMPERUMA, F. N. (1958). Lime as aremedy for a physiological disease of rice associated with excess iron. *Int. Rice Comm. News Letter*, **7** (1), 10–13.

[497] PREVETT, P. F. (1959). A study of rice storage under tropical conditions. *J. Agrl. Eng. Res.* **4** (3), 243–54.

[498] RAKITIN, JU. V. *et al.* (1961). [Pre-harvesting chemical desiccation of rice]. *Izv. Akad. Nank. SSSR.* (*Bull. Acad. Sci. USSR*) Ser. Biol. 1961. No. 5, 729–39. Eng. summary, Kuban Exp. Sta. for Rice.

[499] RAM, K. and CHETTY, C. V. S. (1934). The development of pigments in the glumes and apiculus of rice varieties. *Ind. J. Agric. Sci.* **4**, 642–55.

[500] RAMACHANDRAN, C. K., KAMALANATHAN, S. and ANNAPPAN, R. S. (1960). Cultivation of cotton in the rice-fallows of Madras State—The need for a proper approach. *Madras Agric. J.* **47** (7), 303–9.

[501] RAMANUJAM, S. (1937). Cytogenetical studies of Oryzae. III. Cytogenetical behaviour of an interspecific hybrid in *Oryza*. *J. Genet.* **35**.

[502] RAMANUJAM, S. (1937). 11. Cytogenetical behaviour of an autotriploid rice. *J. Genet.* **35**, 223.

[503] RAMIAH, K. (1927). Artificial hybridization in rice. *Agric. J. India*, **22**, 17.

[504] RAMIAH, K. (1934). Lodging of straw and its inheritance in rice. *Indian J. Agric. Sci.* **4**. 880–94.

[505] RAMIAH, K. and HANUMANTHARAO, K. (1936). Inheritance of grain shattering in rice. *Madras Agric. J.* **24**, 240.

[506] RAMIAH, K. (1935). The inheritance of red pericarp colour in rice. *Madras Agric. J.* **23**, 268.

[507] RAMIAH, K. and RAMANUJAM, S. (1935). Chlorophyll deficiency in rice. *Proc. Indian Acad. Sci.* **2**, 343–68.

[508] RAMIAH, K. and RAMASWAMY, K. (1941). Floating habit in some varieties of rice known as deep-water rices. *Indian J. Agric. Sci.* **11**, 1–8.

[509] RAMIAH, K. and RAO, M. B. V. N. (1953). *Rice Breeding and Genetics*. Ind. Council of Agric. Res. Sci. Monogr. No. 19.

[510] RAMIAH, K. (1935). Rice genetics. *Proc. Assoc. Econ. Biol. Coimbatore*, **3**, 51.

[511] RAMIAH, K. (1937). *Rice in Madras*. Madras Govt. Press.

[512] RAMIAH, K. (1954). *Factors Affecting Rice Production*. FAO Agric. Development Paper No. 45.

[513] RAMIAH, K. (1957). Scent in rice. *Madras Agric. J.* **25**, 173–76.

[514] RAMIREZ, D. A. and UMALI, D. L. (1956). The nature of lodging in rice. *Philipp. Agriculturist*, **40** (7), 335–51.

[515] RAMPAL, A. J. and BHATT, J. G. (1959). Some responses of the rice plant to growth-regulating substances. *Trop. Agric.* (*Trin.*) **36** (2), 96–99.

[516] RANEY, F. C. and FINFROCK, D. C. (1961). *Rice J.* **64** (12).

[517] RANGANATHAN, S. *et al.* (1937). Changes in chemical composition brought about by cooking. *Indian J. Med. Res.* **25**, 45–65.

[518] RAO, C. H. (1958). Field tests of insecticides against paddy borer in Taiwan from 1953–56. *J. Econ. Ent.* **51** (5), 571–73.

[519] RAO, P. R. and VARATHARAJAN, G. (1962). Sex-ratio of rice stem-borer. *Int. Rice Comm. News Letter*, **10** (4), 70.

[520] REDDI, P. B. V., MURTI, K. S. and FEUGE, R. O. (1948). *J. Amer. Oil Chem. Soc.* **25**, 206–11.

[521] REED, J. F. and STURGIS, M. B. (1939). Chemical characteristics of some Soils of the Rice Area of Louisiana. *La. Agric. Exp. Sta. Bull.* 307. pp. 31.

[522] Report (1931). *Manual of Green Manuring*. Dept. Agric., Ceylon.

[523] Report (1934–5 to 1937–8). Rice Research Officer, Burma (GRANT, J. W.)

[524] Report (1935–6 to 1936–7). Annual Report, Rice Station, Berhampore, Madras (JOBITHRAJ, S).

[525] Report (1936). Rice Markets Survey No. 9, Dept. Agric., Burma.

[526] Report (1939). Annual Report, Rice Research Officer, Raipur, Central Provinces (DAVE, B. B.).

[527] Report (1942). Agriculture in the West Indies, Colonial Office, No. 182, H.M.S.O.

[528] Report (1944). Burma Rice. Burma Pamphlet No. 4. Longmans, Green, London.

[529] Report (1945). Co-operation in the Colonies. Allen and Unwin, London.

[530] Report (1947). Report No. 86 of Supreme Command for the Allied Powers G.H.Q., Nat. Resources.

[531] Report (1947). Report No. 93 of Supreme Command for the Allied Powers G.H.Q., Nat. Resources.

[532] Report (1948). Coating Process Restores Vitamins to Rice. McGraw-Hill World News and F.I. Staff Report, reprinted from *Food Industries*, **20**.

[533] Report (1948). Report of British Guiana and British Honduras Settlement Commission [The "Evans Report"]. H.M.S.O.

[534] Report (1948). Report on the Mission to Siam. FAO, Washington.

[535] Report (1948). Report of Nutrition Committee, Food and Agriculture Organization, on Nutrition Problems of Rice-eating Countries in Asia. FAO. June, 1948.

[536] Report (1948). Report on the Rice Meeting, Baguio, Philippines. March. FAO, Washington.

[537] Report (1949). Report on the First Session, FAO International Rice Commission, Bangkok.

[538] Report (1950). Colombo Plan for Co-operative Economic Development in South and South-east Asia. Report of the Commonwealth Consultative Committee, Sept.–Oct. 1950. H.M.S.O.

[539] Report (1950). Report on the Mahaicony-Abary Development Scheme to 31 Dec. 1948. *Daily Chronicle*, British Guiana.

[540] Report (1953). Annual Report, Department of Agriculture, Bihar.

[541] Report (1953). Report of the Joint U.K. and Australian Mission on Rice Production in Ceylon 1954. Publ. June 1955. Sessional Paper 11, Govt. Publication Bureau, Colombo.

⁵⁴² Report (1955). The Stabilization of the International Trade in Rice. Commodity Policy Studies, Aug. No. 7.

⁵⁴³ Report (1956). Report of the First Session of the Consultative Sub-committee on the Economic Aspects of Rice. FAO. 9 Nov.

⁵⁴⁴ Report (1956). Progress Report on the Work of the International Rice Commission for the Years of 1955 and 1956. (CHANG, C. W.) *Int. Rice Comm. News Letter*, No. 20, Dec. 1956.

⁵⁴⁵ Report (1957). Rice Growing on the Murrumbidgee Irrigation Area, N.S.W., Australia. Dept. Agric., N.S.W.

⁵⁴⁶ Report (1957). A Symposium on the Operating Costs of Machinery in Tropical Agriculture. Col. Advisory Council of Agric., Animal Health and Forestry. Pub. No. 4. H.M.S.O., London.

⁵⁴⁷ Report (1958). Report on Asiatic Rice Mission. *Rice J.* **61** (9).

⁵⁴⁸ Report (1958). Report on the U.S.A. Asiatic Mission, 1957. *Rice J.* **61** (10).

⁵⁴⁹ Report (1958). Annual Report of Government of Thailand for the Year 1956–7 to FAO, Min. of Agric., Bangkok.

⁵⁵⁰ Report (1960). Annual Report Nat. Agric. Viet-nam 1960–1, 232–4.

⁵⁵¹ Report (1960). FAO Commodity Reports: Rice No. 11, Aug. 1960.

⁵⁵² Report (1963). FAO Rice Report, 1963.

⁵⁵³ RHIND, D. (1950). *Notes on the Improvement of the Yields of Paddy in Ceylon.* Govt. Printing Press, Colombo.

⁵⁵⁴ RHIND, D. (1955). Paddy Notes, prepared in connection with the Mwea-Tabere (Kenya) Scheme. (Not published.)

⁵⁵⁵ RHIND, D., U BA THEIN and U TIN (1943). Growth and yield studies on irrigated rice in Upper Burma. *Indian J. Agric. Res.* **13**, 335

⁵⁵⁶ RHIND, D. and U TIN (1948). Results of the continuous use of an ammonium phosphate fertilizer on rice in Lower Burma. *Nature, London,* **161**, 105–6.

⁵⁵⁷ RHIND, D. and U TIN (1952). Residual effects from superphosphate, basic slag and bone meal on some paddy soils in Lower Burma. *Trop. Agriculturist,* **108**, 102–7.

⁵⁵⁸ RHODES, P. L. (1961). Weed control in drilled rice. *Fiji Agric. J.* **31**, 3–8.

⁵⁵⁹ RICHARDSON, H. L. (1961). The improvement of soil fertility. *Emp. J. Exp. Agric.* **14**.

⁵⁶⁰ RICHARDSON, H. L. *et al.* (1944). The use of organic and inorganic manures with rice: a continuous factorial experiment. *Emp. J. Exp. Agric.* **12**, 35–50.

⁵⁶¹ RICHHARIA, R. H. (1960). The possible use of vegetative propagation in rice (*Oryza sativa* L.). *Sci. and Cult.* **26**. 239–40.

⁵⁶² RICHHARIA, R. H., MISRO, B. and SEETHARAMAN, R. (1961). Recent approaches in rice breeding and genetics. *Indian. J. Agric. Sci.* **31**, 27–30.

⁵⁶³ RICHHARIA, R. H. (1960?). *Recent Research in Rice Breeding and Genetics. Span* (Supplement), Shell Int. Chem. Co.

⁵⁶⁴ RICHHARIA, R. H. and GOVINDASWAMI, S. (1962). Fewer varieties with wider adaptability. *Rice News Teller,* **10** (4), 80–82.

⁵⁶⁵ RICHHARIA, R. H. and MISRO, B. (1962). Evolutionary tendencies in rice based on genetic evidence. *Bull. Nat. Inst. of Sciences of India*, No. 19, 1962.

⁵⁶⁶ ROBERTS, E. H. (1960). The effect of Gamma BHC on the growth of rice seedlings. *Emp. J. Exp. Agric.* **28**.

⁵⁶⁷ ROBERTS, H. E. (1960). Dormancy of rice seed. 1. The distribution of dormancy periods. *J. Exp. Bot.* **12**, 318–29.

⁵⁶⁸ ROBERTS, E. H. (1962). Dormancy in rice seed. III. The influence of temperature, moisture and gaseous environment. *J. Exp. Bot.* **13**, 75–94.

⁵⁶⁹ ROBERTS, E. H. (1962). Design of some inexpensive growth chambers for growing rice plants to maturity under controlled light and temperature in the tropics. *J. Agric. Eng. Res.* **7** (4), 316–19.

⁵⁷⁰ ROLSTON, L. H. (1961). Aldrin treatment of seed rice. *Ark. Farm Res.* **10** (2), 6.

⁵⁷¹ ROSCHEVICZ, R. L. (1931). A contribution to the knowledge of rice. *Bull. Appl. Bot. Gen. Plant Breed. Leningrad*, **27** (4).

⁵⁷² ROSEDALE, J. L. (1939). The nutritive value of rice. *J. Malay. Branch B.M.A.* **4**, 213.

⁵⁷³ ROSSIN, M. (1948). *La Riziculture aux États-unis*. Bul. Agron. No. 2, Ministère de la France d'Outre Mer.

⁵⁷⁴ RUINEN, J. (1953). *Nitrogen-fixing Bacteria in Tropical Soils*. Paper R. C.

⁵⁷⁵ RUSSELL, E. J. (1950). *Soil Conditions and Plant Growth*. 8th ed. Longmans, Green, London.

⁵⁷⁶ RYKER, T. C. (1947). *J. Amer. Soc. Agron.* **39**.

⁵⁷⁷ RYKER, T. C. (1947). Seed treatment with rice. *Rice J.* **50** (12), 11.

⁵⁷⁸ SAHASRABUDDHE, D. L. (1928). Assimilation of nutrients by the rice plant. *Dep. Agric. Bombay, Bull.* 154, p. 17.

⁵⁷⁹ SAKAI, K. (1935). Chromosome study of *Oryza sativa* L. 1. The secondary association of the meiotic chromosomes. Abstract in *Pl. Breed. Abs.* **6**.

⁵⁸⁰ SAMPIETRO, G. (1934). [On the proportion of straw to grain in rice.] *Risicolt.* **24**, 237–39.

⁵⁸¹ SANDS, N. H. (1933). The vegetation of the rice lands of North Kedah. *Malay Agric. J.* **21**, 175–76.

⁵⁸² SANDS, W. N. (1933). The storage of padi in Kedah. *Malay. Agric. J.* **21**, 678.

⁵⁸³ SANTOS, J. K. (1953). *Philipp. J. Sci.* **52**.

⁵⁸⁴ SARAN, A. B. and PRASAD, M. (1952). Ratooning in paddy. *Curr. Sci.* **21**.

⁵⁸⁵ SASAKI, T. (1932). A preliminary report on the form of the root system in rice plants. *Proc. Crop Sci. Soc. Japan.* **4** (3), 200–25.

⁵⁸⁶ SASAMOTO, K. (1957 and 1958). Studies on the relation between the silica content in the rice-plant and the insect pests:
(1957) *Botyu-Kagaku Inst. Insect Control*, **22** (1), 159–64;
(1958) *Jap. J. Appl. Ent. & Zool.* **2** (2), 88–92: and **3** (3), 153–56.

⁵⁸⁷ SASATA, U. (1938). *Jap. J. Med. Sci.* **11**, Biochem. **4**.

588 SATO, K. (1937). *J. Agric. Exp. Sta Chosen*, **9**.

589 SATO, K. (1938). The influence of fertilizers on the root development of the rice plant. *Ann. Agric. Exp. Sta. Chosen*, **9**, 475–92.

590 SATO, K. (1957). Starch content of the culm related to lodging. *Proc. Crop Sci. Soc. Japan*, **26** (1), 19.

591 SATYANARAUSNA, P. (1956). The nutritional requirements of rice. *Fertilizer News, India*, **1** (5).

592 SCHUSTER, W. H. (1949). On the food of bendang (*Chanos chanos* Forsk) in Indonesian ponds. *Med. Alg. Proefst. Landb. No. 86, Buitenzorg.*

593 SCHUSTER, W. H. (1955). Fish culture in conjunction with rice cultivation. Paper at Int. Rice Commission, Tokyo. Abs. in *World Crops*, **7** (1 and 2).

594 SENGAPTA, G. C. and ROUT, G. D. (1957). Control of rice stem borer with Endrin. *J. Econ. Ent.* **50** (2).

596 SETHI, R. L. (1930). Root growth in rice under different conditions of growth. *Mem. Dep. Agric. Indian Bot.* **18**, pp. 57–80.

597 SETHI, R. L. (1940). *Manuring of Paddy.* Imp. Coun. Agric. Res. Misc. bull. 38.

598 SHEN, T. H. and KUNG, P. (1954). Rice production and improvement in Taiwan. *Int. Rice Comm. News Letter*, No. 9.

599 SHIBUYA, K. and SAEKI, H. (1934). The effect of vanadium on the growth of plants. *J. Soc. Trop. Agric.* **6**, 64–73.

600 SHIBUYA, K., SAEKI, H. and KATAGAI, D. (1938). Utilization of nitrate and ammonia nitrogen by plants. VI. The reaction of nutrient media. *J. Soc. Trop. Agric. Taiwan*, **10**, 38–54.

601 SHIBUYA, K. and SAEKI, H. (1939). Utilization of nitrate and ammonia nitrogen by plants, VIII. The physiological relationship between phosphoric acid, potash and the different forms of nitrogen nutrients. *J. Soc. Trop. Agric. Taiwan*, **11**, 66–75.

602 SIL, S. N. (1917). Paddy experiments at Sabour. *Dept. Agric. Bihar and Orissa Agric. J.*

603 SIMMONS, K. V. (1957). Establishment of legumes sown with rice. *Agric. Gaz. of N.S.W.* **68** (4), 198.

604 SIMPSON, I. A. (1940). The antineuritic value of parboiled rice. A comparison with undermilled rice. *Inst. Med. Res. Fed. Malay States Bull.* 4 of 1939.

605 SIRCAR, S. M. and SEN, N. K. (1941). Studies in the physiology of rice. I. Effect of phosphorus deficiency on growth and nitrogen metabolism of rice leaves. *Indian J. Agric. Sci.* **11**, 193–204.

606 SIRCAR, S. M. and KUNDU, M. (1955). Effect of auxins on the flowering behaviour of rice. *Nature*, London, **176**, 840–41.

607 SIVAN, M. R. (1922). Availability of Trichinopoly phosphoric nodule as a manure for paddy. *Agric. J. India*, **17**, 560–63.

608 SLUYTERS, J. A. F. M. (1962). Milling studies on parboiled rice in Nigeria. *Trop. Agric. (Trin.)* **40** (2), 153–58.

609 SMITH, R. J. JR. (1957). *10th Southern Weed Conference*, Jan.

610 SMITH, R. J., HINKLE, D. A. and WILLIAMS, F. J. (1959). Pre-harvesting

desiccation of rice with chemicals. *Publ. Agric. Exp. Sta. Univ. Ark.* 619, 16.

[611] SMITH, W. D. and JONES, J. W. (1937). *When to Cut Rice.* USDA Leaflet 148 : (2).

[612] SMITH, W. D. (1955). The use of Carter Dockage Tester to remove weed seeds and other foreign material from rough rice. *Rice J.* **58** (9).

[613] SMITH, W. D. (1955). The use of the McGill sheller for removing hulls from rough rice. *Rice J.* **58** (10).

[614] SMITH, W. D. (1955). The use of the McGill miller for milling samples of rice. *Rice J.* **58** (11).

[615] SMITH, W. D. (1955). The determination of the estimate of head rice and of total yield with the use of the Sizing Device. *Rice J.* **58** (12).

[616] S.N.T. (1962). Parboiling. *Rice News Teller*, April–Sept., 1962.

[617] SONNIER, A. (1960). Catfish, crayfish and rice. *Rice J.* **63** (5) 8–9.

[618] SOONG, M. K. (1948). Fishes in the Malayan padi-fields. I. Sepat Siam (*Trichogaster pectoralis* Regan). *Malay. Nature J.* **3** (2).

[619] SOONG, M. K. (1949). Fishes of the Malayan padi-fields. II. Aruan: Serpent-head fish. *Malay. Nature J.* **4** (1).

[620] SOONG, M. K. (1954). Fish-culture in paddy fields in the Federation of Malaya. *Int. Rice. Comm. 4th Session, Tokyo.*

[621] SOONG, M. K. (1950). Fishes of the Malayan padi-fields. III. Keli: Catfish. *Malay. Nature J.* **5** (2)

[622] SOONG, M. K. (1947). Preliminary report on Sepat Siam investigations in Krian. Paper No. 9 Office of Special Commissioner South East Asia Fisheries Conference.

[623] SOONG, M. K. (1951). The fitness of ecological niches into which fish are introduced at various ages and the survival of the transplanted fish. *Proc. Indo-Pacific Council*, Sect. III.

[624] SORIANO, M. F. (1934). Influence of amount of fertilizer in soil on growth of rice and composition of its leaves. *Philipp. Agriculturist*, **23**, 295–316.

[625] SPEARS, J. F. (1963). Hoja Blanca vector eradication program in Louisiana. *Rice J.* **66** (5), 30–1.

[626] SREENIVASAN, A. (1946). Nutritional improvements of rice. *Curr. Sci.* **15**, 180–4.

[627] SRINIVASAN, V. and SUBRAMANIAN. (1961). A note on natural cross-pollination in rice at Agricultural Research Station, Aduthurai, (Thanjavur District). *Madras Agric. J.* **48** (7), 292–93.

[628] SRIVASTAVA, M. G. (1958). Effect of hormone herbicides on paddy *Oryza sativa* L. *Proc. Natl. Inst. Sci. India. B. Biol. Sci.* **24** (5), 258–71.

[629] STAHEL, G. (1934). Influence de la teneur du grain sur la décorticage du paddy et la pourcentage de brisures. *Riz et Riziculture*, **8**, 396.

[630] STAKER, E. V. (1958). Green manure crops in relation to paddy rice production in Southeast Asia. *Int. Rice Comm. News Letter*, **7** (4), 1–20.

[631] STAMPA, G. Utilization of rice husks. *Int. Rev. Agric.* **32G**.

512　　　　　　　　　　Bibliography

632 STEPHENS, C. G. (1953). *A Manual of Australian Soils*. C.S.I.R.O. Melbourne.

633 STERMER, R. A. *et al* (1963). A rice photometer for measuring the degree of milling of rice. *International Rice Yearbook*, 1963, 22–26.

634 STURGIS, M. B. (1936). *Changes in Oxidation-Reduction Equilibrium in Soils as related to the Physical Properties of the Soil and the Growth of Rice*. La. Agric. Exp. Sta. Bull. 271.

635 SUBRAHMANYAN, V. (1937). Some aspects of the chemistry of swamp soils. *Curr. Sci.* 5, 25.

636 SUBRAHMANYAN, V., SREENIVASAN, A. and DAS GUPTA, H. P. (1938). Effect of milling on the chemical composition and commercial qualities of raw and parboiled rices. *Indian J. Agric. Sci.* 8, 459–86.

637 SULAIMAN, M. (1944) Effect of algal growth on the activity of azotobacter in rice soils. *Indian J. Agric. Sci.* 14, 277–83.

638 SUNDARARAMAN, S. (1936). Administration report of the Government Mycologist, Madras, for the year 1935–6.

639 SURE, B. (1955). Effect of amino acid and vitamin B_{12} supplements on the biologic value of proteins in rice and wheat. *Amer. Dietet. Assoc. J.* 31, 1232.

640 SUWATABANDHU, K. (1950). *Weeds in Paddy Fields in Thailand*. Tech. Bull. No. 4, Dept. Agric., Thailand.

641 SUZUKI, H. (1935). Studies on the influence of some environmental factors on the susceptibility of the rice plant to Blast and *Helminthosporium* diseases and on the anatomical characters of the plant: II. Influences of differences in soil moisture and in the amount of nitrogenous fertilizer given. III. Influence of differences in soil moisture and in the amount of fertilizer and silica given. *J. Coll. Agric. Tokyo.* 13, 235–75; 277–331.

642 SWAMINATHAN, M. (1942). Effect of washing and cooking on vitamin B_1 content of raw and parboiled milled rice. *Indian J. Med. Res.* 30, 409–16.

643 SZOKOLAY, G. (1956). Ratooning rice on the Swaziland Irrigation Scheme. *World Crops*, 8, 71.

644 TAKACS, F. and VAMOS, R. (1957). The part played by the nitrogen and weather in the appearance of the Bruzone. *Kopancsi Allami Gazdasag*, Hungary.

645 TAKENAKA, C., HU, H. and TATEOKA, T. (1955). Karology of *Oryza sativa* L. I. Karylogical studies on haploid rice. *Ann. Rep. Nat. Sci. Inst. Genetics, Japan*, No. 6, 47.

646 TANAKA, A. *et al*. (1959). III. Partial efficiency of nitrogen absorbed by rice plant at different stages of growth in relation to yield of rice (*Oryza sativa* var *indica*) *Proc. Indian Acad. Sci. Sect. B.* 49 (4), 207–216.

647 TANAKA, A. *et al*. (1958). Studies on the nutrition of rice plant (*Oryza sativa* L.). II. A comparative study of nitrogen requirement of *indica* and *japonica* varieties of rice. *Proc. Indian Acad. Sci. Sect. B.* 48 (1), 14–27.

[648] TARCHETTE, A. (1912). *Latest mechanical developments in the rice industry.* Paper read at 4th Congress of Cult. Rice at Vercelli, Nov. 1912.

[649] TEMPANY, H. (1932). The Italian rice industry. *Malay. Agric. J.* 20, 274–292.

[650] TEMPLETON, G. E. and WORAWISITTHUMRONG, A. (1962). Leaf smut of rice. *Ark. Farm Res.* March, 1963.

[651] TEN HAVE, H. (1959). [Foundation for mechanization of agriculture in Surinam, New-Nickerie, Surinam.] *de Suriname Landbouw.* 7, 39–50.

[652] THOMAS, K. M. (1931). *Madras Agric. J.* 19 (1).

[653] THOMAS, K. M. (1933). The "Foot-Rot" of paddy and its control. *Madras Agric. J.* 21 (6), 263–72.

[654] THORP, J. (1936). *Geography of the soils of China.* Nat. Geographical Soc. of China.

[655] TIDBURY, G. E. (1947). The cultivation of rice land between successive crops. *E. Africa. Agric. J.* 12, 212–15.

[656] TING, Y. (1949). [The origin of rice cultivation in China.] Agron. Bull. Sun Yatsen Univ. Ser. III. No. 7: 18.

[657] TING, Y. (1960). *Agrobiologija* 1960: 563–67. (In Russian.)

[658] TISDALE, W. H. (1921). *J. Agric. Res.* 21, 649–58.

[659] TISDALE, W. H. and JENKINS, J. (1921). *Mitchell Farmers Bull.* 1212, U.S.A. Dept. Agr.

[660] TOBATA, SEIICHI. (1958). *An Introduction to Agriculture of Japan.* Maruzen Co., Tokyo.

[661] TOGNATO, L. (1912). By-products of the cultivation and milling of rice. *4th Congress on Cult. Rice. Vercelli.*

[662] TOKUNAGA, Y. and TOKUOKA, M. (1957). [Influence of sulphur on growth of the rice plant.] *J. Sci. Soil, Tokyo.* 27, 415–18.

[663] TOKUOKA, M. (1938). *Soc. Trop. Agric. Taiwan,* 10.

[664] TOKUOKA, M., DYO, S. T. and GYO, S. (1940). The fertilizer effect of urea nitrogen. V. Field experiments with rice and sugar cane. *J. Sci. Soil, Tokyo.* 14, 403–10.

[665] TOKUOKA, M. and MOORUKA, H. J. (1936). Effectiveness of urea nitrogen for rice. III. Comparison of urea-gypsum and ammonium sulphate for varieties of rice. *J. Soc. Agric. Taihoku Univ.* 8, 197–210.

[666] TOMLINSON, T. E. (1957). Changes in the sulphide-containing mangrove soil on drying and their effect upon the suitability of the soil for the growth of rice. *Emp. J. Exp. Agric.* 25. 108.

[667] TOMLINSON, T. E. (1957). Seasonal variation of the surface pH value of some rice soils of Sierra Leone. *Trop. Agric. (Trin.)* 34, 287–94.

[668] TOTHILL, J. D. (1948). *Agriculture in the Sudan.* Oxford.

[669] TSUTSUI, K. (1959). Pests of paddy rice in Japan. *Span.* 2 (3) 119.

[670] TULLIS, E. C. *et al.* (1934). Panicles of Rexoro rice injured at emergence by sun scald. *Phytopath.* 24, 1043–44.

[671] UEKI, K. (1958). The influence of temperature of irrigation water upon the growth of paddy rice in the warmer district. IV. On the influence

of water temperature at tillering period upon the growth of rice. *Proc. Crop Sci. Soc. Japan*, **27** (4), 426–28.

[672] UMALI, D. L., PARKER, M. B. and DUMLAO, R. C. (1960). A preliminary study on the cancellation of dormancy period of rice seed. *Philipp. Agriculturist*, **46** (6), 279–89.

[673] UPPAL, J. D., PATEL, M. K. and DAJI, J. A. (1939). Nitrogen fixation in rice soils. *Indian J. Agric. Sci.* **9**, 689–702.

[674] U TIN (1936). Developmental variation in the paddy grain. *Indian J. Agric. Sci.* **6**, 396–459.

[675] U TIN (1941). Eleven years' results of continuous manuring of paddy at Mandalay. *Indian J. Agric. Sci.* **11**, 21–30.

[676] VAMOS, R. (1956). The role of the soil's excess nitrogen in the Bruzone of the rice. *Acta Biologica.* **2**, 103–10.

[677] VAMOS, R. (1957). Nutrition conditions of rice at the time of the appearance of the Blast (Bruzone). *Acta Biologica*, Szeged, Hungary. **3**, 239–45.

[678] VAMOS, R. and MERAI, J. (1957). The rice product and the weather in Hungary. *Kopancsi Allami Gazdasag*, Szeged, Hungary.

[679] VAMOS, R. (1958). Factors of the Bruzone in Hungary. (Manuscript.)

[680] VANOSSI, L. (1956). Bibliography of 200 items on rice published in Italy during the period 1800–1879. (Italian.) *Il Riso.* **5** (12), 28–31.

[681] VAUGH MASON (1954). Mechanization of the small farmer. *Int. Rice Comm. News Letter*, No. 10.

[682] VASCONCELLOS, J. DE C. E. (1953). *O. Arroz.* Min. da Econ., Lisbon.

[683] VAVILOV, N. I. (1930). The problems of the origin of cultivated plants and domestic animals as conceived at the present time. *Pl. Breed. Abs.*

[684] VAYSSIÈRE, P. (1948). Hermetic storage, the process of the future for protection of foodstuffs. *FAO Agric. Studies*, No. 2.

[685] VEEN, A. G. VAN (1940). *The Rice Problem in the Dutch East Indies.* Health Organisation of League of Nations. Bull. 9.

[686] VELASCO, J. R. (1943). Studies on the nutritive value of Elon-elon rice grown in different parts of the Islands. *Philipp. Agriculturist*, **29**, 238–52.

[687] VENKATACHALAM, S. (1955). The intake of silica by the rice plant with reference to rice blast. *Madras Agric. J.* **41** (9), 304–10.

[688] VISWANATH, B. (1931). *J. Mysore Agric. and Exp. Union.* XI, No. 3

[689] VOLK, R. J. et al. (1948). Silicon content of the rice plant as a factor for influencing its resistance to infection by the blast fungus, *Piricularia oryzae. Phytopath.* **48**, 179–84.

[690] WALKER, R. K. and STURGIS, M. B. (1947). Fertilizers and methods of applying fertilizers to rice in Louisiana. *Rice J.* **50**, 17–19.

[691] WARD, M. M. (1956). *Weed Control in Rice.* Report No. F/S/41 : Fernhurst Res. Sta. Plant Protection. (Not published.)

[692] WATANABE, A., NISHIGAKI, S. and KONISHI, C. (1951). Effect of nitrogen fixing blue-green algae on the growth of rice plants. *Nature*, London, **168** (Oct. 27), 748–49.

⁶⁹³ WATSON, R. (1956). *Rice Production in the South Pacific Region.* Technical Paper No. 97, South Pacific Commission, Noumea, New Caledonia.

⁶⁹⁴ WATSON, E. B. *et al.* (1929). *U.S.A. Dep. Agric. Bur. Chem. and Soils.* No. 4, Series 1925.

⁶⁹⁵ WENT, F. W. (1957). *Experimental Control of Plant Growth.* Chronica Botanical Co., Wather, Mass.

⁶⁹⁶ WESTGATE, R. (1960). Agricultural mechanisation in China. *World Crops,* **12** (6), 228–30.

⁶⁹⁷ WHITLOW, S. (1927). Nitrogen fertilizers used as a top dressing for better yields in Texas. *Rice J.* **50**, 28.

⁶⁹⁸ WHYTE, R. O. (1960). *Crop Production and Environment.* Faber and Faber.

⁶⁹⁹ WICKIZER, V. D. and BENNETT, M. K. (1941). *The Rice Economy of Monsoon Asia.* Food Res. Inst. Stanford Univ., California.

⁷⁰⁰ WICKRAMASEKERA, G. V. (1941). Some results of harrowing a growing rice crop. *Trop. Agriculturist,* **97**, 14–17.

⁷⁰¹ WIJIWARDENE, R. (1957). *The Mechanization of Tropical Agriculture.* Colombo Apothecaries Co., Colombo.

⁷⁰² WILLIAMS, W. A. and FINFROCK, D. C. (1963). Vetch as green manure increases yields. *Calif. Agric.* **17** (1), 12–13.

⁷⁰³ WIT, TH. P. M. DE (1960). *The Wageningen Rice Project in Surinam.* Stichting voor de Ontwikketing van Machinale Landbouw in Suriname. Koninginnegracht 66, The Hague, Netherlands.

⁷⁰⁴ WITTER, S. H. (1959). Foliar feeding can provide needed nutrients. *Soils and Crops,* **11** (10), 17–19.

⁷⁰⁵ WYATT, I. J. (1957). *Field Investigations of Padi-Stem Borers 1955–56.* Bull. 102, Dept. Agric., Malaya.

⁷⁰⁶ YABUTA, T. and HAYASI, T. (1940). *J. Imp. Agric. Exp. Sta. Nisigahara, Tokyo.* 3, 365–400.

⁷⁰⁷ YAMADA, N. (1959). Some aspects of the physiology of bronzing. *Int. Rice Comm. News Letter,* **8** (3), 11–16.

⁷⁰⁸ YAMADA, N. (1959). The nature of fertilizer response in Japanese and *indica* rice varieties. *Trop. Agriculturist,* **115** (3), 163–72.

⁷⁰⁹ YAMAGATA, M. (1958). Studies on the limit of possibility of the increase in number of leaves and grains of the main stem of rice. IV. Influence of sunlight intensity. *Bull. Fac. Agric. Yamaguti.* No. 9, 1001–10.

⁷¹⁰ YAMAGUCHI, Y. (1918). Beitrage zur Kenntnis der Xenien bei *Oryza sativa* L. *Bot. Mag. Tokyo,* **32**, 83.

⁷¹¹ YAMAGUCHI, M. and NAMIKI, K. (1956). Studies on technical improvement of paddy culture on ill-drained fields. II. On the effects of Baido in ill-drained paddy fields. *Proc. Crop. Sci. Soc. Japan.* **24** (4), 268–70.

⁷¹² YAMASAKI, M. and HANDA, Y. (1956). Hastening root-formation of rice seedlings by means of supplying straw-ash to the nursery bed. *Proc. Crop. Sci. Soc. Japan,* **25** (2), 67–68.

[713] YANG, S. T. (1948). The cultivation of regenerated rice and its future in Nunan and Szechwan. Abs. in *Field Crops Abs.* **1**, 91.

[714] ZIMMERMAN, R. B. (1938). Malted rice as a brewing material. *Comm. Wallerstein Lab.* No. 4, 7–14.

[715] ZIMMERMAN, P. W. *et al.* (1950). Practical control of water hyacinth with 2,4–D. *Agric. Chem.* **5**, 45, 49, 81, 93.

ADDITIONAL REFERENCES

[716] ATKINS, J. G. *et al.* (1957). Preliminary studies on root parasitic nematodes of rice in Texas and Louisiana. *International Rice Comm. News Letter*, **6** (2), 8–11.

[717] AUDULOV, N. P. (1931). Karyo-systematische untersuchung der familie Gramineen. *Bull. Appl. Bot. Suppl.* 44, 429.

[718] BOR, N. L. (1960). *The Grasses of Burma, Ceylon, India and Pakistan.* Pergamon Press, London.

[719] BROWN, F. B. (1955). Rice hybridization in Malaya. *Int. Rice Comm. News Letter*, No. 15.

[720] BROWN, K. F. (1963). Nematode-Destroyers of world's crops. *Span.* **6** (2) 98–100.

[721] CHANDRARATNA, M. F. (1964). *The Genetics and Breeding of Rice.* Longmans, Green, London.

[722] CHATTERJII, D. (1947). Botany of wild and cultivated rices. *Nature*, London, 160, 234–37.

[723] CRALLEY, E. M. and TULLIS, E. C. (1937). Effect of seed treatment on seedling emergence. Severity of seedling blight and yield of rice. *Bull. Ark. Agric. Exp. Sta.* No. 345.

[724] HICKLING, C. F. (1961). *Tropical Inland Fisheries.* Longmans, Green, London.

[725] HIGGS, J. W. G., KERKHAM, R. K. and RAEBURN, J. R. (1950). *Report of a survey of problems in the mechanisation of native agriculture in tropical African colonies.* H.M.S.O., London.

[726] JOHNSTON, H. (1908). *George Grenfell and the Congo.* Hutchinson, London.

[727] LUIGI BORAZIO (1929). Studi e Ricrche sui terreni e sulle aeque d'irrigazione. *Il Vercellese.*

[728] MENON, M. K. (1955). On the paddy field prawn fishing of Travancore-Cochin. *Proc. Indo-Pacif. Fish Coun. 5th meeting.*

[729] MISU, H. (1929). Availability of nitrogen of air-dried green manure for rice. *Ann. Agric. Exp. Sta. Chosen.* 4, 167–72.

[730] RAJAGOPALAN, K. (1959). Studies on drought resistance in rice. *Madras Agric. J.* **44**, 195–205.

[731] RHIND, D. and SUBRAMANIAN, V. (1931). Red grain in paddy. *Agric. and Livestock in India.* **1**, 135.

[732] SHANMUGASUNDARM, A. (1953). Studies on dormancy in short-term rices. *Madras Agric. J.* **40**, 477.

[733] YAMADA, N. (1961). Photosynthesis and dry matter production in the rice plant. *Symposium on Rice Problems, Pacific Sci. Congr.* 1961.

[734] Abstract Bibliography of Rice. 4 vols.—1926–40; 1941–50; 1951–55; 1956–60. Mimeo. Univ. of Philippines College of Agric., Laguna, Philippines.

INDEX

Abdominal white, 68, 112
Abnormalities caused by hormone weedkillers, 269
Abortifacient from straw ash, 393
Acclimatization of varieties, 94
Achlya spp., seed disinfection to control, 346
Acidity of soils, 17–19
Acorus calamus, 362
Adlay, giant, 262
Aeroplane: application of weedkiller from, 272, 274; sowing seed from, 187
Aeschynomene aspera as green manure, 252; *A. virginica* (L) B.S.P., control of, 271, 272; as weed, 261, 272
Afghanistan, area and production of rice in, 422
Africa: area and production of paddy in, 423, 435; exports and imports of rice, 434; mechanization in, 204, 211, 217; land tenancy in, 447; origin of rice in, 3, 4; possibilities of paddy cultivation in, 420; water hyacinth in, 262; yield of rice in, 425
Africa, East: introduction of rice to, 7
Africa, Equatorial: *O. perennis* Moench. in, 4; possibilities of increasing production in, 420
Africa, West: introduction of Asian rice to, 3; mechanization in, 204; origin of rice in, 4; *O. glaberrima* in, 56
Akiochi disease, 248
Albania, area and production of paddy in, 422
Alcohol: from hulls, 325; from rice, 389
Aleurin cells: layer, 374; position of in rice grain, 66
Algae: as food for fish, 277; in North Sind, 264; rôle in nitrogen fixation, 221, 222
Algeria, area and production of paddy in, 422

Alisma plantago, 261; hormone weedkillers on, 268
Alkali injury causing sterility, 341
Alkaline soils, 14; improved with sulphur, 228; technique for washing in Egypt, 51–2
Alluvial soils, 14
Alterraria spp. in stored grain, 354
Altitude, effect on yield, 11
Aluminium in soils, 18, 19, 20
America, area and production of paddy in, 423; red rice in, 264; water hyacinth in, 262. See also under States
America, Central, 10; glutinous rice in, 88; introduction of rice to, 8; red rice in, 265
America, Latin: area and production of paddy in, 435; exports and imports, 434; land reform in, 448
America, North: glutinous rice in, 88; red rice in, 264; rice exports and imports, 434
America, South: area and production of paddy in, 423; dryland paddy cultivation in, 167; glutinous rice in, 88; introduction of rice to, 8; red rice in, 264, 265; white tip disease in, 339
Amino-acid: content in rice, 396; analysis of protein of rice, 398
Ammannia coccinea, 261
Ammonium sulphate, effect on soil acidity, 19
Anabaenas algae, 221
Anabas testudineus (Bloch), 278, 283
Analysis, sequential, of paddy, 267, 465
Anatomy of root, 59
Andosols, 14
Angkor, irrigation in, 40
Angousmois grain moth, 358
Anguillulina oryzae (Breda de Haan), 339
Aniani, 146

519

16'70